The Dawn of the Cursed Queen

GODS & MONSTERS

ALSO BY AMBER V. NICOLE

GODS AND MONSTERS
The Book of Azrael
The Throne of Broken Gods
The Dawn of the Cursed Queen
The Wrath of the Fallen

THE DAWN OF THE CURSED QUEEN

GODS & MONSTERS

AMBER V. NICOLE

KENSINGTON
PUBLISHING CORP.
kensingtonbooks.com

Content notice: *The Dawn of the Cursed Queen* explores some potentially triggering themes. A list of content warnings can be found on the Rose & Star website.

KENSINGTON BOOKS are published by:

Kensington Publishing Corp.
900 Third Avenue
New York, NY 10022

kensingtonbooks.com

ISBN 978-1-4967-5808-8 (hardcover)

First Kensington hardcover printing: October 2026

10 9 8 7 6 5 4 3 2 1

Printed in China

Cover design by Opulent Designs

Map design by Dewi Hargreaves
Chapter illustrations by Marta Riva (Marta Into The Forest)
Endpapers and stencil art by PalinLineArt
Interior design by Cassandra Farrin & Aubrey McConnell

The authorized representative in the EU for product safety and compliance
is eucomply OU, Parnu mnt 139b-14, Apt 123
Tallinn, Berlin 11317, hello@eucompliancepartner.com

TO THE READER

"The scariest monsters
are the ones that lurk within our souls."

—Edgar Allen Poe

ONUNA
ECANUS
Pamyel
Silver City of Hadremiel
Boel
SANDSUN ISLES
Jaéoul
AARIN
Omael
Adonael
Valoel
Charoum
Conah
Tadheil
BAIRNISLE SEA
NAIMER SEA
NOCHARI
Ecleon
San Pavlão

THE DEAD OCEAN
NOVA'S ISLAND
Kashvenia
Hayyel
IPIUQIN
Naaririel
Arariel
Ruuman
THE UNKNOWN DEEP
Eoria
NAIMER SEA
Ophanium
El Donuma
EL DONUMA
Morael
Chasin
ZARALL
Tirin
THE DEAD OCEAN

Previously on—

No, I'm kidding. Logan showed me this show one time where they do funny recaps, and yeah . . . anyway.

You know those times when you're relaxing after a long day? You put your feet up, thinking life can't get any better? No? Yeah, well, me either. I thought I'd experienced the worst thing that could happen the day Rashearim fell. The world I knew crumbled, and my family was torn apart. I thought, it can't get worse, right? Xavier would have slapped me if I'd said that aloud, but man, did I think it.

Samkiel, our king and loyal . . .You know what? I can't even say loyal because that bastard left us for . . . I'm getting ahead of myself. Anyway. You think you know a guy, right? We'd partied together, fought side by side, and even fucked in the same room. Don't make that face. It is necessary to blow off some steam after battle, and we had fought together in several fucking wars. When you get so desperate for a release that you no longer care your friend is across the tent, then we'll talk.

Anyway, we'd spent hundreds of years with Samkiel before Rashearim fell. After that, he changed, but I'd be a liar if I said it hadn't started long before. It had all begun with the change in Unir. Honestly, I should have paid closer attention. To everyone.

Samkiel deserted us after the destruction of Rashearim. He left us instructions on maintaining the rest of the worlds and then disappeared for centuries. Then the fucker shows back up with a super hot—and I mean quite literally will-burn-your-face-off—girlfriend.

Everything changed with Dianna, and I mean everything. She didn't just scorch a path of destruction across the world to avenge her fallen sister, but she burned so damn bright she revealed secrets buried within our family and ourselves.

Xavier, Imogen, and I were stationed on the remains of Rashearim, completely unaware that Samkiel had not only come back but was working with our archnemesis, the Ig'Morruthen—see hot girlfriend above. Apparently, they were searching for a relic. But all of it went to shit, and Dianna lost the one person she loved. Then, she tried to kill us all in her devastation and grief. It was no joke. I quite literally held my own guts in my hands.

Samkiel, always the hero, was able to break through that crazy shell of hers. He even remade his home and hid her, keeping her safe from the council. Those shady bitches wanted her head. Sure, maybe I was sleeping with one of them as a distraction from what I was feeling for my best friend, but everyone has problems, right? Anyway, let me get back on topic.

Dianna, as fierce and loving as she is—don't tell her I said that—was not the worst thing in the world, not by a lot. Apparently, her maker, Kabitch—sorry, my pen slipped—Kaden had a plan far grander than any of us suspected, and none of us knew it wasn't him at the helm.

I thought I knew pain. The day Xavier told me he was dating someone made me want to claw my eyes out, but when I found out how horribly we had all been betrayed, it was devastating. Faced with the reality that Vincent, a man I considered my damn blood, had been working with Kaden, sent my world spinning again. He lied, manipulated, and turned my family into perfect, uncaring, unfeeling soldiers.

Once more, I thought that was the worst that could happen until Kaden dangled Xavier as bait to lure me in. I offered to come willingly, to give up not just my physical freedom but the freedom of my mind. I would join them as long as we could stay together, but Kaden had other plans. We were all dumb enough to believe we knew all the secrets the gods harbored. But none of us were prepared to face the all-powerful children Unir had hidden away. Locked away for ages, they were finally free and intent on blood and revenge.

Yeah, you heard me right. Papa Unir was not just getting hot and sweaty and making one kid. No, no, he had three. Three hell-bent children set on making Samkiel and all of us pay dearly for his crimes.

Although, technically, the jury is still out on how they were created. I don't remember Unir sneaking around the palace with different partners like Samkiel. I knew of his amata Zaysn. She was cool and a complete badass who could make Unir cry with a look. I doubt she'd let any affairs fester, but I am getting off topic again. Why do people entrust me with these things?

I know, I know, you're all really concerned about me. I get it. And, well, I guess you'll have to wait and see what happens with me. But I can say that everything is different now. Completely different.

I assumed we would always come out on top. It was arrogant of me, yes. We fought for what was good and just in the world. Despite that, we all failed fucking miserably. Not only did we lose, but we lost our home again. I still have nightmares of watching the remains of Rashearim burn, of seeing Samkiel beaten and bound on the floor. Now, his power spills across the sky, the last remnants of him. Nismera reigns over the realms, and we are all trapped beneath her rule now. I thought we had experienced the worst, but I was wrong. So fucking wrong.

I know Dianna is still out there. I know she will want retribution for Samkiel's death, and a part of me hopes she burns this whole fucking thing to the ground. If I must die a fiery death at her hands . . . I just hope I go with my Xavi.

— *Cameron*

I

Camilla

I beat at Vincent's shoulder, fighting against his grip as he dragged me through that damned portal. It sealed behind us, the sound slicing through the air. Vincent released me with a shove, and I stumbled before finding my footing. I brushed my hair out of my face and shot him a glare before looking around. We hadn't arrived in another darkened dungeon or cave but a city of light. I squinted, my eyes struggling to adjust to the sunlight piercing through the clouds.

People continued on their way, talking and laughing, utterly unfazed by the soldiers that had suddenly appeared. A city of tall buildings constructed of various pale stones was spread out before us. Overhangs, balconies, banisters, and roofs were littered with hanging florals, adding cheerful pops of color. Clean, bright cobblestone streets wove through the city, all seeming to lead to a large, open center. Small flying creatures with double sets of wings flew across the hazy pink sky, calling to each other. It looked peaceful and happy, an entire city living in harmony. For a moment, I could believe this was paradise. But then the thickly armored general appeared at my side, and I remembered this was not paradise, not in the least.

"Take her to the palace. Nismera will need us all there for the convergence."

My head snapped toward Vincent and the tall, winged, feather-covered general near him. The general sneered at me before taking flight, and the rest of us walked forward, following Vincent.

The walk, or more so drag, felt as if it took forever. I tried to remember every alleyway, dip in the road, and building because I planned to find a way to get out. I would find a place to hide and leave this damned city as soon as I could. My throat bobbed as I wondered where I would go. I knew nothing of this realm or this world, and I had no friends or allies.

My feet skittered on the ground as the glistening cobblestones changed to a smooth, sleek surface. My head reeled as a large, breathtaking stronghold appeared before us. The palace gleamed nearly white in the sun, a pearl amongst bright gems. I had to tip my head all the way back to see the top. Spires, partly obscured by clouds, pierced the sky. Every winding line, curve, and window whispered wealth, but the whispers turned to screams of horror when you knew what those prestigious doors harbored.

Vincent's grip tightened on me, interrupting my gawking. My head swiveled toward him, but he wasn't glaring at me for once. He was looking at the palace as I was, and his jaw hardened with apprehension. Even covered in armor, I saw his muscles flinch. He glanced at me and realized he had revealed more of his thoughts than he intended. His eyes went blank again, and he shook his head before pushing me forward.

"Move." Vincent's voice was gruff and filled with anger, as if I were the one that made us stop. The generals towering over us may buy his act, but I saw the crack in the armor he hid behind so well.

Vincent was afraid.

II

Vincent

One week later

I scooted across the long rumpled bed, picking up my pants and stepping into them as the water from the bathroom shut off. Steam cooled and spread in tendrils, attempting to escape the beast it had just cleaned. My eyes roamed, looking for a distraction and catching on the intricate shell sitting on the carved dresser.

My head tilted. "You kept this?"

"Yes, it's yours or what's left of the first piece of armor I gave you. I told you I have missed you, pet," Nismera purred from behind me, the floral scent of bommsberries coating her skin. It was another attempt to hide the lethal creature beneath. She may not have had horns, scales, or fangs, but a beast made of light was still a beast.

I watched from the corner of my eye as she ran her hand through the ends of her silver hair, separating the pieces that had curled around one another.

Pet. Always a pet. I wondered if that was truly how she saw me, but I knew the answer. Missed me was a loose term. Nismera never loved like others, never cared like others. She used what she had, and when she could no longer use it, she eradicated it.

I turned as she walked across her room, my eyes following her naked, lean-muscled form as she grabbed her garbs off the large, claw-foot chair. I watched without a hint of lust or longing, not craving her as I once had eons ago. What I'd done in this room with her had been out of survival, duty, and perhaps a belief that I deserved it. Maybe I did deserve her after the way I had betrayed my family. I swallowed the bile rising in my throat, refusing to reveal the disgust I felt for myself.

"What of me now?"

She spun, zipping up the side of her shirt. "You will assume your position as if you never left. The High Guard of the legion, Hectur, will be demoted. He was merely keeping your spot occupied while you dismantled Samkiel and The Hand, anyway."

The Hand. The way she said it made it sound like a curse. Guilt ate at my gut, causing it to roll, and I swallowed my apprehension. "It will cause an uproar, I am sure."

Nismera smiled as she jumped and wiggled, sliding into the sleek dark pants before buttoning them and sitting on the bed. She slipped on steel-heeled boots and met my eyes. "There will be none. Anyone who disagrees will be strung up like a new flag outside the stone walls that border this city. They will fly high as a warning to anyone who dares challenge me."

I nodded, knowing she meant every word. The scent of decaying flesh lingered in the air. I had smelled it the second the portal closed.

She was on her feet and beside me in a flash. A single finger ran under my chin, turning my gaze back toward hers. She wore that famed three-skulled cape around her shoulders, the hollow eyes mocking me even here.

"Worry not, pet. You were Samkiel's second for so long. Maybe you forgot your place is and will always be by me."

I shook my head. "I never forgot."

"Good." Her finger curled beneath my chin, and even though it was but a small, simple digit, I could feel the power beneath her touch. I knew, without a shadow of a doubt, that with one flick, she had the strength to fling my head off my shoulders and toss it across the room as if it were nothing, as if I were nothing. I knew I was nothing to her.

"I also have your room prepared. You are in the east wing, top floor."

I swallowed, trying to hide my satisfaction. The east wing was far from her large rooms here on the west. Excitement thrilled through me that I'd at least have my own place.

"You will accompany the witch to and from her station."

My excitement died.

"Pardon me, my liege?" I asked, trying to mask the bitterness I felt.

Nismera clamped the large, circular pin that held her half-cloak to her shoulder, her legless beasts engraved into the metal. "Which part was hard for you to understand?"

"The witch."

"Camilla is a magnificent power source, my only one since Santiago proved useless. I need her to repair an ancient artifact of mine, but I do not trust her. You, I trust. You will accompany her to and from unless I need you, then I will ask the other guards. Your room shall be across from hers. I need to make sure she follows my rules. Too much freedom given to any beast, and they assume they can roam freely." Her smile was as cold and empty as any abyss.

"Yes, my liege." I forced a smile to match, even though I loathed this plan of hers.

Her hand dropped as she smiled at me. "Now go mingle with the other generals below. I need you to be cordial with your legion. I have other things I need to address."

I simply nodded, and she left the room.

My boots echoed off the cream and gold stone flooring, tiny specks dancing beneath my feet as I walked. It was a sign of royalty, something this whole city reeked of. Nismera was king of all twelve realms now and wanted to make sure everyone knew it. As I walked out of her chamber and toward the lower foyer, I was met with bowing and downcast eyes. The wardrobe assigned to me had too many tassels and chains, and I did not care for any of it. Nismera loved power displays. She always had. Power was all that mattered to her. Every piece of furniture and glass column was hand-crafted and placed how she liked it. All of it was as gaudy and wild as she was.

Laughter and hollering sped down the long, wide corridor, reminding me of the family I had condemned. I moved toward it, my chest clenching.

I pushed the large, thick, chiseled doors open, the music and laughter dying. All eyes shifted my way. The hall was almost as large as the main entranceway, with long wooden tables hugging the walls. There were chairs hidden in almost every corner and a staircase lined with jewel-encrusted tapestries.

A long table held a feast. Battered and dirty generals sat in various spots. Some watched me with food hanging out of their mouths, others with cups held to their lips, forgetting to swallow. They stared at me with two sets of eyes, others with four or more. Some had tentacles where arms and legs should be, and others with wings large and thick, jutting from their backs. I didn't see any of Grimlock's reptilian horde, but I assumed they wanted answers on why their general went with Nismera and Isaiah and did not return.

A throat cleared as a burly troll, cloaked in furs and leathers, stood and raised a glass the size of my head. "Welcome our High Guard of the legion, Vincent."

My lip curled at the loud, boisterous display, my ears ringing as everyone cheered. The troll who shouted moved from the back of the room, making his way to me before clasping a hand on my shoulder and shoving the massive drink into my hands.

"Come, sit with us."

"Who are you?" I asked, brushing his hand off.

"My name is Tedar, Commander of the Eighth Legion."

Maybe it wasn't just generals in here.

He led me toward a large seating area in a dim corner of the room. I went because I had nowhere else to go. The chair he plopped into fit him, but its match almost swallowed me whole. The liquid in my glass sloshed to the side, spilling some on my hand. I leaned forward and placed it on the center of the table before wiping my hand on my pants and leaning back. Laughter and chatter filled the room once more as Tedar leaned forward.

"You're a legend now, you know that? Every whisper among realms speaks of what you did, and now you are High Guard?" He whistled between thick teeth. "You're above every commander and general now. They'll hate it."

"You don't."

"Gods, no. There are only six High Guards now, including her brothers, so less responsibility for me. You and your legion will always go first into battle now."

My brows lifted. "Battle? I don't think so. I think we will just follow orders."

"Say what you want, but the sky bleeds silver now. The World Ender is dead, and The Hand of Rashearim now walks around blindly, listening to every demand like a whipped hound. There are, and will always be, those who jump at the bit when the largest power player exits the field, and guess who just did?"

I swallowed, trepidation burning in my throat. He was so callous, so joyful for what I did, and I felt grimier than sludge upon a boot. I reminded myself that I had no choice. He did not know my will was Nismera's will. I shook my head as Tedar rambled on.

". . . I have to say it's such a relief. No one ever thought he'd die. That's gotta feel amazing for you. You did it. You helped."

My stomach rolled. I had avoided looking toward the sky since then, especially at night when his power seemed to mock me, begging for answers. My chest tightened, and the air suddenly became far too tight.

"I serve my king now, as she wishes. Nothing in the world has the power to rival Nismera now," I repeated.

Tedar leaned forward, drawing attention to a large, chipped tusk as he smirked. "Not from what I heard."

My brow ticked up, and I scanned the room, noting a few generals glaring our way, speaking in low tones amongst themselves. "And what did you hear?"

Tedar leaned closer as if to whisper. "Listen, everyone talks, and after they cleaned up the massacre in the East, everyone knows now."

My face scrunched in confusion. I had heard nothing of this. "The East? What happened in the East?"

"The World Ender had a lover and not just a fling like in his past. They say she is a beast made of flame and hate, and she followed you lot back. His beast.The female Ig'Morruthen."

Dianna. He meant Dianna.

I nodded and sat up a bit straighter as he rambled on, the sounds of this room fading into the background.

That power radiated from the doorway, the same as his father, and I didn't need to turn to know Samkiel was leaning against the doorway of the foyer. I rubbed my wrist, shaking my head.

"Let it go."

"Is that any way to speak to your future king?"

I heard the concern in his voice.

"Future. You still have to surpass your father."

Heavy boots echoed as he entered, his battle armor encompassing him entirely, that damn sigil cape flowing behind him. It's the same one his father wore every damn council meeting.

"Why do you let her—"

I cut him off, spinning to face him. "I don't let her do anything."

His eyes widened a fraction, and he watched me carefully as he said, "You can join Logan and me. My father wishes for me to have my own kingsguard even though that will not be the name you claim."

A snide snort left my lips as the large curtains blew near the opened expanse of a window.

"I decline, future king."

"Why will you not let me help you?"

I glanced toward the door as if I could see her watching me, waiting.

"Vincent."

His voice snapped me out of the trance I had fallen into.

"Why do you always wish to help so many?" I asked. "What's in it for you? You are destined to rule this realm and everyone in between.

You don't have to pretend to be benevolent. They will lick the dirt from your boots, regardless."

Samkiel shrugged, lifting a single shoulder, his hair curling around the shoulder of his armor. "I just want a better realm, a better world. This one is kind of shit, and I am over egotistical gods."

"Respectfully, I feel like yours is a mirror."

His lips quirked. "Mine is bearable."

I believed him. I believed he wanted something more, something better, even if the world he saw was only a fantastical dream spun by oracles.

"Even if I participated and won, she would never let me leave. Her claws are too deep, my prince."

His eyes shifted, the silver glow similar to Unir's and Nismera's. "You let me worry about her. Just come, try, and meet the others. There is no harm in that."

Harm. He didn't get it. No one did, but against all reason, I nodded. He said nothing else before he left, and I stared at that empty expanse of a doorway. He said try, and try, I would.

The memory faded as the roaring and whooping came back, glasses slamming against each other and tables. The generals from across the cosmos, all vicious and vile, cheering and celebrating his death. All of them know her next move will be to liberate the realms. She had taken and converted the most cruel and deadly for her reign, and now, nothing would stop her. Nothing ever could, so what choice did I ever have?

Samkiel was a light. He promised peace and change, and I had helped snuff it out. A part of me hoped I burned in Iassulyn for eternity for it. Another part of me knew Dianna would hunt me, hunt us all like she did for her sister. I would be lying if I said I wouldn't welcome it.

III
Kaden

"We will never tell you anything," he said, spitting at Nismera's feet.

Her lip turned up as she shook it off her pointed, armored boot. "That's fine." Her smile was cold as she lifted a hand. Power erupted from her palm and scattered across the sky. Lightning, pure and blinding, ripped back as she created and controlled the sparks of energy, shooting them toward the floor. Runes lit with her silver power, and the floor beneath our feet spun. I jolted to the side. Beside me, Isaiah did not even falter, as if this was a normal occurrence to him. The floor opened in a massive spiraling vortex, saltwater reaching toward the ceiling with a hollow roar. The rows of chained armored men glared toward it as the room stopped shaking. Nismera walked behind them, one by one, and fear coated the air.

"I know you won't talk, and I don't need that from you. The Eye is, and has always been, about the same dribble. Why else would they send their little pawns? I know they hide from me, too."

"The Eye does not hide," an older, graying soldier spat from the end of the line. "We wait for the perfect opportunity—"

Nismera barked an ugly laugh. "An opportunity. Oh, Sir Molten. I've been dying to have my hands on you. You've been nothing but a pain in my side."

"Your day is coming." He straightened his back. No fear rolled from him, at least, none I could smell.

"When exactly? You lot have been trying to overthrow me for how long now? I'm a bit bored, honestly." She leaned toward the soldier nearest to her, and he shook. "But I have a hungry beastie, and what better treat to feed it than traitors? I think fear quenches its appetite the most."

Nismera shoved the soldier into the vortex, the man's scream cut short by a loud crunch. Chaos erupted as the others saw what had befallen their companion, and most tried to shuffle to the side to escape. One by one, Nismera's gold and black army kicked the remaining rebels in, and one by one, their screams were the last thing we heard before they disappeared below. The last soldier, older by far with a gray beard tied at the end, didn't even so much as blink as she came to him.

"And will you beg, Sir Molten?" She dug her nails into his armored shoulders as the material cracked against it. He did not so much as falter.

His chin held high, the age lines creasing across his face as he sneered and glared at her in his last act of defiance. "I hope their prison remains locked for eons."

Nismera's hand whipped out faster than light, severing his head from his body. Blood coated her front and splattered her face. She blinked rapidly, chasing away the overwhelming anger that filled her expression.

Their prison? The question rattled around in my thoughts but died as the severed head rolled toward me over the stone floor. I lifted my boot, stopping its path. Unseeing eyes stared back at me, hair clipped close to the scalp with shaved markings on the side—markings of rebels.

"Four hundred and seventy-two rebels. Four hundred and seventy-two heads." Nismera cleaned her hand. The room stayed deathly quiet as she stepped forward.

"Take Sir Molten's head to Severn." She nodded toward the large male armored guard to my left. "I want to send a message to any rebels who think now is the time to attack. We have far too much to do."

Isaiah made a noise in his throat and shuffled. Armored boots echoed in the carved stone room as the guards did as she commanded and left. Nismera kicked his remaining corpse to the beast in the water below before sealing the floor.

Isaiah whistled low. "You seem uptight, Mera. It's been weeks. Shouldn't you be the least bit happy? Big brother's home and all the realms now belong to you."

A warm smile spread across her face as she glanced behind us, making sure every guard had left as if she didn't want them to see she did have emotions. She glared at me, her temper barely leashed. "I am happy, but The Eye seems to think now, above all else, is the time to attack."

"Attack is overstating it," I said, nodding toward the closed floor behind her. "An attack would imply they have a chance."

She merely shrugged before stalking past us both, heading for the main entrance of her ostentatious, shimmering white fortress. Onuna changed my perspective on architecture. I had forgotten how massive most palaces were, and Mera loved the finer things above all. Drapes embroidered with the twisted, legless, mighty ryphors along the hem hung from the top of every entrance. The long tassels of her war banners danced across the pristine floor.

We turned and followed after Nismera. Isaiah wrapped his arm around my shoulder, squeezing once. "You've been so quiet since your return. Brother, I thought you'd be far happier to see me."

I swallowed the growing lump in my throat. I was happy to see him. Happy to be off of blasted Onuna, but another aching pit ate at my gut. One thing I could not, or had not, forgotten.

"You're a monster," she said, sneering at me and pulling at the restraints.

"I halted plans for you, searched for that damned book, hoping there was another way that I could keep you." My hand slid across her jaw as she pulled away from me in disgust. "I love you."

We strode down the gold and cream halls, the reflection of the ceiling splayed across the dark shiny floors, the stone unscuffed even with the guards shuffling about. Nismera climbed the massive stairwell, prattling on, but my mind wasn't present and hadn't been for weeks. I was thinking of her and how to bring her back, but I had a plan this time. Samkiel was dead. No one would be left in any of these realms for her, no one but me.

Guards pushed open the large doors, and the chattering inside the room died, the massive stone war room quieting. The Order surrounded the rectangular raised table, maps and scrolls scattered over the top, with small totem-shaped beings in between. Nismera's guards followed inside, taking their place in the four corners as she headed toward the back of the room. The war drapes were yanked open with one flick of her hand.

Sunlight flooded the room, giving the impression of warmth and peace, when I knew damned well the goddess that controlled this realm could wipe us all away with a flick of her brow if she so deemed necessary. Unir and Samkiel were nothing but dust, and neither Isaiah nor I could match her power. No living being could.

"Good dawn." Nismera tipped her head as a guard pulled out her seat for her. With a toss of her sash on her shoulder, she sat. Once she was seated, Isaiah and I took ours, one on her left, the other on her right, and the room soon followed.

"Good dawn," the others repeated as she clapped her hands on the table.

"These are barely a fraction of the relics and scrolls we took from the remains of Rashearim," Jiraiya said.

Jiraiya was the councilman who, like the others, tricked Samkiel into thinking they worked for him, but Nismera had ruled The Order since The Gods War. She had put her people in place, securing their seats one by one without being caught until only her sept held power. She was a master strategist who had taught me well.

Jiraiya shifted the records toward her, and she glanced them over. Sweat built at his brow, and I could smell fear on every being around the table. Smart of them.

"Why does he keep glancing at the blonde one?" Isaiah asked, nodding toward Jiraiya.

My eyes followed, and I watched. He did glance toward Imogen even as he spoke to Nismera.

I shrugged. "I believe they fucked when she had her mind."

Isaiah made a noise of disgust.

Imogen was the only member of The Hand left here. Nismera had the others shipped off and sold to the highest bidder for battles or gods-knew-what. Imogen stood stiffly near one of the orc generals, staring straight ahead. Nivene was his name. Isaiah had said he was one of Nismera's new favorites, but I couldn't care less. Even with half the table between us, his scent confirmed he was just another brute who had worked and slain his way to the top.

Imogen stared off into space, her dull blue eyes not moving even when the council members raised their voices. She wore the same dragonbane armor as all of Nismera's higher-ranking soldiers did. Her hands were clasped behind her back, her posture straight, and her long twisted braid draped over her shoulder.

I didn't need to see Imogen's fingers to know they were bare. Nismera had those silver rings melted down the second she had a chance. She hated the color and what it reminded us all of. Instead, she now bore two forsaken swords strapped to her back. I was surprised she had let her keep even that, but I knew my words had imprisoned her brain. She was no longer capable of independent thought or free will.

Nismera stood and moved around the table to lean over a scroll, the general at her side explaining what they had learned and brought back from Onuna.

"He's so puny." Isaiah sighed next to me. "It couldn't have been pleasurable."

I glanced at Isaiah. He studied Jiraiya with a predator's intent before glancing at Imogen again.

"Why do you care?"

"Call it curiosity." He shrugged.

I rolled my shoulders and leaned forward, clasping my hands on the tabletop. "Your curiosity will enrage Veruka."

"Ah, so Mera told you about that." Isaiah merely shrugged. "She's just fun. Plus, the things she does when you pull her tail are very satisfying."

My gaze bored daggers into him. "She's one of the High Guards. I told you not to shit where you eat."

"Says the one who turned and fucked Samkiel's mate."

My nostrils flared, which only garnered a grin from him. If I could punch him without pissing off Nismera, I would.

Elianna stood and glanced down the table at us before clearing her throat and opening the worn journal she had carried for ages. All eyes turned toward her, everyone listening intently.

"Speaking of blonde ones, where is your celestial?" Isaiah asked, not giving a shit what Elianna had to say.

"Cameron is in the low levels still." I folded my arms as I leaned back, at least attempting to pay attention.

"The pit fights?" Isaiah asked.

I nodded. "He needs to work out his new powers, and he's not fucking them out so that leaves fighting and feeding."

Isaiah scoffed. "Thrash."

We called it thrash because, at some stages, all you did was thrash from side to side as your body overheated. Those able to be turned to Ig'Morruthens experienced it. Dianna had. The first few weeks, I had her chained as I had Cameron when he arrived. The first blood rage was always the strongest as their bodies carved out their insides, making room for the new ones. Power surged through them, replacing what they once were. If they survived and didn't turn into a beast, they were as we were. But the thrash could take weeks to resolve, sometimes months. The blood lust makes them damn near animalistic. They could level a village if left unattended. Uncontrollable urges were so strong they could rip their victims to ribbons. I had seen Dianna leave nothing but shards of tissue in her wake when she first changed, another reason among many for her bloodthirsty name.

"Nismera will want you to make more, you know?"

I glanced toward Isaiah. "It's not that easy."

"Good luck telling her that."

"Cameron is the only other one I made like her in a thousand years. I've tried. I just end up with beasts."

Isaiah nodded and opened his mouth to respond but was cut off before he could say anything.

"Something you two wish to share?" Nismera asked.

We turned toward her and shook our heads. Isaiah extended a hand and gestured, urging her to go on.

"Good," Nismera said. "Then, if you two don't mind, please pay attention."

Her smile was anything but sweet or kind. It never was. Sometimes, I wondered exactly what Unir made her from. I always assumed a cold, dying star. That's what she felt like, even with every soft word or mild joke. She was empty. The only emotion she displayed that was not manufactured for effect was rage, and it swirled ceaselessly behind her eyes.

Nismera folded her arms, turning back to Elianna. "Why has the incentive increased?"

Elianna pushed a map near Nismera and leaned over the table, pointing to a region past the stars. "It would appear, Your Highness, The Eye seems more determined since the slaughter in the East."

All eyes turned toward me.

I held a hand up. "I haven't been to the East."

"No," Nismera said calmly, the word dripping with hatred. "I have reports of an assault on some legion officials making their rounds in the far eastern tip of Tarr. I sent soldiers to see what they could find, and they did not return. But you know who was spotted? Eyewitnesses said a large, dark, scaled Ig'Morruthen flew across the sky before landing. She then proceeded to dismember my loyal soldiers and spread their remains across the field in a warning."

I swallowed the lump in my throat, along with the hint of amusement and the tiny flame of pride at just what she could still accomplish.

Nismera clasped her hands, cocking her head toward Elianna. "What was spelled for me once more?"

Elianna looked as if she wished to be anywhere but here as she folded her hands. "Umm, come get me," Elianna cleared her throat, looking around the room, "bitch."

She looked at Nismera, afraid she was about to be reduced to ashes as if she called her that herself. No one spoke in the room, and all eyes were on me. However, I did catch Isaiah's look of utter shock. No one spoke to Nismera that way or ever had and lived long.

"If that is true," I said. "I can handle her."

"Handle." Nismera smiled, tapping her fingers against the table. No one moved or even breathed. "Samkiel's mate still lives. Even if he does not, she will wage war in his name." She paused, the line in her jaw clenching. "Do you know what happens to the psyche of an amata when the other is slain? No, you don't because you don't have one."

My fists clenched on my thighs, my foot tapping. It was a jab and a dirty one to throw at me. Yet I knew how Mera spoke in her chamber meetings. I knew she had to show she did not pick favorites, even if it was her own blood. To them and everyone else, I was merely a High Guard who disobeyed orders.

"One can go insane with grief to the point of not existing, or they can rage and burn worlds, and it seems she has chosen the latter." Nismera prattled on. "This is why I wanted her dead the second he was, or better yet, dead long before. Do you see the problem, Kaden? Your wishes to keep her will likely result in an uprising."

No other general or commander turned toward me, but I felt the room shift. The discomfort was apparent in the sound of shuffling feet and the clench of scaled hands. Those with tentacles wrapped them around their bodies protectively.

"You told me to mold her, make her over, and I did. Now, it is an issue. You wanted a killer. I created one."

"They are calling her winged death. You know how names spread. They build, fuel, and feed into imaginations. I do not want The Eye thinking they have any leeway over me or my kingdom."

"I have a plan for that." My voice echoed into the silence, and every eye was on me.

"Care to enlighten the rest of us?" It was a member of The Order that made the challenge. I recognized him, but his name, like most of these people, I didn't fucking care to remember.

"No." I smiled widely at him, making sure the tips of my fangs showed. "That is information meant for only the highest ranking to hear. You and The Order do not make the cut, to say the least."

The room filled with tension.

Nismera sighed and shook her head. "Our main concern is capturing Harwork Bay at the moment. The remaining threats will be dealt with by the higher-ranking officials, as my brother has so politely said."

No one questioned Nismera. They never did because to do so was to risk their lives. The room turned back toward her and continued talks of siege and war.

As soon as every commander, general, and the last member of The Order filed out, Nismera turned to us. Her guards remained outside. She removed her cloak with one hand and hung it over her chair before striding toward an alcove. She returned, carrying two bottles and a few glasses, falling into a seat with a huff.

"I wish you would not argue against me in meetings, Kaden. They are not used to my voice being spoken over, and you're not a flunky that I would need or would ever wish to correct."

She poured the sparkling yellow liquid into her glass before sliding the other bottle and glasses toward Isaiah and me. Isaiah caught them and popped the top off the bottle with a single hand. The sweet, coppery smell of blood filled the air, and I dared not ask where she got this. Isaiah poured himself a glass before sliding it to me.

"My apologies, *king*." The last word I enunciated with a smirk. "Why do you insist on that title?"

"Because it was one all aspired to have. Why change it now?" Nismera shrugged. "Besides, I love watching the lords curl their lips when they hear it. Since I have a pussy, they prefer queen, but we all know in our world the title of king holds more power."

"That it does." I snorted.

Nismera smiled behind her glass. "Also, you don't have to call me that here. There are no soldiers or guards or fucking council members asking for help. I am not our father. I will not demand respect or for you to use my title every hour of the godsdamn day. Besides, I have missed you."

Isaiah cleared his throat, and Nismera rolled her eyes.

"We," she enunciated, "have missed you."

"I technically missed you more," Isaiah added, cutting a glance toward Nismera. "She's been quite busy, and I've asked every day since that damn portal sealed when you were coming back. I even have the place marked where it closed because it was the last place I saw you."

Something inside my chest flickered. It was as if a small light was switched on in a dark, dusty room. It was so strange to hear that someone missed me. Especially after how long I'd been gone and remembering those I surrounded myself with. The last form of affection I'd received had been years and years ago with Dianna. Emotions now felt weird, to say the least. They made me uncomfortable because they never felt real. All acts of caring or kindness could be yanked away, evaporating like mist on the wind. I was locked in Yejedin for so long that perhaps the part of me that believed in such things had died and rotted there.

"You sentimental fool." I sneered at him, and Nismera laughed.

But I did picture it. Isaiah had grown a reputation of blood and gore long before the realms had ever closed, and Nismera had told me he had only gotten worse after I left. He used that damn power of his whenever he could, bending blood by pure will, honing it to perfection. Nismera told me how he didn't even have to touch anyone anymore to make their blood boil or, worse, rupture. He was a beast in every form of the word, just as I, another reason we had been locked away so godsdamn long.

She said they called him Blood Scorn, and he liked it. Personally, I thought he liked it because it proved we were stronger now. We were no longer those scrawny teens with unkempt powers who so easily believed all of Unir's lies. How innocent we were so long ago, yet it seemed like a flash of memory. We had grown up in the silver palaces, amongst the beauty and florals, but Yejedin, with its smoke and flame, shaped us.

So I didn't blame him for latching on to that name or me. I had protected him then and promised to protect him always, so I laughed at the image that coursed through my brain of the large, muscled High

Guard of Death covered in blood and armor waiting at the edge of a portal that never opened again. Sentimental fool, indeed.

"Call me whatever you wish. I'm just glad you're back, and now you can have all the blood and pussy you want."

I choked on my drink as Nismera sighed, placing her armored boots on the table. "Speaking of that, tell me your plan, Kaden. Why would I need another Ig'Morruthen when you so kindly brought me the blond one?"

I glared at Isaiah, wiping the edge of my mouth before turning back toward Nismera. "Dianna's power is unmatched. She would be a great asset."

"To me," she swirled her drink in the glass, "or you?"

I did not try to hide my feelings. It seemed that had only made everything in my life so much worse, so I only nodded. "I spoke to you daily. You knew my feelings, and they have not changed."

"Ah yes, but hers definitely have. Now, I have rebels crawling around, believing they can't be touched. Hope that she's given them."

I tapped my finger against my glass. Isaiah said nothing, watching us both. "Another reason she can be here, a prime example to take that hope away. Show that you can tame the most untamable. It would give you even more power. Who would ever even think of questioning you then?"

The corner of Nismera's lip twisted. "And how do you expect her to stay here under our rule? We slaughtered her sister. We slaughtered her mate. Do you not think it's time to give up on this useless dream?"

"I have a blade," I said, and Isaiah sat up straighter. "It has runes engraved on the sides. Think the words of Ezalan, but more. I could erase all her memories and replace them. She would want only to serve you, I swear it. Dianna is a weapon I crafted, and a damn good one. She slaughtered Tobias and Alistair with ease. We need her."

I need her, but I did not say that aloud.

Nismera glared at me. "I wanted her away from her mate. You failed that, and yet you think you can accomplish this?"

My skin crawled, unbridled power arcing beneath it in defense of her words. But this was Nismera. The only one who gave a shit about us, so I willed it down. I had not realized how the darkness in the room crept forward until I calmed down, and it receded.

I took a calming breath before saying, "Unir trapped them in the same realm, not me. I kept them apart for a thousand years."

His name was ice in my veins, and the room grew heavy. Nismera simply went on, "And now his death has sent her on a course that will only get in the way of our liberation."

"I did everything you said to make them hate each other. *Everything*. I ripped the false sister from her exactly as you wished. This is as much of your problem as it is mine."

"Except I do not love her."

That made my pulse quicken, and I knew they heard it. Nismera's eyes narrowed into slits, but I could not lie to her or myself. Not anymore. I glanced at my glass, the red liquid darker than the blood on Onuna. "I cannot help the way I feel."

"You know, I have skinned traitors and hung their flesh on poles to wave in the wind for less. Shall I do that to you, Brother? I think our deal of you keeping her as a pet has ended after the display on the remains of Rashearim, don't you? I am down a general and now a handful of soldiers. There must be repercussions." A sly, slick smile formed on her face.

"Are you to make an example of me, then?"

She tapped her sharpened nails against the table. "No, but your beasts will be slaughtered in the great hall. I'll hold an impromptu meeting, and while that occurs, you'll sit in the dungeons for a moon's turn."

My gaze locked on hers. No hint of a smile or joke flowed from her lips, and her shoulders locked as if she meant every word.

"Don't look at me like that. You must be made an example of, my brother or not. My soldier, my legion, will think I show mercy if I don't exact even the smallest punishment for your betrayal. You understand, yes?"

My throat tightened, but I wouldn't show her my fear. I learned eons ago how to mask it, hiding all my emotions. Above all, I couldn't let Isaiah know. But to be locked beneath the palace, I didn't know how far it was, how deep . . . how dark.

"Of course," I said, hoping my voice did not crack or shake.

Nismera tipped her drink back once more before placing it on the table, the clink ringing through my head as my anxiety grew.

"It's merely a week in the holding cell. You've succumbed to darkness far longer than that."

It felt as if all the air had been sucked from the room, and my heart thudded. I had, and I hated every part of it. Most assumed I loved it as it was part of me, but it was the one thing I was truly afraid of. I had grown up with so much light, Unir and Zaysn the epitome of it. Then he shoved us into Yejedin, and the light went out, where only darkness, the scratch of nails along stone, and flames, hot smoldering flames, existed. How ironic was I? The boy who was so afraid of monsters in the dark that I became the very thing I feared.

"Of course," I said again with a cold smile before raising my own glass to my lips. The blood did nothing to settle my stomach. A week. I could do a week . . . unless she forgot about me and left me there to rot like he had.

"I told her a week was enough." Isaiah's voice cut through my thoughts. "She assumed the others would push for a harsher sentence, like a month, but it seemed far too cruel for someone who killed the World Ender."

Right. Isaiah wouldn't forget. I had my brother. He was here. I blew out a breath, squaring my shoulders. "I said okay." The words came out as cold and miserable as I felt.

"Don't be upset," Nismera said. "Isaiah was right, and I did miss you, and I need you for what's coming. I want you to have somewhat of a normal existence now that you're back with us, and if this allows it, so be it."

Isaiah relaxed at her answer, and I caught his smile.

"Thanks." It was small, but all I could manage to say. Maybe I had been away from them both too long, but even the beast beneath my skin refused to settle.

"Do you have it?" Nismera nodded as she poured another glass. "The blade?"

I forced the Ig'Morruthen beneath my skin to calm as I raised my hand. With a flick of power, the blade formed from the darkness, appearing on my palm. I held it at the hilt, the lightning flashing through the table, reflecting in the sharp steel curve.

"I made Azrael make it before his untimely demise. I had planned to use it after we killed Samkiel, but Dianna broke free, leaving with Samkiel's body," I said.

Nismera's lips tightened. "I had soldiers return for Azrael. All that was left of the area was crumbled stone and singed walls. Even his book was gone. I assume she finished him off in her rage when she broke free."

I nodded. I had assumed the same, given the order I forced upon him.

Nismera sighed, unimpressed with the outcome, but leaned forward to study the blade. "And this would work? Make her ours, as you say?"

"Yes."

Her eyes cut to mine. "And that's all you want with your return? Her? Not more power?"

"You say that as if you doubt me."

Nismera didn't even blink. "Call it old trauma, but yes. The Eye has grown restless, and no matter how many I kill or burn, no matter how many places I siege, they continue to grow. Betrayal has become the norm."

"You have nothing to worry about from me. You know that. The throne is yours, Mera. I have no use for it. I never have. Grant me just this."

Her silence was deafening as she watched me, and I knew she was weighing her options. I just hoped they leaned in my favor. The corner of her lips finally tipped up. "The mate of our fallen brother and another weapon in this ghastly rebellion. I suppose it would help. The rebels would lose what little hope they have if we claim someone who has so publicly fought back. Fine. Fetch your toy, then. You explain to the two remaining Kings of Yejedin why you brought their fallen executioner here."

Isaiah chuckled and kicked his feet up. "Speaking of which? Where are those two?"

Nismera shrugged her shoulders, her eyes still on the blade. "Busy. I have them taking care of something." And that was that. We continued to talk, but not of war or plans of siege, just a recollection of our time apart. Laughter filled the battle room until Nismera yawned and excused herself.

Isaiah whistled low through his teeth as he leaned back, his boots resting on the table. "I have to say I've never seen you this enamored with another."

I said nothing as I reached into my pocket and took out the bloodstained coin. I flipped it between my fingers. A thousand years I had with Dianna, and that damned part of me that still hoped and cared wished I had more. I thought I would have forever.

"It wasn't supposed to be like this," I whispered to Isaiah. "They weren't supposed to find one another."

"How did they? Mera never really said. She just threw a table through a stone wall and squished a few guards to death when you told her. I didn't press any further after that."

My lips pressed into a thin line, and I met his eyes. "Truthfully, fate, probably. The plan was for Samkiel to come back after the weapon was made. Dianna would help me kill him before she ever felt the bond and knew what he was to her, but I was wrong. Maybe she was seeking that connection on some level. She killed Zekiel, which brought Samkiel back. They hated each other, and by the time I realized they had teamed up and were looking for that book, it was too late. They have been inseparable since."

Isaiah glanced at the coin in my hand before meeting my eyes. "What's it like? To love?"

I swallowed and clenched the coin in my hand. Isaiah always asked me for guidance as if I were the oldest and he was the youngest. We were all we had. We spent eons trapped in Yejedin, locked away by the one person who was supposed to love us no matter what. Love to us was deadly, powerful, and, above all, something we would rip to pieces to keep.

"Being around Dianna was the first time I truly felt anything besides anger or hate or bloodlust. For us?" My eyes held his. "Love is a terrible, cruel thing."

Isaiah finished his glass in one long gulp before placing it on the table. "Very well then. How exactly will we find her?"

"I have an idea."

IV

Cameron

One week later

A fist made of sharpened bone hit the side of my head so hard I face-planted on the floor. I felt the blood leak from my gash before my skin tingled, and it healed.

Cheers rang out, a thousand voices screaming as the ghastly beast stomped around me. He tossed his massive arms in the air, all four pumping wildly, encouraging the crowd. The bands strapped around his biceps carried small bone fragments of his last victims.

"Puny celestial scum," he snarled as he turned toward me.

I spat at his feet and pushed myself up, every muscle aching. The floor shook as he walked toward me. The screaming of the crowd grew tenfold, row after twisting row of armored beasts and beings from every walk of life. Some seemed to be on a break, puffing smoke from the cigars that hung from their mouths. Others slammed tankards of shimmering liquid against each other, toasting as they watched the fights. A few beings skulked around the edges, trying to blend in. Regardless of who they were, they were all here for the blood sport.

"Your precious World Ender's remains float amongst the stars now."

He kicked the side of my head hard enough that my vision blurred. Flashes of Rashearim burned behind my vision. Images of all of us sitting around laughing, Samkiel's face the brightest.

"You all thought you could best us!" he roared.

Another kick had me spinning through the air, my back hitting the rusted, mangled fence surrounding the arena. I crashed to the floor, my ribs cracked, and my back screaming. I suppressed the healing of my wounds a little longer just to feel the pain.

"War songs were made for you and your ilk. Now look at you. Pathetic."

His foot slammed into my back hard enough to crack the ground beneath me. Even that pain didn't slow the memories of that damned council room. I again saw the symbols etched into the floor, and chains strong enough to hold the god I knew wouldn't last much longer, and it was all because of me. One glance and I hated myself, hated as I turned away and followed after Xavier, the entire time knowing the consequences.

"No more protector for you." Another kick to the face, the crowd growing hungry for more bloodshed.

He was right. There was no one, not anymore, not for me or them. This was Iassulyn.

I tried to push myself up again.

"I think when I am done with you, I will find the rest of your precious Hand brethren and finish them too."

I coughed a laugh as he kneeled and grabbed me by my hair, ripping my head back.

"Maybe I will start with the dark-haired one. What was his name? Xavier?"

I was on my feet in the next second. Gasps overtook cheers as I rammed the jagged talons that replaced my nails through his chin. Pure hate oozed from his eyes, followed by blistering pain. I hoisted him up, my hand driving a fraction deeper, spearing through the fleshy tissue of his tongue. He glared at me and gripped my wrist with two hands while the others flailed, trying to fight me off.

"I think you talk too much." Fangs replaced my teeth, and I brought him closer. "Let me help you with that."

His pulse quickened, and his heartbeat was erratic. Blinding hunger ripped through me. My fangs sank into the rough flesh of his neck, blood thick and heavy filling my throat as I fed. My nose and ribs snapped back into place, the lacerations, scrapes, and bumps tingling. I gorged, gulping greedily, the viscous liquid dripping down my chin as every wound disappeared. His heartbeat slowed, and his body jerked before the last beat fluttered to a stop, the resulting silence destroying another part of me. I leaned back and took a deep breath before tossing him to the ground. He landed with a thud, and I eyed him with disgust, swiping my hand across my face.

The silence lingered for a few stunned moments before the crowd burst into screams even louder than before. Cheers turned to whoops as a voice cracked through the room, but I didn't stay to hear the announcement.

I stalked to the gate, and the guards stepped aside, not even trying to stop me. I grabbed my discarded shirt and tossed it over my head, not slowing down as I headed for the exit. The crowd bickered, yelled, and exchanged money as I ducked around them.

I felt him more than heard him. Spinning, I avoided his outstretched hand. A single curved horn protruded from his head, Nismera's damned gold and black armor covering his body. A commander from some fucking legion. He had been eyeing the entire fight, watching his favorite soldier pummel me.

"You owe me a fucking soldier," he snarled at me.

I snorted. "I don't owe you shit."

The crowd grew louder as two new opponents stripped out of their armor and stepped into the ring, the sound of fists against flesh punctuating the noise. Commander Hornhead, or whatever his name was, took another step forward, blocking my view.

"You give me a soldier, or I take you."

His hand whipped out, attempting to grab me by the throat but stopping a fraction away. A massive hand concealed in dark armor wrapped around the commander's wrist. The room shifted, the darkness growing and filling every corner. The crowd's cheers and murmurs turned to whispers before going silent, and I knew why.

"What do you plan on taking?" Kaden's voice was soft. Maybe it was my newly enhanced hearing that made it seem foreboding. "Tell me again."

The slits of the commander's eyes dilated as he realized who held him. Kaden towered over him by a foot and a half, his shadow of a brother looming on his left. Both men were massive and powerful, demanding the attention of anyone in their shared space. The room felt heavier now, thicker, as if the air had fled in fear.

I didn't know why I hadn't seen just how much they resembled Samkiel until now. They were all one and the same, containing too much power in a single form. One glance, a single motion, and even the strongest would tuck tail and run. The only difference was Kaden and Isaiah didn't carry that flicker of light Samkiel had. They did not smile or ease others as he had. There was no happiness in them, no real joy. They were monsters that stripped away the last living ember of hope this realm or the next had, and I had been an instrument in that.

I hated myself.

Chaos erupted as every single being in here grabbed their armor or belongings and headed out of the arena. I didn't know if it was because Kaden and Isaiah had shown up or the fact that Nismera was never too far away. Either way, no one wished to stay.

"My apologies, High Guard. I was simply seeking reimbursement."

"Reimbursement?" Kaden laughed and looked at his brother. Isaiah's smile was a thing of nightmares.

Kaden's hand tightened on the commander's wrist until he gritted his teeth and fell to his knees. Kaden didn't let go until the commander screamed. The commander cradled his wrist with his free hand.

"I think you've been fully reimbursed, yes?"

The commander nodded, jumped to his feet, and fled. Kaden didn't even spare him a glance as the fleeing commander pushed past the dwindling crowd.

"I think he may have pissed his pants," Isaiah quipped, watching him leave before turning back to me.

"Well, well, well." Kaden glanced at me the way a predator gazes at a nervous fawn. "The little hunter is all grown up and winning pit fights."

"And beating berserkers." Isaiah whistled, grabbing the collar of his armor. "I'm impressed."

"While this is lovely, I'd rather not talk to either of you. Ever." I spun on my heel and made it two steps before my body froze. Every muscle tensed, leaving me completely immobile. I couldn't talk or move. The only things that still worked were my lungs and eyes. What the fuck?

Kaden and Isaiah stepped in front of me. Isaiah's eyes glowed red and swirled with power. He'd done this to me. Oh gods.

"Release him," Kaden said.

Isaiah smiled as I half fell forward, trying to adjust to having power over my body again.

"What the fuck?" I snapped.

"It's not important right now, little hunter." Kaden smiled. "What is important is that I need something from you."

"Oh yeah? Go fuck yourself."

My knees bent, hitting the floor. I growled and glared at Isaiah. "How the fuck are you doing that? Mind control?"

"Nope." Isaiah smiled.

Kaden kneeled near me as I clenched my fists at my side, fighting Isaiah's control. "You might actually like this request, though. I need you to find Dianna."

My head reared back. "What?"

"That's right. We both know you were Samkiel's favorite tracker, and now your power is magnified. I bet you'd find her quicker than an entire legion."

I thinned my lips, trying not to laugh as realization hit me, but it didn't work. It started as a snort before I chuckled, then morphed into full-on laughter.

"You want me to be your little bitch? Fuck you. You turned me, left me to deal with the insatiable hunger, and above all, you let your bitch sister take Xavi."

Isaiah growled and stepped closer.

Kaden raised his hand. "Stop your whining. You've been fed, and Xavi is not yours to keep. If you wished that, maybe you should have acted sooner."

"Xavi?" Isaiah asked, glancing at Kaden.

Kaden waved his hand as if he meant nothing. "The dual blade wielder. Nismera shaved his head and sold him."

My heart lurched, remembering how they had to drag me out of the room when I learned what she was going to do. How Kaden chained me up for a week because the Ig'Morruthen beneath my skin rebelled so hard I killed two guards. Nismera had me beaten as if that were a worse punishment. No, the worst punishment was that I didn't even get to say goodbye. By the time I had healed and regained consciousness, Xavier was gone, and no one would tell me where.

"Oh." Isaiah snorted. "I know four men that look just like him. We'll get him a replacement."

Kaden made a mocking face. "You can't. The little hunter is in love."

Isaiah's smile dropped, then his head tilted as he looked at me.

"Actually, I changed my mind," I said, still bound to the ground. "Both of you can go fuck yourselves."

"I'm not asking." Kaden's hand whipped out, grabbing me by the back of my neck. "You're helping me find Dianna, little hunter. It isn't a debate or question."

"So let me get this right. You killed her sister, gutted her mate to actual death, and now you want to find her to what? Make her love you again?" It was my turn to grin. "And you make quips about who I love."

Isaiah sighed. "I told you it was a stupid idea."

"Shut up," Kaden snapped at him, and Isaiah only rolled his eyes.

"You are actually fucking insane, Kaden." I shook my head. "I didn't believe it, but you really think that finding her will help you? You know she hates you just like everyone else?"

Isaiah glared at me, his eyes flaring with power. My back bent, and I gritted my teeth in pain, feeling my blood boil and my body shudder.

Isaiah finally released his hold on me, and I fell forward, my palms pressed to the floor as I struggled to catch my breath. They both stood as I stayed half-crouched, panting.

"I'm not asking for your opinion."

"What are you going to do? Call your sister on me? You know, the one who locked you up for a week. How was that, by the way? I have to admit, that was the first time I'd felt joy in weeks, when I heard what happened to you and those monsters you made. I guess it explains why you're such a prick. Your own sister doesn't care about you."

His fist shot out, the punch landing against the side of my face. I fell to the floor, blood dripping from my cheek.

I licked my split lip and struggled to my feet, small tingles reaching my toes as I regained every ounce of movement back from Isaiah's hold. "No, I'm not helping you. We both know you're asking for death. After what you've done, what I . . ." I paused, my jaw clenching as it ached, the muscle layer beneath healing. "We're all fucking dead, and you're a fool to think otherwise."

I expected him to hit me again, maybe a kick while I was down, but his eyes only bore into mine. "Do you want to find Xavier or not?"

My eyes narrowed on him, and he smiled, knowing he had me practically by the balls. I'd prefer to be kicked.

"That's right." He added. "You find her, and I'll tell you where he is. You say no, and I can make sure you never find the outpost where she shipped Xavier. I know you've been looking, asking too many questions."

My teeth worried my lip before I sighed. "You won't have to worry about finding Dianna, trust me." I pushed myself up on my feet. "After what you did, what you all did."

"What you helped *us* with as I recall," Isaiah snapped, defending his hellish brother.

"I'll do it," I said. "But take it from me. You won't like what I find. Samkiel's death will have broken her. We all saw what Gabby's death did to her. Dianna will find us and make everyone pay. She's probably slaughtering her way through realms as we speak."

V
Dianna

Two weeks later

Plates clattered to the floor, every bit of breakfast I had laid out for us ruined. The table beneath me creaked as I bucked my hips against his mouth, a desperate moan escaping my lips with each swipe of his tongue. My back arched, his tongue running from my center to my clit. He sucked my clit into his mouth, and my skin burned, every nerve sparking. He alternated between sucking and swirling his tongue in that demanding way that made my toes curl, and my eyes fuse to the back of my head.

"Fuck," I gasped. "You're supposed to be eating breakfast."

Another swipe of his tongue had my body bucking with helpless pleasure.

"I am," he practically purred against my swollen, wet flesh.

I rested my cheek against the table and lifted my knee, giving him more access from where he kneeled behind me. His big hands gripped my thighs, spreading me even further, intent on devouring me completely. His tongue slid over my pussy again, and I saw stars. I bit my lip hard, trying my damnedest to be quiet, but it was pointless. I answered every groan he made against my flesh with a low moan of pleasure and need, pushing back against his face just to feel it again. His tongue speared my core and pushed deep. It felt so good, too good. This was bliss, and I was going to die.

Samkiel knew my body better than I did, and he used that knowledge to edge me again and again. It was senseless agony, but he liked to hear me beg, hear me whine as I called his name over and over again.

We hadn't had sex in six weeks, not since we arrived. The healers had been working to mend the still-healing wound in his abdomen. They had given him the go-ahead yesterday, and as soon as his eyes opened this morning, he had stalked across the bedroom, past our balcony door, and straight to me. He hadn't even looked at the breakfast I'd made for him before slanting his lips over mine. He'd ripped my sleep pants away and bent me over the breakfast table, cutlery, and food be damned.

"Ah, Sami. Right there. Right there," I whimpered, my fingers clenching at the edges of the table in a desperate attempt to ground myself before I fell off. "*Please.*"

My hips bucked as I pressed harder against his face, the scruff on his cheeks another illicit sensation I practically craved now. The breeze flowed across the outer balcony, swirling and caressing my skin, goosebumps rising everywhere it touched. My back bent, and I knew the needy god between my legs was doing more than just devouring me.

"Come on my tongue, akrai," Samkiel demanded, his hands gripping my hips tightly, holding me still for his assault.

That was all it took. With one more flick of his tongue, my back bowed, and I came. Wood splintered beneath my hands as my orgasm ripped through me like wildfire, intense and burning.

My body was still rippling with aftershocks when Samkiel stood and pulled me to my feet. My legs wobbled as he turned me and gripped the back of my thighs, lifting me against his body. The cool air teased at my sweat-slicked back before curving around my nipples to pluck at them teasingly. Samkiel walked me to the balcony wall and sat me on the ledge, the cold of the stone doing nothing to alleviate the heat between my legs.

He placed his fingers against the flat of his tongue, wetting them before lowering his hand to grip my pussy. "This is what I need. You. Just you. I want to bury my cock in you balls deep. Then I want to fuck you until you can't walk. I want you to feel me for days, akrai."

Samkiel pressed close, and I felt encompassed in him as he slipped his fingers into me. Pulling out, he ran my slickness along his swollen, thick cock. My breath caught watching him stroke himself, knowing he was covered in me. I lifted my leg as he watched me with pure, unadulterated lust and rested my ankle against his collarbone. His eyes blazed molten silver as he looked me over with possessive need. The sound rumbling in his chest nearly sent me over the edge once more.

"You want that too. Wicked, wicked girl."

"Only for you." I ran my tongue along my lower lip.

He stepped closer, angling his hips to lock his cock at my entrance. I whimpered and pressed closer, needing him inside me.

Samkiel slapped my thigh, the sting only adding to the aching heat at my core. "Greedy girl."

I nodded feverishly as I watched him. He spread me with the thick crown of his cock, but he barely pressed in a few inches before pulling back. "I've missed how good you feel," he groaned, and I watched between us, my body trembling at the sight. "You missed it too?"

"Yes," I whimpered at the teasing, bracing one hand on the balcony behind me and the other on his biceps.

He pushed in a little deeper, then pulled out. His lips brushed mine, and he whispered, "Five hundred." I growled at his teasing when he thrust in and pulled back out again. I gripped his hair, barely able to grasp the short strands, and pulled him close. He kissed me deeply, my toes curling as our tongues danced. I panted against his lips when he broke the kiss and said, "And four hours is too long to keep us separate."

I moaned as he sank into me again, my body welcoming him with a flood of heat. "You counted," I gasped out.

His lips slanted across mine before he nipped at my lower lip. He gripped the back of my head and met my eyes as he slammed his full length into me and hissed, "Yes."

I cried out and shuddered at the shock of his entry. The angle with my ankle resting on his shoulder and my other leg barely reaching the floor, the thickness of him, and how he filled me so quickly, it was all almost too much.

"Fuck. Fuck, fuck, fuck."

It was all I could think or say as he moved inside me. Every thrust sent waves of heat through my core and into my entire being. It never felt like this before. My powers had dampened so much, but now it was pure, blinding bliss.

My nails raked across the railing right as he started slamming into me. He pounded into me relentlessly, my moans turning to screams. He was no longer worried about hurting me as he had been when we first were together, and this time, he wasn't holding back. A small part of my brain whispered that we should be taking this slower. He had been so wounded, so hurt, and we hadn't fucked for weeks. We had teased, and he had more than once slipped his hand between my thighs or used his mouth on me, but we hadn't done anything like this. Not until now.

I clenched tightly around him, drawing a string of curses out of him. Pleasure shot through me, and I clung to his arm, feeling that building ache as I chased my release. He gripped my waist, pulling me into his thrusts in a brutal rhythm. I could do nothing but hold on, every stroke carving another wave of pleasure from me. His need and his blistering hunger consumed me.

I felt my heart struggle to match his heartbeat, used to the sensation now. The sound of his rushing blood drew my eyes to the veins across his arms and hands. I licked my lips, and my fangs extended. My mouth gaped, a moan escaping me as he nipped at my throat. I caught my reflection in the window, seeing exactly what I feared. My eyes were burning red, and my fangs fully extended as he thrust into me. I snapped my mouth closed, willing that part of me back under control. I rested my head on his chest, hiding from the realization of my beast.

It felt like when I first turned and was out of control. At that time, I was nearly incapacitated by the overwhelming hunger to fuck and feed and rip. I held onto him harder, focusing on the feel of him, the sounds he made, and how I'd never hurt him like that. Never. Never. Never.

His hand gripped my hair, pulling my head toward him. Samkiel leaned in to kiss me, and I turned, exposing my throat. He didn't even notice, taking it as a sign of what I wanted him to do. He nipped and sucked on my neck as he continued to slam into me.

"Talk to me," I gasped. "Tell me filthy, dirty things."

I didn't want him to feel my fangs. There was no way I could feed on him, not now while he was still healing. I felt that hunger subside as I focused on how deep his cock drove into me.

"Fuck." He groaned. "I'm trying to concentrate on not coming too fast." He groaned once more, pulling my head back to look at me as he slowed, one deep thrust, then another. "That will push me over the edge."

"Good." I licked at his kiss-swollen lips. "Fall over the edge with me."

He growled low in his throat and gripped the base of my neck, his lips fusing over mine.

"Treacherous."

Thrust

"Filthy."

Thrust

"Woman."

Sweat glistened across his skin as he fucked me harder. I loved watching his face contort with absolute ecstasy when I tightened around him.

"And you love every second of it."

"Yes." He groaned, nodding frantically. "Every second."

His eyes bled silver as he gripped the back of my hair so tight I moaned.

"Tell me what makes you come harder. When I call you my Dianna . . ." He flicked his tongue over my pulse before pressing kisses along my jaw to my other ear, his cock slamming so deep my eyes crossed. I ran my tongue over my teeth, finding them smooth and flat. He pulled out almost to the tip before plunging deeply into me again. "Or akrai."

My back arched, pushing against him, taking him deeper, needing more of his cock, needing him to be a part of me.

"All of it, but my favorite is when I do this, and you say . . ." I clenched around him, strangling his rigid cock.

"Fuuuck," he groaned out, his eyes rolling back.

I smirked, nipping at his lower lip. "That."

Samkiel's head fell to the curve of my neck, his face contorting in an expression somewhere between pleasure and pain. His knees buckled for half a second as he groaned, and I watched the hardened lines of his abs shudder. His head dipped, my eyes closing tightly as his mouth latched onto my breast. He nipped and sucked at the turgid tip, his fingers tormenting my other nipple, pinching and squeezing. I cried out as he licked and sucked and bit.

Knowing how wild I made him was my favorite thing in the world. There was something so satisfying in seeing my Samkiel lose control and become absolutely unhinged, but there were consequences to driving him to this place. He gripped my hip with one hand, the other slipping between our bodies. His fingers found my clit and circled it once before pinching it, sending a frisson of pleasure mixed with pain through me.

Samkiel bent me back and readjusted his angle before driving into me. With every thrust, he hit that damned spot inside me, forcing a scream from my throat. My head fell back as my belly clenched.

This was payback, and dammit, I loved it. The inhabitants of Jade City probably hated us so much for this, but I couldn't care less.

His thrusts turned feverish, and I knew he was close. "That's my girl," he groaned. "My pretty, pretty girl."

My hands reached for his arms, desperately squeezing the muscles there, trying to hold on as my body burned with pleasure.

"Look at you, taking every fucking inch of me."

My toes curled as I closed my eyes and threw my head back. I felt myself clench around him, another orgasm building.

"That's it. Come for me again. I want to feel it," Samkiel demanded. "Give me what I want."

My back bowed as I did just that, drawing a string of curses from him in return. Those filthy fucking words from him sent me over the edge every time, and he knew it. Samkiel knew how easily he could control my pleasure, and a part of me loved that, too.

He buried himself to the hilt as my body combusted around his. My pussy clamped down tight on his cock, and his body jerked as he came inside me. He groaned, low and deep, his hand leaving my clit and gripping my hips, my sides, anything he could reach.

"Gods," he groaned, lowering his head to the curve of my neck, his cock twitching inside me. "You are divine."

A breathy laugh escaped me. "Depends on who you ask."

Samkiel chuckled, lowering my leg and placing me on my feet. His hands ran up and down my thigh as if soothing a sore muscle. We stayed there for a moment, catching our breath and coming down from our high.

Sometimes, I didn't know where I ended and he began, but I didn't feel like wondering about it any longer. All I knew was the world faded away when we were together, and I would burn anyone and anything to ashes to keep it. If the afterlife was perfect, I wanted mine to be this with him forever and ever, but this was not paradise. It was reality, and reality, like a cold-hearted bitch, snuck her way between us. I felt the shift when it was no longer about us. The insidious whispers reared their ugly heads, reminding us of exactly what had happened, where we were, and what was ahead.

He leaned back, his hands sweeping across the sides of my head and fisting in my hair. He kissed me once, twice, three times. "Good morning."

I smiled against his lips. "The best morning."

He pulled me to him, his arms wrapping around me completely as if having me pressed against his body solved all his problems. Maybe it did help. Gods, I hoped it gave him at least a moment of peace. My hand pressed against his chest, feeling the solid, reassuring thump of his heart. His head rested atop mine, and I could feel the edge of his scar along my abdomen as he held me close. I swallowed, trying to steal a few more moments for us.

I traced the glowing lines on his skin. They pulsed gently, matching the beat of our hearts. I knew they showed up when he used extreme power, but knowing I drew them from him when he was lost and blinded by the pleasure I gave him had a cocky smile playing across my lips. I hoped he only glowed for me.

I didn't know they had a name, but we had talked a lot over the last six weeks, and Samkiel had told me what the adyin were. They trailed all through his body, swirling thin lines, godly marks that manifested when his power was roused.

The light slowly dimmed, his skin returning to the smooth brown hue. Samkiel didn't say anything or move as the weight of the world came crashing back down. He clung to me as if I were his only anchor. I knew what shadows lurked near him, what monsters nipped and clawed at him. He still struggled with them at night, new nightmares haunting him now. I hated it and vowed to burn the world in retaliation for what it took from him.

"You know," I pulled back, looking up at him, "I was just thinking, who knew the terrifying World Ender required cuddles after mind-blowing sex?"

His brows lifted, and I saw the shadows retreat to the farthest corners of his mind. "Mind-blowing, huh?"

I shrugged. "Okay, you got me. Mediocre. I just didn't want to hurt your feelings."

"Hmm." He nodded, but I caught the slight grin. My laughter died on a squeal as he yanked me off my feet and tossed me over his shoulder before striding away from the mess of our breakfast.

Samkiel leaned against the tub with his eyes closed as I used the bubbles to mold the longest part of his hair into a ridge along the top of his head.

"You could probably go to sleep here, huh?"

He smirked, his arms hanging off the sides of the tub, his body almost too enormous to fit. "Mm-hmm."

My hand ran over one eyebrow, chasing away the small line of soap sliding toward his eye.

"Where did you even find bubbles? Their soap here usually turns into that murky cream color."

"I asked Miska."

My head reared back, my lip turning up. "Who is Miska?"

His grin widened, and his hand patted my butt. "Calm down. She's one of the youngest healers here, and I'd say the nicest."

My lips tugged to the side. Samkiel knew most of them by name since they were with him the majority of the day, trying to heal his side. I only remembered them by their hair. Some had short or long, some wore jewels in the strands, and that one with a ponytail whose eyes lingered far too long on Samkiel. I disliked her the most.

I sat up a fraction in the tub, the soap clinging to me. "Did she give you these because she's nice or because she has a raging crush on you?"

Samkiel peeled one eye open, that damn smirk still curving his perfect lips. "Relax, akrai. On your home world, she would be no more than fourteen. She is merely a sweet kid."

My jealousy instantly died, the Ig'Morruthen in me curling up and going back to sleep. "Now that you mention it, I haven't seen any kids here."

"There aren't. She's the youngest, and from just what I've seen, she has no friends. So, yes, I asked for bubbles since you hate the other soap, and I was being nice."

I smiled, leaning back into him, but before I could speak, he hissed and half sat up. I jerked forward, water splashing to the floor as panic outweighed any critical thinking in my head. The memory of that tunnel flashed through my mind when his face crumpled in pain and his skin turned gray, his light dying.

"What is it?" I scanned him wildly.

"Nothing." He shook his head, failing to convince me with his fake smile. "You pressed . . . I'm just sore, that's all."

"Maybe having sex so soon wasn't a great idea. Maybe we—"

"No!" He sat up straighter, and I snorted.

"A few more days or even a week isn't going to kill either of us. Besides—"

"No." He clasped his hand with mine. "It's another way to spend time with you, and it's the only time I don't think. I just feel. If you don't wish to, that's fine, but don't hold back from me because you think I cannot handle it."

My hand swept across the side of his face, his hair still sticking up in different directions. "Okay."

"Besides," he lifted a shoulder, "I've fought battles that left me limp and damn near immobile and still had sex afterward. This is nothing."

My hand dropped hard enough that the water splashed. "With who?"

His laugh echoed off the walls as he wiped a few stray bubbles from his face. "I was just trying to distract you."

"Distract me?" My nose scrunched. "Oh, so funny. I'll distract you."

I leaned toward his laughing mouth, my lips hovering over his as a swirling mass of energy formed in the doorway.

"Roccurem," Samkiel said, but it was not the playful tone I heard mere seconds ago. Now, he was agitated. "Knocking is a pleasantry I'd like you to adopt."

I snickered as Samkiel shifted in the tub, trying to hide me behind his massive frame.

"My apologies, my liege. I did knock, however, to no avail. The queen requests you. Her subjects have been persistent in wanting to remove the remaining stitches this morning."

The muscles along Samkiel's back flexed at that, and I drew a face in the soap bubbles that slicked the heavy muscles.

"That was to happen at midday."

"Yes, my liege. It is way past."

My finger stilled. "Wait, what time is it?"

I pushed at Samkiel's shoulder, trying to move around him. He whipped his head toward me, a low noise of disagreement rattling in his throat.

I rolled my eyes. "Would you stop? Roccurem has seen both of us naked and together, I might add, probably several times. You know fate and destinies and all."

Samkiel waved a hand. "It does not matter. Roccurem can wait outside while we get dressed."

I could have sworn a light smirk touched the fate's face, but it was gone just as quickly. "As you wish," Roccurem said, seeming to approve of Samkiel's protectiveness toward me.

He disappeared, and I stepped out of the tub, Samkiel right behind me. I gave him one of the towels and wrapped one around my body. "So territorial," I said with a smirk.

He flicked my nose before kissing it. "I don't share the naked sight of you with fate or otherwise. Now let's get dressed."

"Yes, my liege," I said, lowering my voice like Reggie's.

"That's not funny."

"It's kinda funny," I quipped, following him out.

VI

Dianna

Samkiel kissed me once more before leaving to meet the queen. My smile dropped from my face the second the door closed behind him.

"What?"

The air stirred as Reggie formed. "You made a mess in Tarr."

I fell from the sky amidst a rush of flames, my wings fanning the fire. Soldiers yelled and brandished their weapons. The townspeople, not hiding, watched from their windows, gaping at the brutality. My form shifted, the dark mist swirling around me before dissipating. I walked forward, yanking a sword from the gut of a fallen soldier as I stepped over him. I stopped in front of the lot of them and raised the bloody weapon. My fangs scraped across the metal as I licked the blood dripping from the blade. This would be a nice way to release some steam.

Eyes narrowed behind the gold and black plated armor, and they shuffled, stepping back as if they had anywhere left to run. These were Nismera's, and they weren't leaving. I raised the sword between us, pointing to the largest brute.

"Who wants to die first?"

No one moved, and as a group, they held their breath.

I sneered at them in disgust and stepped onto the body of the downed soldier, using his head as a step. I spun to face the watchful city. Spreading my arms wide, I yelled, "Let it be known that I do not fear your wretched king. Know and tell all, I will hunt every being who wears her colors or screams her name in praise. I will feast on you and your loved ones, making you watch as I do it. Nismera will be a footnote in history, and all who follow her will die screaming."

A soldier charged forward, and I twisted my sword, piercing him through the middle.

"Like that." I yanked the sword from his body and tossed him to the ground, not bothering to see who closed and locked their doors and windows first. It was time to send a message.

"I might have been a *little* dramatic." A small smile lifted my lips as I turned toward him. "You said to cause a distraction in the East. I did. They think I'm there. They will never look toward the west of the realms."

"A distraction, yes, not a taunt." Reggie's gaze didn't falter. "You made a bloody mess. You burned and tore her soldiers to pieces. That's an act of war for Nismera. Did you not think I'd see the colorful note you left her? She knows."

I snickered. "Did she? What was that like?"

"Dianna," Reggie said, exasperated.

"I thought I did a good job."

"It is not a game," Reggie said. "Her power is unparalleled. There is a reason she has so many allies that bend so freely to her. Powerful, terrible allies."

"Like you once were?" My head tilted toward him.

Reggie did not falter. "And I betrayed her for you."

He did. He had when he helped me get to Samkiel and then in the tunnels.

"I know. That's why you're still breathing," I said and moved to the balcony, stepping over the scattered food and broken plates.

"Did you see anything from their memories? A location, perhaps?"

My body froze. "No."

"No?" he asked.

I hadn't told him that my blooddreams seemed to stop after I woke up on the slab in those tunnels. I assumed it was due to being drained, but I was still unsure.

"My head is just scattered," I lied. "Maybe I just can't see anything right now? Maybe I overate, and all the noise just canceled out. I don't know."

Reggie glanced at me in disbelief, but I knew he wouldn't push it. One thing I could rely on with fate is that he already knew it and was testing me, waiting for me to figure it out since, technically, he was not supposed to intervene. I wouldn't tell him how thoroughly he had already failed at that. His eyes flicked toward the room.

"He needs to know."

"Which part?" I smiled innocently.

"All of it," Reggie said. "But most importantly, his demise."

Demise. That word rattled my bones. It made it seem so permanent, but it wasn't. Samkiel was alive . . . very alive and whole if this morning was any indicator. Yet still, as if death's cold embrace waited in the corner, I halted. No, we were fine. Everything was fine. Nothing waited in the shadows of my room. I was just experiencing another weird symptom of my grief. Sucking in a breath, I waved Reggie's comment off and started to clean up the mess we'd made.

"You're hiding him away from the world," Reggie said.

I stopped with a broken dish in my hand. "I don't know what you're talking about."

"What of The Hand?"

The dish shattered in my grip, and I swallowed the growing lump in my throat. I slowly turned toward him. He stared back at me, not wilting beneath my glare.

"Am I wrong?"

"They're dead anyway, in case you forgot."

"Do you really feel that way?" Reggie asked with the slightest bit of censure in his tone. "This family you found and grew to love, you truly believe they are gone and will do nothing?"

No. I didn't. I felt . . . I sucked in a breath, trying to calm not only my nerves but my anger.

"Don't do that!" I snapped back.

"Do what?" he countered.

"Act as if you don't know I killed Azrael because he couldn't be saved."

"Your father," Reggie corrected as if he'd actually been that to me.

"Azrael." I drug the name out, letting it hang in the air. "Because he couldn't break the hold. They are just as dead. He said it. You really think I want Samkiel to see the ones he loves the most that way, or worse, they try to kill him?"

Reggie clasped his hands in front of him. "And does Samkiel know this?"

I dropped the plate and advanced on him, stopping a hair away from him to hiss, "Don't you dare tell him!"

"It will not be enough for him, and you know it. Regardless of why you wish to keep them separated, he will not rest until he finds them."

"You don't think I know that? But there is no way he's even remotely strong enough or ready to go searching."

"Then get him ready. Help him." Reggie didn't back down, and for a second, I was worried as to why. It sent a chill down my spine to see him this persistent.

"For what? Another disappointment?" I turned away from Reggie, blowing out a breath.

"Are we speaking about him or you?"

My fists clenched at my sides. I hated how right Reggie was at times. "Listen, he just needs a break and time to heal before he sets out on another heroic mission. He's not ready. The *wound* hasn't fully healed. He's still sore and can't move in certain ways without severe pain."

Reggie only glanced at the mess on the balcony before meeting my eyes. "Or perhaps you are not ready."

I said nothing for a moment, but I knew the truth, and so did he. I couldn't imagine if the roles were reversed. If Gabby's mind had been taken over, and she'd tried to kill me. I wouldn't have been able to do it. I'd much rather turn the blade on myself, and I feared he might have to face that, too. He loved them deeply. Maybe I was keeping him away from that pain. He had shielded me from such. How could I say

I cared about him and not try to protect him, even if it made me seem heartless? I also knew the one harrowing truth that would make even Samkiel hate me if he knew of it.

"My father, as you like to put it, raised a weapon to me in those caves while under that spell," I said, pausing to make sure I had Reggie's attention. "A spell *he* created. He fought, but he wasn't strong enough. Samkiel needs to be if we encounter them because if they raise a weapon to him, try to hurt him, Hand or not, I'll kill them myself."

Reggie nodded as if finally understanding why I hesitated, but when I really looked at his expression, I wondered if maybe he'd just wanted me to say it out loud.

"You are amata. I'd expect no less."

I nodded and returned to the mess on the floor, determined to clean it up. Despite my words and bravado, my entire life felt out of my control. I couldn't even tell him of the fear that lived in me that I would still lose Samkiel. No matter what else might happen, I could fix this.

"Has he inquired more about that?" Reggie asked as I passed him, dumping bits of fruit and bread in the trash.

"Only every day, in some way or fashion," I said, heading back to the balcony.

"And what do you tell him?"

A harsh laugh left me as I kneeled. "Oh, I say, 'yeah, babe. So we had a mark. It only formed when you died, and I threatened the universe to get you back. It was there for a while, then disappeared, and fate and I have no idea what that means. Oh, by the way, did I mention you died?'" I glared at Reggie as I stood up, making my way back inside to the trash.

"How did he take it?"

"Reggie." I shook my head. "I'm lying, just like I am to him. I haven't told him, and I don't know how or what my price is for him being back."

"You need to," Reggie said again.

"I know," I said, tossing the pieces of broken plates away. "Reggie, I will. I just don't know how, and a part of me worries that if I say it out loud, he will disappear. You know, I watch him sleep just to make sure he's breathing. I feel like I am going insane."

Reggie watched me make another pass by him, continuing to clean up and carry things to the trash. He waited for me to stop and look at him before saying, "If Nismera learns he is still alive—"

"She won't," I interrupted and nodded toward the balcony. I needed air. Reggie followed behind me.

"Nismera will hunt you, and if she gets close to you, she gets close to him."

My hands splayed across the ledge. "She won't."

Reggie sighed as he stood next to me. "How can you be so sure?"

The breeze shifted across the hairs along my hand, causing me to wrap one around my ear. "I've been doing this far longer than you have. I'm pretty sure I know how to be the villain."

"Is that what you wish? Do you want to build a throne out of fear?"

"One, I'm not building a throne. I'm carving a path of blood and destruction to hide him from the world. Second, do you think they follow Nismera because they *like* her? They listen to her, including Kaden, because they fear her. If anyone made a throne from it, it's her."

Reggie ran a hand over his face. "Your methods are not ideal. I am just afraid that with one slight mishap, she will learn he is alive."

My heart clenched because I knew her first order would be to kill him permanently, and no matter how tough I thought I was, I knew her power was greater than mine.

"I'm afraid, too," I admitted. "Afraid if she does, I won't be able to stop her. Samkiel gets worn out even with the smallest use of power right now. He thinks I don't notice, but I notice everything about him. Nismera has a whole legion at her beck and call. Allies, his two hateful brothers, and I don't know shit about these realms."

"To admit fear is a sign of true strength. I hope you are aware of that. By saying it, you take that control back."

I glanced at Reggie, knowing now that was what he'd wanted. He wanted me to say it out loud, to admit the truth. Maybe he was worried, as Samkiel was, that I'd regress and hide my feelings. But I was not the same woman they had met on Onuna, and I'd never be again.

"I do know one thing more than any," I said, holding his gaze.

"What's that?"

"No matter what, I will kill anyone and everything to make sure she doesn't find him. Even if he hates me or I die in the process."

His eyes bore into mine, but I meant every single word I said. I was finally comfortable in my own skin, happy with who I was, and no matter what, I wouldn't let that change. For the first time in centuries, I knew who I was. Samkiel may have died in that tunnel, but the part of me that was conflicted about the darkness living within me died with Gabby. Anything good in me didn't survive the loss of them.

The balcony grew silent. Wind whistled between us as the clouds rolled in, fog forming at our feet with how high we were above the planet.

"There is one other matter I need you to consider seriously." Reggie focused on me, his expression as grim as I had ever seen it.

"What now?" I all but rolled my eyes.

"Resurrection is forbidden for a reason. It has not been performed for any reason. Even the strongest, most deadly necromancer can only revive tissue, not the soul. Who knows what it has done to you and him? What if it is not permanent? If he is not permanent?"

"Don't," I said, unable to keep the growl from my voice. I wouldn't even allow myself to think about the possibility of that.

"I am not trying to upset you, but you need to consider all possible outcomes. Even for yourself."

My head whipped to him. "Why are you being so headstrong about this? It's been weeks. If something were going to happen, it would have by now. I mean, he seems—"

"My visions are sporadic. Some come in waves or fragments, but they are all broken."

Dread clenched my gut, goosebumps flecking my skin. "What?"

Reggie shrugged a shoulder, and I realized he was slowly starting to seem more mortal than fate. "The whispers, the words from the universe, have never behaved this way before. I even have days where I see nothing but darkness, no matter how hard I manifest it. Whatever you did in that tunnel altered more than you think. The universe will always have its balance. There will always be consequences. I know mine, but what are yours?"

"Reggie." I stood up straighter, reaching for his hand.

He pulled back. "I do not tell you this for pity, but you must be aware. If this has happened to me, what else has been altered? For you? For him?"

"I don't care what happens to me," I said, pulling my hand back, an easy, honest smile curving my lips because I meant it. "If you think I'll ever regret it, you're wrong."

"I do not. I know your selflessness well, but I worry nonetheless."

I clicked my tongue and smirked. "A fate with a heart. Who would have thought?"

The tension between us seemed to melt away then. Reggie cocked his head with a small smirk. It was such a mortal expression from one so ancient. "Perhaps I have just been in your presence for far too long."

"If I'm your role model, you're definitely fucked." My chuckle made even fate's lips twitch.

"You are far too hard on yourself."

"Maybe, but now that you've mentioned it, could this be what is affecting Samkiel's healing?" I asked. "I mean, it's been weeks, and while it's better, it's still bad."

"They think you two being unable to stay off of each other is slowing the healing process," Reggie said, glancing at the half-cracked table behind us.

I snorted even as heat flushed my cheeks. "Kissing and sex are two very different things. We just had sex this morning for the first time in weeks. That is not the problem."

"I am only telling you what they whisper," Reggie said. "Everyone has heard the hidden moans after training or between his healing sessions. They are only concerned."

The smile on my face was pure mischief. It was true that we hadn't had sex until this morning, but that didn't stop Samkiel from kissing and touching me since he awoke. For days, I'd been so damn worried when he hadn't even opened his eyes. When he did, I needed that closeness.

A week after he woke, we had attempted to be together fully, only for him to nearly pass out from the pain. Since then, we hadn't gone farther than his hands pressing and squeezing, dipping between my legs. It was more than sex for us. That intimacy was another way we proved we were alive and still together. Of course, orgasms are always a plus.

My eyes narrowed. "Concerned? Yeah, okay, I've seen the way they look at him. I think their only concern is if they can have a turn." I looked at Reggie and put my hands on my hips. "It was the one with the ponytail, wasn't it? She's always watching him. I wonder if anyone would notice if I pushed her off the balcony. Wait, can they fly?"

Reggie made a noise of disgust and covered his face. "Dianna."

I went on but noticed he didn't answer if they could. "Listen, besides my murderous tendencies, I think the magical death spear that was shoved into his gut and ripped the realms open is what has slowed his healing. You know, the one he died from? Not us fooling around."

Reggie nodded. "Well, yes, but we cannot tell them that, I presume? Maybe their healing techniques would be different if they knew what he was stabbed with?"

"No."

"I merely mean it may speed the healing process."

"And the process of our enemies knowing he is alive. I don't trust them enough to share that. Besides, if they are these miraculous healers, they should've been able to heal it without knowing. We stick to our original plan. If anyone asks, he is a soldier from The Eye, and I'm the defected Ig'Morruthen."

Reggie sighed and rubbed a hand over his face. "Very well."

I exhaled, watching him carefully. "Is there something else?"

I knew Reggie, knew those wheels were turning in his brain.

"How's your appetite?"

I glanced toward the food piled in the small trash. I had brought enough for us both, thinking he'd eat first, but also to maintain the illusion I would, too. Over the last few weeks, I had tried to eat, but I couldn't help how bland it tasted or how my stomach churned with every bite. I would wait until he was gone and hold out as long as I could before it came back up.

"Everything is . . ." I wanted to lie like I so casually did with Samkiel, but I feared Reggie had already seen the truth. "Bland, except . . ."

"Blood."

The word hung between us.

"It's all I want, all I crave now. It's never been like this before. Even on Onuna, after Gabby passed, I could control it. If I don't feed, staying in the same room with anything living is hard. The last time I remember it being this bad was when I was first turned."

"When was the last time you fed?"

"Tarr."

"That was over a month ago."

"Well, I ate half an army. I thought it would last longer." I took a shuddering breath and looked at Reggie. He was my friend, the only one I had right now, and I knew I could trust him even with everything that had happened. I glanced down at my hands to see I was sliding my fingers over the spot where my mark should have been. "When Samkiel and I were . . . I would never hurt him, but maybe you're right. Maybe something is wrong with me."

Reggie was silent for a moment, and I didn't dare to look up. "Do you feel you are regressing?"

I nodded. "I feel I denied who I was for too long, and now it refuses to go back. My powers came back with a vengeance, but Kaden bled me out in that tomb. Perhaps there is no more celestial part of me left."

Reggie sighed. "Perhaps it is more than that. You spoke of your dreams once when we returned. Do you still have them?"

My heart thundered. "Yes."

"And?"

"And nothing has changed. It's still that man sitting on that throne made of bones. All I see before I wake up is him beckoning me to him and then nothing."

"Do you remember what he looks like? Perhaps a ruler of the Otherworld senses your power? Maybe he wishes for an alliance."

I shivered, running my hands over my arms. "I don't know. All I remember is walking through the darkest part of the world. There's no noise, not even a breeze. It looks like a monstrous graveyard. Bones stick up in every direction as if a hundred massive beasts had fallen from the sky and died right there. I always take the same path through the mouth of the largest beast. The walls are dark and jagged, and he's there, sitting, watching me. I see orange eyes and hair made of spikes."

"Spikes?"

"Horns? I don't know. Even in my dreams, it's too hard to tell." I rubbed my arms, a chill running across my body. "He doesn't move, just sits like he's waiting for something."

"Do you see any type of armor?"

My lips pursed as I tried to recall. "His shoulders, yes, I suppose some type of armor, but it's blurry. I don't know. All I know is it's happened a few times, and I'm startled awake as though he's in the room with us every time."

"I assume you haven't told Samkiel this either?"

My eyes narrowed. "That I'm dreaming of another man? No, I haven't. It's just another thing I'll have to explain when I tell him I brought him back to life."

Reggie was nothing but cool and complacent as he turned from me. He watched the billowing pink-tinged clouds. "You should tell him soon, my queen. Secrets have buried rulers faster than any blade."

Uneasiness swept in before I could smother it. Reggie was right. I needed to tell him, tell him everything, actually. I just didn't know where to begin.

VII

Samkiel

I exited the healers' quarters, lowering my shirt. Soft giggles and whispers followed me out, but I ignored them as I turned down the hall. The scents of flowers and healing herbs filtered through the air. An assortment of lush plants and vines grew from the walls, columns, and ceilings, twisting and twining through the infrastructure of the palace.

I slid my hand across my scar, and a small hiss left me. It was still sore but better than before. At least with the last few stitches out, I felt I was progressing.

As I made my way to my next appointment, I took a deep breath and ran through the cover story Dianna and I had decided on. Lying was not my strong suit, but I knew what I had to do. I grabbed the curved door handle and twisted it without knocking. The door opened easily, and I stepped inside. Frilla looked up and giggled, her flower-patterned lace dress skittering across the floor as she rose. I noticed the rare green jewels that graced her fingers and wondered just how well they paid the Jade City healers that she could afford those. I offered her a soft smile, wincing as I curled one arm in front of me and bowed. I hoped my smile still seemed genuine when I rose, with no hint of the twinge of pain that still lingered.

"Please." She chuckled slightly, waving her hand. "You do not have to bow, Cedaar. You are a guest here."

Cedaar. The name Dianna and Roccurem suggested, along with this elaborate ruse. I smiled and stood upright as she waved me over.

The large carved-out windows allowed the clouds in. They spread inside and dusted the floor in a pink haze. Plant life spread over every portion of this luxurious room as it did this entire world. Large baskets, overflowing with brilliant flowers, hung every few feet. Several plush, elongated ottomans were placed about the room, each paired with a small table lined with bowls of fruits and pastries.

"You summoned me, my queen."

It still felt peculiar to have that roll off my tongue. Dianna was my queen, the only one who would receive that title from me, the only one I'd bow to. Yet I had to play the part, so I forced myself to use the correct terms.

Frilla blushed, the lavender hue across her cheeks darkening. Her consorts glared at us, the two men and women sitting at the far end of the room, whispering as they finished their morning meal. I couldn't help the small smirk that curved my lips, remembering my own breakfast.

Frilla stopped before me, clasping her hands in front of her. The intricate flower crown she wore rose high on her head, parts of it twisting like vines on trees with small flowers that seemed to open and close.

"Pennynickels," I said, nodding toward it.

She giggled as she raised her hand to touch it. "Yes. Are you familiar? They are a lost jewel."

I swallowed. "My mother had a garden when I was younger. She liked them and said they winked when they were happy and well-taken care of."

I didn't mention how my father had surprised her with a whole bush of them one year with as many colors as he could find just to make her smile. How every early morning, she would take me on a walk to see them since they seemed to enjoy sunrises the most.

Frilla didn't press the conversation, taking my words as flirtation as they were meant to be. Her cheeks heated as her lashes beat a fraction harder. "Come sit with me."

Flashing a brief smile, I nodded and followed after her as she turned, the train of her dress flowing behind her. I glanced around the room. I knew there were no exits besides the main bay windows and the door, and the florals she had in here were all harmless, but I could still smell the tinge of something more potent. A male servant pulled a chair out for her, and a woman appeared, filling her cup with a liquid that filled the air with a sweet aroma.

I sat at the small table as another man brought me the same drink.

"Thank you once again for helping as you have and letting us stay."

She smiled, interlacing her fingers as she leaned forward. "Of course. Any member of The Eye is a friend to us. Nismera and her legion have been a disease on these realms, you know."

"Yes, very well."

She took a sip of her wine, savoring it. Placing her cup down, she ran her finger over her lower lip, catching the drop that had threatened to fall onto the white lace of her dress. She held my gaze as she slipped her finger into her mouth and sucked. A bold and flirtatious move, and one I had to pretend to enjoy even though it did absolutely nothing for me.

Her consorts seemed to dislike it as well, shifting restlessly and avoiding meeting either of our gazes.

"Even with the request to meet alone, I sense the Ig'Morruthen through these walls. She does not stray too far from you, does she? Not that I blame her," she all but purred.

A smile spread across my lips. I assumed she'd nap until I went back upstairs after this morning, but I shouldn't be surprised. Since Rashearim, she hadn't left my side. Even with the thick walls separating us here, I still felt Dianna as if she were next to me.

"No, she does not." I nodded. "She's protective."

"I've noticed." The queen raised her brow. "How serious are you two?"

She is my everything. The words floated across my mind, a truth that lived deeper than my flesh and bone, one buried in my very atoms.

"You know war." I shrugged, forcing a smile. "It breeds closeness but not permanence."

Her eyes flicked across me, and I tried not to show my disinterest.

"I must say, it is quite intimidating for us to be this close to one." She giggled. "An Ig'Morruthen. We heard the stories of how the Primordials made them from a fraction of themselves to best the gods. They were granted the power to devastate cities, yet this one seems most content to just be in your presence." She reached forward and grabbed a small piece of fruit from the tray. Popping it into her mouth, she chewed and swallowed before saying, "Tell me, just out of curiosity, what deathly gift does she possess? The most legendary could breathe lightning like the gods long dead."

I buried my uneasiness at her question, instead reaching for my glass and taking a sip. "Flame, your majesty."

"Fire? That's . . . old."

"Old?" I raised a brow.

She ignored my question, shooting a glance at the woman fluttering about near the fruits, something unspoken passing between them. Frilla turned back to me and asked, "And how did this partnership bloom? I'd never thought I'd see such a close connection between two warring sides. The Eye, no offense to you, always seemed to be above petty things. The rebellion is what matters, you see."

Memories flooded my mind. A small smile flickered across my lips when I thought of the truth. I leaned forward, my hands wrapping across my elbows. "To be honest, we didn't like each other at first, quite the opposite. I think it's because we were too much alike. Stubborn. Hard-headed. Strong-willed. But we were forced to work together for a common goal. That closeness formed something stronger than dislike. We got to know each other and realized we had far more in common than not."

I didn't tell Frilla how being with Dianna made days feel like minutes, how time started to not exist the closer I had gotten to Dianna. After a while, against my better judgment, she was all I saw, all I thought about, and no matter how much I lied to myself in the beginning, she was all I craved. She lit a spark inside me, chasing away that harrowing darkness, and all it did was burn brighter the more I was with her. I never wanted it to go out, and I was afraid of what lengths I would go to keep it.

A sparkle lit her eyes before she cleared her throat. "Are you sure you two aren't in love?"

"Mutually beneficial, I assure you." I winked at her. "Maybe we can be as well."

Someone dropped a tray in the far corner. The man was dipping to his knees and apologizing as he gathered the fruit onto a plate. Frilla's cheeks heated once more as she cleared her throat and adjusted her posture, attempting to appear more appealing.

"I can tell you what we have discovered since you arrived. There is no more Samkiel. The fabled God King is dead, it seems. It happened while you were unconscious, so I apologize for breaking the news like this. I know The Eye had been hoping for his return."

She shrugged as if my supposed death and the realms crumbling were no inconvenience to her and went on. "The Hand is dismantled and under Nismera's rule. Hope, what fleeting ounce The Eye held onto, is gone."

I swallowed as if she hadn't just twisted a blade in my already wounded gut with her words. The images plagued me every godsdamn second. Every time I closed my eyes, I saw my body on that damn floor, bleeding out, as my family walked through those portals, their eyes vacant. They were the perfect soldiers my father had warned me of eons ago.

"My faction does not see that as the end."

Her head tipped toward me as the words left my lips. "How so? Nismera is a goddess of war. The strongest in this realm or the next, now that Unir and his prodigal son are dead. She has the same Ig'Morruthen beasts as you, only now I hear she has three."

That was another slap to my already bruised soul. Cameron.

"To assume all hope is lost would be a grave error, in my opinion. As long as you are alive and have a willingness to help, hope is never lost. It's when you truly give up, when you quit, that it's gone forever, and regardless of size or numbers, I refuse to give up hope."

Frilla pushed back in her chair, steepling her elegant hands. "Maybe that is why The Eye is still present after all these years. You all give riveting speeches."

A soft chuckle left my lips, and with that, the meeting was over.

I stepped out into the hall, the large doors closing behind me. The sweet smell of pivorgreen filled the air, sticking to the walls with its small stalks of white, rounded bulbs. This entire palace was covered in vines and ferns. The flowers along this corridor followed my movements as if watching me, and I had a sneaky suspicion they just might be.

A sharp whistle up ahead caught my attention. Dianna leaned against the wall, her arms folded across her chest, wearing one of the lean, black ensembles I had made for her days ago. She wanted something similar to what she'd worn on Onuna when we worked out, something easy to move in. She dazzled me no matter what she wore, but I had to admit the tight clothes that hugged her every dip and small curve were my favorites.

"What are you doing?" I asked, bracing one hand against the wall beside her head and leaning my body into hers. My free hand curved around her back, reaching one of my favorite curves. "I figured you'd be resting."

She smiled up at me before ducking under my arm and taking a step away. "I had to take the trash out. You're a messy eater."

Even as she distanced herself from me, my body buzzed with electricity at her double entendre and the memory of this morning. She caught whatever expression crossed my face and rubbed a spot behind her ear. I turned, remembering the signals she'd taught me, and saw a few healers coming toward us. They slowed their pace as they passed us, and we waited until they were gone before Dianna spoke.

"How did your date with our girlfriend go?"

I shrugged. "Absolutely riveting."

"Learn anything?"

My eyes darted toward a few of the flowers above her head. "I feel dirty."

"River?"

"River." I nodded.

VIII

Samkiel

I darted under a hanging branch, turning quickly through an overgrown patch of trees. I leaped over the fallen log, hearing her paws beating the ground behind me. Fuck. I dodged left, then right, and then there was silence. She was fast. Too fast. I smelled the river up ahead. I had a mile left and focused on propelling my legs harder. The muscles in my abdomen burned, but I ignored it. I had been stabbed before. This wasn't new. I'd been damn near bitten in half and survived, so I knew how wounds healed. It had been long enough for me, so why did my side still sting?

I ducked and sat, sliding on my ass. I rode the slope down and landed on my feet. A quick look back showed massive jaws snapping closed at the top of the hill, her piercing red eyes glowing from the darkness between two collapsed logs. I couldn't help but grin. I had seen the new path a few days ago when she caught me here and knew it would buy me some time. A low growl rumbled from her throat, and I knew she was proud but pissed.

The slap of water against stone greeted my ears. I was so close. I jumped up, sprinting toward the river's edge. The small creatures of the forest scurried into hiding, their skittering heartbeats telling me my Ig'Morruthen was not far behind. My hand whipped a pile of overgrown brush out of my way as I ran faster. Sunlight dipped between the trees, and I could smell the rushing water as it flowed and toppled off the end of the world. Small patches of wild grass grew along the bank, and a burst of energy shot through me. This was the farthest I had made it since we started this game, but my victory was short-lived as a massive dark form tackled me from the side.

Air rushed from my lungs as we toppled over one another before coming to a stop. I groaned, pain slashing through my abdomen. The massive, dark wolf hovered above me, her piercing red eyes boring into me. Her lips were pulled back in a snarl, exposing glistening fangs. A low growl rumbled in her throat right before I felt teeth around my ankle, dragging me over the small rocks and back toward the brush, away from the river's edge.

Just past the thick brush, she released my leg. Her form melted and flowed from her beast back into her lithe form, her dark hair spilling over her shoulders as she looked down at me.

I sat up a bit, bracing myself on my elbows as I glared up at her. "Ow."

"Your enemies won't be kind to you." Her eyes darted to my side. Part of my shirt lifted to show the still bruised flesh beneath it. "We have seen that much."

I huffed and pushed myself to my feet, wiping dirt from my pants. "Yes, but I thought you'd be. You're not my enemy."

I saw the tension in her shoulders, even if she tried to hide it beyond one of those adorable little smirks. "In our scenarios, I need to be."

I glanced toward the river's edge, past the brush of the forest. "I made it closer."

She snorted a laugh, her arms folded as she looked between me and the river. "Barely."

My eyes narrowed. "I don't remember you being this hard on me the last few times we've tried."

A look crossed her face quickly as she buried whatever thought crossed her mind. She squared her shoulders. "I want you to survive with that wound," she said, nodding toward my middle. "I can't go easy on you. It won't help, and you can't go light on me either. You could have used a burst of power small enough to throw me off, but you didn't."

She was right, as usual. Achingly beautiful and brilliant, she was definitely deadly in more ways than one. The only problem was I wouldn't use it. I could have tossed her away from me, but burning her in the process was out of the question.

"I won't risk hurting you, even if we are training," I said.

"Well, that's the problem," she snapped. "How will either of us get better if we hold back here? I'm not fragile, Samkiel. You, above all, should know that."

"I never said you were." My brows furrowed. "Where is this coming from? You were fine this morning. Is this about the queen? You told me to flirt."

"What? No." She shook her head and sighed as if just realizing how harsh her tone was. "I am fine. I'm just saying that we can't stay in this floating city forever, and you can't leave if you can't even outrun me. What help are you if anything other than me gets a hold of you?"

"Dianna," I said, raising a single brow. "You're being mean."

Her eyes softened, and she stepped closer, unfolding her arms. Recently, her attitude had seemed to get the better of her, more so than before. There were days when she'd snap, not meaning to. It was worrisome because Dianna was not mean, not to me. At least not anymore. I knew something was bothering her deeply. The only problem was she would not tell me. No matter how many times I asked, she blew me off, and other times, she quite literally blew me.

The tension left her shoulders, and I wondered what had happened to bring it so fiercely to the surface. We had been getting along so well lately, and to have her come at me again like this worried me. Was it something I had done, or was it that secret she refused to share with me? These were questions that I would address.

Dianna reached her hand out, and I grabbed it. She tugged me to my feet, and I twisted, brushing away pieces of the forest floor.

She sighed before plucking a leaf from my shirt. "I'm sorry. I just need you well if we plan to leave here, and holding back isn't helping either of us."

"Okay." I nodded, watching her.

Her eyes flashed, and my pulse quickened. One look, and gods above, mean or not, I was fucking putty.

"Did I hurt you?" she asked on a whisper.

"Do you mean emotionally or physically?"

Her smile was small, still picking at the forest debris along my sleeve. "Which one hurts the most?"

I shrugged nonchalantly. Pain was suddenly not on my mind, not when she looked at me like that. "I mean, the fall wasn't the best," I said.

Dianna took another small step, her breasts damn near touching me, and I could see her nipples tighten beneath the thin, dark material covering them. Her hand splayed on my chest, and she pushed. I took a step back, hitting the tree behind me.

"I'm sorry if I was too rough with you. With both things." She picked another small blade of grass off of me, and even that small touch made my breath catch.

"Thank you for apologizing," I said, my body heating with her nearness. "I understand where you are coming from and the need to be stronger, heal, and test my limits."

She nodded, sliding her hands over any part of me still covered in debris. "You almost made it," she said, taking another tiny step toward me, her hands coming to rest against my chest.

I cleared my throat. "Farther than the last few times."

Her hand slid down my chest, dipping lower. I didn't even feel the slight twinge of pain as she crossed my abdomen. She cupped me through my trousers, and I grunted, my cock twitching under her touch. "Want a reward?"

"What do I get?" I panted. "This is by far the closest I've gotten to the river. I think it should be a *very* big reward, especially given you crashed into me."

Her bottom lip protruded ever so slightly as she opened my pants. "Poor baby, let me fix it."

Words and all coherent thoughts left my brain as she kneeled in the brush before me. Her eyes, those godsdamn eyes, made my heart race as she glanced up at me. Never breaking eye contact, she reached inside my trousers and fisted my cock, dragging it out in one solid move.

Dianna's lips curved in an absolutely wicked smile, and I nearly groaned. "Already slightly hard for me, huh?" My body jerked as she placed a single kiss against my bare hip and nuzzled her cheek against me, her breath a warm rush over my shaft as she said, "Let's see if we can make it harder, yes?"

Her tongue darted out, flat and thick, sliding along the underside of my cock. A soft moan left my lips as she watched me. Now I knew why she'd pressed me against the tree. It was the only form of stability I'd have while she tortured me into oblivion.

My hips moved, chasing her mouth as she licked one side, then the next in long, devilishly wicked laps of her tongue. She watched me through her lashes and delicately traced the side of my cock, my body twitching with each lick. She wrapped her hand around my base, squeezing and releasing rhythmically before stroking. The veins pulsed along my length as she did exactly what she said she would and made me fucking hard.

I groaned in earnest as she flicked her tongue underneath the head, my cock jumping in her hand at the sensation, but it was the wicked smile and kiss she placed atop the crown that drove me fucking mad.

"I thought I was to be rewarded," I groaned. "Not tortured."

Her laugh was downright evil before she leaned forward and took my cock in her mouth. My head fell back against the tree, and I twined my fingers in the silky tresses of her hair. She took me deeper and deeper, sucking and swirling her tongue in that feverishly skilled way that drove me mad.

Dianna braced her hand against my thigh, swallowing me damn near whole. I didn't care who heard my moans and gasps as Dianna devoured me. She pulled back, sucking at the head, her luscious lips wrapped tight as her hand stroked my shaft in tight, rhythmic circles.

My hands fisted in her hair, urging her on as she took and took from me. I felt her moan around my length, and I felt myself rush toward the precipice, pleasure gathering at the base of my spine.

"Fuck, Dianna." I groaned as my hips followed her every movement.

Dianna purred in response as if she enjoyed every single sound of pleasure I gave her. She cupped my balls, rolling and squeezing gently, using the exact pressure she knew made me wild. My Dianna set my whole body aflame. She always did, even when I was too stupid to realize what was between us. She was my living flame.

Another stroke and everything disappeared. I no longer felt the dull ache of pain in my abdomen, but with her near me, my failures, my vicious, cruel mind reminding me how, even with all my power, I was not enough, went silent. When she looked at me, touched me, and spoke to me with admiration and determination, I truly believed I was more than enough.

With another wicked flick and roll of her tongue, she twisted her hand, and I lost it. My pleasure barreled through me, and I groaned loud enough to shake the damn trees above. My skin flushed, heat boiling up from my toes as my hips thrust forward. Dianna braced herself and leaned into my push, stealing every last drop from me, sucking lovingly as I finished in her mouth.

Dianna's smile was filled with wicked satisfaction as she leaned back and ran her thumb underneath her lip. I smiled, knowing that even though we played and joked about her rewarding me, I already had the biggest reward life could have offered me. It was her. It was always her.

We headed to one of our favorite spots here in Jade City. Past the winding hills and through a few miles of forest was a field close to the edge of one of the floating rocks they called home. This spot was covered in trees and glittering moss. Two smaller floating rocks hovered above, partially concealed by pink clouds. Dianna loved to watch the sunsets from here, and it was far enough away we could train and speak freely without eavesdroppers. Plus, the view was gorgeous.

I had missed the beauty of the other realms, how oddly unique they all were. The first time we came up here, Dianna had assumed her wyvern shape and flew between the aerial islands, making sure it was safe for us. Then, a few other times, just for fun when we made it up here. I liked to watch her after training as she glided between rocks and clouds. She couldn't smile in her wyvern form, but her little chirps as she flew seemed like a laugh.

"I wasn't trying to be mean earlier." Dianna's voice cut through my meditation, her pacing increasing tenfold. "I just meant we need to get serious."

A soft chuckle left my lips as my hands rested on my crossed legs. I took another deep breath, and my side tingled, the small nerves around the edge of the wound healing but too damn slow.

"I thought we were pretty serious," I answered on an exit breath.

"I meant with training. You can't save the entire cosmos if you can't wield a sword," she said. "It's been a few weeks. We can start incorporating more pull-ups and push-ups. You know, upper body strength."

"Uh-huh."

She turned again, continuing to pace feverishly. "Maybe have you throw a boulder around or something. Really work the obliques."

I peeked one eye open as she chewed at the flat of her thumb. "All right. And where has this boulder-throwing idea come from, per se?"

She paused, looking toward me as she waved her hand. "Close your eyes. Less talking, more meditating."

I grinned even as I asked, "This would not have anything to do with Roccurem immediately going back to you after I left?"

I felt rather than heard her stop in her tracks. "What? No. Yes, but no, not when you say it like that."

I knew I was right. Even with my power at an extreme low since that spear, I still felt the air circulate as he formed behind our bedroom door. I wanted to turn back, curious about what he so desperately needed to tell her when I was away, but the healers and their persistence were unmatched. I also figured Dianna would tell me later.

"Mm-hmm, how else would you prefer I say it?" I asked, trying to keep that part of me that was so damn possessive of her at bay. "You two have been very secretive lately. The small conversations that cease when I am around. I don't like it."

"Careful, big guy." She snickered. "You sound jealous."

"I am not jealous. That would assume Roccurem is better than me, which he isn't."

She barked a small laugh. "There's that cocky god we all adore."

I rolled my shoulders. "I'm mildly annoyed at best."

"Okay." She snorted. "Whatever you say."

My lips tilted as she squealed, a rush of water dousing her from the nearby spring. I rolled my shoulders, relaxing once more and focusing. The sun beat against my skin, easing the ache of my muscles. I breathed in, then out, absorbing the energy of the heat. I could feel my power beneath my skin, only a fraction of it remaining, but there nonetheless. It swirled and danced across my skin, sparking at my nerve endings. All of it coursed toward the wound in my abdomen, and a chill ran up my spine. My body kept trying to heal itself, yet something was blocking its ability.

Another twinge of pain had me gritting my teeth, but I subdued the hiss that wanted to leave my lips. Between the teas, medications, and myself, it was a process, a slow one, but a process nonetheless. The barely closed wound stretched from just below my abs on my right side and slashed across my abdomen to end just below my left pectoral. The edges were less of the grayish burnt color that had been so alarming and now were just a fraction paler than my complexion. But it was the small purple veins that had started to spread from it that concerned me. I prayed that the change and the continued pain didn't mean it was infected. The weeks we had been here were stacking up, and my family had been stuck with Nismera for nearly a month. I had to heal so we could get them back.

My control slipped, and I opened my eyes, breaking my trance. The world came rushing back, the sounds of animals moving about and the wind dancing between the trees. I watched Dianna wring droplets of water from her hair.

"He's harmless. You know this. Only arrogant gods make me hot," she said, walking toward me.

"They better," I joked, letting the humor hide the emotions that threatened to drown me all over again. Until Dianna, I hadn't known jealousy, but I was jealous as I had been before with that damned vampire. I wanted all of Dianna's time, her smiles, her laughs, and above all, her secrets. There was something she was not sharing with me, but I didn't want to pry it out of her. I wished for her to trust me, to love me enough to tell me everything, to share her thoughts and dreams with me. I was just so damned scared to ask for it. If it wasn't freely given, was it truly love?

"Regardless, there is a bond between you two," I answered honestly. "Fate does not listen to just anyone."

Worry creased Dianna's brows, and that wasn't what I wanted. She sat across from me and leaned forward, just brushing her lips across mine before pulling back. "Not a bond like that gorgeous mind is probably concocting, but he is my friend."

That prickle of jealousy eased when she said that word. My Dianna had lost so many friends, both through death and betrayal. I wanted her to have people she could trust and lean on. She deserved that and so much more.

"I know," I said. "I apologize. I suppose I am irrational, especially when it comes to you. It's just the mark has not formed. There is no binding letting everyone know you are truly mine."

"I thought I left plenty of those." She smirked wickedly.

I squeezed her knee playfully. "I'm not talking about your little love bites."

She did leave an array of those on me. Small little nips that made my body flush in heat. Usually on my neck, arms, or chest, any place she could reach. Certain kisses seemed to drive Dianna wild, and she would leave a trail of nips and bruises along my neck while my hand worked between her legs. I had missed them when we could not fully be together. No matter how much I enjoyed that, I still ached for the one that should have burned into my flesh, the one that would never heal, never disappear.

I chewed on the inside of my cheek and leaned back, glancing at my bare finger. "You know which one I'm talking about."

She leaned back, her eyes scanning mine. "Do we need a mark for that?"

I looked at her. "No, but does it not bother you it has not shown?"

Dianna's gaze dropped to my scar as it often did. "I don't need a mark for that, and besides, maybe we did the ritual wrong? We kind of did everything backward, and I was evil for a while."

I laughed, shaking my head. "Never evil."

She shrugged. "Many would disagree. Listen, let's worry about healing you first, the mark second, okay?"

I glanced down, absently touching the edges. Those didn't hurt. It was the center that still felt fresh at times, even if the skin there was closed. "All right."

"Do you think their tea is helping?"

"Yes." I dropped my hands, resting them back on my knees. "It's an effective pain reliever for sure. My theory is the blade was meant to kill me, and even though it didn't, the price may be that I'm stuck this way."

A haunted look crossed her face. My chest ached, knowing that even the mention of losing me stirred memories in her that would break anyone. Yet here she was, trying to help me, refusing to give in to her fear and all she went through.

My strong, beautiful girl.

"Hey." I scooted closer until our knees touched and grabbed her hand. Her eyes met mine, the pain fleeing as if she'd returned from whatever memories that had taken her. "I'm okay. You saved me. In the most reckless way possible, but you saved me nonetheless. I don't know what would have happened had you not gotten there in time."

I thought it would make her smile, reminding her of just what she'd done, but she only dropped her gaze from mine, looking at our intertwined hands. She ran her thumb across mine and asked, "What do you remember?"

I took a shuddering breath. We hadn't had this conversation since I had awakened. She had only told me how Roccurem had told her where to go, how he had betrayed Nismera for her, and that I had been asleep for a few days. A part of me knew she wished for me to focus on healing and getting better, and not what I experienced, but I was glad to voice it finally.

My hand stayed in hers, a grounding force I so desperately needed and knew I couldn't live without. "I remember being held down with those runes by the council. I remember Kaden arriving and . . ." I swallowed. "I remember being stabbed and that blistering pain. It felt as if my entire being had cracked open. I remember the realms opening and how much it hurt. Millions of voices exploded inside my skull. I felt them, everyone at once, and then it disappeared. I remember The Hand leaving. I remember Nismera standing over me, and I felt weak, so damn weak. Then all I remember is you."

Dianna's brows creased. "Do you remember the tunnel?"

I glanced away, recalling flashes of light and Dianna's arms around me as I slipped away. "Very vaguely. I remember being cold and tired, and you holding me was the warmest I have ever felt. It's sporadic from there, and then I remember waking up in Jade City."

Dianna nodded, but the smile she forced was anything but a happy one. I did not tell her I remembered telling her I loved her or that she did not say it back. That part I kept to myself, fear a heavy, dreadful thing that told me no matter what we did or shared, she did not love me. There was still so much she kept from me, and like a fool, I was too afraid to ask. My heart could not take it if I spoke those words again, and the look that she wore now formed. How ironic was it that I had slayed beasts larger and deadlier than me and spoke to gods and deities who bowed to me, yet with her, I was utterly and completely terrified?

"That's all I remember. I'm assuming I passed out from blood loss, and you got us here. How did you, though?"

She shrugged. "Reggie showed up in the last second. Told me where to go."

I squeezed her hand, seeking to comfort her. She met my eyes again, and I struggled to define the emotions in her gaze. "You are truly amazing, Dianna. Reckless, fearless, and brave. Even if it annoys me." A soft chuckle left her lips. "I don't know what I'd do without you."

Her smile faded, and she pulled her hand from mine. Uneasiness churned in my gut. I meant to offer her comfort, but at times, it seemed all I did was make her retreat deep into herself and farther from me. Even with all we shared, it seemed she still kept me at arm's distance.

"Okay." She wiggled in place. "Let's try more meditation." She opened her hands, offering them back to me, palms up.

"What is this?" I asked, taking her hands again.

"Well, since I'm such an all-powerful badass like you said," she winked at me, and I snorted before she went on, "borrow some of my power. Maybe I can help you heal." She relaxed and straightened her back, a small smirk on her lovely lips. "And then we fight until the sun sets. You really suck with a sword now."

I threw my head back and laughed, my side aching with the stretch, but oh, it felt good. "I still best you."

"You can barely lift it for long periods of time."

"And?" I added, not denying it. "I still won against you."

"Sure." She dragged the word out. "You were just on the ground yesterday and the day before because you were taking a little rest in the middle of our sparring session."

"I wanted to be there." I leaned forward, bringing her fingers up to press a kiss to her knuckles. "It was all a part of my plan. To have you on top of me."

"You do not need us to train for that."

I laughed again. This was better than any meditation.

IX

Miska

A few days later

I covered the teacup with my hand as I walked upstairs. Smoke curled from it with a slightly bitter smell wafting off it. After reading through my mother's herbal text she'd left me, I knew it would help. All wounds needed healing from the inside, even if the others didn't believe me. My stomach curled at the thought. I didn't know why I wished they would accept me so badly. Maybe because even though this was my home, it hadn't felt that way since my mom passed.

Carefully, I climbed the vine-covered spiral staircase. Moonlight from the twin moons spilled through the half-opened walls, their smooth stones cut out to let the light in. One thing I loved about this place, and quite frankly, the only thing, was how much our queen let nature have its way.

A small giggle had me glancing up, and I heard the turning of a page. I hurried along, coming to the top of the stairs as the hall branched outwards. I stopped outside the carved door right as that laughter stopped. They sat in the center of the room, surrounded by a mountain of books.

I had watched Cedaar and Xio before. The girls whispered about how they liked his body but always hushed when I entered the room.

They had never shared anything with me, but it still stung. I had heard how the queen wished him for her own, but she thought the fling with Xio was far more than he had let on. I had to agree. His eyes never left her, and she was always a step or two behind him. It was impossible to think they were a fling. It all seemed so real and genuine, especially now as I watched.

Xio laughed and playfully swatted at Cedaar. He backed away, grinning wildly as she said something in that language I didn't know. I wondered what it was like to love, to be loved. I never saw it here, not like that. Here, it was only hushed whispers and secret meetings, most matches based on politics and greed.

I smiled as they played, and I could see why the other healers were so enamored with him. He was sculpted like the old gods in the stories they used to tell us. Maybe that's why the men here in Jade City were jealous and made jokes about his weird haircut. Either way, I didn't care. I only wished to help. I only wanted a friend. That was why I stayed up after the others went to bed. I would pull my mother's book from its hiding spot and read through the night.

Glancing at the tea in my hands, I pursed my lips and went to turn. I was intruding like I did when Sashau and Killie talked, and I didn't want to get in trouble. I'd visit them early in the morning instead.

"Miska. What brings you up here so late?" Cedaar asked, and I stopped, half-turned from the doorway.

Concern furrowed his brow, and judging by the books and texts before him, it seemed they were up late with another lesson. I knew from the others he had been teaching her how to speak our language and a few others when he wasn't sitting in a herbal bath, or they weren't making those grunting noises upstairs.

"I made tea," I said, my voice fluttery. I was nervous and had every right to be. He may be beautiful, but they were a part of The Eye, trained killers and rebels who didn't fear the one true king. The other girls whispered stories of how they could probably kill us with a spoon if they so wished. Years and years of training had made it so they didn't fear anything. It must have been brutal, and even though our queen was helping, she did not trust them.

"I made tea," I said again, trying to make my voice steady and more confident. It wasn't him I feared. No, it was the dark-haired one that never left his side, the same one currently staring at me. They called her a shadow, for that was what she was. Every move he made, she countered as if they were in a constant dance. She let nothing show in her expression, but it felt as if she was afraid of something. I swallowed and squared my shoulders. Our queen said we weren't allowed to visit them alone, but I was tired of them not listening to me. Nothing they did seemed to help, and I could tell he was getting worse.

"It is from my mother's texts, one I remember her using on another who had twisted his leg nearly off. It worked as if by magic."

I swallowed and took a step inside. Quicker than any living thing had the right to be, Xio was in front of me. I froze, the tea clattering on the small tray I held as I gripped it hard, trying not to spill it.

She leaned forward, watching me as she inhaled, her nostrils flaring. She made a face. "It smells bitter."

My throat went dry. "It's the gravanl seed."

She cocked her head to the side as if that word was unfamiliar to her. Cedaar translated, and she glanced toward me, the tea, and then shrugged.

"Okay."

Xio stepped aside, allowing me to pass. I didn't hesitate, afraid she would change her mind or, worse, kill me with a spoon. My footsteps echoed against the stone floor. Cedaar gave me a small smile as I placed the tray on the table.

He picked up the cup and raised it to his lips. "Miska, why are you awake so late? No matter how kind the gesture, it cannot be just to make me tea."

I nodded, too afraid that if I lied, she would smell the truth. "It's the only time the other healers are all asleep. I needed to borrow a few ingredients from the cupboards they keep sealed."

Xio whistled softly, and I felt that overwhelming power behind me. "Oh, naughty, naughty. We have a little thief."

I half-turned, shocked by how well and quickly she had learned our language. Nausea gripped me, and I realized she was right. I was a thief.

"Please don't tell." I turned back to Cedaar, knowing I would not find mercy with Xio. He took a sip of tea before lowering it. "If the queen finds out, she'll have me blistered with the thorny vines she keeps."

A look passed across his face, one I didn't know how to decipher. He glanced behind me at Xio, and his smile returned like morning sunlight on the hills. "We will not speak of it. Promise."

I nodded quickly. "I am sorry to disturb you both. Please let me know if the tea helps." I turned and darted across the room, the long fabric of my gown wrapping around one leg. My hand reached for the door, but a delicate hand slapped against the wood before I could open it. I gasped at Xio standing there, blocking my exit. She stared down at me, and I gulped.

"You brought me those soaps, didn't you?"

"Y-yes. Cedaar asked. I knew a recipe my mom showed me because we used to travel a lot, and I hated the water we used, so she made bubbles to distract me . . . Now, I'm rambling."

"I liked them. Thank you." Xio pushed off the door and folded her arms, grinning slowly.

"Please, Miska, have a seat," Cedaar said.

My skin prickled with warning, unsure of what I may have walked into. My eyes shifted toward Xio, and I could not stop the words that fell out of my mouth next.

"They say you are a terrifying beast," I whispered, and an edge of red ringed her deep brown irises. "That you can shape to any form and feed on the very lifeblood that keeps us all breathing."

"Do they?" A corner of her full lips tipped up, and she leaned in closer. "Flattery will get you everywhere, princess."

"Xio," Cedaar said, his tone filled with warning.

Her name made her smile widen, and she flicked her gaze from Cedaar back to me. "Don't worry. I promise not to bite and be on my best behavior. Besides, I'd hate to cause his pretty face to grow a stress wrinkle."

She nodded toward Cedaar, and I gulped. There was no way I was leaving here without sitting with them, and a part of me was terrified. I said nothing as I wrung my hands, turning from her and heading back toward the table. Cedaar stood and grabbed a chair for me.

"You're so kind," I whispered as I curled my dress under me to sit. "Most aren't like that. Not anymore."

Cedaar pushed my seat in before pulling out Xio's chair. She sat and asked, "Are the other healers mean to you?"

My eyes flashed to her as Cedaar finally took his seat. "Sometimes. Well, only when they talk to me. They usually avoid me most of the time."

"Why?" she asked, leaning forward on her arms. "What did you do? Steal a boyfriend? Girlfriend?"

Cedaar made a noise in the back of his throat, both of them speaking in that foreign language. Then she gave him one of those dashing smiles across the stacks of books before turning back to me.

My fingers twisted in the edge of my dress as I shook my head. "No, the boys here hate me, too. No one liked my mother. She questioned our queen too much, which got us kicked out in the first place. But when she died, I had nowhere else to go, so I came back."

Xio turned those striking eyes toward him as he spoke once more in her language before sipping more of the tea. I didn't know what was said, but she responded with a crooked smile that changed all her features. It softened them, and a part of me softened too. The tension in my shoulders left as she leaned toward him, and I saw it then.

If he was the sun, by the old gods, she was the moon. Powerful, dark, and overbearing at times. She never left him, nor he her, as if they danced around each other for eternity. He didn't respond but smiled and shook his head before turning to me.

Cedaar set the teacup back on the tray. "This is quite lovely, Miska. Thank you for that. You said it has healing properties, yes? Enlighten me on which ones."

I stayed in that study with them far past the time the moon crested in the sky. He asked me about ingredients from my world and how they were used. He asked me about my mother and then about the things I liked. We spoke of how I was rescued and came to be here. In return, they told me where they had come from.

Xio told me of treats so sweet it would make your face tingle, and she smiled about it. They both did. Against my better judgment, I did too. She didn't seem like the beast they whispered about, the one they feared. She seemed so normal, especially when she looked at him. I didn't know why I was ever afraid to be around them, and now I felt silly for ever thinking that way.

The moon drifted toward the horizon as I helped them both with more words from my world. We studied and even made somewhat of a game of it. I realized I was having fun, and I was not used to having fun. They seemed so focused on me, as if I was the one who needed healing and not him. It wasn't until Cedaar yawned and Xio soon followed that I realized we had stayed up the entire night.

X

Dianna

"You know, this whole sneaking-in thing really does something for me."

Samkiel chuckled under his breath as he half turned, peering over my head. I wore the skin of one of the healers, using it to check if the coast was clear before he followed. Luckily, the hall on the lowest level of Jade City was empty. It seemed the healers stayed on schedule. Lights out meant lights out here. A wink and a snap followed as he sent a tendril of his power into the locked door. A flow of silver crept over the square metallic lock, and then the door opened.

My hands snaked around his waist, connecting as I rested my head against his shoulder.

He patted my hand, snickering. "Don't get too excited. This is merely recon. We are simply gathering information about why a city full of healers would keep secrets from their own."

I smiled and stepped in behind him, tracing a lazy path up his back. "Still turned on." I walked past him, glancing into the room. It was a lot smaller than I would have thought, given the massive spelled lock on the outside. A staircase covered in vines and flowers of every color led to a balcony that wrapped around the room. Two tables, with an array of empty vials and worn pages, took up most of the space.

The room was dark, without a single candle lit. Shelves took up the farthest walls with a mix of small leafy plants to colorful large shrubbery with thorns growing from the side. I moved closer, taking a look as I heard Samkiel's footsteps head toward my right. He was doing the same.

My hand reached out, ghosting over some of the clear, smooth jars. A bioluminescent plant in one seemed to follow my fingers, pressing against the glass.

"Pretty."

Samkiel's hand grasped my wrist with a smack, pulling me back.

"And dangerous."

I glanced at him. "What?"

He nodded at the jar. Sickly yellow shimmering lights replaced the previous beautiful colors. The plant, or I suppose not plant, let out a small, high-pitched screech. It opened its circular mouth, exposing its serrated teeth, and suctioned itself to the glass.

"What the fuck is that?"

He slid his thumb over my pulse before letting go of my wrist. "A shurvuae. They are often used in ancient magics. The old ones said they could suck out the most lethal poisons, but if left too long, they could be fatal. Although poison seems to be their favorite meal."

Samkiel stepped forward, and the small creature in the jar seemed to vibrate. It turned from me and focused on him, latching onto the jar closest to him. The sound it made had my skin crawling.

I stepped closer to him. "Does it think we are poisoned?"

"No, I believe it senses power as well. Most creatures above a certain rank or order can."

"Well, then, you must be a buffet to him." I playfully smacked him on the ass before turning away to look around the room. "Why keep that? Why all of this? I know I am new to this world, but why lock it up? Are they afraid of their own people?"

"I doubt it. It could be a precaution because of Nismera's rule, but half of the vegetation here seems illegal."

"Maybe that's why they don't tell Miska."

"Perhaps. She is young. Under the right pressure, she would reveal any secrets."

"Like the ones she spilled last night?"

Samkiel nodded and formed a silvery ball of light in his hand before lowering to a squat and moving a few jars out of the way. He held a smaller one in his palm, the beige prickly fern stuck to one side. "Like this? This is used to sedate beasts far larger than you can turn into."

"Maybe they are not just treating people in the city."

He placed the jar back and stood, but I saw that corner of his jaw twitch. I watched as he chewed on the inside of his cheek and knew what was running through his mind.

"They haven't said anything about this or given you an indication of what they are doing?"

He glanced at me before moving forward to another shelf. "No, no, they have not."

"So." My hand danced across the table near me. "Do you want me to kill them now or later?"

A deep sigh left his lips as he continued to look around. "I prefer no killing, my akrai. I wish to know what they are doing with so many illegal works here, and I plan to ask the queen herself."

"Well, that's no fun." I blew out a breath. "There should at least be some corrosion."

He cut his eyes toward me, that storm-colored gray flashing. "Dianna."

"Samkiel," I repeated, lowering my voice in a mocking tone.

"Please do not kill anyone for me." His brows flicked at me. "All we know is they have illegal products."

"Which probably means they are evil," I said.

"Or," he added, "they are trying to make do or make ends meet in a turbulent world. I've seen no signs of wrongdoing besides these products, and they have helped us. Circumstances can make people go to lengths they usually wouldn't in order to survive in a new world."

His words hit a part of me I hadn't thought about in a while. I wondered if that was how he saw me in the beginning: a woman desperate to survive.

"You're so sweet. It's sickening," I said, smiling at him. Hopping up onto one of the tables, I crossed my legs and drew a slash across my chest before holding my hand up. "I promise not to maim or kill anyone unless they hurt or threaten you. If that happens, I'll burn them alive. Deal?"

"Deal." Samkiel snickered and shook his head as he turned back to the shelf nearest him, still holding that silver flickering ball of power. My stomach dropped when his eyes didn't linger on me or run over me in the way they usually did when he thought I wouldn't notice. My eyes roamed over his back, legs, and up once more. Hunger, sharp and painful, pierced my gut.

"You know." I dragged the word and leaned back on the table, thrusting my breasts forward. He didn't so much as glance at me. "Since we already know they are harboring plants that have been banned, we could do something else since we are here."

He looked at me over his shoulder. "And what's that?"

"We can role play."

Samkiel cocked his head as if I'd spoken a foreign word. "And what's that?"

The smile that danced across my face was downright dangerous as I slid off the table. "I can be a slutty healer who wants to tend to your wounds." I worked the off-white gown open, pushing the sheer sleeves off my shoulders. The material fell, bundling at my waist, revealing rose-colored breasts, not my own. I expected his eyes to dart there and stay, waiting for that darkening they did every time I made a suggestive comment. I always loved it, though. He responded so completely to me, and it was my favorite thing to press his buttons and have him unravel at my feet, but the reaction I got now was the complete opposite. His lip curled as if I just insulted him, and his eyes held mine. There was no lust or overwhelming passion, not even a flicker.

"What?" I asked, swallowing the growing lump in my throat.

A single snap from his free hand had the dress covering me and tied once more. "Why would I want that?"

I was confused, especially given the tone he used. He sounded angry, the complete opposite of what I wanted.

"It's just for fun."

"Why would being with another be fun for me?"

"It's not another." I shook my head, perplexed. "You know it's me."

His frown deepened, his lip curling up in disgust. "It's you wearing the flesh of another being. That, by definition, is another."

"Well . . ." Now, it was my turn to be dumbfounded. I stumbled over my words, unsure of what to say next. In my thousand years of existence, this had never once happened to me. Other lovers I had before him never minded. Most of them even encouraged it. Kaden actually preferred it on most nights when he could stomach me, but I wished to bury those memories deeply. "I wasn't trying to make you mad. I just thought . . . I don't know what I thought."

"I am not mad, perhaps a little taken back at such a ludicrous suggestion, but not mad. That . . . does nothing for me."

That sinking, dreadful feeling in my gut suddenly dried up, and another emotion, just as poignant, seeped in. "Wait, really? Nothing? Not a single tickle of excitement? A half swell in your cock?"

"I promise, there is zero swelling." Samkiel didn't grin or smirk, not even a small chuckle as he stared at me. "Is this a common thing you used to do? Before?"

My stomach dropped, but I said nothing as if my lips had suddenly been sealed shut.

Samkiel chewed the inside of his cheek once more before slowly nodding. "With all due respect, akrai, do not compare me to him or what you've experienced with your past lovers. I don't need nor want any other form but the one you wear daily. Do you understand?"

"I didn't mean it like that."

"You might not have, but that is how it came across. You, Dianna, my dark-haired, fiery vixen, are and will always be enough for me. No shape or form or thing you bend to will ever make any part of me swell, as you put it, like you. Understand?"

I hopped off the table and walked over to him, not stopping until I wrapped my arms around him. He rested his cheek against the top of my head, and I hugged him tightly. He wrapped his arms around me, engulfing me in his arms. Perhaps it was truly a funny thing not to realize how broken or damaged you were until someone came along and picked up every single fractured piece and showed you how just being you was enough.

"You really mean that? I couldn't tempt you in another form?"

Samkiel's chest rumbled as he laughed before placing a kiss on my cheek.

"While you can take any shape you want, your true form is the one I prefer. So no, not even on your best day."

My form shimmered, my bronzed glow replacing the pink-hued skin. Thick dark curls spilled over my shoulders, the ends tickling my lower back. I pulled away and glanced up at him.

This time, when he looked at me, that swirling emotion I had expected to see deepened in his eyes. "There's my girl."

I raised up on my tiptoes, my lips brushing across his in a chaste kiss.

"Now that," he made a noise in the back of his throat as his thumb danced back and forth over my cheek, "that does something to me."

"Good." My hands snaked from the planes of his back and slid lower.

He grabbed my hands. "Stop." He laughed a deep, throaty chuckle before prying my hands from him and playfully pushing me away. "Help me figure out why they would keep these plants and herbs so carefully hidden away."

I smiled, nodding as I held my hands up innocently. Samkiel turned back toward the jars lining the shelves. So many samples carried either small, fragmented bits or chopped-up versions. I paused at a jar with dark specks floating in a blue liquid and opened it. My nose curled as the smell hit me, and I gagged, putting the lid back on and placing it back where I found it.

"Maybe we can put this one in the hair care of the girls being mean to Miska."

"Dianna," he said, his tone laced with warning.

"What?" I joked, inspecting another jar. "I'm not going to."

Maybe. I smiled to myself as I found another with what looked like a crushed root, the small branches scattered at the bottom. The hairs on the back of my neck stood, and I glanced over my shoulder, catching Samkiel looking at me. He saw and looked away, clearing his throat.

"What?" I asked, knowing that look as I moved to another shelf.

"What?" he asked, standing.

"You tell me." I reached for another jar, this one with crushed leaves. "You're the one with the questioning face."

He was silent for a moment. The only sound in the room was the tinkling of glass as he replaced a jar.

"Very well, I do have one question."

"Hmm?"

"Are you feeling all right? Physically? Do you feel well?"

Dread crept in, and not one of past insecurities. It was one built on a lie, or more so, a truth I had not told him yet. "Yes. Why?"

He shrugged, pretending it was nothing, yet he glanced at me over his shoulder quickly. "You just seem more . . . ravenous than normal. Not that I am complaining, but if there is something I am not doing right or well enough, you would tell me, correct?"

I nearly dropped the jar I was holding on the floor, and a snicker left my lips. My hand rushed to cover the sound as he scowled and turned to face me fully.

"This is not funny. I am being beyond serious."

I dropped my hand. "I know. That's why it is hilarious. Sami. Please. Do you really think I am not satisfied?"

"I don't know." He scratched his brow. "It's stupid. Forget I said anything."

"It's not stupid," I reassured him.

Of course, my descent back into thrash would be weird for him, too. My need for blood, sex . . . all of it, had increased. I was ravenous as if the void inside of me had grown and was begging me to fill it. The only problem was, I couldn't tell him that. He'd ask what had changed, and then I'd have to explain everything to him. I was not ready for that.

I had seen the world honestly, and now, thanks to him, I had also seen realms and places I never knew existed. I had seen stars and moons far larger than my own, which astonished me. But nothing compared to this powerful, beautiful, handsome god king shoving his heart toward me and praying I did not hurt it. He was by far the most shocking and wondrous thing I had ever experienced.

I stepped closer to him, constantly drawn to him as if he had his own gravitational pull on me. I placed my hands on his biceps, drawing lazy circles with my thumbs, his muscles jumping beneath my touch.

"I promise it's not stupid, nor am I laughing at you. I'm just surprised that you, out of all the people in the universe, would think I would not be satisfied. Maybe you're just too good, and it makes me even more greedy."

With that small, simple compliment, I watched his ego re-inflate, and I would not replace it with worry.

"Well . . ." He half shrugged, glancing away, but I saw his devilish smirk. "When you put it that way, I suppose it garners some truth."

I smiled. Regardless of if I hadn't told him the full truth, he knew me better than anyone. My heart fluttered, and my stomach sank. I hated I couldn't tell him that truth. He was right. I was hungrier and in more ways than one. I wasn't sleeping either, not nearly as much as I used to. No matter how well he fucked me or how my body should crave sleep after our long training sessions, I just lay awake. Reggie was right. Something happened in that tunnel. Something had been wrong with me since we arrived, and I kept burying it under the guise of stress, but I knew the truth. I gave up something down there in the cold when death visited. I gave up something valuable so he could live, and I didn't know how to tell him. He would be mad at me for lying and then mad at me for what I did.

But right now was not the time to tell him. Now we had a bigger issue to deal with. Or was that just another pretty little lie I told myself?

The skin on the back of my neck prickled. Samkiel's eyes widened one second, and he grabbed my arm, moving us to the back of the room. He pressed me to the wall in between shelves of jars as the door opened.

As she stomped in, the woman hissed and slammed her satchel down on one of the tables. She was one of the older healers. Lyrissa was her name. I remembered because she was the bitchiest. She moved toward the shelves farthest away from us, cursing to herself and grabbing a few jars to stuff them into her bag. She kept speaking to herself, but it was too fast for me to catch. I held my breath as she stomped toward us and gripped the back of Samkiel's arm. A wave of energy wrapped around us, and the room faded to gray. Samkiel's head whipped toward me as Lyrissa looked right at the space we were in and reached out to grab a jar right by Samkiel's shoulder. She turned and grabbed her satchel before storming out, closing the door behind her.

I let go of Samkiel's arm as he turned to me. "The in-between?"

"Yeah." I nodded and glanced at the door. "I haven't tried that in a while, and I'm glad it worked."

Samkiel said nothing, staring at me in pure astonishment. He went to speak, and the room went blurry.

"That's weird," I said, my voice sounding odd to my ears.

"What?"

"There's two of you," I said just before darkness claimed me.

XI
Dianna

"She seems well."

I blinked my eyes open. The sunlight made me hiss, and I turned from it, covering my face with my hand. The bed sank, and large hands ran across my forehead.

"What's happening?" I groaned and propped myself up, hating how my head throbbed.

"Killie is here to help you." Samkiel's voice drew me further from the darkness. "I told her you hit your head pretty hard in training."

I blinked, confused at what he was talking about, as my eyes adjusted. Samkiel sat next to me. Killie hovered on my other side, clasping her hands. Reggie stood behind Samkiel near the wall. Training? Oh, yeah. Right. I went to the in-between with Samkiel to cloak us, and then I must have passed out. I smiled weakly at Samkiel. He was learning how to lie for me. I was so proud.

"Yes." I groaned, rubbing my temple for effect as Samkiel glanced toward Killie and patted my hand.

"Well, you look fine. I left a remedy on the table for you. Just chew the leaves, and any swelling you have should go down."

I smiled at her, Samkiel gripping my hand. After seeing the storage room with all those jars, I knew even Samkiel doubted their trustworthiness.

Killie beamed at him, and I caught the flush of her cheeks. "It's also time for your treatments."

My eyes narrowed at the word *treatments*. Treatments, my ass. I was starting to think they weren't helping at all. I had noticed the small purple and red lines forming around the edges of his scar, but when I asked him about it, he said it was nothing and probably just part of the healing process.

Samkiel shot me a brief smile, noticing my death glare. "Are you sure you're okay?"

I turned away from Killie to look up at Samkiel. "Yes." I raised my hand between us, my small finger grasping his. "Pinky."

He squeezed back before leaning forward to place a kiss on my forehead. "I'll be right back."

I smiled and nodded, and he started toward the door with Killie.

"Killie, perhaps it is better for Xio if you stay. Make sure she is okay, given her head injury," Reggie suggested.

Samkiel glanced at Reggie, a look passing between them that made me snicker. Killie looked sad she couldn't walk Samkiel to his treatment but agreed to stay. Samkiel gave me one last look before closing the door behind him, his footsteps retreating. Reggie went back to standing sentinel against the wall.

"Do you feel nauseous?" Killie asked, with a little less pep in her voice. She sat on the end of the bed.

"Yes, but it's not from a head wound. I know what it is."

She pulled back, tilting her head slightly at me. "What is it?"

"I'm starving."

Fangs erupted from my gums, and I jerked forward, grabbing her by the throat. My hand covered her mouth, and she screamed into my palm as my fangs pierced her neck. I moaned as her blood hit my throat, and I drank deeply. My eyes rolled back in my head as I fed. It had been too damn long. Liquid filled my stomach, my entire body tingling as I drank and drank.

I heard her heartbeat and knew it was close to time to stop, but I couldn't control my hunger or myself. My moan vibrated against her throat as she slowly fell limp in my arms. A hand clasped my shoulder and pulled me away. My eyes flared open, and I snarled, my fangs bared and dripping blood. Reggie held up a hand. "You keep feeding, and you will kill her. Do you want her to find Samkiel that quickly?"

As if a switch flipped, the world came back into focus. Killie lay half-sprawled on the bed. Reggie lifted her and sat her in a nearby chair. I glanced at my reflection, grimacing at the blood coating my chin and my burning red eyes.

"I'm sorry."

Reggie didn't scold me. "Heal her enough and let her stay here until she can at least walk."

I kneeled in front of her and pressed my thumb to my fang. She fell limply in my grip as I smeared my blood over the bite on her neck. The puncture marks healed, and I cradled her head.

"Killie," I said as she blinked. "Look at me."

Her eyes snapped open, and her lips trembled in fear. She pushed at me, her fingernails digging into my arms as she fought to get free. She opened her mouth to scream. I clamped my hand over her lips and said, "Hey, you're fine. Calm down, everything is fine."

She went slack, her eyes gaining that all-too-familiar glaze.

I dropped my hand slowly as she stared at me. "You have been overworked, and you're tired, that's all. Tell the others you need a nap." Reggie glanced at me, and I shrugged before going on. "You helped heal Xio, and she never bit you or fed from you, okay?"

"I'm overworked and tired," Killie repeated, her eyes still blank and glassy. "I need a nap."

"Thatta girl."

I moved away from her, standing as she rose to her feet. Reggie grabbed a cloth from the washroom and handed it to me. I cleaned her neck, made sure no blood had spilled on her dress, and then sent her on her way. As soon as the door closed, I faced Reggie.

"That was stupid and reckless." I pushed my hair from my face, my stomach still gnawing at me. It craved, demanded more.

"You are not satiated."

"Why does everyone think I'm not satisfied? I am satisfied," I growled.

When I looked back at Reggie, I realized that was not what he meant. His eyes held no flicker of understanding, only stared at me, scolding. "You have not fed since Tarr. How long did you think you would last without sufficient feeding? You must tell Samkiel or risk his exposure."

"You do not tell me what to do," I snapped back.

"I do when it endangers us all." He shook his head. "An Ig'Morruthen that is starved and deprived of their basic needs could cause immeasurable damage. If that happens, if you snap while you are so concerned for him and not yourself, you will damn us all, and his entire resurrection will be pointless. Is that what you wish?"

The air sucked from the room. I had never heard Reggie even slightly raise his voice, yet here he was.

"What have you seen?" I asked, realizing what had instigated his sudden spark of anger.

His eyes met mine. "I saw Jade City ablaze." He didn't lower his gaze. "I saw it crumble and fall to the waiting sea below."

XII
Miska

"All that means is we need to move up our timeline."

Pots and pans rattled as I made my way into the kitchen. The voices always stopped when I entered. I wiped the sleep from my eyes as Sashau and Killie looked at me. Both were dressed for the day, their shimmering hair swept back from their faces with the royal blue of our queen on their lids.

"Am I-I," I stuttered. "Did I miss an announcement?"

They looked at each other. It reminded me of the secrets they all shared and how I was always left out. I always assumed it was because I was the youngest or maybe because my mom took me away when I was a babe, but either way, I still was and always would be unwelcome.

"Yes," Sashau said, circling the long table. "The queen requested dinner tonight with Cedaar. A big announcement or something."

"Or something." Killie snickered behind her, and Sashau waved her off.

"Oh." I wiped my hands on my pajamas, not able to hide the nerves and my shaking hands. "I'll need to prepare, then. I can help with whatever is needed."

Stupid. I always did this, offering to help when they never wanted it or me. It seemed I couldn't stop myself. I wanted to fit in here, to belong, and the more I tried, the more they laughed or ignored me.

Sashau smiled, but the expression didn't reach her eyes. The kitchen staff avoided us and kept busy, scurrying about their tasks. One healer walked in with a large assortment of flowers and vines, a few others following. Big dinner, indeed.

Sashau's hand stayed on my shoulder as she led me out of the kitchen and into the hall.

"Actually, we do need your help."

"Really?" I didn't know why I sounded so happy, nor did I care. "Yes. I mean. Whatever it is, I wish to help."

I changed clothes, hoping the long sheer dress they gave me looked appropriate. The dress was far too long for me, but none of the other girls here were even close to my age or height, so I made it work. I didn't even realize I was smiling until I passed one healer, and they looked at me a little too long. I was just so happy they wanted my help and I could do something. It made me feel less alone. I neared the bathing chambers as voices picked up. I walked through the large cut-out door, and the voices died.

The one Xio called Reggie stopped speaking and glanced toward me. The healers had whispered how he was probably Xio's consort, but she never touched him like she did Cedaar, nor did they share the same longing glances or quick kisses. I told them he was just their friend, but they laughed at me, claiming I didn't know anything, so I stopped talking.

"Hello, Miska of Vervannia."

I smiled every time he said that. Reggie had caught me outside late one night. I had escaped my room to read my mother's journal in peace. We had talked, and I shared some of my past with him. He'd said that he didn't sleep much, and most of the time, I didn't either. He said there was a word in Xio's language that described my nighttime routines, but I could never pronounce it. It made me happy that he remembered my mother's home. It made her real when he spoke of it, and it made my life with her real.

I grabbed the edges of my gown and bowed. "Hello, Reggie."

"Ugh, please don't ever bow to him. I can only handle one ego at a time."

Xio sat on the edge of the large mort tub. Even sitting, she defined elegance. She was half reclined, her leg crossed over the other, blocking my view of Cedaar. He lounged in the murky, flower-infused bath. Sometimes, I thought the other healers just enjoyed watching him bathe. I truly didn't think they helped, but again, I kept it to myself.

My cheeks flushed as I spun away. "I do apologize. Sashau said he was done."

Oh gods. She lied to embarrass me. I knew it. She and Killie were probably laughing upstairs at how stupid I was. I couldn't help the tears that pricked my eyes or my raging heartbeat.

"I'll come back."

I took a step back and turned toward the door. "Reggie," Xio said. She did not raise her voice, and her tone was calm.

Reggie blocked my retreat.

"Miska, don't be so dramatic. You're fine. He's not even naked, just half," Xio said.

Reggie glanced down at me with that same warm smile. He nodded behind me, encouraging me to turn back around. I swallowed and spun to see Xio still sitting lazily on the carved rim. Cedaar looked up at her with a small smirk and shook his head.

The other healers made comments about him. They liked his physique, his smile, the way he walked, and other things that sent me scurrying from the room. But I think my favorite thing about him was how he never seemed to want to leave Xio's side. He looked at her as if she hung the stars. It reminded me of the texts I loved to read. The others laughed at me for it, but I'd rather dream of magical princes than whatever this life held for me. Cedaar reminded me so much of the knights, protecting what he deemed precious. I didn't see in him the rebel our queen described.

"See," Xio said and stood, fully exposing Cedaar's chest and shoulders above the water. He sighed and lowered his head, rubbing the bridge of his nose. "Not that I trust any of your healers anymore. Tell me," she clasped her hands and took a step forward, "just between us girls, which one has a crush on my Cedaar?"

"Di—Xio."

I swallowed the lump in my throat at her approach. Even if she didn't mean to, the power she gave off made my skin crawl. When she wielded it, I had the overwhelming urge to run and hide. The queen hated she was here, complaining that she had brought darkness to their city.

"Ummm." I looked behind her at Cedaar, afraid to say anything. His eyes were on her, not in anger but soft, as if something she'd said had shocked him. "I-I . . ."

"It's fine, you can tell me. You're not in trouble." She stopped in front of me, placing her hands on her hips. Reggie shifted closer to my side.

"Xio," Cedaar called from behind her, the water sloshing as he leaned forward.

She ignored him, keeping her gaze on me. It reminded me so much of the others when they would make fun of me or laugh at me for how I spoke, but I didn't get that feeling from her. They called her a beast and lusted after Cedaar, but she had never been unkind to me. No, they made me feel like they actually cared when I talked, especially after the other night.

"Most of them do," I whispered.

Xio made a sound of victory and turned to point at Cedaar. He groaned and rolled his eyes. She spoke to him in that language I didn't know, and he quickly responded. He waved his arms, opaque water flying everywhere as they seemed to argue.

"They are harmless," I added, drawing her attention back to me.

Cedaar whispered a thank you and ran his hand over the top of his already slicked-back hair.

"Oh, well, from what I heard, they weren't in the beginning when we arrived," Xio said.

"They fear you. They wouldn't do anything to make you mad. Not to you, at least." I didn't mean to let the last part slip out, but Xio seemed to catch it. The whole room did, and they grew quiet.

"They would do something to you?" Xio asked, and for a second, she looked . . . concerned for me.

I shrugged. "I don't think so. They don't mean it." It's a lie I tell myself far too often. I shifted restlessly and looked away as Xio continued to stare at me.

"Xio," Cedaar said again, and the warning was clear this time. Perhaps I had made her mad, too.

I shook my head. "Sorry, I'm getting distracted. I came for a reason." I twisted my fingers in the long sleeves of my gown. "The others are gathering supplies and food to prepare for the meeting tonight, but we have a small problem."

"What problem?"

"We used the last batch of herbs for the healing lotion, and the plant we need is in another realm. Sashau said we weren't expecting to use so much given his wound, but we are out."

"Okay." Xio waved a hand. "Go get more."

"That plant only grows at the edge of Requmn."

Xio glanced back at Cedaar, who rested his folded arms on the edge of the pool, watching her.

"You say that like I know where it is."

Cedaar sighed. "It's at least a few hours from here, but with a portal, it would only take a few minutes."

"Let me guess, we have to go get it?"

I nodded.

"If the queen wishes for us to be at dinner tonight," Cedaar cut in, "I suppose we can go now and be back in time."

"We?" Xio asked.

Cedaar rose from the opaque water, and even though he had clothes on, I averted my gaze, staring at Xio's feet.

"Yes, we," he said, stepping from the pool, water hitting the stone floor.

I watched Xio's feet move toward him, stand close, and then back away. Material danced across the floor before wrapping around him and nearly covering his feet.

I glanced up then to see Xio shaking her head at him. He was sliding one arm, then the other, into his shirt. Concern scrunched my face when I caught sight of the wound across his abdomen. It was not healing, and now purple lines zigzagged from the edges of the slash.

"You," Xio poked him square in the chest, "are not going anywhere."

"And you're not going alone," he retorted.

"I won't be alone. I'll have my right-hand man, Reggie."

Reggie made a sound somewhere between shock and denial. Cedaar whipped his head toward him and glared. "No offense, but what self-defense does Reggie have that I do not?"

"Well, first, there is no need for self-defense. I am only bringing him so that vein on the side of your head doesn't poke out from worry when I leave, and two, do you really think I need someone to protect me?"

Cedaar made a face. "Yes. Have you met you?"

She swatted his shoulder, the slap drawing a smile from them both.

"I'm going. You are going to have your magical meeting with a queen." She grabbed the front of his shirt and pulled him close. She placed a kiss on his lips hard enough that it left a smack and stepped back. "And then I'll be back to give you dessert."

Cedaar's eyes widened a fraction, and I wondered what the word *dessert* meant.

"What's dessert?" I asked Reggie.

He only shook his head. "Some things are better left unknown."

XIII
Samkiel

I stared at my reflection as I laced my pants. A sharp pain pierced my side, originating from the slash across my abdomen. I winced and pressed my hand over it, surprised at how much it still hurt. Not that I would tell Dianna. She was worried enough. She'd been asking often and always watching me. I'd been forcing smiles, pretending it didn't ache every damn second. I felt weak and off balance, and my power still danced across the sky.

I carefully traced my fingers along the wound. The damn thing nearly split me in two. The purple lines along the edges were new and another cause for her recent hypersensitivity. I bit back a curse as I pulled the white tunic over my head, letting out a shaky breath as it settled. The laces that crisscrossed my chest stayed untied. The clothes were already a tight fit.

Turning from the mirror, I glanced at the empty room and prayed to the old gods the root Dianna brought back would help. I thought of last night and how I'd awakened in such intense pain that I had to run to the bathroom. A small smile curved my lips as she sat with me in there, her hand running across the back of my head as I expelled my previous meal. She talked to me, comforting me with stories of her past with Gabby and all the things she still wanted to do. Gods above and below, I loved her even more for that.

I was half afraid that if I didn't heal soon, she would start threatening the healers or, worse, burn the whole damn place and send it to the seafloor. Although what the healers were doing didn't seem to be helping. The only remedy that seemed to provide any relief was the tea Miska snuck off to make. I padded toward the edge of the bed, holding my side as I slipped my shoes on.

Someone knocked on the door, and before I could answer, it opened, and the healer named Killie entered.

"She will see you now."

The dining hall was overdone, to say the least. Flowers and vines decorated the tables, and lillievines climbed so high they breached the open ceiling. Frilla sat at the head of the table, and one of her consorts leaned over, pouring a liquid of shimmering yellow into her glass. She stepped back, and Frilla took a sip. The cream garment she wore twisted and curved high on her shoulders, rising behind her neck and head in a mock crown.

"Cedaar, you look well," she greeted, waving her hands. "Please, have a seat."

I smiled at her, my hand instinctively going to my side as I sat. "How are you this evening, Queen Frilla?"

Her cheeks flushed as she sipped her drink. "Very well. I hope you don't mind that I called this dinner."

Her consorts walked around the room, placing plates of fruits and meats in front of Frilla, then me. I tried to hide the curl of my lip at the smell. My stomach still had not settled.

"No, not at all. I've been meaning to speak with you as well."

"Oh?" She tipped her head toward me as a glass of wine was poured near me. "What of?"

"The youngest healer here," I said, raising the glass of wine to my lips. The others in the room froze. "I don't think she is treated fairly by the older ones here."

Frilla bristled. "I assure you she is. She has a room, a bed, food in her belly, and the opportunity to learn the art of healing. She is just young and thinks the world is against her. You know teens."

My stomach pinched as the liquid settled, and I placed my glass down. "Yes, I am also aware that less than kind words or tactics at such a young age can affect growth and development," I said, glancing at a few healers who had stopped eating and were openly listening to our conversation.

"She's young," Frilla said. "She probably embellished stories of how she is mistreated, hoping a daring, young male will swoop in and save her. Are you to be her knight now?"

The words were laced with an edge of bitter hate, and I knew Miska's words rang true. They did despise her mother for whatever she had done and were taking it out on Miska.

"I am no knight, I assure you, just simply an observer."

Frilla's sweet demeanor melted away. She didn't like to be challenged. That seemed to be the only thing we had in common. The doors behind me opened and closed as a healer entered and shuffled across the room. She didn't spare me a glance before leaning in close and whispering to her queen. I grabbed my side, another pinch of pain making me nauseous.

The healer and the queen finished their hushed conversation, and the old woman hurried from the room. A look of pure contentment crossed Frilla's face as she sipped her drink.

"I'll be sure Miska is well taken care of. How about that?"

I offered her a soft smile. "Fantastic. I'd hate for any harm to come to her in retaliation for me merely inquiring."

She sat up straighter and pointed toward my plate. "Are you all right? You haven't touched your food."

"Oh, yes." The smile I forced was anything but friendly. My trust in her and this city was dwindling by the minute. "I am just not hungry. My apologies."

"Well, that makes sense, given your wound."

I nodded.

"Especially since I've been slipping a tiny bit of poison into your food every day for the last few weeks. In your drinks, too, even the water you bathed in. It was such a small amount that even your blood drinker did not detect it. It will work on her, too, since you share so much."

The room spun, my side pulsating as nausea once again crept forward. I stared at my drink, my vision blurry as I tried to focus.

"I was kind of worried you'd catch on at first." She plucked a small needle from her hair and slowly rose from her chair. "The extract in these zeile seeds can knock out even the strongest beasts. It attacks the blood slowly, hindering the healing process before targeting the nerves. Objects that weren't heavy before suddenly are. It can cause headaches, dizziness, nausea, and even a fever. Given your history, I needed to be sneaky about it, and I needed time for them to arrive. They have been so busy in the realms, you know. Securing our one true king's power."

Her laugh was vindictive and cruel, but she was wrong. Dianna had not been feeding on me, but she had eaten the food. Fuck. I needed to get to her, to warn her. I struggled to my feet but nearly collapsed when my side split open. Those lines, it was the poison and why I wasn't getting better.

My hand pressed flat on the table as I tried and failed to push myself up. A sharp pain echoed through my gut, and I fell back into my seat. Frilla stopped at my side, the needle seed still in her hand.

"Jade City was renowned for its healers. You and your beast have corrupted it."

I coughed, and the room spun sideways.

"We are still known for it, but only for those under our king's rule. Our specialty now lies in poisons. It is what truly makes her happy."

Frilla trailed a hand over my throat and leaned in close to me. I flinched as the needle pierced my neck, and my limbs went slack.

"Undiluted, the seed can act as a paralytic for a short period. It's how it protects itself in the wild. I figured this would make it easier for you to transport." Her hands trailed along my shoulders and biceps as she leaned forward. "Given all the extra muscle you have."

Nausea hit my gut, and it wasn't all from the poison.

"You truly are a lovely specimen. I wished to keep you, kill that bitch you came with, and make you one of mine, but our king does not handle defectors, such as The Eye, well. She will require you both to return and face your punishment. At least I will be well off once she has you."

Frilla forced my head to the side as she looked at me.

"If you touch me, she will burn you and your precious city alive."

"Doubtful. She will be dead soon enough. I made sure of it."

"What did you do?" I sneered.

Frilla yelped, her hand dropping from me as she shook it. Tiny sparks of electricity bit at her palm but flickered out quickly.

"How?" she asked, gaping at me.

Her question went unanswered, the doors bursting open. Armored boots echoed through the hall as soldiers covered in gold and black armor entered, Nismera's legless creatures emblazoned on their shoulder plates. They came to a stop in unison at the back of the room.

"Queen Frilla," a voice called, and the soldiers parted to reveal a tall commander.

My body swayed, the room fading in and out of focus. Sweat coated my skin, and I began to shiver. I watched the commander place a parchment in her hand before they exchanged a few words. He turned toward me, the single eye in his head blinking once as he stepped closer.

Fucking cyclops.

His hand gripped my hair, turning my head to the side as he looked at the mark Dianna had shaved there. Our ruse was holding true.

"A member of The Eye," he whispered close to my ear. "I cannot wait for our king to disembowel you."

It was the last thing he said before he slammed my head into the table. I didn't worry for myself as darkness crept closer and my body slumped.

My last thought was and always would be her. I feared for the world and what they'd unleashed.

XIV
Dianna

"You know, in a land full of so-called magical plants, you'd think a green flower with red and white speckles would be easier to find."

I tossed my arms in the air as Reggie glanced at a large, opaque shrub. The planet she sent us to was nothing like I expected, putting the forests of Onuna to shame with its thick foliage and the trees that damn near touched the sky. We had walked for at least an hour, looking for the damned plants they'd sent us to find.

"I agree."

We stopped short when the forest parted, revealing a lush, rich meadow. I brushed a piece of hair from my face, curling it around my ear as I kneeled in a bunch of plants that seemed to have recently bloomed.

"Miska said it would help keep him stable." I sighed. "He got violently ill last night. I'm so afraid that the spear messed something up on the inside, something that won't heal."

"They are magnificent healers," Reggie said from behind me. "It is surprising that his wound has not healed yet."

I stood, wiping my hands on my pants as I turned. "Another jab? I don't remember you being this sassy."

"The price you paid has changed you on some level, so I am not surprised if it has also changed him."

"Reggie," I said, "can we not?"

"I understand you don't wish to speak about it, but—"

I narrowed my eyes at him. "Do you? Because you keep throwing this big consequence in my face. I can't think about the possibility that he doesn't exist anymore, okay? I just can't."

"I'm merely saying you need to think of all possibilities."

My heart thudded. "I have, okay? And when I think about them, I tend to go off the deep end. All I know is that I can't lose him. I wouldn't survive it. The pain I felt in that tunnel was as if every molecule in my body split and fractured. It was worse than any stab or punch. I thought I was broken before, but . . . my soul cleaved in two, Reggie. I felt it. A part of me died when Gabby did, and whatever part was left, whatever he helped heal, died down there with him, too."

Reggie's eyes softened. "I fear for the changes is all I am stating. Your appetite, in all aspects, has increased. Your behavior and temper are erratic, and you know it. I fear it is only the beginning of what you gave up."

I said nothing for a long moment, the rolling stalks of flowers blowing between us. "You think I'm turning into a monster?"

"I do not know what you are turning into, but you have evolved past what you were, and it changed things. You brought a god back from death, Dianna. That act alone has never been done and will have required equal payment in return. If you think there will not be dire consequences, you are a fool. Can you look at me and say you don't feel it, too?"

"Well, I wouldn't worry. As long as he stays alive, the universe will continue to spin or whatever it does."

Reggie stepped closer, something that looked like concern darkening his eyes. "I thought you would have come to the conclusion that him knowing what happened in the tunnel would be beneficial, yet you seem determined to carry this secret to your very grave."

"I don't plan to. It's just not the time."

"When is the time?"

I sighed far too loudly and turned away from him. I walked under a half-fallen tree, if you could call the overgrown plant a tree.

"I don't know, but right now, it doesn't feel right," I said, dropping one of the overgrown, broken branches. I heard Reggie's feet behind me, only a hair away.

"The longer you wait, the harder it will be for both of you. He has a right to know. They are healers, but not even their potions can alter a death wound."

I stopped. "Is that what it is?"

"I assume only," Reggie said. "I have been searching through archives. It exhausted me to look through time as such, but all I found as of right now is that death wounds can be permanent. They even remain with the reincarnated ones."

"Reincarnated?"

"Those with enough power to transcend lives are born once more, over and over, until their true purpose is reached. The blade was imbued with your blood and ancient magic. It was meant not only to kill him but also to open every realm. It has succeeded in both of its objectives. I fear normal healing potions and concoctions will not suffice."

I shook my head before rubbing a hand across my face. "I can't trust them, not fully."

Reggie lifted a single brow. "Yet you trust them enough to give him medicine, to try, and fail, to heal him."

I spun from him, knowing damn well he knew why. He wanted me to say it once more. Maybe I was selfish. Maybe I needed to push Samkiel even harder, and maybe I was still taking it easy on him, but I couldn't escape that godsdamn tunnel every time I closed my eyes. I would never forget holding him as his skin turned ashen and cold.

"Why is this such a huge issue for you?" I snapped. "Because you can no longer see?"

Reggie stopped behind me, and I was waiting for him to say something. When he remained quiet, I sighed and turned around. Reggie's gaze was focused on the tree line, and I stopped to listen. A whirring sound echoed through the forest and then stopped.

"We were followed," I snarled.

"Not followed," Reggie said. "A trap."

I pushed past him and strode toward the forest's edge. He whispered my name, but I didn't stop until I reached the clearing. There, behind a closing portal, was a tall man with one eye in the center of his face. He closed the top of his gauntlet, sealing the portal. Soldiers surrounded him, all wearing that ridiculous gold armor Nismera outfitted her army in.

Reggie whispered near me. "There are at least thirty, including the commander."

I smiled softly, patting his shoulder. "Good, I'm just going to go say hi. You stay here."

"Be careful." Reggie nodded to the soldiers. "Nismera knows what you are. She would not send soldiers without something strong enough to subdue you."

"Duly noted."

I cleared the brush, and all eyes turned toward me. "So, since you are all here, I take it Nismera got my note?" I pouted. "Such a shame she did not come herself. Tell me, does she always send her lackeys?"

"So, you are the Ig'Morruthen she so desperately wants?" My eyes fell on the one-eyed general as he stepped forward. He towered over the other soldiers, and they fell in behind him, their hands resting on the hilts of their swords. "I expected you to look different, scarier perhaps. You are tiny."

I glanced down at myself, then back toward the towering, one-eyed commander. "I think everyone is tiny compared to you."

"It makes no difference." His voice echoed as the soldiers near him moved in formation. "You are hereby detained by the Twenty-third Legion."

I folded my arms, planting my feet firmly on the ground. "Oh? Am I? I think you'll need more, honestly."

The commander laughed, placing one hand on his stomach, then looked back as his soldiers joined him. "Oh, I don't think so."

I held my hand out, a swirling ball of flame growing before I turned back to them. "You sure about that?"

One by one, the soldiers with him reached behind their backs, and one by one, chains fell from their hands, glowing and barbed.

"Well, shit."

A severed limb hit the tree, and the general grunted beneath me.

Reggie stepped from the brush and approached me, his feet crunching on the burnt grass. My heeled boot still pressed on the general's throat, my hands on my hips as I turned to Reggie.

"You were right about the weapons." I nodded to the pieces of soldiers that littered the ground. A few of the chains still glowed as they lay near their corpses. The back of my arm still burned where I had been hit. After that first hit, I learned how to dodge a little quicker.

"I assumed as much," Reggie said before looking at the general I held beneath my foot. He clawed at my leg, trying to breathe, his one eye bloodshot now. "Are you all right?"

I shrugged. "A few minor burns, but they are not nearly as trained as they should be if she expects them to defeat me. I'm fine."

Reggie nodded solemnly. "And what of him?"

Pursing my lips, I tilted my head sideways and twisted my ankle. His body went limp, his arms falling to his side. "What of him?"

"I assumed you'd keep one alive . . ."

"I did." I leaned over and ripped the sole eye from the commander before walking over to the half-crumpled soldier leaning against the tree. She sat up and grabbed her stomach, the cut deep enough that she hissed. I ripped the fractured helmet off of her head, and she cursed at me in a language I didn't know.

"Reggie, translate this for me, please."

Reggie nodded.

I crouched before her and showed her the eye of her general. She turned away from me. "I want you to take this back to Nismera. Show her what's left of her precious legion."

Reggie spoke in her language, repeating what I said. Her face blanched. She'd assumed I was going to kill her.

"Now tell me how you found me."

She shivered, her blood leaking between her fingers. She spoke, looking between Reggie and me.

"We were sent to capture the wild Ig'Morruthen."

I glanced at Reggie. "I could guess that much. Ask her why?"

Reggie repeated. She glanced at me but spoke to him so he could translate.

"Yes, Jade City is full of healers, but they specialize in poisons. They follow the one true king."

I sighed and stood up. "Samkiel and I were right. They have a ton of jars containing rare and dangerous plants. Samkiel didn't know what they were doing, but we knew something wasn't right. Okay, we need to go get him, and then—"

The female soldier let out a sharp laugh, followed by a wet, pained cough. She glared at me as she spoke.

Reggie's eyes widened, but he said nothing.

"What did she say?"

"You must promise . . ."

"What did she say?" I closed the distance between Reggie and me.

"She said you are wasting time with her, but it will not matter. The traitor you work with is already captured and will face execution when he reaches Nismera. She said you have already lost."

All control and reason snapped in that second. They went to Jade City first. That harrowing darkness in me rushed forward like wildfire. I spun and grabbed the soldier by her throat, pressing her into the tree.

"Tell me where they took him," I growled, "and I might let you live."

She coughed, pulling at my wrist, but I pressed harder before letting her lungs fill with air.

She glanced at Reggie, her voice broken when she spoke. Behind me, Reggie translated. "She did not tell us. She only entrusted Fig, the general whose eye you currently have," Reggie answered.

"Fair." I shrugged. "But he wasn't going to talk, so that leaves you. What do they know?"

I waited for Reggie to ask and translate her answer. "That you are a traitor's whore, and the ones that work with and help you will suffer greatly. A cargo vessel for Nismera is already well on its way with the traitor from the city. They plan to take him to her for . . ."

My skin prickled. Did Nismera know Samkiel was alive? No. It was too soon. He could barely hold a blade. The veins along his scar had darkened the last few days, and it was all I could do to keep myself from going on a murderous rampage. I knew he was getting worse. I knew it when our training days had decreased and when he didn't even want to touch me but preferred if we just held each other. There was no doubt when he was emptying his stomach in the bathroom last night. Reggie's words danced across my brain, filling me with dread. What if Reggie was right? What if I only brought him back temporarily?

I heard nothing else.

Felt nothing else.

He was limp in my arms, that deathly gray taking up his entire face now.

The color was stripped away.

My light was stripped away.

"I would have loved you then, too."

Love,

Love,

Love,

"Remember, I love you . . ."

Fangs erupted from my gums, my mouth descending as I ripped into her neck. She screamed beneath me as I fed until there was nothing left. Her body thudded to the ground, and I turned away from her. Using my sleeve, I wiped the blood from my face.

"Dianna," Reggie scolded me. "This is what I am talking about with control. You could have attained more information."

"I don't need any more information. I just need power." Pushing past him, I reached the fallen general's body and grabbed the gauntlet off his arm. I tossed it to Reggie. He caught it in one hand and looked at me.

"Where are you going?"

I stomped away. "Where do you think?"

"Dianna."

"Don't." I spun, my hand whipping out to point a finger at him. "I am teetering on a fucking edge right now, Roccurem. So don't tell me what I need to do. I will not lose him a second time. I can't."

Not like I lost her, but those words never left my lips.

"Dianna." Reggie stopped in front of me, his hands on my arms. He pulled back with a hiss as if my skin burned him. "That child does not deserve your wrath."

He was talking about Miska. My vision changed, and I knew my eyes had gone red. "You think I'd hurt a child?"

"If you burn that city in a blind rage, if it falls, she will go with it."

I turned away from him, not stopping this time when he called my name. "Hold onto that gauntlet, Reggie. I'll be back," I said.

My arms grew, forming wings, and scales replaced my skin. A roar ripped through the air, my body changing faster than ever before. I cut a path through the sky, my gaze focused on Jade City.

XV
Miska

I knew I was going to die here. I'd never see the massive, stone castles my mom wrote about or the trees that changed colors with the seasons. I would see none of it because of what they did.

They laughed with the queen, sparkling glasses clinking as they spoke of the prize Nismera would reward them with and how Jade City would be the epicenter of the new realms. The laughter and cheer died when darkness spread across the room, blotting out the sun. But it was the roar that shattered glass that made my bones tremble. The sound would live in my head forever. Tables shook, the food rolling to the floor right before she hit. I had never heard anything so loud or felt anything so hot. The world shook, and it was my fault for not realizing they would never accept me; they only used me to drive her away.

Now, death had found us and set our world on fire.

Another mighty whoosh of flames rained down, and more screams echoed through the crumbling halls. I covered my nose and ran faster, heading downstairs. The smell, oh gods, the smell. My eyes watered as I clutched the sides of my dress, allowing my legs the freedom to move.

She let out an ear-splitting roar, and I fell against the nearest wall as the entire place shook. I collapsed against the stone and pulled myself along, running toward the cut-out window.

"Oh, gods."

My hand covered my mouth in horror. The city had cracked in half and was covered in flames, falling toward the thrashing sea below. My heart pounded in my chest. I needed to get downstairs, take the remedies I could, and find an escape raft. I remembered Sashau and Killie talking about them when they planned to sneak out of the city one night and how easy they would be to steer.

Wasting no more time, I cut a path through smoke, fire, and fear as the world around me continued to end. In the bowels of the palace, the hall at the bottom of the stairs was rarely used other than for storage. Only the elder healers were allowed down here. Shadows danced on the walls, light spilling from one of the rooms. I wasn't the first to think of this.

"You see what she did and what she brought down on us?" someone hissed from inside the room.

"We have to leave now," another female voice responded as the walls shook again, almost knocking me off my feet.

No. If they left, I'd be stuck here. Or worse, burned alive like the others.

I hurried, not caring if they saw me or what they said. I just wanted to leave, but I came to a sudden stop when I stepped into the room and saw what they were doing.

Their heads whipped up, the eldest healer, Franzceen, grimacing as she saw me. There were several other healers with her, including Sashau and Killie.

They had satchels slung across their bodies, filled with gold, jewels, and rare herbs. It looked like they had raided the queen's treasury.

"You're stealing while the city falls."

They sneered at me.

"How, out of all the people here, would the most annoying one still be alive?" Sashau snapped.

Two of the girls clutched their satchels as if they thought I would try to steal them. The room shook violently, the entire palace groaning. I stumbled, catching myself against a table.

Everyone steadied themselves and looked around nervously. "We have no time for this. Let's get to the rafts," Sashau said.

The rafts. There were only two, and by the looks of things, I wasn't getting a spot.

My eyes widened, and we all stared at each other for a moment before they turned and ran toward the door. I followed but was stopped by a sharp pain blooming in my face. I yelped and fell to the floor. Tossing my hair back, I cupped my throbbing cheek and looked up at Killie. She stood above me, her hand still fisted.

"You're not going, freak," she practically spat. "Stay here and die nobly, unlike your mother."

Tears pricked my eyes, and I couldn't fight them. I never fought anyone and knew I would burn here or be swallowed by the ocean.

"Killie," Sashau called from a door at the end of the hall.

"Both of you, come on. We don't have time for this," Franzceen hissed. "We need to—" There was a soft squishing sound, and Franzceen gasped, her face freezing in a grimace. Her arms went limp, and her eyes rolled back in her head. As if in slow motion, she leaned forward and fell to the floor.

"What was that last part?"

Xio.

Her hand was outstretched, a fleshy mass resting on her bloody palm. She wrinkled her nose and dropped it, the heart hitting the stone with a wet thud.

The healers screamed in fear, and the room erupted in chaos. I covered my ears and turned away, curling into a tight ball on the floor. I cried, knowing I was next. She'd find me and rip my heart out next, and I was weak. I couldn't do anything to stop it.

Sashau screamed and then gurgled as if she were choking. I heard a body hit the floor, followed by a low, vicious growl. There was a scramble of footsteps and more screams. I recognized Killie's voice, pleading for her life, and then nothing. The only sound was the crackle of fire, but no flames touched my skin, and nothing seemed to move. Had she left? I waited until I could no longer bear the quiet, and breathing through my nose, I cracked my eyes open.

I screamed, but the sound died quickly in my throat, terror stealing my ability to make a sound. Her face was mere inches from mine. Bright red eyes stared intently at me. Her hand whipped out and grabbed my chin, her grip painful. This was it. I was sure she was going to tear my head off, yet she didn't. She tipped my head, inspecting my cheek where Killie hit me. I could feel the throb of it and imagined a bruise had already formed. She hissed and abruptly let me go.

"Get up," Xio commanded.

I held up my hands, unable to stop the tears that blurred my vision. "I really didn't know. I've only been trying to help. You have to believe me. They tricked me like they always do and told me I was helping, but I wasn't. They told me of the plant, the one ingredient we needed for more medicine, but we weren't out. I found it when I went downstairs to clean. Then, I heard the commotion when the soldiers arrived, and I hid. I heard the healers talking, but I didn't know. I swear. They wanted you far enough away that it would take you a while to get back. The queen poisoned him. They took him a while ago."

I hiccuped as I waited for her to lunge at me, but she only wiped the blood from her chin and said, "I know."

My throat bobbed as I swallowed my sob of relief. "You know?"

She nodded. "Let's start over, shall we? My name is not Xio. It's Dianna. Those people took someone from me who means very, very much, and now I need your help to get him back, okay?"

I nodded, my heart easing its frantic pace. "So you aren't going to kill me?"

She smirked and stood, holding her hand out to me. "No, Miska, I'm not going to kill you." Then she looked over her shoulder and said, "But I am going to kill everyone else."

The old texts spoke of the great darkness that would fall across the land, how it would cut out all light, leaving nothing in its wake. Here it was, only it wasn't cold or quiet, but a blister against the skin and carrying the pure stench of death. That's what she was, yet when I placed my hand in hers, I felt warmth there, her touch soft and protective, not hurtful. Maybe that's what Cedaar saw in her, too.

"I didn't know they were going to take him. I really believed they wanted more herbs to help heal, I swear."

Her eyes scanned mine as she tilted her head to the side. "I know.

I think they have been poisoning him. Your tea seemed to be the only thing that helped him. Do you think you can make some more?"

"Yes," I said. "If I know which poison, maybe I can make an antidote? I need to get my mother's book and some herbs from here."

She let go of my hand and began collecting the bags from the bodies on the floor. She tossed them to me and nodded toward the room. "Grab what you need, then we will go talk with your queen."

I picked my way through the gore, my gaze landing on Sashau's body. Her lifeless eyes stared back at me, her throat ripped out. I ran to the shelves and started gathering what I needed, focusing on the supplies. The room rocked again, but the fear was no longer there with her at my back.

I gripped the satchel harder, making sure I kept hold of the herbs we needed. I had packed enough that the bag weighed me down. Dianna rubbed her brow and glared at Queen Frilla. She lay on the floor, holding her side, and she wasn't looking well. Dianna had burned off half of her hair, the wounds continuing down her face to her side.

"Ask her what poison again."

I did, and this time, the queen didn't make a smart remark but trembled as she answered. If she did not get help soon, she was going to die.

"I know what it is. I can make an antidote. We just need to find him," I said, keeping my voice quiet.

Dianna flexed her hands at her sides before wrapping them around her body. "Great. Now ask her where they took him."

I turned back to Frilla and asked. The queen replied, her tone shaky but filled with venom.

"Miska. Sweetie. What is she saying?"

I swallowed as the queen glared at me. Even covered in soot and blood, she loathed me.

"She says it doesn't matter, anyway. You took her city, so the deal she had means nothing."

Dianna nodded. "The deal with Nismera."

I nodded.

"Where are they now?"

When I asked the question, the queen laughed before coughing. She tried to sit up further and winced.

Dianna waited for me to tell her, my lip curling when I looked at her. "It was vulgar, but in short terms, she won't tell you. She hopes you die with him."

Dianna shook her head and chuckled as she smiled at the queen. "You know, you don't even know who he is." She bit at her bottom lip. "Samkiel would have helped you, saved you and your people. He would have bent over backward to offer you peace. Unlike the old gods, he is kind and caring." Her eyes darkened to a brutal crimson as she raised her hand. "Everything I am not."

Flames roared from Dianna's palm, and I yelped. The queen had no time to scream before she was engulfed. She burned until nothing but a smear of darkened ash remained where she'd sat. Dianna called the flames back to her, and I wiped my brow, the heat making me sweat.

"Now." She turned to me so quickly that I jumped. "We need to go get a fate I left on another planet."

She grabbed my sleeve and dragged me with her, the world shaking and rumbling. The stone beneath our feet cracked with a bellowing rumble, compromising the city's stability.

"Wait, you said a god? And fate?" My mind reeled.

"Yes." She kept pulling me along with her. "His name is Samkiel, and the fate's name is Reggie. We need to go get him before he throws a fit."

I stopped in my tracks as she turned to look at me. "*The* Samkiel?" I gulped. "The World Ender?"

A smile, short and brief, curved her lips before sadness crept in. It was as if even the mention of him brought her joy. "Yes, the one and only. Now we have to go save him."

"But . . . but he died. They said . . . but his light is in the sky . . ." My heart thudded. "How is he alive?"

She started forward again, and I followed. I studied her back as we passed the open door and turned toward the massive hole in the wall. From the size of it, this was where she'd entered when she first arrived.

"How do you feel about flying?" she asked, ignoring my question.

We stood at the opening, clouds rushing past us. My stomach dropped as we stood at the terrifying precipice. I gripped the satchel tighter, my eyes widening as I realized what she meant. "I've never flown anywhere before."

She shrugged. "Well, there's a first time for everything."

Dark, thick smoke encircled her, and her form grew massive. I jumped back, my gasp dying as scale armor covered her body. Massive wings tore through the walls and ceiling as she spread them. I had a second to decide what I wanted, and the answer came easier than I expected. I would finally leave this crumbling place behind. The darkness offered me a new life, a new choice, and I took it. I shifted the satchel and started to climb, using her scales to pull myself atop her back. I had barely settled before she leaped out of the building, destroying the entire wall as she went.

The wind tore the scream from my lips, and I gripped the spikes along her neck so tight my hands ached. Her wings beat soundlessly, propelling us through the sky as we shot up. The floating Jade City, along with every bad memory it held, was in pieces and on fire as it fell.

XVI

Camilla

Nismera sat at the head of a massive, carved stone table. I watched in awe from the shadows as living lightning danced beneath its surface. It whipped and coiled toward her and back, a physical manifestation of her power. I had heard stories of her, the other witches whispering her name in fear. Sweat rolled down my back at the thought of her catching me, but I needed answers. I'd felt a shift when we'd arrived here, and that harrowing feeling had done nothing but grow. Something old, powerful, and angry was stirring, and I couldn't place a finger on it. A deep sigh parted her lips as she placed her hand on her brow and shook her head. Temper flared, and even the holographic image of a soldier in thick armor shuffled on his feet.

"The legion sent to retrieve her has failed, my liege."

I watched her clench her jaw so tightly a vein pulsed on her forehead. A memory of the World Ender flashed through my mind. How similar yet so vastly unalike they were.

"How many casualties?" she snarled, her voice guttural.

The soldier paused. "All of them, my liege. There was nothing but ashes and scorched ground left." A commotion behind the soldier had him looking behind him before refocusing on Nismera. "And Commander Fig's eye was . . . detached, my king."

Nismera covered her mouth with her hands and turned toward Vincent. A feeling I couldn't quite name hit my gut as he placed a hand of comfort on her shoulder. Her loyal general in that damned dragonbane armor. So many spikes and rigid lines, just like him and his damned soul.

He had been by her side from the moment we'd arrived in this realm. If he wasn't escorting me to and from my workstation, he was with her. He was more than her general, and it turned my stomach sick. I still hated how he was practically my damn shadow, and I was even more pissed that our rooms were practically conjoined, with only the hall separating us.

"But before the legion perished, they did collect her companion. He is being shipped to the prison."

That got her attention.

"Companion?" Vincent asked, one perfectly sculpted brow raised.

"The fate," Nismera corrected. "I did not kill him. He is the one helping her now. It has to be him."

A member of the Order cleared his throat and said, "Perhaps we should focus on her, my king? While a nuisance, the Eye has not caused the mayhem she has."

Nismera's head whipped to the Order member. "I am not concerned with Samkiel's whore. She has no one. Her friends are here under my thumb, her family slain, and Samkiel is dead. She has no protection. She is no longer a threat to me. All she is doing is acting like a hurt child, burning all in her path. It means nothing to me. We have more important issues to worry about. When and if she gets close to me, I will execute her. I will make such a display of it that any thoughts of defying me festering in anyone's head will be extinguished."

Nismera sighed and leaned forward, clasping her hands in front of her. The map she'd laid out shimmered on the table. The pieces were carved and imbued with witch magic. She watched mountains, small buildings, hills, and clouds smaller than my finger shift across the landscape, keeping an eye on her enemies. With a swipe of her hand, the image changed, and I sucked in a breath. Oh gods. She had a living map of the realms. How?

Vincent watched her like a starved beast desperate to feast. My lip curled at how entirely obsessed he was with her. He always watched her or was a hair away from her. I couldn't believe the almighty, powerful goddess felt the same. My gaze locked on to him, and I swallowed hard, trying to picture it. With all the options she had tossed at her feet, why did she choose Vincent?

Secure in my invisibility, I allowed my eyes to linger on him a fraction longer. His long, dark hair spilled down his back, but he'd pulled it off his face on one side and woven it into a warrior braid. The dragonbane armor Nismera's highest-ranking people wore added bulk to his already large, muscular frame.

I suppose he was handsome, but that beauty faded once you knew him, knew what he had done and was capable of. It was a shame, though, a shame to be so beautiful and ugly at the same time. Maybe that's why they fit each other so well. I wondered if she would wed him, make him her consort officially. Would they rule over the wasteland she left in her wake?

My gaze returned to his face, and my breath caught. He was looking right at me. Impossible. I glanced down, noting the twitch of green flame in my pendant. The spell was still working. I was invisible, yet . . . I moved back, sinking deeper into the shadows. His eyes didn't follow. Good. Maybe I was wrong. I took a deep breath and forced my attention back to the room.

Vincent leaned forward, clearing his throat. I could have sworn his eyes cut to me once more. All eyes immediately focused on him, but her armored guards didn't flinch in his presence. He clasped his hands behind his back. "With all due respect, my king, I feel we should persist in seeking out Dianna's whereabouts."

Nismera rested her chin on her hand. "And why is that?" she all but purred. She only spoke to Vincent that way, and I didn't know why, but it made me want to hurl.

"Because we are not dealing with Ayla. Ayla died the second Kaden got a hold of her. We are talking about Dianna. We are not dealing with Samkiel's mate. We are dealing with Kaden's."

The room went deathly quiet, and I was lucky more creatures in here had heartbeats because mine pounded like a drum.

Nismera chuckled, but the room remained stagnant, the air clinging to itself and flavored with fear. Everyone watched her carefully. If those devilish eyes lit up, there would be no escape. All it would take was one flick of her hand, and everyone would burn, destroyed by the devastating god power she wielded so competently.

"Vincent, Kaden has no mate. He was not born of flesh."

"He does now. He made her, crafted her when he found her. They spent a thousand years together. He trained her, made her a killer, and respectfully, my king, a damn good one. She killed Alistair with her bare hands. I was there when she flattened his entire organization. I was there when she came back from Yejedin, covered in the ashes of Tobias. There for it all. She may have been made for Samkiel, but she is Kaden's blood, his anger, rage, and, above all, power. After what we did to Samkiel, she will not rest. She nearly leveled Onuna for Gabriella. What will she do for him?"

We waited. We all did. Even the Kings of Yejedin did not flinch.

Nismera took a deep breath as if contemplating, then leaned back in her chair. She tapped her perfectly painted nails on the table.

"You think I should fear her?"

"Absolutely not, my king, only that leaving her to continue on her warpath may bring your rule into question. You do not want to send the wrong message to those still poised against you."

"The boy has a point," Gewyrnon said.

My skin prickled at being this close to another King of Yejedin. Even the witches feared them. Gewyrnon could manipulate disease and spread a plague with his bare hands. The witches had long memories and remembered the last time he had wreaked havoc with his powers. His counterpart was just as dangerous. Ittshare could sculpt ice without so much as blinking. His hair was spiked with frost and I could feel the icy chill emanating from his skin from here.

"How so?" Ittshare interjected. "The Evunin realm may be a frozen wasteland now, but the bodies crystallized in my ice were not just those who would not bend, but rebels, as well. If she is of Kaden and she is against us, she will be seen as a weapon to dethrone you. Just as they saw with Unir."

Nismera rubbed a hand under her chin, glancing at the others in the room. "She is Ig'Morruthen. No one, not even the Most High, would follow her."

"The God King and his son may be dead, but she could be a beacon of hope no matter how violent. They do not need to follow her as long as she opposes you," Ittshare said.

Nismera's eyes bore into each one of them, and I held my pendant a fraction tighter.

"Very well. It will be taken care of," Nismera said decisively. She stood, and that was that.

Vincent stepped back, and the others stepped forward. Nismera didn't mention anything else of Dianna as she stood over her map of the realms.

My mind reeled. Rebels? Against Nismera? And mention of the Most High? Who was that, and why did it give her pause? I listened as they spoke, but there was no more mention of rebels or the Most High. She only talked of places she wished to secure next, food for the palace and troops, and how to cut off supplies to certain areas. A messenger entered, telling her of a shipment heading her way in a few days.

The room shifted at last, and everyone started clearing out. I stuck to the corner of the room, waiting until every last one was gone before I moved toward the table. Checking one last time to make sure no one remained, I tried and failed to make the map move.

"Come on," I whispered, and yet nothing. My magic hit a brick wall and bounced back into me. It remained just a cold, empty stone slab with indentations and scratches.

Shaking my head, I moved around the table, looking for anything I could use, a torn piece of paper, an item left behind, but there was nothing. I bent and checked under the table, but even the floor was scrubbed clean. I cursed and stood, my gasp cutting off when a large armored hand wrapped around my throat.

My back slammed against the unyielding stone of the table, his devastating grip unyielding. He forced himself between my legs and pressed his weight against me.

"What the fuck are you doing in here?" Vincent hissed.

The scales from his armored gauntlet cracked the pendant between my breasts. Magic flickered and crackled until it spluttered out. Cool air rippled over me as my form solidified. With his arm pressed between my breasts and his hips spreading my thighs, I struggled to ignore the brief flash of heat that burned deep in my belly. I shook my head. What was wrong with me? Holy burning gods.

"How did you know I was here?"

"I smelled haughty witch the second you walked in here. You're lucky they didn't," he hissed in a whisper, and I realized even with the brute fucking force he was using, he wasn't yelling or alerting anyone.

My hand wrapped around his wrist, and a soft emerald glow formed.

"Let go of me, or I'll melt your cock off."

A corner of his lips twitched, but he stood up and glanced at the open door before saying, "Do it. You'll only be doing me a favor. Maybe she would leave me alone for a day."

I rubbed my throat and looked down at my pendant. I grabbed it. "You broke this."

"You're a witch. Fix it," he said, shrugging his massive shoulders.

He moved away from me and closed the door as I did just that.

"Why do you say I am a witch like it is a curse?"

"Isn't it?"

I glared at him as the pendant in my hand slowly mended. "No."

"They use you for your power, not caring what or who you are. They don't care what your favorite food is or if you sleep with a light on for comfort in a strange new world. No one will ask about your dreams or your greatest fears. You are nothing but power to anyone here. Sounds like a curse to me."

My head reared back, and I paused. Why would any of that matter to him? "Are we talking about me or you?"

Vincent glared at me. "What was your plan, anyway? Even if you eavesdrop and find whatever information you think you need, you'll never escape this place. No one escapes Nismera."

"Maybe no one has ever tried hard enough," I said, folding my arms.

A haunted look flickered across Vincent's features, disappearing as quickly as it came. We didn't have the relationship, nor did I care enough to ask what it meant.

"Come on," he said, tipping his head toward the door. "We're leaving."

"No," I said. "I'm still looking."

Vincent stalked toward me with the grace of a predator and gripped my arm. "That wasn't a request."

He pulled me to the door. After making sure it was clear, he opened it and tugged me into the hall.

I pulled against his hold, not liking the sparks that danced through me from his touch. "Stop dragging me around like a brute, would you?"

"I will when you start listening to me and go where I ask," he said without even looking at me. I knew he hated this. Nismera had thrust us together the second we got here. I couldn't even piss without Vincent or some other guard being in earshot. I was trapped here in more ways than one, and gods above, I refused to be treated like a barely tolerated pet.

"When you ask me nicely and not order me around like I am beneath you, I will," I snapped back. His grip eased, but he didn't let me go. "Where are we going, anyway?"

"To get you food," he said, the guards we passed bending their heads to Vincent.

"Food?"

"Yes." This time, he did glance at me over his shoulder. "You haven't eaten today."

My brows furrowed. "And how would you know that?"

He let me go near a dining hall, voices clamoring from within. "Because I am your guard, remember? And I haven't escorted you today."

Fair, but the way he said it had my magic standing at attention. Not in fear or an attempt to protect me, but in a whisper, almost a purr. I mentally slapped it. *Stop that.* He was a traitor, a betrayer. He'd do the same to us.

"Okay."

Vincent opened the door, and the voices within died when they saw him. A few beings grabbed their trays and scurried out. Those that remained kept their heads down and their voices low, avoiding eye contact with him. I saw Vincent tense, but he said nothing. Maybe he didn't like the negative attention, but it was his own damn fault. I didn't feel bad for him, not for a second.

He held out his arm, inviting me to proceed with him. Varying beings mixed and mashed a plethora of food, but none was familiar to me.

I took a step forward and paused. "I don't know what to get."

"What do you like?" he asked.

"Eggs?" I shrugged. "It's early, so breakfast."

"Go sit down. I'll be right back," he said before leaving me alone in the center of the room. I swallowed the growing lump in my throat and found an empty table. I wrapped the silk skirt around my legs and took a seat. Eyes darted between Vincent, me, and then back, but nobody said anything, not even a whisper. A cook with three horns seemed uneasy just to be here, so much so that he discarded his apron and left. I wondered if they feared Nismera would not be far behind her precious second in command.

Vincent approached and slammed plates down on the table, the sound making me jump. He sat, and I blinked at the large pile of food in front of me, a mix of greens and what looked like orange eggs.

"Sorry, not scrambled. They are hard-boiled. I'm afraid it's the closest you'll get in this realm," Vincent said. He reached for a glass in front of him, the clear, shimmering liquid dancing as he raised it to his lips and took a drink. He then slid it toward me, and I made a face.

"I have two arms. I can only carry so much."

"Yeah, but I don't know where your mouth has been," I said. "Actually, yes, I do, so no thanks."

His eyes darkened. "I promise it hasn't been anywhere your mind is thinking this morning. You're safe."

"With you?" I scoffed. "Doubtful."

"If you're so worried about my mouth and where it's been, just drink from the other side."

Heat flashed across my face. "I'm not!"

His brow only rose as he turned from me, grabbing utensils for his food. "You're the one that brought it up."

My lips quirked, and I sighed. "Fine." I took the glass and drank from the other side.

I made a noise when the liquid touched my lips. "It tastes like orange juice."

Vincent grunted as he went about cutting the food on his plate and eating.

"So why did everyone scurry away from you? I figured you'd be labeled a hero for what you did to The Hand and Samkiel."

His fork stilled halfway between his plate and mouth, a haunted look creeping over his angular features. I watched the line of his jaw flex, and I wondered if he truly felt guilt for his betrayal. I knew a handful of killers who slept like babies after gruesome murders, yet here Vincent was, acting as if I just screamed a secret across the room.

"I am one of Nismera's High Guards. They fear me, thinking she is only a step behind."

"Oh," I said and nodded. I had been right.

"And my word is also law. I could have the cook in the far right gutted tonight for how he's staring at you, and Nismera would allow it," he said, taking a long drink from our shared glass.

I looked up to see the tall, lean cook was doing just that. His pale skin flashed a shade of pink, and his three eyes widened before he quickly looked away.

I returned my attention to my plate. "Please do not gut someone for looking at me."

He shrugged. "I won't." He leaned close for a second. "Besides, that would be half of the legion."

I rolled my eyes at him and continued to eat.

"Since this place is practically empty, I do have a question," Vincent said after a few moments of silence.

"Okay," I said. "What?"

"You're one of the strongest witches in your entire generation. Everyone knows it. So why haven't you tried to escape yet?"

My face burned. "Is this a test? Something to take back to her?"

He shook his head. "No, just curiosity."

I took a deep breath. To be honest, I had no reason but one. "Well, where would I go? My whole life was on Onuna. That's gone now and has been for a while."

Vincent only looked at me before nodding. "Fair."

"My turn," I quipped. "Why her?"

His posture went rigid. "Pick another question."

"Fine. Why are you being so nice to me? I know you're my guard and all, and I can't even breathe without you near me, but why?"

He didn't say anything for a moment, and I thought he would ignore me as he stabbed at his food. Then he sighed, not daring a glance at me as he said, "Because I think you feel just as alone here as I do."

The tension in my shoulders eased because it was true. I had no one, no friends or family, nothing anymore. Our entire worlds were turned upside down, and now here we were in a strange new world with each other. He was right. I'd never felt so alone.

We sat in silence for the rest of the meal, but I couldn't hide the fact that both of us, betrayers at our cores, seemed to bond over the silence. Maybe it meant nothing. Maybe it meant everything.

XVII

Samkiel

She sweeps the wet cloth under my lip as she hums to herself. My hand grabs her hand, lowering it. "I can do it myself. You don't have to coddle me."

Her lips tipped up, and she pulled her hand from mine. "Very limited coddling," Dianna said and turned back to the sink, rinsing the cloth once more. She reached for the small cup of paste and handed it to me. "I will hold your hand when you're sick and clean up your mess, but I will not brush your teeth for you. So very limited coddling."

I chuckled, the burn in the back of my throat subsiding from losing my dinner. I took it from her and ran my hands under the water before using the small bristle brush. She said nothing as I clean, just watched me and rubbed a soft hand up and down my back.

I turned the water off. "I just don't want you to see me like this."

Her hand stopped as she looked at me. "Why? There is nothing wrong with you. I'm blaming that weird shellfish food they served you. Gabby had this lobster once and puked on the brand-new rug I had bought her. I spent an hour cleaning it while she slept."

"But that's your sister." I paused. "I guess I just don't want you to see me weak."

She faked a gasp, placing her hand on her chest before raising it to lay the top of her wrist lazily across her head. "The mighty Samkiel, taken out by a stomachache. You're right. You're too weak. I must leave you now for all my other, more powerful suitors."

"I'm being serious." I frowned at her and poked her in the side.

She snickered. "As am I. I have several. It was only a matter of time."

I put both hands on my hips and glared at her. "Are you finished?"

"Yes." She smiled wickedly before she placed her head against my arm and wrapped her small hand around my biceps. "But, Sami baby, there is nothing weak about you. I think we are both used to doing everything alone, even taking care of ourselves. So help feels strange. You know I'll be here when you're healthy and strong and also when you're sick and need me to pick up the slack, all right?"

Warmth filled my chest and spread. It was the same sensation I'd felt the first time she and I ever opened up to one another in a strange motel on a planet I wasn't used to, but I felt it then and have felt it every day since. I didn't know what it was then. I was so unaware of how absolutely fucked I was until it was too late, and she was gone.

She held up that small finger, wiggling it at me as she grinned. "Your burdens are my burdens, and we take care of each other, okay?"

I clasped her pinky with mine and nodded. "Promise."

"It's practically law, you know." She placed a kiss on our joined hands.

I laughed and did not care for one second that pain shot through me. Everything in this realm and the next was bearable now because I had her.

Pain jolted my body awake and snapped my eyes open. The floor beneath me rose and fell in time to hoof beats. I turned my head and saw steel panels lining the walls. A violent bump shot an ache through my side. I heard a yell and the crack of a whip before we moved faster.

I realized I wasn't in a cell. The smell of dirt and trees wafted through the air. It looked like I was in some type of transportation cart.

I tried to sit up and immediately regretted it. I fell back, but my head didn't hit the hard seat beneath me. Instead, I felt a large hand catch me, and I was staring into speckled lilac eyes the same color as his skin. When his lips pulled back, I saw the tips of fangs. Realization hit me, and even without seeing his pointed ears and long tail, I knew what he was.

Elvian.

I opened my mouth to speak, but he lodged a small piece of bark between my teeth and forced me to chew. After I swallowed, his hand clamped over my mouth. My hand gripped his wrist, and he hissed before whatever he gave me set in. My eyes clouded, sleep filling my head, and for once, my stomach didn't roll with nausea.

I coughed and sat up, water spilling down the side of my face. I wiped the excess off with my sleeve as the world came rushing back. The same damn wagon rolled forward, the sound of hooves like drums. Groaning, I rubbed my temples, feeling as if my head had split.

"You're awake," a deep voice said. "It's been days."

Glancing up, I saw the same elf as before. He half perched on the opposite end of the wagon. He held a small green fruit and took a bite before nodding to the small, wrapped sack on the floor.

"Eat," he said. "You need it."

My back hit the wagon wall as I sat up straighter. "How do you know I can even understand you?"

A crooked smile formed on his lips as he dug into the dirty clothes he wore and pulled out his hand. He opened his palm to reveal my rings.

"Because I know who and what you are, Samkiel."

My blood ran cold. "You have me confused with someone else. I found those on a corpse."

He made a noise in his throat and placed them back in his pocket before taking another bite of his fruit. "Am I? But you speak Elvian fluently as if raised by a royal family who sent you to a royal school. You even use the proper dialect. Plus, that scar along your side looks as if a spear made of fire rammed through you. The rings with runes inside them are just like the ones Unir's famed son wore. Above all, the wave of electricity that runs through your veins gives you away."

He held up his wrist, and my handprint was burned onto his skin from where I'd grabbed him earlier when he shoved that bark down my throat.

"You're delusional," I whispered. "I merely work for The Eye. Everything you have and see is a product of what I've done for them."

"I never heard of any member of The Eye able to produce electricity. Seems like a godly power."

"Well, I suppose we all aren't that smart then."

He went to respond when the wagon came to an abrupt stop. The elf shoved the fruit back into the bag and hid it under the seat before lacing his ankles and hands back into the shackles.

"Regardless, keep quiet. I'll play along with your little game, but do not fight the guards. They would gladly beat you and leave your bloody body here for the beasts to feed on. If you are him, these realms are going to need you."

The doors were yanked open, and soldiers in dirt-smeared armor undid our chains before yanking us out into the blistering sun. I realized at once just what realm I was in and how far I was away from her and Jade City. Trees, crooked and bent, danced overhead as more guards emptied prisoners from the other wagons in the caravan. The elf stood next to me, and we watched all the activity before we were pushed forward.

"What's happening?"

"We are stopping for the night."

"Here?" I whispered as the guards pushed at us once more. "Do they know what lives between these trees?"

The elf glanced at me and shook his head. "They know, and they do not care. Some probably want us to be eaten. It would mean less sharing of food and work."

The woods and land may look dead, but I knew what beasts lived here, what watched us even now. A yip sounded through the air, followed by another. The guards behind us chuckled.

Fire crackled around the few branches that still burned. We sat huddled, the cold night air nipping at our skin. The blankets they gave us were thin, worn, and filled with holes. There were a few campsites set up in the small clearing. Prisoners gathered around each fire, sharing a bowl or two of whatever mush they gave us to eat. Only the elf and I were at our fire, the others staying far away. I wrapped my blanket around me a fraction tighter.

"Do gods get cold?" he asked behind the spoonful of mush.

I glared at him. "I'm not a god."

He nodded. "Still keeping up that ruse, huh?" He shrugged and took another bite. "You need to eat. That gaping wound on your side isn't healing."

"What was it you gave me?" I asked, trying to stop another shiver. "In the wagon. What was that?"

"A bessel root. We all have them. It helps nausea." He lowered his spoon. "And parasites, since the food and water they give us isn't the cleanest. You might shit your brains out, but at least the worms won't eat you from the inside out."

I grunted in response and pressed my hand over the pendant around my neck. It was the only thing I had of her here.

"You know, they tried to take that necklace off you. Three guards attempted it, and it cut their hands. They laughed, saying it was damn near unbreakable."

I glared at him but said nothing.

He sipped on his soup. "Must be pretty damn important."

I sighed in response and nodded toward the other fires. "Why don't you go sit with them instead of pestering me?"

The elf snickered. "Oh, they don't like me. Trust me."

"Winning personality?" I asked.

He only shrugged. "Until you reveal your secrets, I will not share mine."

"I have none."

He took another bite as the fire crackled between us. "Your Eye markings are wrong. You need four shaved lines on each side, not three. They used three before they took Leenon Ridge back."

My hand instinctively raised to the side of my head as he watched me, his tail flicking. I turned from him, and he laughed low into his food.

"Don't worry, god king. I won't tell."

"Do not call me that," I snapped back at him, careful to keep my voice low. Turning, I made sure the other prisoners weren't paying us any attention. The guards watched us but were more concerned with each other.

"Because you don't want others to know? Or perhaps . . ." He leaned a fraction closer, his nostril flaring before pulling back. "Or perhaps it's the female you are protecting. Her scent is faint, but you are covered in her."

I didn't realize I had moved until my side ached, and I was practically snarling in his face. "Watch what you say next."

All I got in return was a toothy grin that made his pointed ears twitch. "So it is a woman. Always a woman. I don't see a band on your finger or the mark, but she must be pretty important, nonetheless. Is that where the necklace you always touch is from?"

I felt the tic in my jaw and wondered if killing him would serve me. I decided it wasn't worth it and stood, yanking the worn blanket with me as I walked toward the makeshift tent. He said nothing else, just snickered behind me as I left.

I ran my hand absently across the necklace as I sat down on the small, makeshift cot. I lay there as the night whispered its song, my mind racing. The caravan held at least fifty prisoners, and we were all being shipped somewhere. I needed more information, and I needed to reach her as well. I lifted the necklace, peering closely at the pictures of us inside. A small smile curved my lips, a small bright spot in this damned day.

XVIII

Kaden

"What's down there?"

Nismera smiled, playing coy. "It's where I keep my fates. Nothing exciting. Now, come on."

I turned with her even if a part of me knew she was lying.

Guards shuffled past the war room as I sat listening to The Order ramble.

". . . and if that's true, only one stronghold can hold it. The shipment is on the way to it as we speak, my king."

I sighed, the sound of my chair scraping across the stone, cutting off their words as I stood. Every eye turned to me as Nismera lifted her head.

"Are we boring you?"

"Slightly, but I have to piss. So I'll be back."

Isaiah cut his eyes to me as if he was about to stand. My brother could pick up on even the slightest lie that slipped past my lips.

"I'm fine. I don't need you to hold my hand."

He flipped me off but smiled before he sat back fully in his chair.

I left the war room, and the voices flooded the room once more, The Order telling her about another outpost that was hit. I walked past the guards she had standing watch at her door and went downstairs. Once I knew for certain no one was following me or watching, I opened my palm, and a swirling portal of black ringed by fire greeted me. I stepped through into the lower levels of the golden palace. The stone and darkened hall was such a harsh contrast to what she portrayed upstairs. I'd known Mera my whole life, and this place was the perfect representation of her. Her fake smile hid horrors and the darkness resting just under her skin.

Her war drapes hung on every mantel as I walked deeper inside. The hall opened into a massive foyer. A large, twisted stone sculpture took up the middle, the beast and man locked in battle, coiling around each other.

The sound of footsteps reached me, soon followed by voices. I backed up, slipping into the shadows as they passed, lost in conversation. They were headed toward the room I was interested in. I waited until they had disappeared before following. I knew where she kept her fates, and it damned well wasn't in the room I saw her leaving the other day.

I passed by an archway to my left, striding through the one on my right and making my way down the stairs. My gut had never led me astray, and right now, it screamed about that godsdamned room. I stopped as soon as I reached the bottom. The twisted doors were locked, but the two men standing guard were what made me curse.

Guards that were not there yesterday.

"High Guard," one said. "Can we be of service?"

Fuck. I could easily kill them both and find out what was in that room, but then she'd know. This was her testing my loyalty and trust. If two of her guards came up missing, she would be on high alert. Double fuck.

"I was . . ."

My words drifted off as their eyes rolled back and their bodies slumped forward in a heap. Green mist swirled around their heads.

I turned, realizing I wasn't alone.

"Camilla?"

She lowered her hands, her emerald magic drawing back into her palms as she stalked forward. "What are you doing?"

"Me? What are you doing?" I hissed. "Those guards—"

"Are sleeping and when they wake up, they will think they slept on the job. They will never speak of it because if she finds out, she'll rip their heads off." Camilla shook her head at me before grabbing my wrist and attempting to make us leave. I didn't move.

Camilla jerked before spinning. "We have to leave."

I yanked my hand free. "*We* don't have to do anything. I need to find out what's behind those doors."

"No, you don't." She sounded exasperated.

I took a step forward. "What do you know?"

We both stopped as footsteps sounded nearby. She curved her lips inward, clearly pissed, and turned from me. "Fine."

She shoved the guards from in front of the door and reached for the handle. "Are you coming or not?"

I shrugged and followed her inside. Once the door clicked behind us, sparks of tiny light erupted from the ceiling, dancing around above, illuminating the place.

"You're lucky they are in that meeting. Usually, this place is crowded too."

I swallowed as I looked around the room. Metal tables took up each corner, machines and wires hanging above them. A hallway branched off and disappeared around a corner. Camilla walked around, looking at the shelves holding myriad jars and tubes. I strode over, glancing at the ones with different liquids, but the tables spread out in the neighboring room made me pause.

The stench of rotting flesh made me cover my nose. I had been on battlefields and seen the worst, but this . . . There were so damn many, and they had been here far longer than they should have. Stalking forward, I moved the tarp off of them. Parts of corpses were spread over the tables. Some still stared at the ceiling with dead, cloudy eyes, and some had no eyes at all. Others were in parts, cut into perfect squares as if the body was forced between some kind of net. Mutilated corpses of all kinds, including some of her generals.

"What is this?" I asked, looking at Camilla.

"I've heard the witches laughing and the guards talking. She has many titles. Nismera the Conqueror and Nismera the Bloody, but I hate Nismera the Mutilator the most." Camilla set a bottle back on the shelf and walked closer. Her nose wrinkled in disgust, but she did not seem surprised. "In our realm, they called it science. Here it's turtisuma. She's been busy while you were gone, it seems."

"She's mutilating her guards?"

"The ones that fail her or the ones she is interested in, I suppose, but most of these look like regular beings. Maybe prisoners of some sort? Traitors."

"Why?" I asked. "And more so, how do you know?"

She lifted a pendant between her breasts. "I have my ways. I've been sneaking around, usually at night when everyone is asleep, and I found this place. My magic was screaming every night she was in here. Whatever she is working on is making my skin crawl. I snuck in during one of her long war meetings the other day."

I said nothing as I walked around the large lab. The remaining bodies were half-covered in thin sheets. It smelled of blood, piss, and darker things, as if most weren't dead when she started whatever the hell it was she was doing down here. "I never knew Mera to be so . . . cruel."

Camilla scoffed and shrugged. "Maybe you haven't known her at all."

I glared at her. "I know my sister."

"You mean the same sister that locked you in her dungeons for a week after you returned?" Camilla said. "I heard how terrible they are. So far beneath the ground, even the light is afraid to reach it."

The memory of them flared back. How I shivered in that corner cell, unable to tell if my eyes were even open with how pitch black it was. The only indication I was awake were the moans and screams. The inhabitants who had been there much longer than me cried and begged for an end, any end.

My eyes snapped to her, but I said nothing. Whatever she read in my gaze made her drop it and return to the jars lining the walls. "I may need some of these." She glanced back at me. "Spells and all."

"And what exactly are you plotting?" I tilted my head a fraction higher.

"Always have to have a backup plan." She cut her eyes toward me, and I knew exactly what dark-haired beauty had taught her that. My heart skipped a beat even thinking of Dianna.

"What makes you think I won't have you detained for this?"

A smile curved her full lips. "Because something tells me your dear sister didn't want you to see this, either."

Checkmate.

I shook my head and scratched my brow, my armored glove cool against my skin. "It makes no sense why she would be so desperate to mutilate so many. It's as if she's studying them. These bodies are fresh. Samkiel is dead. She is the most powerful being now. So why?"

Camilla quirked her upper lip. "From the way she is working and experimenting, something tells me that even with him gone, she isn't the most powerful being in the world."

Before I could respond, the door started to open. I threw my hand up, drowning the room in complete darkness before grabbing Camilla and pushing her between one of the racks. I pressed my body over hers, my hand covering her mouth, and a single finger raised to my lips to hush her.

"See, no one in here, you idiot. The lights would be on," the guard from outside said. "You just fell asleep."

"Me? You fell asleep too, you moron." The rest of their words faded as they closed the doors.

I glanced down at Camilla to find her looking up at me. Her hands rested on the plated dragonbane armor covering my arms. Her throat bobbed, and a look passed between us. Memories were thick between us, but it was a history neither of us wanted to repeat.

"Can you make them sleep from here?" I asked, lowering my hand.

Her gaze darkened. "Of course."

I was about to respond with a snide comment when the wall near her head hissed. We pulled away, and cold air hit us as the wall slid to the side, revealing a hidden room. My eyes adjusted to the pale blue light of the small chamber.

"What's this?" Camilla asked, stepping away from me.

I didn't answer as I entered, feeling her right behind me. In the center was a long, rectangular table, and atop it sat a device. Its insides were spinning wildly. I bent to look and stopped, my blood running cold.

"It's a centrifuge." Her voice was as cold as the room.

I stood up and turned toward her. "And the blood currently spinning inside is of my brothers."

"What?"

"She has Isaiah's and Samkiel's. I can smell it." I took a shuddering breath. "She must have collected Samkiel's when she killed him, but Isaiah's?"

"Kaden."

"What?" I snapped, turning toward her.

She stood there with an empty vial in her hand. "I think all she's missing is yours."

A sleeping spell and a slight jog later, Camilla and I ascended the stairs. A few generals and guards passed us but said nothing. I hoped our plan worked. We had both been gone for more than a minute, and I knew Nismera would have noticed.

"No one can know," I whispered into her ear as I held her upper arm.

"Oh, I'm sorry. I'll just put away the banner I was making where I tell everyone what we found." She tried to pull away from me and failed.

My lip curled as I turned her to face me. "Camilla, I will—"

"I know, I know, threats, dismemberment. I've worked for you for eons, Kaden. But you need to watch after yourself. Nismera is doing something far more malicious than—"

Her words died as I slammed my lips over hers. Her body froze, and I felt magic swirl beneath her lips, ready to rip me to pieces.

"Well, I suppose it makes sense why you'd skip a meeting of importance," Nismera purred behind us.

I pulled back and glared at Camilla, warning her to play along. Her lips thinned in displeasure, promising retribution before she faked innocence.

"Mera," I said, turning to see her and her guards. Vincent was at her side, looking at Camilla with bewilderment, and Isaiah had a shit-eating grin on his face. "You talk too long. I was bored, so I found something far less boring. Besides, I assumed you'd still be blabbing. I was almost back."

A cool smile formed on her lips as she clasped her hands over her sparkling, jagged dress. Her crown never even tilted. "Let's not make this a habit, shall we? Maybe save your trysts for the evening, perhaps?"

"My apologies. Camilla is usually quicker than this." I smiled, ignoring the sharp sting of magic that jabbed into my arm.

Nismera raised her hand. "Vincent, can you escort our lovely guest to her workroom, where she should stay with guards, yes?"

The last part made me wonder. Now that I thought about it, she never let Camilla go too far without Vincent or her guards. At first, I had assumed it was because she thought Camilla would flee, and Nismera needed her power to help the other witches fix Nismera's medallion. But it had been so long now that Camilla wouldn't run. She might snoop and be too damn nosy, but she wouldn't run. What about Camilla had her so concerned?

Not glancing at me, Vincent stepped forward, completely focused on Camilla. They stared at each other as if it was I who had interrupted something. Neither of them said anything as they left.

Isaiah came to my side, shaking his head as Mera left with her guards. They turned the corner, heading back toward the west wing before Isaiah spoke. "Don't shit where you eat?" He snorted, slapping a hand on my back. "Great advice."

I turned to him with no comeback. I wanted to leave and process what I had seen, but worry for him stopped me. Why had Nismera taken his and Samkiel's blood, and why did she want mine? What was she planning that she needed our blood?

XIX
Samkiel

Five days later

My side ached as I moved on the roll laid out in our tent. I was so tired of this constant pain. We were at another stop, only this time in the hills of Klivur, to pick up another set of prisoners and a huge crate. Sweat drenched my forehead as I rolled to my back and sat up.

A groan came from outside, one of pure pain. I turned, glancing toward the side of the tent where the elf stayed, and saw nothing but a tangled mess of worn blankets.

The grunt sounded again, only this time voices followed.

"Slimy bastard."

Tossing off the blankets, I sat up. I headed toward the tent entrance and peeked out. Only a few small fires burned, and there were no prisoners or guards around. There was another grunt, and my head whipped toward the forest's edge. I stalked forward, past wagons and the thick-maned huroehe that pulled them. I worried about their hooves with this terrain. Even as hard as they were, the jagged rocks could cut the soft underside after a while. They huffed, paying me no mind, the thick, long hairs of their tails swatting back and forth as they ate the wiry grass and herbs the guards provided.

I snuck past them, drawing closer to the noise. The light from the fires faded as I reached the front of two wagons and a sharp cry rent the air. I sprinted toward the noise as it grew more distant, my instincts screaming at me to hurry. The wind whipped over the mountains, rustling the leaves. I came to the second clearing and stopped just inside the tree line.

"That will teach you to be a fucking traitor," a guard spat at the crumpled form he dropped. I saw the tail and knew who it was. Another guard lifted his arm, laughing as he pointed. "Drop him off the side of the cliff. No one will know."

"What about Nismera?"

The third guard shrugged. "Accidents happen."

They lifted him, and he groaned in pain. I stepped into the clearing, and the guards spun, their eyes widening as a scowl formed on their faces.

"Beating a man when he does not fight back?" I tsked. "Coward is not the right word in your language, but it is close enough."

One guard drew his blade, raising it to me. "Back to your tent, prisoner, or we will gut you here."

The elf at his feet pushed up, opening one bloody and bruised eye. I pursed my lips, sighing.

"Sorry, I can't do that."

They charged.

One raised his blade. It swished through the air, and I side-stepped, my fist slamming out, knocking him to the ground. The other guard came up behind me, his blade crashing down on my shoulder. His eyes widened in disbelief when the sword bounced off.

I shook my head and turned, yanking the sword from his hand and slamming the hilt against his nose. He cursed and stumbled back, covering his face, blood spurting between his fingers. I broke the blade across my knee. The guard nearest the elf leaned down to push him off the cliff but yelped and grabbed his own neck. He fell to one knee, a small blade sticking from his throat. He tumbled back over the cliff. The elf smirked, and I realized he wasn't as defenseless as I thought.

His eyes widened, and he reached into his pocket. He threw something, and a small silver ring flew through the air. I caught it and slipped it onto my finger. An ablaze dagger formed, and I twisted my hand, stabbing the charging guard under his chin.

A shuffling came from my right, and the last guard gasped.

"No," he whispered. "You're no rebel. You're *him*."

The dagger left my hand and speared through his skull, cutting off anything else he would have said. His body dropped with a thud. I picked up the first guard I'd killed and stomped through the brush as I neared the elf.

He sat up, holding his side as he smiled at me. "Thanks for saving me."

Not saying anything, I tossed the guard off the cliff. I stalked to the other guard and pulled the blade from his head, calling it back into my ring. I leaned down and lifted his body, hissing as my side pulled. But it was not nearly as bad as before. I stood near the cliff's edge and tossed the last guard over before glaring at the elf.

"I know you kill monsters, but I'm surprised you killed them."

"Who said they weren't monsters?"

He swallowed and nodded. I extended my hand toward him, and he grasped it, pulling himself up. "Please tell me you did not get yourself in this predicament to prove a point."

His tail thrashed behind him. "Actually, no. I left to take a piss, and the guards saw and jumped me."

"Why?" I asked. "They mentioned a traitor."

The elf dug into his loose pants pocket. He pulled out the rest of my rings and handed them to me.

"I guess I can tell you my secret since I know yours."

I took my rings back and placed them in my pocket. "Go on."

"My name is Orym. I'm an ex-commander of Nismera's Thirtysixth Legion."

Orym hissed as he finished wrapping the small gash on his side from the guard's boot. "So you really are him. You're the god king."

He faked a bow, and I grumbled. "Stop that. I hate that."

"How . . . how are you alive?" he asked as we settled into the cramped tent. We stayed in the shadows and snuck in through the back of our tent, making it back without the guards seeing us.

I said nothing as I lay back down on my small cot.

"I saw . . . we all saw the sky open. Your light dances across the sky. You're supposed to be dead."

Dead. That's what they kept saying, and by all accounts, they were right.

I glanced at him, noticing his apprehension. "What of you? How does one become an ex-commander? Defection usually means death."

His smile lost its shine. "I told you before. It's always about a woman."

"You lost someone."

Orym lifted his blanket and turned on his side to face me. "Not just anyone. *The* one."

My heart sank. "Your amata."

He nodded. "She was . . . everything. She died along with many more when Nismera destroyed my world." I listened to his heartbeat. It thumped, not in the erratic way of fear or lying, but like he was excited, as if my existence meant something to him. "Her rule is to join or die after she conquers, and we chose the former. My sister and I joined the legion after admitting defeat, or so she thought. We have been working ever since to undermine her. We moved behind the scenes, collecting information for The Eye and waiting for your return. But you didn't show, and then the sky bled."

I swallowed the aching guilt that bubbled in me. "I did not know what was happening behind the realms. They were sealed because of me. I felt nothing until they opened. I am sorry for your loss."

Orym shrugged. "We all know the pain of loss. The only joy I find now is that one day, I'll see her again. So until we are reunited, I'll help as many as I can."

"That you shall." I let loose a breath and absently cradled the wound across my abdomen. I turned onto my back, the new position giving my side some relief.

"I knew it was you when you arrived," Orym said. "They tossed you in the cart, and I saw that gash on your side. That's where she stabbed you?"

I shook my head, my hand fisting in the fabric. "Not her. My . . ." My voice trailed off. Kaden was my brother, a truth a part of me hated to admit. "Someone else did."

Orym made a noise low in his throat. "How did you not die?"

I met his gaze, a soft smile playing on my lips as I heard Dianna's laugh echo through my mind. "Someone I love very much found me and saved me."

"Ah." I could hear the smile in his voice. "In my culture, we don't refer to them as just amata. They are your great love. Is she your great love?"

I nodded, staring at the top of the tent. "The greatest."

"Is she . . .?" His voice trailed off.

I knew his question, knew what he was asking. He wanted to know if Dianna was still alive, and I knew she was. I knew it with every fiber of my being, even if I could not feel her from here. I could not explain it even if I tried, but that warmth, that spot inside my body that burned only for her, still burned vibrantly. That light had not gone out.

"She is."

Orym yawned. "Well, then, I hope you see her again."

"I have no doubt I will. I only worry about the world until she finds me or I find her."

A short laugh escaped him. "So she is a warrior like you? It would make sense."

"She is. She is also brave and way too smart for her own good." I couldn't help the smile that broke across my face thinking of her.

"Is she nice? My Wyella was kind. She would give her last breath to those she cared for. She did exactly that."

I turned my head toward Orym as he spoke of his lost love, and I wondered if he needed a friend more than rescue.

"She is kind . . . well, it depends, honestly. She loves very deeply and cares for those who are hers, but she has nothing but fury for her enemies." I smiled to myself. "I always suggest getting on her good side."

"Ah." Orym grinned. "You have a fiery one."

My smile was pure and genuine. "Oh, you have no idea."

Orym nodded, his smile slowly fading. "Protect it. What you have with her. This world will strip it bare. It's not the same realm you and your father left. Only death lives here now." The tent fell into solemn quiet. The fire crackled outside, slowly dying, and Orym nestled down to sleep, placing his hand over his face.

XX

Cameron

My bed jerked. My eyes snapped open, and I screamed. "Holy fuck! What a nightmare to wake up to."

Kaden's face curled into a sneer, and he folded his arms across his chest. I pulled myself up, grabbing the sheets and tying them around my waist.

"I've been looking for you."

"Oh, that's nice." I cocked my head, tossing an arm up. "I've only been out with one of Nismera's legions scouring Tarr for the last few weeks. Which, by the way, shows no sign of her."

"There wouldn't be. She fought, then left. It was a diversion and a fucking good one."

"How would you know?"

His smile was venomous. "Because I overheard the Eighteenth legion speaking of their trip to Jade City. The whole city burned and is now underwater."

My heart thudded. "Sounds like her, but why there?"

Kaden waved his hand. "It's not important, but we now know she isn't in the East at all. She's far closer to the north region of the realms."

I blew out a long breath. "Okay, what does that mean for me?"

"It means I have a new mission for you."

My chuckle was not one of humor as I stalked around my bed, the sheet dragging behind me. I stopped at my dresser and pulled out the fitted buckled gambeson and a pair of cuffed linen pants that were a part of our armor.

I half-turned, Kaden still standing there waiting. "Do you want to see me naked or what?"

His jaw clenched. One second, he was near my bed and in front of me the next. It was so strange being this close to him. I could see every small familial similarity that connected him to Unir and Samkiel, the bridge of his nose, those piercing, damning eyes, and a jawline that could cut glass.

"You've been feeding recklessly. Isaiah had two bodies he had to dump yesterday. Both drained of blood and hidden in the waste area of the kitchen."

A cold sweat broke out across my skin. I had been starving and had gone there to get something to eat. I sat down and ate the fruits and mash they'd made, but it wasn't filling me up. The smiling cook, with hair the color of the sea, smelled better. I heard her pulse speed up when I looked at her, smelled the air tinge with arousal, and I . . .

"I didn't mean to," I said, lowering my head. "I was actually eating dinner, but she cut her hand watching me and . . ." I took a shuddering breath. "The second person just walked in on us, okay?"

"I don't care what you do, who you feed on or fuck, but don't make Isaiah clean up your mess or bring him into it."

So that's what he cared about, not the ones I had killed and drained. I saw them every time I closed my damned eyes. Kaden, however, only cared for his brother.

A snort left my lips. "Jokes on you. I only fed and then left. I haven't put my dick in anything but my hand."

Kaden scoffed, taking a step back. "Let's share less."

"Sounds great."

Kaden reached into the side piece of his armor, taking out an obsidian slate. It shimmered an inky black as he handed it to me.

"Take this. Head to River Bend, and I'll contact you from there."

Kaden turned on his heel, heading for the door.

"River Bend?" I called out. "Isn't that a fishing town?"

"Yes," he said as he reached the door. "Dianna was spotted flying over an island not too far away. She's erratic, allowing herself to be seen far more than before. She's looking for something, and I don't think she cares who sees."

A part of me wondered if Dianna was trying to get Nismera's attention, but I didn't voice that question. I wanted to find her, but for my own personal reasons. "Well, what are you going to do?" I asked instead.

Kaden paused, a smile tipping his upper lip. "I have to go see a witch." And with that, he left.

I shivered in disgust. The image of him fucking Camilla made me want to hurl, but that was the talk all around Nismera's palace. The two of them had been caught sneaking around at all hours of the night. A small smile curved my lips as I stared at the door.

They may have been caught in some compromising situations and shared a kiss or two, but one thing was for fucking sure. I didn't smell a hint of lust on him now or before when I had bumped into the two of them. Kaden thought he had control over me because of Xavier, but he was hiding something. They both were. If I wanted to see Xavier again, I was going to use it to my advantage.

"Check fucking mate."

XXI
Samkiel

The natural spring near the mountain's edge is damn near freezing, but gods, was I happy for a bath. We had made another stop at a neighboring castle to retrieve something so vicious that they had lost six guards trying to contain it. Ultimately, they managed it, and I felt for the creature. It had screamed all night, scaring away the large predators that hunted these hills. It wasn't until the soldiers opened a crate carrying spears tipped with heated prongs and poked at the beast that it went quiet. Orym had to hold me down so I didn't interfere.

"Still pissed?"

I heard the water splash near me. "No, but it goes against everything I believe in for one to suffer at the hands of another, especially one already caged."

"If you had interfered, they'd have killed you."

"Doubtful."

"Or worse, your entire cover would be blown."

I raised a handful of water to my face, scrubbing at the prickly hair along my chin and neck that threatened to grow back. "Sometimes, it is not about me or what I wish. To let another suffer . . . I can't. If it happens again, do not stop me."

Orym swallowed. "I have to."

My eyes narrowed. "And why is that?"

His eyes darted toward the water's edge and the guards patrolling the tree line. Several of them were talking, but they all watched us carefully.

"I'll tell you tonight."

That was all he said before sinking into the water and swimming away. Frustrated, I returned to my makeshift bath. My side seemed less tender but still sensitive. The ominous lines around the wound were still spreading. I felt weaker than usual, more winded, and I wondered how deep that poison lay.

I just wished Dianna were here. I missed her. This was the longest we had been apart since Onuna, and I hated every fucking second of it. Every crackle of leaves or noise pulled me from my sleep, expecting to see red eyes. I wanted her to find me, but I knew she wouldn't, not until I left here or got a message to her. These realms were dangerous, even for my brave, fiery girl. I needed to know she was safe, alive, and whole.

I glanced down at my finger and the empty space where a mark should be and cursed. She was my amata, and yet it hadn't shown. If I just had it, I could feel her, sense her, and let her know where I was, but it was not there. The patch of skin remained bare, an empty space where my soulmate bond should be.

Worry made my stomach churn, and I was unsure if it was concern for her safety or from the poison digging deeper. I made it to the water's edge before what I ate came back up again.

"Don't stare."

I glanced toward Orym as we sat around the fire. It was still only us, the rest of the prisoners avoiding us. I stirred the slop they gave us every night, my stomach rolling.

"I have more of that root in my knapsack if you need it."

I shook my head. "It's not helping anymore."

"If the healers from Jade City poisoned you, then they are all that can help."

I nodded, stabbing the lumpy mush with my spoon. "Good to know."

Silence fell, the fire pitching a fraction higher as Orym placed another piece of wood. The guards made their rounds, glaring at us and making remarks as they passed. They hated him the most, it seemed. No one had questioned us about the three missing guards. They had continued to go about their business, claiming the beasts in the woods had taken them.

The fire burned brighter, the crackling picking up and the flames emitting a low hiss.

"I need to talk to you." Orym moved closer, eating his food as he watched the surrounding area. "Just pretend to eat."

I didn't look at him but nodded.

"I wasn't just kicked out of the legion for rebellion. I was also a spy for The Eye. My sister, as well."

My spoon froze mid-dip, but I kept looking ahead.

"Veruka is her name. She's there right now and sent me word."

He reached into his pocket, pulling a small piece of parchment out with words scribbled on it. "They are moving us to Flagerun. From what I hear, it's a prison and one of her favorites. A sweeping fortress that burrows into the planet."

"Okay."

"She also said there is something you need to see."

This time, I did turn to him. "You told her about me? Why?"

"Look ahead," he hissed, taking a spoonful of food. "I had to. She won't say anything, I swear. We want what you want. We want the fall of Nismera, and you are going to help us get it."

I snorted. "Am I?"

"Yes, because Nismera has a weapon there."

"A weapon?"

Orym nodded. "Veruka says it is something she's very protective of and won't leave. She says that whatever weapon Nismera is holding at that prison, you will need it for what's coming. Let me help you get it, and you can help me bring my sister home."

I shook my head, my lips pressing into a thin line. "I do not like to be backed into a corner."

His spoon stopped above his bowl. "I need your help. We all do, and besides, it's mutually beneficial. Help me free my sister, and we get this mysterious weapon at the prison."

Placing my bowl aside, I turned to him. "This is not how you build any sort of alliance."

He went to speak as a shriek rent the air. Everyone in camp turned to look at the massive steel cage behind us as it rocked back and forth violently. A golden brown-tipped feather, larger than my hand, flew out of the small window, and my jaw clenched.

"What do you think is in that crate?" Orym asked.

"That pattern and shriek. It's a toruk. I would know that call anywhere," I said. The guards rushed forward, some with those spears, and I knew what I had to do.

"No way." Orym choked on his food. "That explains its desperation to be free, but they realize toruks cannot be tamed, right?"

My fists clenched. "It doesn't need to be tamed. Once it reaches Nismera, she will force it into submission like she does all who follow her."

"Poor thing."

A plan formed in my head, and I turned toward Orym. "Do you have any more of that parchment paper?"

Orym nodded, and I looked away as the guards approached. I forced myself not to hear the shrieks of the toruk once more as my plan solidified. The crate rocked and then stopped, the guards commenting about returning to their posts as the beast settled.

I knew what I had to do, and it would be the perfect way to get a message to her.

Night fell, and the wind slowed to a quiet breeze. Snoring ripped through the air from an ogre picked up and added to the cargo only a day ago. Orym groaned and tugged at his blanket as he shifted in his sleep. Once he settled and his breathing evened, I snuck out.

Guards laughed, sharing a small water pouch as they leaned against a wagon. I crouched and took one last look before running for the tree line. Once I was out of sight, I walked in the opposite direction. I checked where I stepped, skipping over any brush that may crunch too loud or half-dead sticks that may snap.

Solid dirt is preferable but cover your tracks. Rocks are better, but be quiet, nonetheless. My father's words echoed from my memory.

The trees ahead were illuminated as I approached the steel wagon. They had moved it far from camp, hating how often the beast screamed for freedom.

I paused in the shadows, studying the wagon surrounded by brush. They would have patrols checking out here, so I waited patiently. I crouched low as the guard emerged from the darkness, circling the wagon. He was more thorough than I expected. He made one more sweep around the wagon, peering into the night before his footsteps retreated, letting me know he was headed back to camp.

I waited another few minutes before running to the front of the cage. Several locks, thicker than my palm, secured the thick door. My hand dusted over one lock, but I sensed no magic. I glanced behind the wagon, checking for the guards before I yanked at the metal. It crumbled, and I cursed at how loud it was. Another peek around the corner assured me no one heard. I hurriedly broke the remaining locks and jumped inside, closing the door behind me.

The darkness was unrelenting, but I could feel the pulse of power and scent the wildness of this creature. A pair of eyes glowed from the back of the cage, the slitted pupils wide in the absence of light. The toruk glared at me balefully, and I knew the darkness was no hindrance to this creature. I raised my hand and pressed a single finger to my lips, warning it to be quiet.

It watched and waited as I formed a very dim ball of silvery light on my palm. The only thing I heard from the beast was a soft susurration of sound as feathers slid over feathers. The cage creaked as one massive clawed foot stepped forward, followed by another.

The silvery light cast shadows on the beast. Its golden-tipped beak emerged from the darkness. Twin rows of feathers atop its head rose skyward as it watched me. Its eyes narrowed, and I knew it was about to scream. I held my hand out a tad further. It was either the bravest or stupidest thing I could ever do, given the fact it could snap it off with ease. Its eyes widened, and its head pulled back in surprise. There was a shuffle as it tried and failed to spread its wings, its massive beak wide open.

They called this magnificent creature a toruk, but in my world, it was a griffin.

"An Ig'Morruthen ripped the realms to shreds, and it smells as if you've bathed in its scent. Treacherous, murderous fiend." The voice was surprising and decidedly feminine.

My hands lowered. "You can smell Dianna on me?"

My pulse quickened. It had been weeks since we had been together, and a part of me was thrilled to know she was still with me, at least in some way. As I lowered my hands, the feathers on her head flattened.

"You speak Brushnev?"

A soft smile played on my lips. "I speak several languages."

She blinked at me several times before sniffing at the air, transfixed. Her taloned feet stopped gripping at the hardwood below, and her fluff-tipped tail lowered, no longer thrashing. She drew closer, and I could see the fur along the other half of her body. Perfectly circular burn marks marred the beauty of both her coat and wings.

Sadness filled me. Female toruks were fierce, protective, and, above all, loyal. They were the warriors on their home world. While the males had the muscle and strength, the females would not stop fighting until their hearts stopped beating, and she had to put up a fight here. No wonder she screamed and fought, no matter how many times they burned her. She'd never make it to Nismera. She'd die here fighting for her freedom.

"You reek of death. Poison." Her head lowered, and I turned my head away as she breathed me in. "You will perish soon."

My grin was crooked. "Thanks."

I didn't need to tell her I knew that or had assumed the worst. My side was only getting worse. The poison they'd slipped to me in Jade City was making me beyond weak. I couldn't eat without feeling nauseous, no matter how many roots I was given, so I'd stopped. It was a task just to stand most days, but I had to hang on. I had to find a way to get to Dianna. She would help me.

Her beak grew closer. "Ah, you have not succumbed to your wounds yet because you smell of the old worlds."

Another breath.

"Rashearim."

My pulse quickened at the mention of my home. She inhaled deeply again.

"You are another of Unir's blood, only made of silver light like her."

My head whipped toward her. "I am nothing like Nismera."

"No, you are the lost king. Guardian. Protector. You are a long way from home, King of Rashearim." I swallowed, and the chains containing her massive form rattled as she sat. "Your light burned the sky and ripped the world, yet you stand before me. How is this so?"

"Someone I love saved me."

Her head tilted, those two long feathers on her head perking up like a canine with ears. "Love? I've heard you have had a great many loves. Which one saved you?"

A small chuckle left my lips. "I can assure you, I have only had one, and it's the one you smell on me."

Her wings rustled. "You mate with the same beast that has destroyed your world and worlds before?"

"She is not a beast."

Those feathers twitched at my tone, but I was sick of how others prejudged Dianna without knowing her.

"She smells of a beast. One far older than you."

I extinguished my defensive rage. I wanted to help, not lash out. She was hurting, and now, with her words, I finally understood why.

"You know what I know? I know they wish to transport you to Nismera along with me. I also know, by the orange band along your snout, that you are female, and the breeding season passed two moons ago. That cry you yelled earlier was not of physical pain but of devastation. I know it well. You lost something important to you. I would bet you had eggs, and they destroyed them."

Rage faded as an empty, haunted expression filled her eyes. She lowered her body to a crouch, placing one clawed foot over the other, chains draped over her thick back, shackling wings of tan and gold to her form. Lash wounds, partially healed, marked her head and face. Dried blood flaked from her beak and matted her fur. She had fought so hard.

"They took more than eggs, King of Rashearim."

I extinguished my light and put my back against the wall. Sliding to the floor, I resisted the urge to press my hand to my side. "Your mate."

"We may be the fighters of our home, but they are the protectors. They were slaughtered first. Then they destroyed our home. It rains ashes in the mountains now because of Nismera, and the remaining realms will soon follow."

Pain writhed in her golden eyes. Pain that would haunt her forever. My shoulders tensed at her words, determination replacing the empathy I felt for her.

"Not if I have a say in it."

I sighed and pushed to my feet. The toruk stood as well, the steel cage creaking beneath her weight. I peered out the small air hole to make sure no guards had returned, but only the shadows created by the flames of the torches moved outside.

Her wings shifted against her chains again as I reached into my pocket, fishing out the rings there. I placed them on my fingers one by one and called forth an ablaze dagger. A soft glow filled the cell, and her eyes narrowed into slits. I shifted to her side, and her powerful beak opened slightly. She watched me carefully but made no move to attack as I sliced through the chains holding her. I caught them in my hands, placing them on the floor so they did not rattle.

"You free me?"

I kept working until the last chain was released, then moved toward her wing and side. Returning the dagger to my ring, I lay my hands on the small circular burns. She shuffled to the side, her feathers expanding and her tail thrashing in pain. I concentrated on pulling on the energy inside me. Light flickered on my palm, my abdomen aching as the last of my power leaked out of me. I focused until my hand glowed. Carefully, I slid it across the injured bone of her wing, feeling it snap back into place. Sweat beaded on my forehead as I gritted my teeth. The skin smoothed as it knitted, and feathers grew back, thick, golden, and full where they had been burned off.

"You'd heal me when you can not heal yourself?"

I nodded, suddenly dizzy as the power ebbed from my hand. I took my rings off and placed them back in my pocket.

"You have to go. The guards will make another pass soon, and you cannot be here. We cannot allow you to be taken to Nismera. If she cannot break you, she will use your bones as she sees fit, and we both know the magic that lies there."

"What do you wish for in exchange, King of Rashearim?"

I swayed on my feet. Her wing shot out, steadying me, keeping me upright.

"Thanks," I said as she lowered it, and I headed toward the door. Tremors slithered through my body, and I ached. I had used too much power and had little left. I carefully opened the door and glanced out, checking to ensure no guards were nearby.

"I need you to find someone very important to me and deliver a message. If you do this, I can promise you will be free. I promise you a mountain that no one can reach. I promise to save these realms."

The Toruk's eyes blinked once, then twice before she stood to her full height. As that feathered chest splayed, the carriage rocked. She stepped closer, massive, proud, and powerful. I was in awe of her beauty.

"A great darkness hovers around you, King of Rashearim. It smells of the old one. Ancient. Powerful. Bloodthirsty. Perhaps Nismera is not the only evil being in this realm."

I knew she was speaking of Dianna. She could sense her imprinted on my soul.

"Dianna is not evil."

"Your love for a creature of death will be your demise."

"Will you do it or not?"

The toruk lowered her head until her face hovered inches from mine, her powerful beak taking up most of my vision.

"She is your beloved?"

Her eyes flashed bright, shimmering gold, and a warmth spread through my body. I had a second to remember the power behind the eye of a toruk, and I knew, above all, that was what Nismera truly wanted. This was not just a random toruk she wished to use for its magic. No, this was the sovereign who wielded the eye of truth if the legend was to be believed. It was a flash of magic connected to the universe itself. A mythical beast that people would die to tame and keep. That warmth spread, and my mouth moved, only the truth spilling from my lips.

"I've never loved or been so consumed by another, nor will I ever again."

"Very well."

I blinked and stumbled. The daze was wearing off, but I couldn't remember what I said. Shaking my head, I reached up and unclasped my necklace. The small roll of paper felt so fragile as I secured it to the pendant, but it was heavy with hope and love.

I handed the necklace to the toruk, and she leaped from the carriage. Powerful wings beat hard, propelling her toward the sky. She barely cleared the tree line before the shouting started. I moved quickly, jumping to the ground and sneaking into the cover of the woods. Guards rushed forward as I lowered myself into the brush to wait.

It was a while before it was safe to return to camp, and I did it as quietly and carefully as possible. Guards stood outside every prisoner's tent, ensuring no one left during the chaos I had created. I snuck to the slash I'd made in the back of the tent and silently slipped inside.

"You are just as reckless as the great love you speak of," Orym grumbled, staring at me through sleep-heavy eyes. He said nothing else before turning over and going back to sleep.

XXII
Camilla

I sighed, my headache growing as the shards of the medallion continued to fight me. Hilma watched, half-asleep. She sighed a fraction louder, her hand cupping her cheek and her brown hair curling around her shoulders.

She was years younger than me, but for some reason, Nismera had stuck her with me while I was working. I still had no idea why the first thing Nismera demanded from me was to restore the million or so shards of this broken medallion, but I couldn't question it. Even if my gut told me how wrong it was and my magic whispered for me to stop.

"Well, at least you sealed a few pieces," she said, smiling lazily at me.

"Attitude doesn't help," I retorted.

It was a few pieces to her, but it was more than that. I had been at this since I arrived. When they first brought me this project, I'd said no, and a guard had twisted my wrist until it snapped as Nismera watched. That was the first time I realized how alone I was here. No one cared, not even Vincent. He just stood by, but . . . I did find a pack of ice in my room later when I got out of the bath. He never confessed to it, but I knew Kaden wouldn't have left it. Sighing, I placed my hands on the table. It had been months since I'd arrived here, and I still had so far to go with this.

Hilma shrugged, holding two fragments as she tried to piece them together like puzzle pieces. I raised my head as Tessa and Tara laughed as they cleaned up the aftermath of a spell gone wrong from another task they had been assigned. I watched them for a moment, envy rising in me. Tessa could never keep her hands off Tara, always a touch or kiss away. They had found love and happiness in this hellhole, and all I'd found was spiraling hopelessness and depression.

A few days after my little outburst, they had been assigned to this workshop. It made me wonder if Nismera had sent her strongest witches to watch or help me. It was probably both.

I sighed, not really caring. I had no idea what would happen to me once I fixed this medallion. Would she make me her own personal weapon? Would I spend eternity here? Or worse, she'd learn of my snooping and kill me? I wiped a hand across my face. It was late, and I couldn't think about this anymore. I would play along while I fixed this damned medallion and searched for a way out.

"I'm done for tonight," I said, and every head turned toward me. Tessa and Tara squealed, happy to be able to leave. Hilma jolted, almost dropping the pieces she was fiddling with.

"Already?" she asked.

I nodded. "Yes. I'm burned out."

It wasn't a complete lie.

"You should probably work on keeping your energy up and not sneaking off with the High Guard." Hilma winked.

"What?" I all but stammered.

She looked confused for a second as the guards at the door snickered. "Kaden?"

I let loose a breath. Right. That stupid ruse we'd agreed on while we both tried and failed to find out what that blood was for. So far, we had learned nothing. Even sneaking back into that room proved ineffective. The bodies had disappeared, and the room looked spotless. A part of me thought he truly didn't care. I only saw a fraction of true emotion when he was with his siblings. He was evil. I had to remind myself that he wasn't on my side. No one was.

"Yeah," I said and stood up, pushing my chair back against the worktable. "I'll try."

Hilma smiled as she gathered up the shards of the medallion and headed out. I shuffled after her, the guards at my sides leading the way to my room. I forced myself not to look toward Vincent's door and wondered for the millionth time why he was avoiding me. He was probably wrapped up in Nismera. The guards paused as we reached my door, and I slipped in, closing it behind me. I flung myself on my bed and wrapped my arms around my pillow, letting my eyes drift shut.

My feet were silent on the stone steps. I slid my hand along the wall to stabilize myself. Chanting rose as I drew closer, and I gasped as I saw the massive room. There, in the center, was a dark pool. It rippled as if eels swam beneath its inky surface. Several hooded figures surrounded the pool. The faceless forms raised their hands, and bright green magic sparked from their palms, strings of magic connecting them until they formed a glowing circle above them.

A scream curdled my blood. Two forms near the edge of the room dragged another faceless, shapeless figure. I squinted as one lifted its hand above the pool, and the room shuddered.

My hands grasped at the wall, trying to keep myself upright. The pool stilled, but then, at the center, bubbles broke the surface. There were just a few at first, small pops, and then hundreds all at once. A form rose from the middle of the dark pool, and my heart started to pound. I took a step forward, trying to see better. A hand slammed down on my shoulder. I spun, the scream dying in my throat. A thin figure glared at me with the same double set of eyes, white and opaque.

It pointed behind me and whispered, "From one, all will rise."

I bolted upright, drenched in sweat and my hair clinging to my face. I screamed for real this time, seeing a shadowy form staring at me from the corner of my room. Magic flared in my hand, illuminating the room in emerald green. The only thing there was a dresser with clothes hanging from the drawers. I dropped my magic and laughed at myself before wiping my eyes. Nothing was there. My hand fisted in the material of my dress at my chest as I tried to catch my breath. I was just dreaming.

"Just a dream. Not a premonition," I repeated to myself, even if I knew how wrong I was. "Just a weird dream and not a shadow figure in my room. Just lack of sleep."

As I lay back down, I repeated it like a mantra, pulling the silk dress away from my ankles.

A groan sounded from the hall, and I turned toward it. It definitely was not a groaning shadow figure. I thought maybe I misheard, but then I heard another low moan. Disgust raced through my veins. If I had to listen to Nismera and Vincent again, I'd rather rip my own ears off. I raised my hand to speak a noise-canceling spell when another groan came through the wall, this one followed by a hiss. That sounded like pain, not pleasure.

I was on my feet quicker than I could think and at the door. I grabbed my necklace and spoke a small incantation as I slipped out the door, glancing at the empty hall. Vincent was definitely back if no guards stood by my door. Good. I hurried across the hall and opened his door.

I barely had time to grasp the emptiness before a shirtless Vincent shoved me against the neighboring wall. My eyes raked over him even as he held the cold blade of a knife pressed against my throat. Oh. Not a shirtless Vincent, but a very naked, very well-endowed Vincent.

"You're naked," I whispered, shutting my eyes tightly. "Oh gods, I'm so sorry."

"It's my room. I can be," he snapped back, clearly agitated.

Half of his body was pressed against me, and I didn't dare risk a look down to see what else was touching me.

Stop thinking about naked Vincent, you sex-starved psycho!

I shook my head. "How did you see past my cloaking spell?"

"Spend eons around the goddess who created all witches, and you learn a thing or two, like how certain, powerful magics smell like herbs."

"Is there a reason why you are still naked and holding me?" I asked.

"Is there a reason you are in my room well past dusk?"

I swallowed. "Fair point. Can you lower the blade from my throat?"

"Drop your spell."

My spell dropped the second I whispered the incantation, and Vincent stepped back. He turned, giving me the opportunity to examine his perfectly muscled backside, but it was the zig-zag patterns of scars that covered his back that drew my eyes. His long, dark hair partially covered them. I wondered if that was why he kept it long. Did he use the silky strands as a veil to hide things he wished others not to see?

"I heard a groan."

"And your immediate thought was to run toward my room? I could have been with another," he said, grabbing a pair of loose bottoms and slipping them on.

"Nismera will never let another touch you. I've seen the way she treats you. Everyone does. Besides, I know the happy groans from the pain groans."

His brows rose slightly, and I realized what I said.

"I mean, it's not like you guys are quiet." I waved my hand. "Forget it."

He folded his arms over his chest. The movement made his biceps bulge, and against my better judgment, my mouth watered. "What do you want, Camilla?"

His words shook me from my inappropriate thoughts. "I don't know. I guess I just wanted to make sure you are okay." It was the truth, and his eyes seemed to soften. "And maybe to talk to someone I actually know. I haven't seen you in days."

A dark chuckle left his lips. "I'm surprised you noticed. I figured you'd be too busy with Kaden down your throat."

My cheeks burned at his words, but mostly from irritation. Gods above and below, I hated this damn ruse. "He is not down my throat."

Vincent's eyes roamed over me, and my body flushed. "I really don't care where he is at."

"You sound like you care."

"I don't."

I huffed. "Then why are you avoiding me?"

"Funny story, Camilla. My world does not revolve around you."

This time, when my body heated, it was pure rage. I stomped forward and felt the hair on the back of my neck raise as my magic swirled. "It damn sure feels like it. You dragged me here, you tossed me through that damn portal, and now your psycho girlfriend has you as my personal guard. The only time I get to go outside and eat something besides cold soup is when you are with me. Every damn day you are away, it's my room, the workstation, and back. The other guards don't care. So yes, your world revolves around me. I deserve that damn much."

Vincent's brows deepened at the mention of my day-to-day before his eyes dropped. A clear sign he cared more than he let on. "Fine."

"Fine," I huffed.

He turned away to sit on his bed, and I noticed the long red marks across his side. Dried blood still clung to his skin in places, as he'd tried to clean it but couldn't reach it all. That's why he'd been groaning.

"What happened?" I asked, pointing toward the wounds.

"A mission. Happy?"

"You've been doing a shit job at cleaning it." I nodded toward the small table lined with various swabs and some weird liquid. "Why aren't you healing like normal?"

"Celestial healing, while fast, still takes time. To be fair, my side was completely ripped open. What you're seeing is a vast improvement. So this." He waved, wincing slightly. "This is good."

"Ripped open?" I practically squeaked. "By what?"

"Those who disagree with Nismera's rule. Those that won't bend."

"Oh."

Vincent groaned as he reached for another one of those medical swabs. "Go back to bed, Camilla. I don't need pity from you or anyone."

"I didn't come for pity. I just wanted a friend. Back on Rashearim, we used to talk, and I miss it. I don't have anyone else here to talk to."

And it was true.

He glanced at me, nothing but cold, hard steel in his gaze. "We are not on the remains of Rashearim, and I'm not a good friend to anyone, Camilla. Do yourself a favor and find another."

My chest hurt for him, but a part of me knew he was right. We weren't friends because the truth of the matter was I didn't trust him. He was ruthless and had betrayed his whole family for Nismera. He would tell Nismera anything I told him. His loyalty was to her, always her. Everyone else was second best.

I wanted to tell him my nightmares, to talk like we had on the remains of Rashearim. It felt pointless, but a part of me, one I couldn't name, told me how wrong I was. No matter what he said or did, I knew there was something more to the situation. I wanted to find out, to break that damn wall, but he was right. It was useless. I'd only hurt myself in the end, more than I already hurt. He wasn't my friend. He never was. I was only fooling myself.

I had no one, and I had done that to myself.

"You're right." I forced a cold smile and turned to leave the room. "I'm sorry I bothered you."

I could have sworn I heard the bed groan as if he stood up. I could have sworn I felt his hand reach for me, but he didn't stop me.

I paused at the door. "Llewir's eye is great for healing deep wounds. I am not sure you all have that animal here, but a substitute should suffice. Maybe ask the healer." I closed his door behind me and could have sworn I heard Vincent whisper a thank you.

XXIII

Dianna

River Bend definitely fit its name, with numerous twisting rivers all converging at the center of town and flowing out toward the coast. There were so many boats carrying shipments and cargo of all types. A shit ton of fishermen milled about, and the sounds of bustling life came from the small village. Nismera seemed to have sent a handful of soldiers to every thriving city, which was good and bad for us.

"If you hold him too long, he will no longer be able to breathe," Reggie said from behind me. One of Nismera's soldiers flailed his arms. I sighed and lifted his head from the water.

Miska had made herself scarce once we'd found a few of Nismera's soldiers and dragged them to the forest clearing. She had said she was off to find some sort of plant, but I knew she wished to avoid the bloodshed.

"He literally has gills on the side of his neck," I said to Reggie as the soldier spluttered and coughed.

"Those are vents, my queen. Not capable of breathing underwater."

I rolled my eyes and yanked him up with a little shake. His blue skin was almost purple as he gasped for air, his vents working overtime.

"Oh." I shrugged. "They looked like gills to me."

The soldier glared at me with four thick-rimmed eyes before looking at Reggie. He rambled in a language I didn't know. Reggie responded, and the guy started to tremble. He looked at me, shook his head, and then looked back at Reggie. He struggled in my grip, trying to get away from me before speaking so quickly I was afraid Reggie wouldn't be able to translate.

"What's he saying?"

"With all due respect, he thinks you're a psychotic bitch," Reggie said and cleared his throat.

My fingers tightened around the armor in my hands as I stared at Reggie. "Obviously, but does he know where the caravan is going?"

Reggie bit at the side of his lip. "He refuses to say."

My head whipped back toward the soldier in my hand.

"Tell me where it is." A low growl vibrated from my throat, and with how the guy thrashed, I knew my eyes burned crimson now. The soldier's mouth gaped in tangent with the vents on his neck.

Reggie repeated my words, and the soldier's gaze shifted between me and him.

"He asks for sanctuary if he speaks."

I sighed, rolling my eyes. "Fine. Whatever. Sanctuary. Now, tell me."

The tension in the soldier seemed to ease as Reggie relayed my words, and he started to talk again.

"He said the last sighting of Nismera's caravan was on Klivur," Reggie said, nodding toward me.

"Okay, that's a lead." Excitement shivered through me.

"But that was three days ago. They stepped through a portal and have not been seen since."

My heart thudded in disappointment, the hope I had felt moments ago dying a painful death.

"Dianna."

Words faded as Reggie said something else, but so did the river's edge. I was too late again. I felt my skin prickle, rage bubbling inside me. It had been a week and a half since they had taken him from me, and the fear of what that damned poison was doing to him was making me crazy. Miska had made an antidote, but it was pointless if I couldn't find him.

I was beyond restless, beyond worried. Even scouring the air, trying to draw soldiers to me, wasn't enough. It was all taking too long, and I was terrified I would be too late again. I was practically a red fucking beacon, yet it took days for soldiers to show up. We were running out of time, and he could very well be at Nismera's doorstep. The worst part was I didn't even know where Nismera was. I didn't even know what fucking world she was on. I couldn't save my own damned sister. Why did I think I could save him?

A snarl left my lips, and I jerked the soldier to the side. My fangs ripped into his neck, his hands clawing at my arms as I fed. Blood hit the back of my throat, replacing the growing pit of anxiety in my gut.

I pulled away and dropped the limp soldier before wiping the blood from my mouth with the back of my hand.

"Your control is slipping."

A harsh laugh left my lips. "You think?"

"I do not wish to see you regress into what—"

"Into what?" I snapped, taking a step toward him. "A monster? Last I checked, I was one. Hello, I am an Ig'Morruthen, not some celestial princess you saw centuries ago."

Reggie's eyes bore into mine. "This is not the remains of Rashearim, Dianna."

"Don't."

"There is still hope."

"It's been a week." I felt the words leave my lips on a half-cry. "The lead we had went dead days ago, and I still don't know what planet he is on now. There are hundreds and hundreds of them, Reggie. If he . . ." I didn't finish it. I didn't want to.

"Tell me that you'd not feel it if he was with her? If she killed him? Look at me and tell me you'd not feel something."

"How would I feel it?" I snapped, holding my hand up and showing him my bare finger. "I gave it up, remember? For him. I feel nothing, Reggie. No spark or connection, just hunger and emptiness and . . ."

Fear.

But I didn't say it. I just spun, running my hands across my forehead. "Fuck. We shouldn't have left him in that stupid city. It's my own fault for trusting they were actually helping us. When has anyone not had an ulterior motive?"

"It is not your fault. None of this is."

"Isn't it? He's weakened right now with that wound. A fraction of his power is all he has left now. The rest burns in the sky. He needs me, and I don't even know where to start looking."

My leg shot out, kicking a large piece of wood. It sailed through the air, hitting a tree and splintering, nearly missing the hobbled form that had just stepped from the forest. He clutched his fishing pole, took one look at me, at Reggie, and the pile of dead soldiers before he took off running.

My lip curled in a snarl. "And he heard too much."

Reggie called after me as I sped across the forest floor. The man dropped his supplies, ditching them as he headed straight for the village. It took little effort for me to outpace him. I stood in his path, and he ran straight into me, falling to the ground. He crawled back and raised one hand in a pathetic attempt to ward me off. I lifted him and sank my fangs into his neck, feeding deep. Reggie approached, and I dropped the fisherman, allowing him to fall to the ground with a thud.

"Dianna," Reggie rubbed his forehead, "I am merely concerned for you, that is all. You have progressed so well. I merely do not wish to see you regress."

"I know. It's just that I love him, Reggie. Like real stupid, mushy love, and now I am afraid I won't get to tell him." I wiped my chin on my sleeve. "He didn't even remember dying in the tunnel or what we said . . . I'm just—"

Miska hummed from a few feet away, her small feet silent over the forest floor. Reggie and I turned, both of us shifting to stand in front of the body as she emerged from the brush. "There you guys are. I found some more herbs we can use . . . Dianna, why is your face red?"

I wiped my hand across my mouth. "I ate the guards."

Miska looked at me and shrugged. "Okay. Are we leaving now? Did you find where Samkiel is?"

Reggie cleared his throat and said, "Let's go into town and get you some food, yes? Dianna will catch up."

She nodded and turned to head back to the town. Reggie didn't speak to me as he followed. I dragged the fisherman's body back to where I left the soldiers and set them aflame, staying as the ashes floated toward the burning sun.

Cold air whispered around us as we walked down the busy street. Along the wooden piers, fishermen laughed together, others yelled as they tossed crates and bags off boats, and people were out buying food at the small shops.

Reggie tossed some coins I had taken from the dead soldiers to a vendor. Miska bounced toward me with a small sack of treats in hand, telling me how she would save enough to give Samkiel when we found him since we were so close.

Her enthusiasm and kindness seemed to stoke the flames burning in my chest. Her thoughtfulness reminded me so much of Gabby. I said nothing, just smiled as we left and headed deeper into the village. Even with the amount of commerce happening in this village, the people still wore scraps of fabric wrapped around themselves in layers. This town was struggling, like so many we had been to.

"Nismera's rule seems bleak," I said, breaking the silence between us. Reggie had been quiet since we left the woods.

"She only cares for herself," he said, his eyes finally meeting mine.

"Is that a jab at me?"

"Your first instinct should not be to kill." He pursed his lips like a disappointed father. "There are other options."

"I feel like you forget who you are talking to. Did you not spend months with me? I'm not the merciful one. That's Sam . . ." I cleared my throat, afraid to even mention his name in case a guard or someone would overhear. "He is."

"Dianna."

"I'd do it for you, too, if I had to. To keep you safe. What do you think happens if someone runs their mouth and we get caught? You think she will be kind to the fate who betrayed her and survived? Or what about the last living Jade City healer? Do you think she'd welcome a child into her ranks?"

Miska smiled at me, holding her satchel tighter as we wove through the crowd. Reggie, against his better judgment, let his eyes soften, and I could have sworn a corner of his lip twitched under his hooded cloak. I wondered if the fate had ever had friends before, much less anyone willing to protect him.

I pulled the hood a fraction higher over my head. "So yes, I'll be the bad guy. I'll be the one you can all judge or hate, but I'll still keep you safe above all else. You may have seen it as wrong, but if he'd even whispered a word of who or what we are or looking for, he would have been more fucked than he is now."

We passed a few more people, barely brushing their shoulders as the street grew more crowded.

"You cannot rule with fear. You will only create more enemies that way. Not allies."

"Who said anything about me wanting to rule?" I glared at him as he pulled the hood around his head a little tighter. "Besides, a crown on my head all the time? Can you imagine? It would mess up my hair, and I'd have to find outfits to match."

Miska giggled behind me at my joke. However, Reggie did not. We moved through a small crowd gathered around a few stalls full of fruits and loaves of bread. I reached out as we strolled and grabbed a small purple fruit.

I turned to Miska as we continued to walk. "He likes fruit," I whispered to her as I passed it unseen between us. She smiled and took it, stuffing it in her satchel. If she were going to be positive, then fuck it, I would too.

"Ah, yes. Your hair, what a drastic concern compared with peace in the realms," Reggie said, not seeming to have noticed our exchange.

I snorted. "You think they will have peace with me? You have met me, right?"

Reggie cocked a brow as we passed through a family of tall, multiple-legged beings bickering with each other. "Oh, so you expect him to take another as queen? You are his, correct? Is it not what you both scream relentlessly in the dead of the night?"

My eyes narrowed on him. "Remind me to get soundproof walls when we eventually find him and build a new home."

"My question remains. You will rule by his side. Already, others will not accept you for what you are. Will you further prove their point by piling bodies at their feet?"

I didn't say anything for a moment as we carried on. I hadn't thought that far ahead. My focus had been on surviving day to day. I still didn't want to think about it. My main concern was finding and healing him. Crowns, thrones, and saving the realms could come later.

"Let's just find him. Then we can save him, The Hand, and the realms. We will worry about politics later."

Reggie sighed. I stopped and extended my arm, stopping both Reggie and Miska. The crowd moved at their own pace, but a chill ran down my spine. It was a sensation I knew all too well. My head whipped to the side. Across the street, between two buildings, stood a man clad in black. A hood draped his head, covering every part of his face. My heart dropped in anger, replacing all other emotions. Flames burst to life in my hands, and I ran past Reggie, darting through the crowd as he called my name.

Beings yipped and yelped as I pushed through the crowded street, the heat from my flames clearing a path as I ran. The figure was only six paces ahead of me when he turned down an alleyway. I jumped over a cart, the owner stumbling to the side and yelling after me.

I darted past a vendor full of fish and skidded to a stop at the mouth of the alleyway. A ball of flame left my hand with the force of a hurricane, hissing as it flew. It burst against the stone wall at the end of the alley, the fire extinguishing upon impact. I stopped and searched the alley but found nothing but overloaded trash barrels and a few small skittering creatures. The massive wall was the backside of another building. Where had he gone?

"What are you doing?" Reggie asked, coming up behind me, Miska holding his arm.

"Didn't you see him?" I pointed toward the empty alley.

"See who?"

"Kaden," I snapped. "He was standing there back in the city. Watching us."

"Dianna." Reggie glanced behind me, then back, concern filling his eyes. "Kaden is not here."

"I saw him," I said. "I felt him."

"Respectfully, Your Grace, Kaden is not here. You are the only powerful force in this village right now. Even if he were here, the legion would be with him. There is no way he goes anywhere without her regime now, especially when it comes to you."

My chest heaved, the Ig'Morruthen in me thrashing to kill. I shook my head, glancing back toward the empty alley. "I know what I saw, what I felt, Reggie."

"Are you sure you are all right?" Concern furrowed his brow.

I took one last glance at the empty alley and burned wall before nodding and moving past them. "I'm fine."

Neither Reggie nor Miska said anything as we headed back into the crowd. A few looked our way but steered clear. Others pretended they saw nothing as they moved their food carts farther away. We made it past another shop, the worker watching me warily. The whole village probably thought I was crazy, and maybe I was, but I saw him. I swear I did.

"Has this happened before?" Reggie asked. "Have you seen or felt him since the remains of Rashearim?"

"No, not really. Maybe a shadow here or there, but never anything as clear as that." My eyes darted to his. "The only other thing is the man with orange eyes, but that's only in my dreams."

"Why have you not spoken of seeing things outside of your dreams?"

"Because we have more important things to worry about, and I chalked it up to everything that's happened."

Reggie stopped in front of me, Miska by his side, watching us. He placed his hands on his hips, the cloak flaring at his sides. "That's exactly why you should say something because of everything that has happened. The realms are open, which means the Otherworld is open. They have powerful allies that may sense your power, too."

"And so what, they stalk me now? In my dreams or out here around every corner?"

"Perhaps." He scratched his head. "I am not sure."

Screams rang through the streets, interrupting our conversation. Shouts followed, and my heart thundered. I was right. Kaden was here, and he'd brought the legion. I grabbed the dagger strapped to my thigh, holding it sideways as flames lit my other hand, and I prepared for a fight. People ran toward us and scattered as Reggie grabbed Miska, holding her close.

"The sky." Miska pointed.

Reggie and I looked up where the clouds seemed to flutter. No, not flutter, but part. A heavy beast burst through the opening. Its cream-colored wings shot through with gold spread wide. It looked like it was headed right for us. It tucked its wings and arrowed toward the ground. People scattered, leaving only an empty street.

Thick talons on its front feet flared wide as it slammed to the ground, its landing shaking the street. Feathers covered its head and massive chest, its beak glinting in the sun. A tail whipped behind it, long and smooth with a fluff of fur at the end. Its back legs ended in paws bigger than my head, and I suspected they concealed claws that could rend and tear.

The massive beak opened, and it screeched, the sound echoing so loud it could shatter windows. It bore down on me with the lethal grace of a predator, its hot breath blowing the hair back from my face.

"Your dagger," Reggie said a few feet from me, "lower it."

I listened, the dagger clattering to the street as I held my hands up. The flames died on my palm, and the massive beak closed.

"You smell of the King of Rashearim." Her voice held a unique musical lilt.

My heart fluttered as her words slowly sunk in.

"Sami." I shook my head. "Wait, how can I understand you?"

Eyes the color of the warmest gold narrowed into slits and glared at me. "You have the blood of Ro'Vikiin in you. All beasts speak Beast."

"Ro'Vikiin? Kaden?"

Her massive head tilted, the twin feathers atop it rising as if they were ears. "I do not know that name."

I shook my head. "Okay, moving on. You know Samkiel? Do you know where he is?"

Her beak pressed close to my chin. I didn't step back, but I did turn my head away. She took one big sniff, and I had to control myself not to flinch away from it. "Intertwined, yet I see no Mark of Dhihsin." Her massive head drew closer, her sharp beak hovering over my breast as it inhaled. "Peculiar."

I didn't care what it said. She knew where he was. That was all I needed.

"Where is he?"

She yanked her head back, the golden feathers of her chest fluffing. "You do not command me, beast."

"Beast?" I scoffed. "Have you looked in the mirror lately? Now tell me, where is the King of Rashearim?"

The giant birdbrain ignored me, choosing to flare her feathers instead. "I know the blood that runs through your veins. All from the realms recognize it. *Ig'Morruthen.*" She said it like it was a curse. "My eye does not work on you, so I ask, what does the King of Rashearim mean to you?"

"Everything." I didn't hesitate or pause. I didn't have days to think about it, nor would I deny it as I had so many times before. No more would I run from what I felt and have the world suffer for it. I'd lost him because I couldn't tell him, because I was too afraid to tell him, and I was about to lose him once more. "He is everything to me."

If a giant bird beast could smile, I felt this one would have. Her eyes darted to Reggie, and he nodded. I wondered how much fate knew about this creature.

"Just a rare occurrence to witness twice." She cocked her head again. "The King of Rashearim's heart seems to beat for you as yours does for him. I hear it even now."

I started to demand what she meant and where my Samkiel was when she lifted one massive wing. I ducked to avoid being hit. Regal and majestic were the only words that came to mind as I took in the beautiful breadth of her wings. I stood in wonder until I saw the silver chain and pendant wrapped in a piece of worn paper.

My hands shook as I reached forward, carefully untangling the necklace from the soft and surprisingly warm feathers. I swallowed against the dread that ate at my gut, my chest feeling as if the world itself sat upon it. My mind, heart, and being were screaming, remembering the last letter I had received. If this was a goodbye letter, I would burn the rivers to steam here and now. Unraveling the note, I clenched the necklace I had given him between my fingers.

My Akrai,

I am not familiar with how fast toruks can fly. It's been too long, but I hope this finds you quickly. I am okay. I am alive. Please smother the anger and rage I know you may feel at the betrayal. We have more important things to worry about now, I fear. Jade City has been selling poisons for Nismera and insuring shipments for a while, it seems. I also believe they used more than enough on me, which is why my healing has been less than ideal. They are moving us to Flagerun. It is a stronghold similar to the prisons of your world. Roccurem knows the world. Have him show you, but please arrive as quietly as you can. I need to figure out exactly what is being held there. I'll explain more when I see you. I assume you will make some quip about me being a hero, but if I can't help those who need it, then saving these realms seems pointless to me. Please, just be careful and try not to set too many things on fire until you return to me.

I—

It looked as if he had scratched out whatever else he was going to say before simply signing it.

Be careful. Yours always, Sami

A strangled noise left my lips, and I raised the note to my chest. The weight I had carried the last ten days dissolved. I clutched at the silver chain, the pendant dancing at the end of it. I clasped his necklace around my neck, turning toward Reggie before saying, "I know where he is, and I need you to tell me how to get there."

"Of course," Reggie said.

I turned back to my new bird friend. "I need your help."

She gave me a haughty sneer as she rose. "I do not answer to you."

"I don't need you to, but these people are also important to him. I need you to take them somewhere safe until I return with Samkiel."

She looked at me as if I had grown three heads. "You would go and save the King of Rashearim?"

My hands dropped to my hips. "Oh, I would level the universe for him, but he told me to be good, so I'll stick to saving him instead."

"There is no kindness left in these realms, dark one. The King of Rashearim is kind. If you mean what you say, then I shall help. My only wish is that you protect the realms, protect him."

Reggie stepped forward, Miska trembling at his side as she looked past me and toward the creature behind me. I handed him the note, and he read it over before nodding and placing it in his pocket.

"I know where that realm is and how to get you there quickly, but you must wait for nightfall."

"Fine. You can still do your cool misting thing. When it's safe, I'll summon you and let you know what I find."

Reggie nodded. The bird beast lowered her wing and crouched. I didn't realize how large she actually was until Reggie helped Miska onto her back and leaped up behind her. Miska reached into her sack, pulling out the small treat she had saved.

"Here, for when you find him."

"Thank you." I smiled at her before turning and meeting the creature's gaze, making sure it saw my eyes flare pure Ig'Morruthen red. "Take care of them. Get them somewhere safe, or I'll roast and serve you for dinner."

She snapped her beak in frustration before letting out a piercing screech as if to tell me to go fuck myself. She spread her wings wide and lifted skyward with one devastating downward thrust. A powerful boom echoed shortly after, like thunder splitting the air, and then they were gone.

XXIV
Imogen

"She's pretty, that's for sure."

The minotaur snorted in my face. The heat made me want to blink, but I was unable to. I couldn't do a damned thing but scream internally where no one could hear. I fought to yell, to move my limbs, but I was not in control of myself any longer. My body responded to orders I wished it didn't. I was trapped in my head where it was dark, watching my actions as if it were all a movie. My mind was filled with the sound of my sobs, but my body was silent. I missed my friends and my home. I missed it all.

"That she is, and also the perfect weapon. Samkiel really sculpted The Hand perfectly. The last raid we did took less than an hour with her. My soldiers couldn't keep up."

Nivene, the orc general Nismera sold me to, laughed as he chewed on some disgusting goo that turned his sharp teeth black.

My heart ached. Every time they said his name and laughed about his death, I cried for days. I cried because I'd ached to help him in that damned council room. It destroyed me that I'd been forced to leave him behind. I hated myself for not being strong enough to break free, to die trying to save him and my family. A true warrior's death was what I wanted, and that was what it would have been if I'd given up my light for them.

"Ah." The minotaur turned. "What else is she good at?"

Nivene laughed harder. "I haven't tried her, to be fair." He spat that chewing goo on the floor, and I wished I could recoil. He had never brought me up here before, usually leaving me to stand guard with the other part of his legion. They would talk or joke about me, but never like this.

"Let's just say I can attest she is great at that too." I recognized that voice, and my gut rolled.

Jiraiya and a few soldiers entered the room. He walked in, wearing the regal Order garbs. The emerald green and golden tassels reminded me of one of the princes in those movies Dianna showed Neverra and me on the night of our slumber party. It had been her sister's favorite, and she'd wanted to share it with us. I missed them both so much, and I was worried I'd never see them again.

"Isn't that what we are here for?" the minotaur said, and my blood ran cold.

Nivene had lied to Nismera. He wasn't taking me for extra training. They were exchanging money for time with me, and Jiraiya was gladly accepting it. The door to the room closed, one of the soldiers latching it behind him. I willed my hands to move, my toes, any fucking thing. If I could get control, I could cut them to pieces.

Jiraiya stepped closer to me as he tucked the money they'd given him into the pouch he carried. He placed it on the small table before stalking forward. His breath tickled the top of my eyelashes as he stroked his hand down my face.

"We only have an hour here." He stared into my eyes, sliding his thumb along my lower lip. "Don't leave any marks on her, or Nismera will think she is defective and kill her."

Someone grunted in response, and lust filled the air. Jiraiya's lips curved in a sick and twisted smile. Internally, I closed my eyes, turning away. I could not feel my body anymore, only here where I was trapped. There, I could pretend not to see. I could focus, drowning out the sounds, and once I was free, then I could—

"I don't understand," the minotaur said, and everyone looked at him.

A soldier snorted. "We're going to fuck her, dude. Doesn't your race do that?"

Another soldier laughed, and the minotaur's head tipped ever so slightly.

"Oh." He shrugged. "Okay, I just wanted to make sure before I do this."

The soldier who had spoken first screamed, his body pulling tight until blood pooled in his eyes, his nose, and his mouth. He coughed and choked, spraying blood everywhere. He gurgled and dropped, blood oozing from his pores as if every blood vessel burst at once. Everyone stood frozen, their eyes like saucers as they stared at the minotaur. His entire demeanor had changed, and he stood with one hand raised toward the soldier.

"I have been waiting for you to fuck up. Now you have," the minotaur said, only his voice was different. He took a step forward, and Jiraiya stepped back. I knew that voice, remembered it as if it followed me everywhere I went in this place.

Isaiah.

Jiraiya held his hands up, his eyes wide with terror. Inky black smoke dripped off the minotaur, leaving Isaiah behind, wearing his dragonbane armor and towering over the smaller man. "We were just. Well . . ."

Isaiah tipped his head. "Go on. Tell me what you wanted to do, and why you are all away from your stations with one of the elite female guards. Can't get your dick wet with the willing?"

"What did you do to Cluvern?" Nivene asked after his minotaur friend.

The smile that formed on Isaiah's face made me far more scared than what these soldiers had planned to do to me.

"Oh, him?" Isaiah chuckled. "I did this."

He was across the room in a heartbeat, his fangs in the orc general's throat. He fed, drinking deeply before dropping his body as if it were nothing. The other soldiers ran, eager to escape. Isaiah grabbed one of the orcs' longswords and threw it at the door. The blade pierced the wood, nailing the door shut and stopping the fleeing soldiers. Then the screams started, rending the room. I could not move my head to see all that happened, but I did see arms fly across the room and blood paint the walls. I shuddered when I heard a series of crunches, my mind trying to figure out what could make that wet sound.

Jiraiya started begging, and my heart thudded. "It's not what it . . ."

Isaiah growled, low and feral. "Go ahead, lie before you die. Do you think the old gods will welcome you for it?"

There was a strangled gasp as if Jiraiya were choking. "Why do you care so much, anyway?"

"I don't like when people touch what belongs to me."

Belong to him? My mind reeled, fear sweeping through me. Jiraiya's scream died, and somehow, it was worse that I didn't see what had happened. Everything was horribly silent, but then I heard the squeak of boots wading through blood as he drew near.

Isaiah stopped in front of me, but I only saw the jagged chest plate. Cool fingers touched my chin, tipping it up until I stared into those swirling, deep red eyes. They were so much like Dianna's but so different. His face was covered in blood, and while it should make me queasy, the splatter only accentuated his strong jaw and dark brows, making his eyes even more otherworldly.

He looked so much like his brothers. I could see the same nose, the same piercing gaze, and above all, the beauty. Emotion flooded my body, and my heart skipped a beat for the first time since my mind had been taken over. As fast as it came, it was gone. His free hand reached up, gently brushing the hair away from the side of my face. I wanted to laugh. He was such a contradiction, shifting from pure brutality to tenderness so quickly. He had just turned the guards and Jiraiya into a heap of blood and limbs, and now he was touching me as if I were made of glass.

"What is it about you that has me so enamored?" he asked the empty shell that was me. He studied me for a moment longer before shaking his head. "We need to get you cleaned up."

He turned and yanked the longsword from the door. Tossing it aside, he looked at me, his beautiful lips forming the damn word that was the key to my body. Internally, I screamed and struggled, willing myself to resist, but I calmly followed him from the bloodstained room.

"Are you out of your fucking mind?" Kaden boomed as Isaiah washed the last bit of blood from his body. Isaiah's bathroom was wide open, with a shower enclosed by clean glass that didn't seem to fog, giving me a view of all he had been blessed with. I hated that I couldn't move, hated that I couldn't turn away, and even more, I hated the fact that the most perfect body was wasted on such an evil man.

"Which part?" Isaiah called, stepping out and wiping a towel around his waist. He headed into the room, water dripping from his hair onto the thick muscles of his shoulders. He swiped a hand over his face as he went to his dresser.

Kaden came into view and pointed at me. "This? She is not a pet."

"I don't plan to use her as one."

"You killed a legion member."

Isaiah held up his fingers. "Two."

Kaden growled and stalked toward his brother. My body jerked as if I wanted to rush forward and protect Isaiah. Wait, no. That was impossible. I hadn't moved on my own or felt on my own in weeks. No, that was wrong. It had been months. It had to be months, right?

"Mera will have your head for this."

Isaiah dropped the towel and pulled on a pair of lounge pants before slapping Kaden on the shoulder.

"No, she won't. The other two in their unit have been promoted, and I cleaned up the bodies. If anyone says anything, we will just tell them they died bravely in battle."

Kaden frowned. "She was okay with that?"

"Absolutely." Isaiah laughed. "Oh, Brother, trust me. Her soldiers come and go. She is used to it. The rest is a ruse, so the remaining feel she cares for them. She doesn't. They are just casualties of war and all."

Kaden seemed to relax. "As long as you're not in trouble, I don't care."

"I'm fine. Imogen will be with my legion now." Isaiah went to the far corner of his room, and Kaden followed, their voices trailing off as they moved deeper into his other room.

Isaiah had slaughtered them for me, and now I was stuck in his massive bedroom. What if I'd been rescued from one horrible situation only to be fed to an even bigger monster? A door closed, and I heard the padding of bare feet draw close, followed by a feminine voice. Oh, gods. Isaiah appeared back in my line of sight, and I tracked him through the blank windows of my eyes.

"Where was Kaden going so fast?" the female asked. Her walk was carelessly seductive, her mauve-colored tail swishing behind her.

"Probably off to see a witch, Veruka."

She made a noise in her throat. "What's with the elite guard? Is this a new thing you want to try?"

Isaiah chuckled, coming to a stop before me. "No, that's not why I called you. She needs to be cleaned up, and I need another set of battle garbs for her. Black like mine, preferably. She will be with my unit now."

Veruka stopped at his side, placing a hand on his bare shoulder. I knew she was an elf from her pointed ears, mauve skin, and fangs. That also explained the tail.

"She's pretty. Is this your new plaything, then? Since you've been avoiding me."

His eyes cut toward her. "Jealousy doesn't suit you."

"Then pay attention to me," she all but purred, and I wanted to be anywhere but in this room.

"Neither does begging." He shrugged her hand away. "Now, clean her up."

I heard Isaiah's feet disappear into the other room, leaving me alone with Veruka. Her eyes met mine before she said that cursed word, and my body moved.

XXV

Camilla

I sighed and flipped through another book as if the answers I needed would be in there. My mind wandered once again to that damned brute of a celestial and what he'd said the other night, and I sighed, the sting still present. I had no friends here, and I was a fool even to consider there could be anything between us. A fool to wish it. What was wrong with me? Why did I always find myself attracted to the ones who were completely wrong for me? Dianna and now Vincent? I placed my head on the table and sighed again.

"Did you hear?" Hilma asked, her heels scraping against the floor.

My head snapped up. "Hear what?" I closed the book, and with a flick of my wrist, sent it back to the shelf before collecting two more. They streaked through the air, coming to rest on my workstation. I dragged one close and opened it while waiting for her to speak.

"Nivene's soldiers went missing along with that dark-haired council member. Now, no one can find Nivene either, but a certain blonde celestial is still alive, and guess who she is following?" Before I could say anything, Hilma cut me off. "Isaiah."

That had my brows shooting up. "Isaiah?"

She nodded. "Yup, he moved her to his unit, and no one is saying anything. Not that they would. They don't call him Blood Scorn for no reason. You know he made a guy burst into goo once because he stepped on his foot."

I swallowed. "Lovely."

Hilma nodded again. "Yeah, and Nismera won't do anything about it. No one will. He is far too high in the ranks."

"Oh."

"You don't seem to be impressed."

"Sorry, my mind is elsewhere."

Like on muscled celestials with long hair who acted as my personal shadow but didn't speak to me. Or maybe it was the overbearing High Guard general who bothered me for information about the sister he apparently knew was the problem. Or maybe it was because I was a prisoner in a palace run by an insane goddess. But I said none of those things.

I slammed the book closed. "I can't find even a hint of a mending spell strong enough to put that medallion back together."

Hilma shrugged. "I'm sure you will figure it out. Listen, don't tell the others I said this, but even Nismera knows you're her strongest witch now. If anyone has this, you do."

I forced a smile, not knowing if I wanted to fix anything for that lunatic. "Thanks, Hilma."

She flashed a grin at me. "No problem. Now, if—"

Someone cleared his throat at the back of the room, and Hilma nearly jumped out of her skin. Vincent towered in the doorway, and my throat went dry as I met his eyes. Hilma placed her hands in front of her, bowing slightly. I forgot how much respect he got from just being Nismera's lap dog.

"Hilma, Nismera requests you come to the lower levels."

I didn't need to see her face to know she'd gone pale.

"Right away, sir." She didn't give me a second glance as she hurried past Vincent and out of the room, leaving only the two of us.

He turned back to me after making sure she had finally left, and my skin burned from the way he looked at me. I hated I was even remotely attracted to him, especially after everything. I blamed it on my abstinence over the last few months, and I was too scared to take care of the problem with my own hands. Guards stood at my doors, and all I needed was for one of them to hear.

"What does the queen need her for?" I hated how shaky my voice sounded. I also hated how ridiculously hot he looked in that damned dragonbane armor, all sharp, dark edges, dangerous and lethal, just like him. He took a step forward.

"I don't ask questions when it comes to Mera."

"Mera." I scoffed with more force than I meant to, and he caught my disgust. "The strangest nickname for a goddess whose livelihood is death."

"Watch your tongue."

"I'll try my best," I quipped, and even I could hear the emotion in my voice.

The corner of his lips curved as if my jealousy pleased him. I wanted to wipe the grin from his face.

"I wanted to talk to you."

I nodded. "Talk to me? About the other night. Why? It's not like we're friends, remember? It doesn't matter."

Three nights, to be exact. Not that I'd counted.

Vincent took another step forward before passing a glance toward the open door. No boots sounded against the stone path leading to my small coven room. It was just us.

"Right," he said, coming around the other end of my table. Heat pooled low in my belly as he grew near, but I stood firm, refusing to move. "I want to apologize about that. I was rude, but the last few days, gods weeks, have been rough."

I felt my mouth drop open in disbelief. "You apologizing? Color me shocked."

"Also, my comments about Kaden. I guess what you do in your free time is none of my business. We're at war, or on the verge of it, at least. It's normal even for enemies to seek comfort where they can find it."

"Okay, stop." I held my hand up, bile rising in my throat. "I can't do this anymore. Not with you. I'm not having sex with Kaden."

Something wild and rageful in his eyes relaxed. Actually, his whole posture eased. "But?"

"No buts. It's a long story that I don't want to put you in the middle of. The kissing was just a ruse, okay? The last time he and I even remotely got intimate was when I was dating Dianna, and we used to . . . That's not the point. The point is, nothing has happened in hundreds and hundreds of years, nor will it ever again."

My chest practically heaved as a weight was lifted off of it. It felt good to get that out there, even if the man I told probably wasn't the best.

"Okay," was all Vincent said.

"Okay?" I asked, narrowing my eyes at him.

"Yeah." He half shrugged, but I caught it. He didn't seem to stand eight feet tall anymore, his body relaxed. It was like I'd given him the greatest thing in the world—I saw him.

"Are you hungry?"

"Sort of. But I don't want to go to the kitchen. I hate the stares."

"Me too." He thought for a moment and then smiled. He looked at the tall, stained-glass window. "I know a place."

I held onto the collar of his armor, my eyes closed so tightly they ached. He gripped my legs and back, holding me to him until he landed. I pushed off him, putting my hands on my hips and slinging my hair out of my face.

"I know a place?" I screamed. "You didn't tell me we were flying!"

He smiled, revealing two perfectly small dimples. It lit up his eyes, and I was gobsmacked by how utterly beautiful and tragic it was. Gods, when was the last time he had done it?

He placed the two small bags he'd carried up on the smooth stone of the highest point of the palace before sitting down. "You asked me once before where I go, and this is it. Sometimes, I come up here after a battle or early in the morning. It is a place I can just go to get away."

The wind pulled at my hair, throwing it into my face. I pulled it back into a loose knot and walked to him. With a flick of my wrist, a soft blanket appeared beneath him. I sat down with him and turned my face to the sky. The sun hung high, casting a shimmering glow over the city below, and far off at the curve of the planet, I could see an ocean.

"It's beautiful."

"It is. And quiet. No guards or people staring, no whispers. Just silence." He looked at me. "And no one up here looks at me like the bastard traitor I am."

"You mean Cameron?"

He said nothing.

"What about Imogen? Have you seen her?"

"I can't," he said, his voice a whisper. "Every time I even get close to her . . . I just can't. Besides, Isaiah keeps her safe and fed. No one gets close to her."

"And you trust him with her?"

"Isaiah is not like some of the lower generals. He may be powerful, bloodthirsty, and cruel, but he would never touch anyone without consent. He's not that low. Besides, he is screwing the brains out of Veruka."

I snickered at hearing Vincent so candid and relaxed for once.

"What?" he asked.

"Nothing." I smirked. "Have you thought of apologizing?"

"There is nothing to apologize for. It would only make me a liar. I did what Nismera asked from the beginning. I always will." Pain flared in his eyes. "I belong to Nismera. She is who I want, who I have to want. The only one."

"That's not fair to you. What about what you want?"

He met my gaze, something burning in those cobalt eyes. "I can't have what I want."

My skin flushed with the way he looked at me. I didn't know how I felt about his words, but my body understood exactly what he had said. It was all in and ready for whatever he wanted to give.

Vincent cleared his throat and broke eye contact, opening the bags and spreading our food between us.

I pulled my knees up and rested my cheek on them, watching how he moved. "You always brought me food back when I was locked up on Rashearim."

He half smiled. "I remember."

"Can I ask? Why visit me? Samkiel had guards even if you chased them away. Was it just to get close to me for this?"

He glanced up at me. "The plan was always to bring you here. Kaden would have still brought you, regardless of how you felt about it. I didn't have to get close to you."

I appreciated his honesty, even with the uncertainty of my fate. I nodded. "So why then?"

He shrugged, sitting back and unwrapping his sandwich. "You keep my head quiet, I suppose. I can just exist around you. If that makes sense. I don't have to talk or be anything. That's why."

His words touched a lonely, vulnerable part of me, easing the ache of loneliness that had been constant since being here. I'd never had anyone just want to be around me. Everyone wanted me for my power, not just me.

"Does this mean we're kind of friends again?"

Vincent rolled his eyes. "You're persistent."

"Not persistent. Just lonely." I looked up at the rolling clouds. "I kind of hate this place."

I didn't glance his way, but I felt his eyes on me, watching me. That bit of truth slipped between us.

"Me too."

My eyes turned to him then at that admission. I gave him a small smile. "At least talking to you makes it less horrible," I said, feeling my cheeks flush.

He nodded, but I saw his pain as if it hurt him to admit that. I wondered why. "Fine, you win. Kind of friends then."

I smiled, leaning forward and grabbing one of the small triangular sandwiches. "Oh my gods, I am so glad this is not that stupid soup," I murmured while taking a bite. I moaned at the taste. It was so much fucking better.

"Tell me the name of the next guard that brings you soup."

"Okay." I snickered before I swallowed. "How long can we stay up here?"

"I'm not sure."

I looked around, just breathing in the fresh air. "I'd like to stay up here for a while, if that's okay? Pretend the world is okay."

His eyes followed mine. "Me too."

We ate, speaking in between bites like we had on the remains of Rashearim, talking about everything and nothing. Not once did he bring up The Hand or Samkiel. I knew those demons raked at him, leaving him bloody and raw, so I didn't press. After we were done, he took us back to the palace, dropping me off at my workstation. I turned as he went to leave.

"Can we go back tomorrow?" I asked, pointing up.

A simple nod was all I got before he disappeared into a sea of armor.

XXVI

Cameron

The boat rocked to the side as it stalled near the dock. The captain waved me forward. I placed a handful of gold coins in his hand, and he gasped.

"Keep it." I waved him away and jumped off.

River Bend smelled exactly how I thought it would, a blend of sweat from working in the sun and fish, a shit ton of fish. I moved past a few workers and fishermen, heading toward the main boardwalk. A handful of shops were open, their barkers screaming about prices or sales as I made my way through the crowd. I adjusted the front of my shirt as I spotted a small shop selling handmade bracelets. I pretended to shop, tilting my head a fraction higher, letting the scents and sounds wash over me.

The smell of cooking meats hit me first, followed closely by the scent of the river, then sweat and the musk of trash and piss. I closed my eyes, pretending to rub them as I concentrated harder. My eyes snapped open when I caught the tiniest aroma of cinnamon. Choosing a small pink bracelet, I slipped it onto my wrist and placed another gold coin on the rack. I thanked the woman selling them, picked out the thread of that scent, and began tracking that smell. It led me past rows of shops and stalls selling everything from fruits to weapons. I stopped abruptly before a woman selling small purple fruits. There was the faintest scent in the center where one was missing.

"Would you like one?"

My head tipped, and I inhaled deeply again until I could almost taste that scent. Excitement shivered through me. I was almost positive I was right. Maybe my search was coming to an end. "Have you sold a lot today?"

She shook her head. "No. Someone stole one, and then the city was frenzied for a while. People just slowly started coming out of their homes again."

"Frenzied?" I asked.

She nodded. "A woman with fire on her hands ran through the streets earlier."

"She did?" My interest piqued. "Where did she go?"

The vendor pointed behind me. "She ran that way, down the back alleys."

I handed her a few coins and stepped away. She called her thanks and insisted I take some fruit, but I ignored her, heading toward the alleyways. Her scent hit me as I turned the corner. I followed it past another line of sellers until I ended up staring down a dead-end alley. My eyes were drawn to a perfectly round, burned smudge on the back wall.

I hadn't realized I'd moved until my fingers rubbed across the dark spot. My heart thumped once, twice, with a loud, thunderous beat as my eyes burned. I didn't smell anyone else here, just her and the lingering smell of smoke from that burned spot. I wondered if she had taken her anger out over something, or was she just broken without Samkiel? I dropped my hand to my side, sadness gripping my throat in a vise grip as I remembered the last time we were all together at that dinner party. How we'd laughed and joked and how it was over. It was all now burned to ash. Nothing but smudges of memory like the spot on the wall.

"Are you looking for the dark-haired one?"

I turned to see a small woman standing at the end of the alleyway. She carried a bunch of rags and clothes on her hip.

"Do you know her?"

She shook her head before glancing nervously behind her and nodding at me to follow her. She led me further into town, leaving the shops behind. We wove through streets lined with small houses until we reached one I assumed was hers. My guide moved a long, beige tarp away from the door and ducked inside.

"You missed her by a day or so," she said, placing her basket down and turning to me. She removed her hat, allowing her long brown hair to spill down her back.

"She was here then. What did you see?"

She skirted around a dirty table and started a pot of tea, the aroma filling the small, unkempt place with a measure of warmth.

"I know you're one of Nismera's soldiers."

My brows furrowed. "And how do you know that?"

She peeked at me over her shoulder, studying my face. "Your eyes. You don't look like that unless you've been through something traumatic."

I said nothing.

"And, of course, you can barely hide the muscles beneath the clothes we wear here. Our fishermen don't look like that."

"Where did you see her last?" I asked, brushing off the compliment as she poured a cup of tea and took a sip. I watched her throat work the liquid down, and my heart thudded for a different reason. Fuck. When was the last time I'd fed?

"She was in the main square after the fire," she said, placing her cup on the table. I saw the vein in her neck throb. I felt the room pulse, but it wasn't the room. It was the sound of her heart, strong, steady, and full of life. I felt my gums prickle and ran my tongue over the sharpness of my fangs as they emerged. My stomach growled. Or was it me?

"Are you hungry?" she asked, turning back to me. "I'm assuming it's a long trip here, especially by boat."

I nodded, forcing a tight-lipped smile that didn't show my teeth. "What else can you tell me? Where did she go?"

"Oh, yes." She wiped at her brow. "The others won't talk, but she left, burst into the sky as a huge, scaled beast. She blocked out the sun for a second, and everyone scrambled. We thought she was circling to burn us all, but she left right before her friends did."

"Friends?" I asked as she reached for her basket. She nodded, pulling out a sheet and hanging it on a line of wire strung at the back of the room. I stepped closer, crossing my arms across my chest.

"Yeah," she said, leaning down to gather another sheet, the front of her blouse gaping to expose the top of her breasts. Deep blue veins ran just below the cream of her skin, leading back up to the slender column of her throat. My mouth watered. I clenched my hands and turned my gaze from the temptation. "She had a gentleman with her and a child."

My head reared back as I absently counted on my fingers. There was no way Samkiel got her pregnant, and if he had, the child would not be walking yet. I shook my head. I already knew the man with her was Reggie. It had to be.

"A child?" I turned back around as she placed a hand on her hip.

"Yeah, cute kid. They seemed like a nice family. The man and girl left on the back of a toruk. I don't know what direction they went. Like I said, we all went to hide."

I nodded, placing my hand over my lips and speaking around my fingers. "Thank you."

"Sure. I'm glad I could help." She smiled and continued to hang her laundry.

I had to get out of here before I did something I regretted. Maybe I could find something to eat here and travel back before . . . Blood fermented the air right as she cursed.

"Ouch." She sighed. "I forget to take the pins out sometimes."

I was in front of her before she moved away from her laundry, gripping her hand in mine.

"What the . . ." Her words died as she saw my face, eyes, and fangs. "No, no, no. You're one of them!"

A tiny droplet of blood had formed on the pad of her thumb. Her hand hit my arm, trying to get away from me as I placed it in my mouth and sucked. One drop of blood and my entire nervous system went into overdrive. It always reminded me of when Logan and I'd stolen sweets and eaten way too many. My whole body would tingle, only this felt so much better.

"I'm so sorry," I said, dropping her hand and going for her throat.

"Are you calling me?" I sneered, the reflective disk in my hand shimmering.

"Did you find anything?" Kaden replied.

I glanced at the woman near my feet. The twin puncture marks glared at me, her lifeless eyes staring toward the door as if waiting for help that would never come. I wiped my mouth with the back of my hand, wishing I didn't still savor the taste of her blood. I'd found something, all right. I'd found I was just as much a monster as he was.

"Nope," I lied. "Not a thing."

"Hmm." Kaden ran a hand over his face. "She must have gone further north than I thought."

"Must have." I absently scratched my head. "I'll head back now, then."

"No." The word was curt, and even without fully seeing him, I could tell he checked around before speaking next. "I need you to keep looking, but also have an ear out."

"For what?"

"I want to know why Nismera has a vial of Isaiah's blood and why there is an empty one with my name on it. I want to know what my sister has been up to these last few centuries and what she's planning."

I couldn't help the laugh that bubbled up, but I covered it with a cough. "Sorry, but you're telling me the diabolical Kaden doesn't trust his equally diabolical evil sister? There's a joke about karma in there somewhere."

"Cameron."

I glared at the blood on my sleeve and rubbed at it as if I could erase it. "Can't you just fuck the hot witch since you can't have Dianna right now and get answers?"

"Cameron."

"Hmm?"

"If you become useless to me, I will kill you. Again."

The line went silent.

I flipped it off before placing it back in my pocket and rolling my eyes. Well, that went great. Sighing, I looked down at the woman crumpled on the ground. Blood no longer flowed from the twin puncture marks on her throat, and still, my stomach rumbled for more. I took a calming breath, then another, before lifting her into my arms.

"Let's get you a proper burial, love."

I turned from the house that was more of a shack and snuck out the back toward the woods. Hunger was at the top of my list of problems. I couldn't tell Kaden, and even if I did, he wouldn't help. I needed to find Dianna, beg for forgiveness, and hope she'd help me long enough to find Xavier. She could kill me after that. I just needed to find him.

XXVII
Samkiel

For the first night since I had met Orym, we didn't eat alone. We were on the outskirts of Pheliie. We'd reach Flagerun tomorrow evening. As soon as we set up camp and the small fires were lit, several other prisoners joined us, pulling large logs over to sit on and sharing the warmth of our flames.

Orym cleared his throat and rubbed the back of his neck as another joined. "I may have told them about how you saved me and also maybe about releasing the Toruk."

I lowered my spoon, glaring at him.

He snickered. "You are officially the toughest among us, so they will want to be around you for protection. Trust me, it's all a part of my master plan."

My jaw clenched, and I shook my head but said nothing as I stirred that damn mush they served us. My stomach didn't even growl. The aching pit at my center remained, and I was unsure if it was the purple veins spreading from the wound or that the toruk would find Dianna. Quiet conversation flowed around me, the men speaking in hushed tones so as not to draw the attention of the guards.

"So, where did they kidnap you from?"

It wasn't until Orym nudged me that I realized the question was directed toward me. I wasn't used to any of the prisoners talking to me, but now when I looked up, damn near twelve of them were staring at me as they ate, the fire crackling between us.

I shook my head at the dwarf who'd asked the question. His beard was matted, but I could see a scar running along his jaw and across his lips. His hands were just as calloused as mine, and I knew how strong he was despite his size. He was not one I would wish to fight.

"Me?" I asked. "What about you? The mountains of Tarnesshe are not that easy to get to, and your people are far too battle-strong to be taken without a fight."

The dwarf smiled a toothy grin that made his face a fraction softer, as if my words had given him the confidence boost he needed after all that he had lost. He sat a little straighter and prouder at the reminder of where he came from.

"You must not have been in The Eye that long if you're asking us questions." The voice was harsh and bordering on challenging. The men grew quiet, and everyone stopped eating, some staring into their bowls.

The owner of that voice sat hunched over on one of the logs furthest from the fire. He was in shadows, his silhouette large and burly, a worn blanket wrapped around him, covering his head and obscuring his face.

"No," I said. "Recently joined. Nismera took my family from me."

It wasn't a lie, a twist of the truth maybe, but not a lie. She had taken my family, and my involvement was recent. The snap of the logs filled the silence, and I wondered who this man was that the others seemed to cower as he spoke. I couldn't see his features, and by the way he held himself, he didn't want to be seen, but I caught the reflection of cuffs and chains securing his wrists as he pulled his blanket tighter around his shoulders. It was a brief glimpse, but enough that I knew they were not the same as the ones we wore while traveling. I wondered what they kept at bay.

"She takes everything she wants." He grunted, and I felt the relief of the others as if they had been waiting for him to lash out in some way. "They call her a madman, a butcher. Many think she keeps something beneath her city of gold and happiness to create monsters."

"Monsters?"

He grunted in agreement. "No one knows how, but we assume Blood Scorn helps. Now that the other brother has returned, he will make her beasts, and then there will be no stopping her. We are doomed because our only hope now bleeds into the sky."

One of the prisoners sighed, placing his bowl down as if the reality made him queasy.

"Blood Scorn?" I asked, and they all looked at me. "They don't use titles as such in The Eye."

Another prisoner spoke up from across the fire, half of his face covered in scars. "I imagine they wouldn't. Blood Scorn is the one that can kill you without even touching you. I saw it once when she sent him to a rebel village in Napila. He popped a guy's head off without even flinching. He had eyes made of blood."

Ig'Morruthen. Isaiah. He could control blood. I glanced down, flexing my hand. It explained why I didn't bleed out when he took my hand back on the remains of Rashearim.

A prisoner slurped his soup before pointing his spoon at the others. "You shouldn't pinpoint one. It won't matter if he comes for us or all. She has five now."

There was a murmur of hushed whispers, but he went on. "Two Kings of Yejedin remain, along with her brothers and the one he made."

The hooded figure from afar spoke next. "There's not five."

Another prisoner laughed. "Seems like counting may not be your strong suit, my friend."

His back straightened, and I realized he was far taller than I originally thought. "There are six."

Everyone started talking again, gaining the attention of even the prisoners who sat at other fires. Orym shushed them, nodding toward the guards, suddenly eyeing us with interest.

"Six?" the dwarf said. "Can't be. One Ig'Morruthen is enough. If she has six, that's practically the start of the new age. She'd be unstoppable."

"She already is," the hooded figure said, drawing back into himself.

I swallowed the growing lump in my throat as they looked toward me for reassurance, but I wouldn't, couldn't, give them that. I couldn't tell them of her.

"I'm more worried about the general being back here. He slaughtered the World Ender, and now his life force is dancing in the sky," the dwarf said.

"The realms brought something back with it. Something with the blood of the ancient. The first. The fires in the East weren't rebels," the hooded figure said.

"The East?" I asked.

"Yes, her soldiers were slaughtered. They thought it was you guys, but I heard remains were scattered, spelling out a message that enraged her," Orym said. "You'd been long captured by then."

I nodded as if listening, realizing he was trying to keep my cover for me by stretching the truth. Fires in the East with a haunting message screamed Dianna, but when would she have had the time for it? We had been together. Unless it was while I was still unconscious when we first arrived. No, she would have told me. The spoon tapped the side of my bowl as I thought about her expressions when I mentioned certain things. She was a terrible liar, and I'd been too wrapped up in thinking she was lying about her feelings for me to contemplate it could be so much worse.

A younger prisoner laughed and said to the hooded figure, "You're just listening to fables and myths. No Ig'Morruthen would turn against Nismera. They'd have to be insane. The weapons I hear she has could destroy worlds."

"You think I lie? I feel it in my blood. All of us do," the hooded figure sneered before standing and sauntering off to a tent on the other side of the camp. No one spoke again for a few moments, and then the conversation shifted from Nismera and her legion, focusing on what they were eating and whether the prison would serve better food. But my gaze remained on the tent the hooded figure had stepped into.

Orym nudged my shoulder, and I turned to him. He tipped his head toward the tent and said quietly, "They say he is the first prisoner she has taken from the Otherworld. They say he can turn into a beast with three tails. I don't know anything else, only that he killed and ate his future cellmate."

That would explain the chains and why he spoke the way he did. He truly would feel an Ig'Morruthen since they derived from the same place. I nodded but said nothing. The flames grew higher as I sat deep in thought, twirling my spoon in the mush.

A crack of thunder split the air. The sound was loud enough that it startled everyone in camp. Prisoners and guards alike stopped and studied the night sky, a few mumbling prayers in their native languages. I turned toward Orym, his mauve skin a shade lighter. Many prisoners stood and started putting out fires, suddenly ready to retreat to the dubious safety of their tents.

"What's the matter? Has no one heard thunder before?" I asked.

His eyes met mine. "It doesn't rain in Pheliie. Ever."

Murmurs turned into whispers amongst the other prisoners. The guards cast careful looks around the camp, instructing the prisoners to get back to eating.

A few stayed with us, huddling closer to the fire. Orym and the others continued to cast nervous glances at the sky while a smirk danced across my lips.

XXVII

Samkiel

The whistle sounded so low, yet it pierced my soul. I lifted my head and glanced at the back of the tent. Orym glanced at me as he entered and walked toward his cot.

"Don't let them get to you," he said, thinking I was still processing the earlier conversation. "They believe there is no hope, but we know different."

I forced a small smile and nodded, letting him believe that was the reason for my sudden mood change. I lay down and closed my eyes, listening to the crackle of fire turn to a hiss as the guards covered it with water, snuffing it out. Lifting my lashes just a bit, I peeked at Orym. His arm lay across his chest, the slow rise and fall telling me he was out cold. Yet still, I waited.

Whispers turned to murmurs outside, then silence as the guards on watch moved to the front of the caravan. I pulled back my makeshift blanket and quietly slipped from my cot. Taking one last furtive look around the tent, I lifted the flap we'd created in the back wall and ducked through. I crouched and waited, making sure I heard no guards or movement. Once I was sure it was clear, I secured the flap with the stake and crept toward the forest.

I walked deeper into the brush, in the direction I'd heard that small whistle. I continued until I was sure I was far enough from camp and stopped. It was silent, no whistles, no noise, the forest an empty, desolate place. The only heartbeat out here was my own.

The brush rustled to my left and then right. I turned, chasing the sound. A chill ran across my spine, and the rings in my pocket vibrated, screaming danger. But there was no threat in these woods, at least not to me. There was a snap of a twig, and I glanced behind me. A smile spread across my face, joy filling my heart, and every breath came a bit easier. She descended on me, one forearm pressing lightly under my chin, pinning me to the thick tree at my back.

"Didn't they teach little gods not to wander the woods alone? Never know what scary Ig'Morruthen you'll run into." Her smile cracked every single bit of doubt or fear I had these last weeks, and gods, I melted.

"When you see one, let me know."

Her eyes softened, a sheen coating them, and I knew mine matched.

"You found me."

Dianna nodded, lowering her arm. "I'll always find you."

She stepped back, but inches between us after so long felt like miles. It was too damn far for me. I reached for her, but she waved my hands off. "Wait."

My brows furrowed as she reached for her pants.

"I can do that," I said, touching her hands.

She snorted and stepped away. "Wait. I have something for you."

"I know. I'm trying to get it."

Her laugh made me smile, and I waited. She slid a small, thin piece of material around her waist until a tiny vial came into view. It was secured as if it was vitally important to her. She pried it away from the small buttons it was attached to and held it up, the liquid swirling inside as she drew closer.

"Take off your shirt."

I didn't even hesitate, hissing as my arm stretched higher than my shoulder. My muscles had started to lock. The veins of poison on my side had spread up my chest, and I feared what would happen when they grew higher. The horrified look on Dianna's face told me she understood the seriousness.

"Drink this," she commanded, pushing the vial into my hand.

I twisted the top off and sniffed. My head reared back instinctively, the smell horribly acidic. "What is this?"

"Just trust me. Drink."

I didn't hesitate, tipping it to my lips. I watched her the entire time, afraid if I blinked, she would disappear, and I would wake to find this was just another dream. The liquid hit my tongue, and I recoiled, dropping the vial. It tasted exactly how it smelled. It was rancid, but that was the least of my concerns. My body burned, and I grabbed my stomach and hunched over, my entire abdomen pulling tight, every muscle in my body straining. Dianna's hand was on my shoulder as the hot, needle-like pain ripped through me. I fought to stay conscious, and then, all at once, it dissipated.

"Sami," she whispered. "Are you okay?"

I stood, taking what felt like my first real breath since I woke up. I hadn't realized how uncomfortable breathing had become until now. Her eyes roamed over my face, then lower. I glanced down, watching in disbelief as those purple poison veins curled in on themselves, drawing back toward the wound and fading until only the scar that slashed across my abdomen was left.

"It worked," she said, her voice filled with relief. Dianna smiled up at me, her eyes soft with an emotion so profound I couldn't name it. She opened her mouth to say something else but only managed a gasp as I grabbed her and sealed my lips over hers.

XXIX
Dianna

He devoured me like a starving man with lips, teeth, and tongue. I groaned, tilting my head to the side, deepening the kiss, begging for it to last forever. His hands fisted in the bodice of my top. I braced, waiting for him to rip it off me, but he stopped and broke the kiss, pulling away. Cold air slipped between us, and I reached for him, already missing his warmth.

"Wait," he whispered. "I can't rip it. They don't supply clothes, and you'll need some. Otherwise, I'll destroy the whole camp and ruin whatever plan I have."

I nodded, panting. "Okay," I said, aching to have his hands back on me.

Samkiel stepped forward, the bottom of his lip disappearing between his teeth as he reached for me. He spun us, and my back hit the tree. His hands splayed across my ass and squeezed before sliding up, his touch slow and deliberate, savoring every small whimper I made. My body damn near screamed for him, burned for him. I'd missed him so much. I wondered how I'd survived being denied his touch for so long and still managed to breathe.

His fingers worked the laces of my leather top, his eyes never leaving mine as he pulled it off, tossing it to the forest floor. It landed in a pile of leaves with a soft crunch. Samkiel's eyes fell to my breasts, the heat of his gaze in contrast to the cold night air, making my nipples harden to points. His hand curved around my shoulder, the calluses on his palm an erotic rasp against my skin. The rough pads of his fingers raised goosebumps as he ran them over the top of my breast before cupping it. I arched into his touch, pushing the soft curve into his palm. His thumb swiped a path over my nipple, forcing a soft moan of pleasure from my lips.

"I've missed you," he whispered, grazing his thumb over the swollen tip again. I whimpered and bit my lower lip, closing my eyes against the pleasure. "Did you miss me?"

I nodded, and he pinched my nipple, the small bite of pain forcing my eyes to open.

"Use your words, akrai."

"I missed you, Sami. Every bit of me missed you."

Samkiel's smile was downright devious. His hand left my breast, my stomach clenching as his finger slid over my abdomen. His other hand skimmed my hip, his fingers meeting at the laces of my pants. I thought he was going to undo them, but instead, he slipped his hand inside and cupped my pussy.

My hand wrapped around his wrist, and I moaned. His fingers splayed, rubbing on either side of my clit, pinching it gently before slipping a finger inside.

My eyes rolled to the back of my head as he stroked in and out, my pussy clenching tightly, aching for more. "Yes, yes, you did. You missed this. Didn't you, akrai?" Samkiel asked, pulling out to slip another finger into the tightness of my body, the stretch a welcome burn and one I so desperately missed. "You want my cock so deep inside you can't tell where you end and I begin. You want me to fuck you against this tree, out in the open," he whispered against my ear before sucking it into his mouth.

My hips rolled against his hand, his palm a constant pressure against my clit as he finger fucked me against the tree. He kissed and sucked at my neck before sliding back up to my ear again, and I groaned.

"I love how wet you get when I do this." He sucked on my skin again, the heat of his mouth like a brand. "You just love to be tongue fucked, don't you? Love the way it sounds, how it feels. I'd bet you'd come right now imagining my tongue where my fingers are."

I nodded feverishly because he was right. Godsdamn, was he right.

He worked a third finger into my pussy, and I shuddered, the burn intense, but I knew his cock was even thicker. I panted as my body adjusted and pushed against his hand.

"Imagine my tongue in your pussy and come on my hand, akrai."

Samkiel's mouth settled over my pulse. He flicked his tongue against the sensitive skin and sucked hard, and I came undone. He covered my lips with his free hand as my orgasm swept through me. I gripped his forearm with both hands, riding his hand as he pushed and pulled, continuing to fuck me with his fingers. He took every last bit of shaking, trembling pleasure from me.

I kissed his palm, and he dropped his hand. I leaned forward, my pussy still clenching around his fingers as I claimed his mouth in a deep kiss. We both panted, nipping at each other's lips. He slowly withdrew his fingers, and I felt the rush of liquid and the sweet ache as I clenched against the emptiness he'd left behind.

Samkiel stepped back, tearing at his laces, working to free his cock. I struggled out of my boots and fought to remove my pants. My orgasm had barely taken the edge off the ravenous need between us.

Finally naked, I stepped toward him just as he pushed his pants over his hips. I groaned at the sight of him. He bent his knees and caressed my thighs before gripping them and lifting me. I locked my ankles at his back and rubbed my pussy against his shaft, the wet heat slicking the rigid length. He hissed and dropped to his knees, a part of me glorying in his strength.

He laid me back, his weight pinning me to the forest floor. Samkiel braced his arm near my head and licked at my lips, tugging gently on my lower one with small, teasing nips. I ran my hands over his chest and shoulders, tracing the hardened muscle. So familiar, so *mine*.

"I want to be on top," I whispered, pushing at the heavy muscles of his chest and bracing my feet on the ground, lifting my hips.

He smiled and kissed my lips. "Not here," he said, pressing his lips to my brow, allowing more of his weight to rest on me. The pressure helped to calm me, and I wondered at that. Anyone else and I would have burnt them to a crisp for holding me down, but with him I just felt at peace.

"Why?" I asked breathlessly, pulling away as he chased my mouth.

He grabbed my chin, forcing me to look at him. "Because I cannot cover your mouth that well on top. We've learned that the hard way. And with how I've missed you these last few weeks, I am sure you'll be screaming."

My pussy throbbed and clenched at his words. His gaze on me was a molten heat that pooled at my core. I captured his mouth, and he deepened the kiss, running his hands down my sides before grasping my thighs. I had spent weeks looking for him, and I hadn't touched myself since he was taken. My need to find him, save him, overrode any other desire. I spread my legs wide, but he pushed my thigh back, opening me further to him. He fit the head of his cock against my entrance, and I moaned, arching my back.

"Fuck," he whispered. "I've missed you."

I nipped his bottom lip and reached between us, stroking his shaft, my pussy squeezing around his tip, tempting him deeper. "You keep saying that."

His smile was lethal and full of promises. He pushed inside me, inch by glorious inch, and all thoughts of teasing died as my brain short-circuited. I loved the way it felt when he stretched me, filling me up. I knew by the way he groaned and sank so slowly into me that he felt the same way.

Samkiel's body was nearly trembling as he struggled for control. I looked deep into his eyes and squeezed hard around his cock. His grunt was guttural, and I saw the moment he let himself off the chain. "Oh fuck, Dianna. So fucking demanding. You want my cock, akrai? I will give you everything." His voice was deep and resonant, barely recognizable as his. It set my blood on fire.

My mouth fell open on a moan as he thrust inside me, the stretch and fullness nearly overwhelming. His large, calloused hand clamped over my mouth on his second thrust, and my eyes rolled back. My nails raked down his side as I held onto him, my body falling into the familiar rhythm. Gods, it was perfect. He was perfect, and I needed more. His grunts turned to groans as he fucked me into the ground, and I knew his plan would not work much longer.

I was not the only one who was loud.

We weren't that far from camp, but I didn't care. If anyone showed up and tried to take him from me, I would rip them to shreds. Gods, I could destroy the whole camp and sleep like a baby as long as I had him.

Samkiel slammed into me again, sticks and leaves digging into my ass. I arched to meet him, taking him deeper, feeling my pussy clamp around him. It was so fucking good, too fucking much, but oh gods, I needed more. Consequences be damned, I shifted my hands under his arms, and using a move he'd taught me so long ago, I wrapped my leg over his hip and hooked my heel around his thigh. I pushed, forcing him deep and managing to flip us over.

"Diannnna." He stretched my name out, one part bliss, the other part warning.

I sat up and straddled him, biting back a gasp. He felt even bigger in this position. I lifted a single finger to my lips to shush him, smiling wickedly behind my finger.

"Be a good boy and try to be quiet." I rose, my belly clenching as he slowly slipped out of me. Reaching between us, I used my other hand to grip him, my fingers not meeting around his girth. He was slick, and my hand slid smoothly, stroking his thick length. His abs flexed as he took a deep breath.

He watched me, his gaze focused on my hand, not protesting like I thought he would. I pressed his thick crown against my entrance, moaning when I took just the flared tip inside, using my grip on his shaft as leverage. His brows furrowed in confusion when I sank no lower.

I moved, only allowing him so deep as I jerked him off with my hand simultaneously. His confusion died, and he dropped his head to the ground, leaves and dirt tangling in his hair. His hips surged up, and it felt good, fucking good, but it was not enough to make me a screaming mess. My heart hammered in my chest, my pussy clenching around the tip of him as he moaned beneath me. I watched him, his lust-filled eyes locked on where our bodies were joined.

He thrust up, trying to drive more of himself into me, but I didn't let him. Sweat beaded on his strained muscles. His arms flexed, one hand resting on my knee, the other digging into the soil. Every inch of him was pure-blooded warrior, and the sight alone was enough to make me wet, but knowing I was the one who made him whimper and beg had me fucking dripping for him. My slick heat slid over my hand, and I used it to grip him tighter, stroking him a fraction harder.

Samkiel shoved hard against me, grinding against my hand and begging, "Sit on it."

I shook my head, biting my lip playfully. "No, Sami. I am in charge."

"Oh, yeah?" he growled, and I knew that had been the wrong thing to say.

He sat up, and I yelped, the speed of the movement driving him deeper and forcing my fist hard against my pussy. One hand came down, popping my ass, the other gripping my throat, his mouth inches from mine.

"Move your hand and give me what I want," he demanded, the silver swirl of his eyes pinning me in place.

"You're spoiled." I moaned, and Samkiel gripped my ass painfully tight and lifted me off his cock before slamming me back down. "Fuck." A scream ripped from my throat with the sudden rush of pleasure, but I kept my hand between us. He did it again and again, our skin slapping against each other with deep, punishing thrusts. He yanked me forward, crushing his lips to mine.

"Spoil me akrai, give me what I want," he snarled, his voice infused with a dominance that bathed his cock in another rush of liquid heat.

I nodded and finally released my hold on him. He grabbed my hand and sucked my fingers into his mouth, and I saw his eyes flare, heat, lust, and something more intense swirling in their depths as he licked my slickness from them. I clenched around him at the erotic display, and how fucking filthy he was when it came to me. When he released my hand, I wrapped my arms around his neck and sank back onto him fully.

"Yes, yes, yes," I panted, my body trembling with need.

His arms held me in an iron grip, making sure I didn't escape to tease him anymore, and gods above and below, I loved it. I rode him hard and fast, both of us gasping for each breath. He was holding me so close that every time I lifted and slammed back down, my clit ground against him, sending sparks across my entire being. Gods, it felt so good. He felt so good. His lips and teeth scraped at my throat, and I tipped my head back, offering him more. His groans vibrated against my skin.

I was fire and lightning and life and death. Ever since my powers returned, sex had felt different. Better wasn't the word I was looking for. It was always amazing, yet now it felt as though he was not only inside me but everywhere, in my veins, his power encompassing my skin. I felt him in my blood, my very soul. Samkiel's hands slipped to my ass, his grip painfully tight. He moaned, his voice strangled. I loved that sound because it told me he was close.

I bounced on him harder, his thrusts almost brutal beneath me, chasing our pleasure. The swell of pleasure built so high that I didn't even have a warning before it ripped across my flesh. I buried my face against his neck and bit down, muffling my cry against him as my body shuddered with my release. It was hot, quick, and blinding, specks of light sparking behind my eyes. He gripped the back of my neck, forcing my head up and my lips to his as he came inside me. His body twitched, his thighs flexing beneath me as he ground deeper.

"Fuck, akrai, you're going to make me come so hard," Samkiel groaned. I felt his cock throb inside me as he spilled, his grip on my hips punishingly tight as he thrust mindlessly into the wet heat of my body. He pulsed inside of me again and again, filling me to the point of overflowing, his seed running down my thighs. He finally stilled beneath me, his breath coming in thick, heavy pants. Our bodies shuddered with aftershocks as the connection broke and remade us over and over.

My forehead rested against his, both of us breathing heavily as we trembled.

"Gods, how long has it been?"

His breath tickled my lips. "Three weeks, four days, and sixteen hours."

I laughed, sliding my hands over his shoulders and leaning back. "You counted?"

He looked at me as if I'd asked him the stupidest question. "I always count when you're away from me."

I nipped at his nose and smiled. "Stalker."

I leaned in and ran my lips along his stubble, able to feel his grin. His arms wrapped tighter around my waist. He was alive and whole. My fear had faded away the second I had entered this blasted realm and found him. I had hunted the caravan, stalking through the trees as they traveled. I had watched them force the prisoners from the wagons, nerves twisting my insides when I hadn't seen him in the first few. That had died the second I saw him through the brush, every ounce of it disappearing. The guards would meet a gruesome end the second I had him healed, but I was content to know he wasn't dead.

Memories from the tunnel flashed in my head. Water dripped as the world shook, and his blood-covered body held in my arms as life left him. I shook my head, chasing away the images.

"What are you thinking about?" he asked, nuzzling his lips beneath my ear, trailing featherlight kisses. His hands roamed a soft path over my lower back to my ass and back again.

I didn't realize I had been so quiet. I didn't want him to know how it felt with him gone, how empty I felt as if a part of me was missing. It was something I had never felt before, not for anyone, not even Gabby. Nor did I want to ruin this moment by telling him about the bloodshed I'd caused, either. So, I did what I normally did. Pulling back, I purposely tightened around him, redirecting and distracting. "That I need to learn to breathe again."

His smile lit up the darkened forest, and mine soon matched. I picked the tiny leaves from his hair, but there was so much dirt he'd have to wash to get it all out. Maybe I could find us a stream . . . My hand froze, and my smile dropped. I heard them first, quickly followed by the scent. My eyes raked the forest, and I threw myself off Samkiel, my skin prickling. Fur replaced skin, and my paws beat against the forest floor as I chased the onlooker. Teeth met flesh, ripping as I leaped atop him, a blood-curdling scream rending the air.

XXX

Samkiel

A flash of jet-black fur and Dianna was off me, barreling into the woods. It happened so fast that I was still pulling my clothes into place when I heard the scream. I moved, tearing through the woods.

I skidded to a stop, gaping at the sight of Orym struggling beneath a wolf the color of midnight. Dianna held him easily, her lips pulled back in a menacing snarl.

"Dianna."

Her head snapped toward me.

Orym held his torn-out throat, coughing. I dropped to my knees, my hands covering his wound, silver light emitting from my palms.

Jaws snapped toward me, her voice as dark as her fur. "Why are you helping him? He smells of Nismera's legion."

"He's an ex-commander, Dianna, non-active and currently bleeding out."

Orym groaned, his throat vibrating beneath my palms, but the bleeding had stopped pooling, and I could feel the skin knitting back together.

She growled. "Is this what he told you? The smell is too fresh. He's lying to you."

My hands lifted, and Orym sat up, scuttling back so fast he hit a fallen log, still holding his throat.

"You can understand it?" Orym asked, his voice broken, his throat raw and healing.

I ignored him, focusing on her. "Do you truly think I am incapable of discerning threats? He smells of them because his sister is still a spy there. She sends messages by ink. That is all."

The fur standing on her back slowly fell, but a low growl continued to rumble in her throat, her eyes focused on Orym. I realized then that Dianna was hurt and broken, the wounds still raw and wide open. Between the fear of having lost me, the adrenaline, and what had happened to Gabby, she was reluctant to trust anyone near me.

"Dianna. I am safe."

Her eyes snapped to mine, the crimson glow easing a bit. She took a deep breath, and her posture eased, the low grumble in her throat quieting. Dark mist grew from her fur and swirled around her. She shifted, and I was instantly on my feet, blocking Orym's view of her naked body.

I tossed a look over my shoulder, glaring at him. "You even try to look, and I'll rip your throat back open."

He held up a bloody hand in defense and shook his head.

"Dianna, clothes. Now." She rolled her eyes but headed back to where we had left her clothes.

"You followed me?" I asked Orym, still blocking his view of where Dianna was dressing behind me.

Orym rubbed his throat. "I woke up, and you were gone. I was afraid the guards had done something in retaliation, and then I heard the grunting . . . I didn't know. I thought they dragged you off."

"Retaliation?" Dianna asked, stepping to my side as she adjusted the laces of her shirt over her breasts. "For what?"

Orym did not look toward her as if he was afraid to make eye contact, and I could smell the fear dripping off him. "He saved me when he first arrived," Orym said. "I defected from Nismera's army. They hated me and tried to beat me to death."

Dianna's nostrils flared at Nismera's name, but she didn't move toward Orym. Her eyes darted to mine, a smirk flirting with her lips. "Always the hero."

"I can't help myself," I said, and her smile widened at the inside joke.

"So this is your great love?" Orym asked, his eyes darting toward her this time. "The one you spoke about? The one that gave you the necklace?"

My body flushed with heat, my smile dropping as if I had been caught doing something wrong. I had not said that word to Dianna or her to me, and I was nervous to have it spoken out loud. What if what we had was fantastic but not love for her?

Her eyes widened, and her brows rose, her gaze flicking between Orym and me. "Great love?"

I glared at Orym, and he scooted back a fraction. I raised my hand, scratching the back of my head. "We were just talking . . ."

"Uh-huh?"

"And he—"

"She's Ig'Morruthen," Orym interjected and stood. "You did not mention that."

"Why would that matter?" I snapped back. "She's good."

Dianna crinkled her nose and glanced at me. "I mean, let's not lie to him."

"You heard what they said. One of them nearly destroyed these realms. One. Singular. Bloodshed, pain, torment. The sky was black with smoke as villagers screamed below. All under Nismera's orders." The look he fixed on Dianna made my blood boil. "He was right. There are six, and you're hiding her."

I stepped in front of Dianna, blocking her from his accusing finger. "If you look at her like that again, speak to her in that same tone, or threaten her, I do not care about any partnership or alliance we may form. I will kill you," I said, meaning every word.

Orym's eyes widened, and he held up his hands in mock defense. "I'm not being crass or rude, my liege, but—"

"I know what and who she is. You do not." My hand flicked out, and an ablaze weapon formed between him and her. The silver shine glistened in the darkened forest, illuminating us both. "If you are a threat to her, you are a threat to me. I will not repeat myself."

Orym took one look at the blade and then glanced at our hands. "She is not just your great love, is she? That furious blind need to protect. She's more."

Dianna's hand clasped over my wrist, and she stepped forward, flashing a smile toward me, then Orym. "While this bravado and public display of affection is nice, let Orym have his fears. It doesn't matter. We're leaving anyway."

"Leaving?" Orym and I said at the same time.

Dianna glanced at us as if we had grown six heads. "Uh, yeah? I spoke to Reggie, and we have a plan to get out of here without being caught or alerting Nismera's soldiers."

"Dianna, I cannot leave."

"Why?" Her brow flicked up. "You can't go to Nismera's prison. If she finds out you're alive—"

"She's not there," Orym interrupted. "And Samkiel made a promise to me."

She glared at me. "Of course he did. That damn kindness of yours."

I recalled the ablaze weapon back into my ring. "I thought that was one of your favorite things about me?"

"It's becoming my least favorite when you promise detours." Her eyes darted to my side. "We still need to find The Hand, and you're in no shape for an epic rescue, king."

"I'm fine, as I proved just a bit ago. Your elixir worked. I don't feel as fatigued as before. Besides, you're here now, so you can help me, and we will be done even quicker."

Her arms tightened around herself. "Don't throw me a pretty smile and flatter me, thinking I will do whatever you say."

"Please." I stepped forward, my fingers curving under her chin. "Do this for me?"

Dianna stared at me for a moment, chewing on the inside of her cheek before sighing and turning toward Orym. "Fine, what is tall, dark, and heroic supposed to help you with?"

Orym stood, looking at us in shock, before clearing his throat. "Samkiel promised he'd help Veruka and me."

"Veruka?"

"His sister," I replied.

Something passed across Dianna's face, an emotion I knew all too well. As brief as it was, I recognized the lost, angry, and broken look that she had worn on the remains of Rashearim. Her grief lived just under her skin, and I knew even when she joked or smiled or laughed with me, it still bit at her and always would. She would always remember how she lost Gabby and the lengths she went to avenge her.

Dianna glanced at me, and the demons raging behind her eyes retreated. As she held my gaze, another emotion brushed against me as if just the connection with me helped to calm those demons.

"He would." She smiled, but it wasn't a teasing, flirtatious smile. This one was soft, tender, and loving. My heart beat frantically at the sight. If she looked at me like that again, I might have just forgotten about helping Orym, taken Dianna, and left.

I cleared my throat. "She is a spy, as is he. They communicate with wisps."

"Wisps?" Dianna asked.

Orym held up his hand, and a small fluttering wisp landed on his palm. "Wisp. Usually, they will carry a small note, but I haven't received any new ones."

Dianna cocked a brow and leaned closer. "We have those in my world. They are called dragonflies."

Orym scrunched his face. "That's peculiar. They look nothing like dragons."

Dianna shrugged. "Okay, fine. We will save your sister. I'm assuming she is at the prison."

"No," Orym said as the wisp flew away. "She is still under Nismera's rule."

The air shifted at his words. Dianna stepped forward, her lip curling up, exposing gleaming fangs. I held my arm out, blocking her path.

"Excuse me? She works for her? And you want us to help you? Are you out of your godsdamn mind? After—"

"Dianna," I cut her off. "Let him explain."

She no longer growled, but she didn't move back an inch. I knew if he said the wrong thing or reached for me, his head would be off his shoulders with one swipe.

"Fine. Explain to me how we can trust your sister even though she still works for Nismera and her brother is a rebel."

Orym swallowed. "Because she was the one who told on me and got me sent away."

Dianna didn't speak for a second, but I no longer felt her hackles were raised either. "I will not go into all the ways that is fucked up right now."

Orym only shrugged. "We do what we must in order to survive for the rebellion. It gave her a foothold in the legion she is a part of. They trust her completely."

"I promised I would help. We," I said, and Dianna rolled her eyes, "will help you."

"Not by choice." She smiled, and I nudged her. "So, what's the big plan? Go to prison and what?"

"Veruka said there is something there we need. A weapon of some sort. I'm not sure," Orym said.

"A weapon in the prison?" Dianna asked.

"I said I was unsure."

"Apparently." Dianna scoffed. "What kind of spy are you?"

Orym's face darkened.

"Enough." I held my hand up between them. "Both of you."

The sound of leaves crunching made us all turn, and I saw the light of three torches headed our way. Guards.

"Dianna, you have to go," I said, keeping my voice low.

She nodded and placed her hand over mine, squeezing it once. "I'll stay close, so please ask the guards to keep their hands to themselves, or I'll burn this entire camp. Promise or not." She glared at Orym.

I nodded and leaned forward to kiss her. I pulled back, and she smiled. Feathers replaced skin, and a bird as black as night took flight.

XXXI

Dianna

I yawned, stretching the sleek, feline form I wore this morning. My fur matched the foliage, spotted with rosettes of brown and gold. A small, furry creature with a long tail scampered by. It saw my paw and squealed, racing in the other direction. I placed my head on my paw, watching the camp rise. Guards yelled, and prisoners emerged from their tents to pack up before trudging toward the massive steel caravans.

The guards looked pissed, yelling and pushing at the prisoners. Lack of sleep seemed to be affecting them. The six-legged huroehe that pulled the wagons had been restless all night, calling and neighing in panic. They sensed me, and it sent them into a tizzy, but I didn't care. I only cared about the god who had just stepped out of the tent a few feet from me.

I'd never tell him, well, maybe not too often, but he was so gorgeous, even covered in those ridiculous beige prisoner garbs. The thin fabric didn't even begin to conceal the bulge of muscles straining over his powerful physique when he bent or moved. The sight of him set my blood on fire, and I wanted to lick every square inch of him. Of course, I couldn't because he was also the nicest person in the fucking cosmos, which meant there he was again, offering help to the elf that stepped out next to him. Orym said he wanted to help his sister. A part of me felt that and could relate to him, but another darker part of me didn't care. I trusted no one anymore, and no matter what he said, my instincts told me Samkiel was in danger.

Samkiel bent to roll up their knapsacks, and while I was annoyed at his effortless heroics, at least he had a nice butt. He looked up and said something to Orym as he helped him break down the tent. They walked to their caravan, two guards coming by to escort them and open the thick latch on the door.

I stood and stalked along the tree line, spotting a thick, heavy tree branch hanging over the top of their wagon. The powerful muscles in my back legs bunched, and I lunged, digging my claws deep into the bark. Birds took to the skies in a cluster, and I flattened my body against the limb. Everyone below looked up, searching the canopy and the sky. It took a few minutes, but the guards eventually shook their heads and turned away. Samkiel smiled softly as he spotted me and glanced away. He always saw me, no matter what form I took.

The two guards ushered Samkiel and Orym into the caravan before joining two other guards. I spied the small air hole in the top of the caravan and dove, shifting my form to shapeless mist. I slipped through the hole and appeared on the bench next to Orym, one leg crossed and my arm on the back of the seat.

"Gods above!" Orym snapped and grabbed his chest. "Can you all do that?"

"Only the really pretty ones," I said, winking at Samkiel. He smiled at me with pride.

The guards on the outside of the caravan were just far enough away and too lost in conversation to hear us, even with the steel door partially open.

"You really are powerful."

I cocked my head toward Orym. "Why do you say that?"

"You're the one who saved him from dying, right?" Orym said, glancing at Samkiel.

I swallowed the lump in my throat along with the visions of the tunnel, the world ending, *my* world ending. I didn't dare to look at Samkiel, not wanting him to see a hint of the apprehension and pain that lie inflicted every time I had to play along with it. My lips pressed into a thin line, and I reached across the caravan, popping Samkiel on the shoulder. He winced and rubbed his arm.

"Aggressive." He smirked.

"I leave you alone for five minutes, and you tell everyone our secrets," I seethed, narrowing my eyes at him.

Samkiel shook his head. "It was not like that. I saved him, and a part of my power slipped. He saw it, so I told him some minor details."

"Minor details." I groaned and covered my face with my hands. "You trust so easily."

"What does that mean?" Orym asked.

I glared at him. "It means you tell him some sob story about how you and your sister need help to escape an evil ruler, and he helps because he's sweet. I don't buy it, no matter what you preach."

"Dianna." Samkiel moved as if to separate us.

"I did not tell a story. It's true."

Orym glanced at Samkiel as if seeking confirmation.

"I'm sure it is true. I'm sure you want to save each other, but the second something happens—she's taken, or you're blackmailed—you'll switch sides and stab us both in the back."

Orym stared at me, his face turning a shade darker, but the look in his eyes was one I'd seen a thousand times. It was the look of someone doing whatever they could to survive. He nodded and stood, clearly defeated and not wanting a fight.

"I'm going with Hellem's caravan to the prison." He glanced at Samkiel. "I'll let you know if I hear anything else."

He opened the door and hopped out, the guards yelling. I shifted, turning into a small bug. Orym spoke with them, laughing and gesturing toward Samkiel. One of the guards shook his head and approached, reaching in to cuff Samkiel's ankles, chaining him within the wagon. He said something that made Samkiel's jaw clench, then closed the caravan door. I waited until the noise picked up, hooves beating on the ground and the caravan jolting, before I changed back. Samkiel and I were alone.

Samkiel glared at me.

I shrugged, tossing my hands up. "What?"

He sighed and shook his head but didn't say anything as the caravan rumbled forward.

I groaned and kicked Samkiel's knee. He'd been meditating for the last hour, but I suspected he was ignoring me. I even gifted him the wrapped treats Miska had sent for him. He ate it and said she was sweet but then returned to that quiet calm.

I sighed loudly. "How long are you going to act like a child and ignore me?"

His eyes cracked open. "Me? Acting as a child?"

"Oh, there it is." I leaned back, folding my arms.

"Why must you be so difficult?" He rubbed his brow and shifted on the uncomfortable seat. He sat up, breaking out of the pose he assumed when he let his mind wander far from here.

"I'm not."

"You are," he said, his voice filled with frustration. "I promised to help. Can you at least attempt to be nicer?"

My lip curled. "No."

"Why?"

"Why do you trust him so easily, or anyone for that matter?"

He leaned closer, bracing his elbows on his knees. "That's what this is about?"

"Have we learned nothing? I don't trust anyone, and neither should you. How many times do we have to be stabbed in the back to learn that?"

What if I lost you again? My lips didn't form the words, but the sentence coated my tongue like acid. The fear consumed any bit of trust.

I didn't care if he was mad at me for not immediately being Team Orym. I couldn't. His own family, the people he would have done anything for, betrayed him. As a result, he got a death spear rammed through his gut, and they left him to bleed to death on the floor. They didn't just take him from the world but robbed me of him, our future, and any plans we had. They nearly took the one person I cared about the most. I'd never be trusting when it came to him or his safety, never sweet or kind if I thought he was in danger. I wanted to be daggers and steel and something the realms could fucking choke on.

"Dianna." He said my name softly, dipping his head to catch my eyes. "Akrai."

I folded my arms and leaned against the wall. "Don't use that name to make me relax."

"Baby," he said, running his tongue along his lips. "We have to make alliances, especially here and now. Do I fully trust him? No, but I trust you, and you're here. I know you have my back regardless of what we face, as I have yours. He has not once given me any reason to distrust him, and I will not hold him responsible for the sins of others. That's not fair. Not to anyone."

I turned from him. I knew he was right. He usually was, but I couldn't be like him. No matter what life seemed to throw at him, he handled it with grace and understanding, but when someone burned a bridge with me, I made sure that bitch was nothing but pebbles in the waiting abyss below.

"Dianna."

I blew out a breath and dropped my hands, studying him across the space between us. Unable to tolerate the distance, I stood and stumbled forward. The caravan hit a bump, jolting us both, but Samkiel just watched me. I moved his hands out of the way and pushed him back before straddling his lap.

"What are you doing?"

"We are alone, and gods know when that will happen again once we arrive at the prison. Plus, I've missed you." I idly ran my fingers over the shorter part of his hair near his ear. The marks I had shaved in were almost gone. My knees pressed against his hips, and I slowly rocked my heat against his groin.

He shifted under me, his hands cupping my ass and holding me still. "Who is distracting who now?"

My gaze softened as I slid my arms around the back of his neck. "It's not a distraction." I leaned forward, kissing the side of his neck, his stubble rough against my skin. "It's merely a slight pause in conversation."

I ground my hips against him a fraction harder. He groaned and gripped the back of my head, pulling me back.

"Don't try to kiss your way out of a discussion."

My hips moved again. "What if I wiggle?"

He lightly popped my ass. "Stop it. I'm being serious."

I rolled my eyes and sighed. "Fine. I'll play along if we make a deal?"

His brows furrowed. "A deal?"

My hand stilled behind his head. "Gabby was stolen from me because I trusted others. You were . . . I will not do it again. I can't."

His hands drifted to my hips, gripping as if to stabilize me on this plane. It was as if he was afraid if he let go, I'd float away to that damaged dark place where all my demons waited. "I know."

"I told you before, I am not the same as I was before. I will not change, and if that's a problem, you need to tell me."

"It's not." His fingers flexed on my skin. "You're not. All I'm saying is that in this war, we will have to deal with and form alliances with those we may not like or trust. I've done it my whole life. And sometimes that means holding our tongue."

His fingers tipped my chin up, forcing me to meet his eyes. I nipped at his hand and said, "I'll work on that."

"And keeping things from me?" He tilted his head, a single brow raised as if he already knew every single thing I hid. I felt my body flush. Had he figured it out? Did he know what I'd done?

"What do you mean?" I swallowed.

"I thought we had moved past this." His words carved my heart into pieces. "I thought after everything, you'd rely on me more. Tell me your plans. Do you want to tell me about the fires in the East?"

Relief washed over me in a cool wave.

He went on. "I know how cocky you are, but leaving the place burnt to embers and a note for her? That's brash, and it will only fuel her rage when we need to stay under the radar."

I nodded. "I'm sorry I didn't tell you. It was when you were still unconscious. I wanted her to look for us there, far away from the southwest region of the realms and Jade City. That's all."

His thumb stroked across my lower back. "I do have a question, though. How did you even know where to go? Where the soldiers were?"

My lips formed into a thin line, knowing he wouldn't like my answer. "Reggie."

His hands flexed on my lower back before moving to my thighs. "Roccurem sent you to the East without regard for your safety or her numbers? He risked you for a distraction?"

"Technically, he knew how many. I just went a tad bit overboard," I said, holding my finger and thumb about half an inch apart.

Samkiel ran his hand over his face and rubbed his eyes. "I need to speak to him . . . or kill him. I have not decided yet."

A small laugh left my lips, and I pulled his hand away, clasping it in mine. "No killing. It bought us time, okay?"

"To be fair, I am unsure if a god could even kill a fate, but I am persistent and willing to try."

"Stop it."

"I do not like feeling left out when it comes to you. Especially after everything."

I pressed my lips together. He wanted all of me, and I wanted to give it more than anything, but it was so hard, even after everything, to let every wall fall. I needed to tell him about the tunnel, about what happened, but I was so scared. I could claim I wasn't, but I was. Nismera scared me more than anything, if I were being honest. With how he was now, it'd only take a second for her to take him from me again. I feared myself and what I would do if that happened. I could fight her armies and dismember threats, but I could not fight death. It held the upper hand, and I always lost.

"I know," I said. "I'm sorry. Honestly, I've been worried about more important things," I joked lightly, poking at his side.

He didn't wince like he had so many times before when something brushed against him. The antidote had worked, which meant it was the poison that had made him so ill. I was so worried about him even being alive again that I hadn't even thought an outside factor could play a role in his lack of healing.

"I also burned down Jade City," I said, peeking through my lashes.

I expected him to scold me, if only a little, but he just lifted his shoulders. The corners of his mouth turned down as one of the guards barked out a command, and the caravan lurched.

"I expected as much. I assume you saved a few to make the antidote?"

"No, I killed them all. I only saved Miska."

That vein on his forehead throbbed as his brows drew together. "That was a large city, Dianna."

"Full of poison makers under Nismera's rule, Samkiel," I said, matching his tone.

He pinched my ass hard enough to make me yelp, and I sat up slightly.

"I cannot leave you unattended for a second."

"Absolutely not." I smirked back.

He took a deep breath as I settled back in his lap. "We can figure the rest out together, but we will do it together, all right? No more secrets."

No more secrets, as if I weren't hiding the largest one. I was truly the worst of the worst, yet I smiled back at him, digging myself into an even deeper hole. Unable to rip that one truth from my throat.

"Or secret alliances," I added.

He only smiled. "Or secret alliances without discussing it first."

"I accept your terms, my king," I said, wrapping my arms around his neck once more, my breasts pressing against his front.

"Don't call me that here," he said, smiling against my lips.

"Why?" I kissed him.

"You know why," he grumbled as the caravan hit another bump in the road.

"I remember the first time I called you that. You glared daggers at me for it."

His chuckle was soft but heated. "That's because, at the time, I did not like what it did to me when you said it. We did not get along then."

"Oh, yeah?" I grinned against his lips, rocking ever so slightly against him. "What does it do to you, my king?"

He groaned, and I felt exactly what it did to him. A wicked laugh left my lips before I pressed them to his again.

"You're going to get us caught." He nipped at my lips.

"I know, right?" I rubbed myself on him, a slow, harsh grind that made him grip my hips even tighter. "Isn't it fun?"

"You're a very dangerous woman," he all but growled.

"I know. It keeps me awake at night." I smiled, placing a kiss on his cheek, then at his temple, then his nose.

"We . . . umm . . . need to discuss." His forehead pressed to mine, and his hands flexed on my hips. He stifled a groan when I ground my heat against him, savoring the throb of his cock. "The . . . plan."

His words stuttered on a groan, and I couldn't help my wicked smile as I moved a fraction harder against him. I loved him unhinged, on the verge of losing control. I loved it when that tough layer melted away, and he let himself off the chain. I loved how I was the one who caused it, and it only made me want to do it more.

"You're my only plan."

Samkiel groaned. "I can't think when you say things like that."

"Good." I fit my body against his and slid my tongue against his lower lip before nipping it. "No thinking."

"Always." Samkiel's hands slid down my back and gripped my hips, his mouth claiming mine. I moved against him, and he deepened the kiss. His cock hardened, thick and throbbing against me. He tried to be quiet, but I hoped his soft, little whimpers could be mistaken for the bumps we rode over. Gods, did we both love the rough road. Every rock and dip sent another burst of pleasure through us both. I was having so much fun making him squirm beneath me.

"You have to stop." He pulled back, licking at his lower lip as if he couldn't get enough of how I tasted. "I'm going to come."

I nodded, my hand grasping his chin and forcing his lips back to mine. "That's the point."

I fit my mouth to his and sucked gently on his tongue, swirling and teasing. His hips bucked, pressing his cock against my sex, my clit aching from the rub of fabric separating us, and I knew he was imagining my tongue on his cock. I groaned, letting him taste my pleasure and need.

Samkiel's breath came in pants against my lips as he started to move under me. His abdomen tightened as he kissed me deeper, taking control of my mouth again. His grip on my hips turned painfully tight, and he pressed me down harder, grinding his cock against me. He pulsed and twitched beneath me, a groan leaving his lips that I muffled with another blistering kiss.

I dragged every little bit from him before slowing and smoothing my movements and sitting back on his lap. He released my hip, and I could feel the throb where he had held me. His fingers skimmed the pulsing ache between my legs, and I grabbed his wrist, stopping him before his hand could slip inside.

"You do that, and we both know we'll get caught."

He grinned and withdrew his hand, wrapping me in his arms and pulling me close. "I can honestly say I have never done that in the history of my life."

I giggled. "Really? Not even in your wild youth with those handsy nymphs?"

He shook his head and rested it against the wall, completely relaxed and spent. "Not even once. I've never wanted someone as much as I do you."

"Yeah, you better say that," I said, nipping at his chin.

"How do you do that?" he asked, a smile playing on his lips.

"Which part?"

"Drive me completely insane."

"It's a gift." I pressed another kiss to his lips.

Samkiel tucked a strand of hair behind my ear, tenderly swiping his thumb across my cheek. "Can you do it to me forever?"

My eyes softened along with the angry, blackened heart in my chest. "Forever," I said softly.

He only smiled, shaking his head as he relaxed under me. "I cannot wait to show up to this prison with a stain on my trousers."

"Trust me, baby. Your clothes are nothing but stains. They won't even notice."

The caravan jolted sharply to a stop, and Samkiel's hands tightened around me.

"What is it?" he asked as I peeked outside. "Why the sudden stop?"

"Because we made it to the prison."

He moved beneath me, turning to gaze out the steel slits as the caravan started moving again, only much slower now. The higher we climbed, the sharper and more jagged the hills became, snow capping the gray peaks. I swallowed, not realizing how high we'd gone. Clouds billowed around the cliff edge, and I watched another wagon pass over the solid, wooden bridge.

"That's a prison?"

Samkiel grunted beside me. "Yes. That's Flagerun."

It stood out against the mountainscape with its smooth, circular top. There were no windows or ledges as if it wanted to blend into the cliff itself. The only signs of life were the torches lit out front and the guards holding back their large, snapping beasts. As we approached, the felines they kept on leashes thrashed. Even with the whips the guards used, they didn't obey. Fear. They were afraid because we had just snuck an Ig'Morruthen through the gates.

XXXII
Dianna

I peeked my head out of Samkiel's pocket as he walked through the large stone door. A thousand and one smells hit me at once, and I was glad the form of the small rodent creature I'd assumed didn't vomit because that's exactly what I wanted to do. The group of prisoners entered in a single file line, my eyes taking a moment to adjust to the gloom. The guards yelled and pointed, directing everyone forward.

Orym came up behind Samkiel, leaning in to whisper, "Where is she?" Samkiel glanced down at me, and I watched Orym's eyes widen. He tilted his head slightly and said, "That's honestly really impressive."

We approached more of the guards and their fierce beasts. The creatures snarled at the prisoners in front of us, baring large fangs, their claws digging grooves into the stone floor, but as soon as Samkiel passed, they tucked their long tails and pulled at their leashes.

The shouts of the guards echoed in the main foyer, and I peered out a fraction more. Heat blasted from the center of the room, emitting from just beyond the electrified guardrails. Samkiel got closer, and I peeked over the barrier. A large glowing ember spun at the bottom. The guards did not give us time to stop and look, yelling and pushing us forward.

Up ahead, the line broke into three sections, the platform splitting. One group went to the center, another went up more stairs, and the third was funneled toward the bottom. Samkiel's line was directed downstairs, and as he started down the steps, I looked up. High above was a large stone platform supporting what looked like an office or special cells. I noted it as a place I wanted to explore later.

The noises changed as we descended further into the bowels of the prison, but the stench just continued to get worse. Darkness pooled in the space on the other side of the railing. There was only a row of lights far above, providing a sickly glow to illuminate the way. The stairs spiraled for what felt like ages until they opened up to a large room.

Voices picked up, and I looked around. Prisoners sat in what looked like a cafeteria, utensils hitting against bowls and plates. The older prisoners looked toward the new ones but didn't say anything. Their eyes flickered toward the guards walking the aisles above, each carrying what looked like a staff with a ball at the tip.

Samkiel stumbled, and I was jolted, falling back into his pocket. I fought my way back to the top, peering out to see a guard with a tuft of hair bristling along his spine. He snorted and grinned at Samkiel and Orym, revealing dagger-like teeth. Okay, so he'd die first. He used his staff to point toward the retreating prisoners, and I realized it wasn't just me surveying the area.

We moved once more, the sound and smell of fresh water catching my attention. The line stopped as the guards made them all line up, speaking and pointing toward the rows of showers. Mist coated the room, a small fog from the heat of the water. The guard shouted something else, and the prisoners started to strip.

Samkiel patted his pocket lightly to let me know, and I held on as he lowered his pants. The second they hit the floor, I dashed out and away.

Hours passed as I scurried through the prison. I needed to reach the upper levels, but I soon learned there was no way to get there once the doors leading to the stairs closed. At least I had not found one yet.

I had returned to the dining hall and was between two misshapen stones, watching Samkiel and Orym eat. At least he was eating again now that the poison was fully gone. The only problem was, now, I was starving. I couldn't come and go as I needed to in this place, so I had to find a way to eat that didn't include killing or drawing attention. Great, fucking great.

A guard tapped his staff along the railing, and all the prisoners stood up, returned their trays, and filed out of the dining hall. I scampered across the floor, following close behind as they went deeper into the prison.

This level was just as dim as the one above and branched off in two directions. Guards pointed to the jagged cut-out rooms with matching grates, shuffling prisoners in two at a time. Luckily, Orym and Samkiel were to be cellmates. I hopped over the railing, staying in the shadows. The guard said something in a harsh language before locking them in.

The guard left, and I waited for the sound of his boots to recede. When I only heard the murmurings of the other prisoners, I changed back. I stretched my neck and stepped from the shadows. Orym jumped, clutching his chest.

"Holy gods! I will never get used to that," he said as a corner of Samkiel's mouth twitched. "Did you come from the very shadows themselves?"

"Actually, I've been running around as a small rodent for the last few hours, and my muscles feel very cramped and tight," I said, stretching my arm over my head before switching to the other. "Also, you guys don't stink anymore, so that's good."

Orym grunted in response and went to his makeshift cot, unwrapping the blanket and pillow. Luckily, they had given them new clothes, even if they still looked used, a mix of gray and brown garbs that wrapped at the waist and were tight around the ankles.

Samkiel nodded toward the stack of clothes beside his cot. "I got some extras for you since I am unsure how long we will be here."

A corner of my mouth lifted. "You stole clothes for me? How romantic."

"There was a smaller guy here. I just took his. I am sure they found him some others." He scratched his head.

I grabbed the clothes and set them on the narrow cot. Samkiel stood, shielding me with his body and tossing a look over his shoulder at Orym. A small chuckle left my lips as Orym lifted his hands and turned around. "I'm not looking, I swear."

Samkiel watched as I undid the laces of my top and let it slip to the floor. He handed me the shirt first, helping me slip it on.

"I looked all over this place," I said as he pulled my hair free from the top, brushing it back from my face. "It's pretty much an underground fortress."

"I assumed as much," he said.

I reached for my waistband, pushing my pants over my hips. "Once that door up top seals, so does this part. I wonder why they separated you all into three and what that fancy room on the main floor is."

I rested my hand on his shoulder as I took one pant leg off, then the next.

"The first level is those she can exploit for information. The second is workers to keep this place running, and the third . . ." Orym drew quiet as I slipped the pants on, jumping into them and rolling the waistband to keep them up. Samkiel pressed a kiss to my forehead before turning around to face Orym, but the elf still sat with his back to us.

"You can turn around now. I'm decent," I said.

Orym turned around, and Samkiel sat near him. I followed and stayed near the wall in the shadows, keeping their bodies between me and the door in case a guard passed by.

"What is the third level for?" Samkiel asked.

"The third is for the only ones who might make it out of here, and all of them will end up in front of Nismera. That's why we are here. We will only leave when she arrives for us."

Samkiel nodded, but my blood ran cold. "Would she come here?"

Orym shrugged. "I'm not sure. She may. Or she may send one of her trusted High Guards."

"We need to find this weapon and get you out of here before then,"

I told Samkiel. “Even though we eliminated the poison, that wound is still not completely healed, and I’d die before I let her take you.”

“I agree,” Samkiel said, surprising me. For once, he didn’t fight me, and I was glad for it.

Orym looked between us, a strange expression on his face.

“What?” I asked.

He shook his head. “It’s so strange, yet impressive, to see an Ig’Morruthen this close and not feel that my life is threatened. I am amazed that you’d risk your life and fight for him. You two have been enemies far longer than I have lived. There are stories carved in stone about battles between the gods and Ig’Morruthens.”

Samkiel and I shared a glance, a thousand and one memories running through it as I caressed his thigh. “To be fair, we used to hate each other.”

“Oh?” Orym said.

“Yeah,” Samkiel answered, “she tried to kill me several times.”

I nodded. “That’s actually true.”

“Now I can’t get rid of her, which is kind of bothersome.”

My hand shot out, popping him on the shoulder. “Now that’s a lie,” I said, and he laughed.

Orym said nothing, but I caught the haunted look in his eyes as he watched Samkiel rub his arm and grin at me. I recognized the loss and pain in him. It seemed the demons that haunted him were the same that haunted me.

“Who did you lose?” I asked, feeling Samkiel tense next to me.

Orym’s eyes found mine, and he forced a smile, telling me I was right. “It doesn’t matter. What does matter is that I am unsure if Veruka can send me messages while I am here.”

“We will figure it out.”

Orym nodded. “Another question to answer tomorrow, then.” With that, he lay back on his cot. I stood and stretched, walking toward the front of the cell. I’d just reached the door when Samkiel grabbed my elbow.

“Where are you going?”

"To see what else I can find while this place sleeps."

Samkiel looked at me as if I'd said the silliest thing he'd ever heard. He grabbed my hand and pulled me toward his side of this carved-out cavern.

"Absolutely not. You can explore during the day tomorrow, but I have not slept beside you in weeks. I refuse to wait any longer."

The smile that played on my lips was genuine. "Needy."

Samkiel unfolded the bedroll they gave them, ignoring the cot and spreading it on the floor. He shook out the blanket that looked as if it had seen better days. "Very," he said, dragging me onto the ground with him. We settled against each other, my back to his chest and his arm under my head in a makeshift pillow. His broad back blocked the view so that if anyone glanced in, they would not see me tucked against him.

"I'll sneak out before they make their morning rounds."

"Mm-hmm." Samkiel draped his other arm across my chest and pulled me tight against him, tucking his knee between my thighs. He rested his face on the back of my neck and inhaled deeply. Gods above, he fell asleep the minute he placed his head on me. I savored the experience of being surrounded by him, allowing his touch and the sound of his breathing to ease me. But as wonderful as this was, I still hungered.

I waited until Samkiel and Orym were deep into sleep, then slowly extracted myself from him. My stomach ached, the Ig'Morruthen begging to be fed. I silently snuck out of the cell and went hunting. The guards allowed their beasts to roam free at night, and I quickly took one down, finally satiating the gnawing pit in my stomach. Afterward, I found a small crack in the catacomb wall, fresh mountain water trickling from it, and cleaned the blood from my face and hands.

I made it back to Samkiel right as he went to turn over. Slipping back into his arms, I wrapped him around me with a deep sigh. He relaxed again, falling further back to sleep, and for once, I did too. But in the depths of my sleep, I dreamed of the orange-eyed man that beckoned for me.

XXXIII

Dianna

It had been two days since we arrived here, and I knew for a fact this was not like the prisons of my world. These prisoners were left here to rot and die while they waited for Nismera to come. The guards made sure they were fed and forced to take one cold shower a day, probably to keep the stench to a minimum. Beyond that, no one truly cared what happened to them.

There were prisoners here who had gone mad in their darkened cells, scratching at the walls, wishing for death, and cursing the guards who kept them from taking their own lives. I wondered how many were just forgotten, truly and utterly alone, locked in a cave below the ground in the dark.

I carried my tray of food toward Samkiel and Orym. They sat at their regular table near the wall, huddled together and talking. I snickered at the rumor running through this place about the two of them being lovers. I could see why. Samkiel was the prettiest one here, even with the overgrown five o'clock shadow. I supposed I should be jealous, but no one here was a threat to me, and I was more than happy to stir that rumor just for fun.

"I told everyone you two are in love," I said, sitting down in a heap. I still wore the look of a short man, my head shaved, and a scar running across my jaw. He was someone I had seen on the streets back on Onuna, and I'd assumed his form to blend in here.

"You did that?" Samkiel asked, his spoon half raised to his mouth.

"Yup," I said, taking a bite of what looked like some type of fruit, struggling not to gag in front of him. Solid food was not my friend. I wanted and craved blood, but that was a conversation for another time.

"Why?" Orym hissed, his tail flicking.

"Two reasons." I held up my finger. "One, it gets the guards off all of your backs when you are seen huddled and whispering to each other all the time, and two, for my own selfish one that if now I want to have my way with Samkiel and he happens to moan too loud, they will never think twice."

Samkiel snorted around his food and shook his head. Orym scowled and glared at me. He knew it was a good plan. He just hated to admit it.

"Listen," I said, taking another bite of my fruit. "I can only be strong for so long, okay? You think far too highly of me, and I have been without him for weeks. How much control do you think I have?"

Samkiel nudged my leg under the table. "Stop teasing him." He grinned and kept his leg against mine.

Orym shook his head, mixing the mush on his tray before taking a bite. "While I think half of that is a great idea, it does put a mark on our backs. What if they separate us?"

I waved my hand. "Pfft, they won't. I was doing my normal surveillance of the area, and the guy with the tentacles back there and Mister Uptight Guard with the goatee were not sleeping last night. Trust me. They don't care."

Both Samkiel and Orym turned to look at the two. The prisoner with the tentacles sat with a bunch of others but kept glancing up as the guard walked along the catwalk high above. He nodded, and Mister Tentacle got up and left as we watched. Samkiel and Orym grinned at me, and Samkiel went back to eating.

"Told you," I said, taking another crunch out of my fruit. "Also, I wonder if the tentacles kind of hurt and if he's into it. In my world, they had these tiny suction cup things."

"It depends on the species," Samkiel said, and then his spoon stilled in his mouth as both Orym and I stared at him. He lowered his spoon, his eyes widening a fraction as he looked at me. "Not that I would know or remember . . . ever."

My eyes narrowed. I banged the fruit down on my tray and pulled my leg away from his. When I scooted away from him, he reached under the table and tried to pull me back. I slapped at his hands, both of us in a small match of push and pull before Orym cleared his throat.

"I heard they moved Savees to the lowest level after he ate a guard's arm off when they tried to touch him. Only a handful are forced to stay down there."

I raised my brow as Samkiel tried to put his foot near mine, and I stepped on it. "Who is Savees?"

Samkiel glared at me.

"Savees is a prisoner that was with us on the trip here. I still think they did it because of what he is," Orym answered.

"Savees is one you stay away from," Samkiel said, folding his arms and leaning on the table.

I ignored him and looked at Orym. "What is he?"

"I don't know, actually. All I know is he is from the Otherworld."

Otherworld. My heart thudded. Reggie said some beings from the Otherworld may look for me since I'm here now. My mind reeled as Orym kept talking, but I ignored him. I needed to find Savees. What if he was the orange-eyed one that had been calling me? My dreams had not relented, and the one the other night felt so damn vivid, even if all he did was sit on that throne, begging me to come to him. I didn't realize I'd stood until Samkiel grabbed my arm.

"Where are you going?" Samkiel asked.

"To investigate a little further."

"Dianna," he hissed. "What did I just say about staying away from him?"

"I thought we had a conversation about alliances, remember? What if he can help us? You trusted Orym. Let me talk to him and see if we can trust him, too."

"Why? Why do you think he'd even help? Beings from the Otherworld are not that . . . giving. They always require something in return."

"Oh?" My brow flicked upwards. "Slept with one of them too?"

Samkiel reached for me, but I shoved his hand away. "Dianna . . ." he said as I moved past him.

"You're in trouble," I heard Orym say, a hint of humor in his voice.

"Yes." Samkiel sighed, watching me leave the small cafeteria. "I am in trouble."

I complained about a stomachache to one of the guards. It wasn't a complete lie. That damn fruit upset me. He walked me toward the lower level where the cells were located. We reached a dark hallway that I knew was rarely used. My hand reached out, catching him by the throat, my grip hard enough that he couldn't call for help. I dragged him toward the dark corner, out of sight of anyone walking by.

His eyes widened as the shell of the man I wore melted away to reveal my true form. I rose in height, dark hair spilling down my shoulders. "Don't panic. Everything is fine."

His jaw grew slack as he blinked.

"Good boy. Also, I wasn't lying," I whispered. "My stomach does hurt. I can't keep anything down, and I've already eaten all the wildcats you had here. I need something more."

My fangs emerged, and I tipped my head back before striking. I bit deep into his throat, warm, smooth blood filling my mouth. My eyes rolled back, and I almost moaned. This was what I needed, what I craved. I felt his heart slow and realized I couldn't leave a dead guard here. I forced myself off him, slicing my thumb and healing his throat. He looked at me, woozy and dazed.

"Go lay down. Tell your little friends you're just tired and need a break, okay?"

He nodded.

"And you never saw me. Good?"

"I never saw you."

"That's right, cupcake." I patted him on his back and watched him leave before wiping the blood from my chin and licking it from my finger.

I changed forms again, assuming the small rodent creature with large ears and a tufted tail. I scurried down the stairs, jumping down each step and continuing past the level with the cells.

The stairs ended, opening up into a dark and oppressive damp room. Water trickled in from the cracked walls, leaving puddles on the uneven floor. I didn't hear a heartbeat or breathing and wondered if Orym had gotten it wrong. Or maybe whoever they sent down here was already dead.

"You smell . . ." a voice echoed from my right, "old."

My ears perked up, and I turned. A giant rock leaned against the wall, and now I knew why I hadn't seen any cells. They had barricaded him in. I shifted back to my natural form and placed my hand on the jagged, circular rock. I shoved it aside and immediately wished I hadn't. The stench of death filled the air, and when I stepped in, I saw why. Rotting corpses hung against the wall, but luckily, it was the living one at the center that spoke to me.

I pressed my hand against my nose and took another step forward, my gaze remaining focused on the hanging body. He seemed smaller than my dreams, more sleek. His skin was pale, making the red rings around his arms stand out starkly. They looked like some type of tattoos.

He lay against the wall, his arms suspended above his head and pulled tight, wrapped in chains that cut into his muscles. He smiled a toothy grin, the dried blood on his face cracking. I swallowed and stepped closer, just now noticing the pointed ears. They were like Orym's. Only this creature had a tuft of hair that looked softer than feathers at its tips. When I stepped closer, I saw his one good eye was a swirling white shot through with blue. They were not orange. My heart settled, and I blew out a breath.

"I knew it was an Ig'Morruthen that landed that night. No thunder sounds that deadly," he said, and I wondered if his fangs were sharper than mine. "You're a fool if you think they don't know it, too. That she won't know what's being held at her prison."

"What do you mean?"

"Why would an Ig'Morruthen come to a prison buried in the Death Mountains if not to collect something?"

"What do you know?"

His smile was pure feline. "I know a lot. But what do I get if I tell you? Everything has a price."

I didn't feel the air stir behind me, but his overwhelming presence caressed my every nerve.

"I told you to stay away from him," Samkiel said, stepping in front of me, his arms folded across his chest.

"Ah," Savees said. "You are not with The Eye at all, are you?"

Samkiel said nothing.

"Is he what you came to claim, dark one?" Savees asked.

"Something like that," I replied. "Now I'll ask you again, and this time you will tell me what you know, or I will open your belly." I raised my hand, extending my talons slowly. "With my claws."

A sick smirk formed on the creature's face. "You'd only be doing me a favor. You think I want to stay in a world where that godly cunt rules? I'd rather die like my brethren than be subjected to her deeds."

I dropped my hand and shot Samkiel a quick look. We did need alliances.

"What if I could offer you something better?" I asked.

Savees lifted his head and gave me another toothy grin, his fangs flashing in the low light. "I could think of something better before I die here, but I think the foreboding one next to you would protest."

Samkiel took a menacing step forward but stopped when I lifted my hand, the back of it resting against his chest. "Stop. He's just horny and dying like most prisoners here. It means nothing."

"It's disrespectful," Samkiel all but growled, and I wondered for a second who was more beast, the guy on the wall, me, or Samkiel, when someone talked badly about me.

"You should probably apologize," I said to the Otherworld being on the wall. "He will kill you."

"I don't care about any blood rebels from The Eye," Savees snarled, snapping his teeth.

I knew what was coming but stepped back regardless. Samkiel slipped those rings on his hand and was at Savees's throat in a second, an ablaze weapon held against his neck. Samkiel shoved him hard enough against the stone that it shuddered.

Savees's eyes got so big I wondered if they would pop out of his head.

"Told you to apologize." I shrugged, keeping my arms folded. "He is not fond of anyone who is mean or crass to me."

"Y-you're . . ." Savees couldn't catch his breath. "You're supposed to be dead."

"I am not, but you soon will be if you ever speak to her like that again. Apologize," Samkiel snarled, tipping Savees's head back a fraction more, the blade cutting a thin line across his throat, blood running down his neck and pooling at his collarbone.

Savees's ears flattened against his head. "I'm sorry. I swear. I'm sorry."

Samkiel let him go, not bothering to check on him. He flicked the blood off his blade and called it back to his ring. He stood behind me, his presence a comforting warmth at my back. Samkiel was a sword and shield, always my protector.

Savees gasped for air, his body trembling. "What do you need from me?"

"I need to know how to get into the upper room."

After a long talk and less back talk from Savees, we officially had a plan. It was half-cocked, but I was willing to try, even if Samkiel was less than keen. We barely made it out of the room before Samkiel whirled me around, pushing my back against the cool stone. His hand clenched on my jaw, and his lips slanted over mine in a punishing kiss.

"Don't pull away from me again."

I blinked, not knowing what he was talking about, but then I remembered what happened in the dining hall earlier.

"Seriously?"

His leg wedged between my thighs, the hard muscle pressing against my sex at just the right angle. I moaned, and he ate it with a kiss, claiming the sound. "I don't like it," he said against my lips.

I bit at his lower lip and tugged *hard*. "Well, I don't like you reminiscing about the good old days with beings that aren't me."

His brows furrowed. "I wasn't, nor would I ever. I'm extremely comfortable with you, Dianna. That means I can be my entire self. I may say things, but I never meant to hurt you. I share every part of myself with you. Besides, there is no competition when it comes to you. Not for me."

I swallowed as my blood heated, pumping harder at his words. I wanted to kiss him again, to ravage him against this wall, but I also heard his heart. It thudded wildly, matching my own. The pulsing vein along his neck taunted me, begging me to feed. I fought the urge. I couldn't, wouldn't hurt him. Not when that wound on his side still caused him pain.

I nodded in response to his words before placing my hands on his chest and pushing him back. He released me, but I caught his expression.

"That's not fair."

"What isn't?" I asked, starting up the steps.

"So you can touch me, but I cannot touch you?"

I halted, turning ever so slightly. "Do you really want me screaming in this prison? We still haven't found that stupid weapon, and I don't need Orym pouting because our cover is blown. After all, you fuck too good."

He nodded, and his brows ticked up as if he agreed fully with what I said. It wasn't a lie, but it also wasn't the full truth. I was way too hungry at this point not to rip his throat open the next time he was inside me.

"All right," he said, glancing down at me. "But when we leave here . . ."

"Yes." I rolled my eyes dramatically. "You can ravage me for hours once we are out of here, my king."

"Dianna," he warned.

Shrugging my shoulders, I smiled and sauntered up the steps. I had to cover the yelp when he popped me square on the ass.

We made it back to his cell. Orym wasn't there, and Samkiel sat down next to me. He sighed and asked, "Are you so pissed at me that you'd venture down there when I told you to stay away?"

"No," I said. "And I can handle myself in case you forgot."

"I didn't, but you do not know every Otherworld being, Dianna. I have no idea who or what he is. Some can kill with a glance, others with gas you'd never smell until it was too late."

"Well, he doesn't look like he can release a deadly smoke bomb. He literally has hair on his ears. He's probably not dangerous at all. Maybe he is a soft, squishy feline."

"I do not care what he has. Do not risk yourself like that again. Please," Samkiel growled low in his throat.

"I won't . . ." I paused. "I'll try not to."

"Well, work on that." The corner of his lip tilted as he rested a hand on his knee. "Why did you go, anyway?"

I let his question hang in the air for a second before I released a breath. I needed to tell him. My dreams weren't stopping, and after seeing things out of the corner of my eye back in River Bend, I started to worry that maybe I was being followed.

"I have to tell you something, and you are going to be mildly upset."

He was quiet for a second before he nodded. "All right."

We sat knee to knee as I told him of my dreams. I told him of the place, the man with orange eyes, and how long it had been happening. He said nothing as I finished. Only looked at me with a twinge of hurt flashing through his eyes.

"Are they . . ." He chewed on his words, growling softly. "In your words, sexy dreams?"

I couldn't help but smile. "No, never. I only have those about you."

The haunted look left his eyes, replaced by one that made me think of when he showed up for our ice skating date. He looked surprised or excited. I wasn't sure, so I went on.

"It always starts the same. I'm in this bone graveyard of massive beasts, and I know where to walk, where to go. When I make it, he's just sitting there on this throne. Waiting."

"Waiting?" he asked. "Waiting for what?"

"Me."

His face hardened as if I'd just threatened him. "He will not have you."

I placed my hand on his. "I know, it's just creepy, I guess. When Orym said someone from the Otherworld was here, I went. I had to know if it was him, but it's definitely not."

"Why would you think he was from the Otherworld?"

My lips pursed into a thin line. "Well . . . Reggie may have said since I was here, powerful beings from the Otherworld may reach out."

Samkiel sat back and nodded, glaring at the wall. "All right, so Reggie told you, and you confided in him over dreams of a mysterious man."

I leaned forward, grabbing his face and forcing him to look at me. I made him face me, placing a kiss on his lips. "Don't be jealous. I was going to tell you, but it's not like we have time."

"We've had plenty of time. You could have told me anytime, and I could have told you just the same, if not more."

"I'm sorry."

His eyes didn't soften at my words. "What else am I missing, Dianna?"

You died.

It was on the tip of my tongue. It was right there. If I told him, it would make sense to him why I'd asked Reggie and not him, why I felt so empty when it came to feeding, and why, above all, I had been so overprotective. I could tell him, and then I'd have to tell him everything. It would ruin his hope for The Hand. I would have to tell him I had given up the one thing he wanted most of all, traded it for his life, and a part of me was terrified. It meant I'd have to tell him my one true fear and why touching him reassured me so damn much. Why I desperately needed to know that I was wrong and that he still wanted and cared for me. What if I'd given up our mark, and we weren't mates anymore? What if I had saved his life but, in turn, ruined mine?

"Nothing." I shook my head, and he stared at me. "Nothing."

He leaned back a fraction, gazing at me, and I thought he knew just how terrible I was at lying. I thought he knew it all, but my stress died the second he held his hand toward me, his pinky finger extended. "Pinky swear."

"Pinky swear?" I repeated.

"Yes, it's the law and an unbreakable promise, as you said before. I will only believe you if you do."

I couldn't stop the grin or the god-awful feeling I had when I hooked his finger with mine and lied and lied and lied.

I was a cruel, awful bitch.

And I loved him.

XXIV

Cameron

Moans filled the air. Whoever was behind the wall sounded as if they'd gotten their organs rearranged, but I didn't care as long as it drowned out what I was doing. I stood up, his body at my feet. I took a deep breath and wiped a hand across my face.

My eyes adjusted to the dark room, and I inhaled deeply, filling my nostrils with the smell of sex, smoke, and booze before the scent of death coated the air. I slid my fingers through my hair, the short strands sticking up from the blood I had just wiped on myself. I looked at the bodies scattered around me and couldn't stop the sick laugh that exploded from my lips or how my eyes welled with tears.

I had done that. I had killed them because I was so fucking hungry.

My pocket vibrated again. I knew who was calling. That damn mirror was worse than a phone. I ignored it as I had several times before and stared out over the dark water, unable to look at what I had done. I had jumped on board this ship when it docked at River Bend a week ago, tracking down a lead. Only I was stupid and hadn't realized it was headed to another major port and was filled with too many rich drunk aristocrats that wanted to fuck their way back to wherever the hell they'd come from. The man at my feet was the one I had come to see. He claimed to have seen a toruk flying south across the evening sky.

I blew out a breath, frustrated at information that made no sense and pointed me in too many directions.

My pocket buzzed once more. I reached in and grabbed the obsidian stone, throwing it at the wall with all my might. It didn't smash against the wood as I so desperately wanted it to. Instead, a fist closed around it, stopping its forward momentum.

"So you have been ignoring it," Kaden said, his voice filled with anger.

"What a massacre," Isaiah said, stepping out of the shadows. Imogen followed him, and my breath died in my lungs.

"What are you doing with her?" I hadn't realized I was in Isaiah's face until Kaden placed a hand on my chest.

Isaiah laughed. "Get your bitch in line, Kaden, before I rip him to pieces."

"Both of you," Kaden said, pushing me back, "calm the fuck down."

"Why do you have her?" I asked again, unable to look away from Imogen. She just stared straight ahead, her blue eyes so far away it broke my fucking heart. I had been avoiding her because I couldn't look at her, couldn't see her, without needing to take her away from this, to save her. If I did that, I knew I'd be locked up somewhere and skinned alive. Then, I'd never be able to save them. I had to find Dianna.

"I'm the only thing keeping her safe," Isaiah said.

"Bullshit!" I spat. "You, like him, only give a shit about what you can own or use. There isn't an ounce of care in you."

Kaden's fist connected with my face, and I stumbled back. I caught myself and spat dark blood on the deck. "Oh, my mistake. I guess you do care about one brother."

"I've been calling you."

I rubbed my jaw as it healed. "Yeah? Well, go fuck yourself. I haven't found anything."

"I don't believe that," Kaden said, stepping closer to me. "I think you have, and you're chasing it. So I'm going to ask you once, then I'm going to take something you love very much."

My chest heaved because I knew the evil bastard would.

"Someone said they saw her on the back of a toruk headed east again. I was following that."

It wasn't a complete lie, just twisted enough that he wouldn't sense it.

"A toruk?" Isaiah said. "Wasn't that a gift for Mera?"

Kaden nodded. "It was."

"What does that mean?" I asked.

Kaden looked at his brother and then back at me. "It means that fate is keeping Dianna one step ahead of us all."

"Mera has to know, Kaden."

My blood chilled. I had lied to save her, but I may have damned her.

"I know, but we will worry about that later. It's time to go home." Kaden slapped me on the back before raising a hand and opening a portal. Before we stepped through, he said, "Clean that up, Isaiah."

Isaiah scoffed, but I watched him raise his hand. The blood on the floor seeped back into the bodies before they rose, their eyes swirling red. I had a second to process what Isaiah was capable of and what he was going to make them do before Kaden pushed me through the portal, and it closed behind us.

We arrived back at Nismera's palace, passing a few guards before Kaden pushed me into an alcove.

I smacked his hands off me and fixed the front of my shirt, adjusting the buckles across my chest. "Hey, I get it. I'm even hotter as an Ig'Morruthen, but this isn't going to happen," I said to him.

His face darkened, and I wondered if he was about to split my head in two. "Shut up," he snarled and slapped me across the head.

I felt my eyes flare red, but I just chuckled. "Listen, all I'm saying is everyone is a little gay. We've all sucked dick before. We're immortal. It's normal, but I won't be your willing sex slave like Dianna."

"Cameron, if you don't shut up, I'll kill you here and now." He held his hands close to my face in half-clenched fists, his claws extending.

I put my hands up in mock surrender. "Well, what's the secret meeting in a dark part of the castle for then?"

"Are you out of your fucking mind?" he sneered, too damn close to me.

"About which part?" I smiled back. "You have to be more specific."

"You leave bodies across every fucking world you touch. You think I wouldn't know? Wouldn't smell it on your fucking breath?"

"Then I suggest backing up," I said, not backing down for a second. My blood thrummed in my ears, my pulse quickening. Kaden took a step back.

"How careless are you trying to be? Ig'Morruthen or not, she will have your head. She is too close to a summit and will not tolerate any fuck ups."

"Oh, it's so sweet you care." I threw him a closed smile. "Since you showed me how to feed once and left."

His brows furrowed, his lips turning upwards. "I thought the instructions were pretty clear. Feed, erase their memories, and be gone. Not drain."

"I'm starving," I practically yelled. Kaden slapped a hand over my mouth, pushing me back further.

"Shut up," he hissed.

I just waited. He dropped his hand when he realized I wasn't saying anything back. "I'm starving. I can't even change forms. Did you know that? I have zero idea how to do it. That's what took me so long to even get to River Bend."

Kaden shook his head, rubbing a hand across his brow. "It's not my fault you're defective."

"You're a dick," I snapped. "And a terrible maker. No wonder Dianna left the second she had a chance."

His eyes bled red before he punched me square in the gut. I didn't even have time to breathe before he grabbed me by the back of my neck and shoved me out of the alcove. He dragged me down the hall, the guards watching. He stopped in front of Nismera's war room, and his hand tightened on my collar as he leaned in close to whisper, "I'd suggest you tell her the truth. Otherwise, you can say goodbye to Xavier."

He didn't give me time to respond before opening the door and shoving me through. Every eye turned toward us. Nismera stood with Vincent at her side, the members of The Order looking more than stressed.

"Cameron here has a lead, my king, and I think you will want to hear it."

Nismera glared at me and said, "Well, let's hear it then."

The war room doors closed behind us, and I was reminded again that Kaden wasn't the worst thing in the world, not compared to her.

XXXV

Dianna

"This is the weirdest place to have a meeting," I said, my nose still wrinkled against the rotten smell.

Orym had snuck food in for Savees, and he was currently sitting on the floor eating. It was guaranteed that they fed him little, if at all. I leaned against the wall with Samkiel at my side.

"Does everyone have a tail here?" I asked, glancing at Savees. His twin tails, tipped with dark fluff, bristled.

Orym shook his head, but he thrashed his tail, too. "How can we get to the upper room?"

"Why do you want to go there?" Savees asked as he ate the skin off whatever small bird they served this morning.

"I think there is a weapon there for me. It's the only place it could be because Dianna has searched everywhere else."

"Plus," I added, "when we arrived, I felt . . . something up there. I can't explain it."

Samkiel nodded, his arm braced above my head and his body hovering protectively over mine as he leaned against the wall. I smiled to myself and wondered if his need to show everyone we came across that I was his would wane. Not that I was complaining. It was nice to be wanted so much for once and not just for what I did when we were naked.

"I felt it, too," Samkiel said.

Savees cleaned the bone in his mouth until it shined and tossed it toward the disgusting cell.

"Good luck getting topside. Those doors won't open unless Commander Taotl opens them. He has a chip set in his wrist to unlock all the doors."

My face scrunched. "But the other guards and the food, all that gets here. You're telling me it's not delivered?"

Savees picked up another small bird leg and sucked it into his mouth. "It is through the system they have topside. It's a bunch of tunnels that squeak all night. I can hear them through the wall."

"And this commander? What does he look like?" Samkiel asked.

"He's Estiine. You can't miss him."

Orym cast a glance toward Samkiel while I looked confused.

I held my hand up. "Okay, can you guys tell me then? Sorry, I haven't been to this realm in, let's say, ever, and all you're doing is throwing one word after another like you think I know what you are talking about."

Samkiel hid a snicker as Savees and Orym looked at me. "He's the tall one, skin a mix of spots and a short coat. He has hooves," Orym said finally.

"The guy that looks like a huroehe? With the long face, mane, and big ass weapon?" I asked.

"Yes, that is the one. He is a sadistic bastard," Savees said, chewing on the words.

I nodded. "Okay, I'll find him, kill him, and take his form. Then we grab the weapon and leave."

They all spoke at once, and I held my hands up. "One at a time, please."

Savees jumped in before the others could. "Don't leave me here to rot when you leave."

I cast a glance at him. "I'll think about it." Then turned to Orym. "You?"

Orym only shrugged. "I was going to say if you kill him, you need to make sure he has the key on him first. Otherwise, you are wearing a useless shell."

I nodded before turning toward Samkiel and resting a hand on his chest. "And you?"

"I was merely going to suggest for you to be careful. Also, he only wanders the lower levels of the compound in the morning. Then he returns topside. If you are to get him, we will need a diversion to distract everyone first."

My head reared back. "I'm actually shocked. I thought you'd suggest it was immoral or something."

He shook his head. "Taotl is cruel. I smelled it on him the second we entered. He is unkind to the others here. I saw how they cowered."

"He is also from the Otherworld," Savees joined in, tossing another bone.

Samkiel and I looked at each other. I assumed the Otherworld would be the first to rebel against her, given they fought the gods for eons. Instead, she had collected the meanest and used it to her advantage.

"Why would an Otherworld being bow to a god?" I asked, patting Samkiel's arm. "No offense, baby."

Savees cleared his throat. "From the moment the sky opened, the Otherworld erupted into chaos. There are seven rulers, and from them to the lowest of us, we saw an opportunity to have our own, so to speak. Some rebelled and died, and others ran topside."

"Why would beings in the Otherworld run to her? Don't gods hate us?" I asked.

"Every being wants a home, a territory. The Otherworld is like any empire. They sit above us. Nismera offered a way to overthrow even them so . . ." Savees shrugged. "The enemy of my enemy is my friend."

I glanced toward Orym, who looked just as shocked as us. "What does that mean . . . Wait, are they going after The Eye?"

Savees snorted. "They'd rather be ashes than help them, not that The Eye would care. No one cares about anyone but themselves now. It is a fight for survival, and everyone is running scared. Those who do not join Nismera die, and most are just striving to survive."

"They came for you," Samkiel said. "That's why you were taken prisoner, why they keep you here, starved and beaten."

Savees refused to look at any of us. "I ran topside too. The sun does not shine in parts of the Otherworld, and I saw an opportunity for freedom."

"Freedom from what?"

Savees's eyes turned to me, their nocturnal shine glowing from the torches outside, and I wondered just what beast he turned into. "That's none of your business." He all but growled.

"Watch it," Samkiel said from behind me, the air in this chamber stirring. Savees lowered his gaze in a sign of submission.

From the scars along his arms, I was willing to bet most of his body held them. I didn't need to know what beast he turned into, only that whatever it was, it was powerful enough that the ones who had him in the Otherworld had forced him into submission, too.

"It's okay. I was prying." I tossed a smile toward Samkiel, who still glared daggers at Savees. If he even flinched wrong, Samkiel would take his head off.

"Well, I think we all make a great team," I said, trying to lighten the mood.

I only got two eye rolls, which was significantly better than earlier.

"Stick to the plan," Orym said as we sat in the cafeteria the next morning. I nodded, but my brows lifted when I saw he was looking at Samkiel, not me. "I'm talking to him."

Samkiel opened his hands from where they had been fisted on the tabletop and growled, "I will."

Orym clicked his tongue. "I see how you look at her. She's strong. She will be fine. Don't run off the second it happens."

Samkiel glared at Orym, and I smiled. I could feel his embarrassment at being called out for his protectiveness, but I adored it.

"He will," I said, patting Samkiel's thigh. "And as soon as I get the weapon, I'll be back, and we can plan our escape."

Samkiel nodded, and we all glanced up. There, stomping through the guards, was Taotl, holding his battle ax across his shoulder. His skin was ivory and speckled with freckles. A dark mane spilled down his head and along his neck, the same texture and color as the tail swishing behind him. His hands were like ours, but his hooves clattered against the metal as he stalked along the catwalks. He was speaking to a guard draped in mostly cloth, only a couple of pieces of metal armor along his arms and calves.

I nodded at Samkiel, and he hid his hands beneath the table, placing a single ring on his finger. I saw the change in him but knew no one else would notice. His rings weren't just for his weapons but a way to focus his powers.

Samkiel raised his pointer finger, aiming at the burly man off to the far right. A tiny spark of electricity snapped at him, quick and sharp, hitting him in the thigh. He yelped and stood up as if he had been stung, glaring at the guy closest to him. He didn't even hesitate before throwing the first punch, and then all hell broke loose.

Guards pushed and shoved, trying to wrangle the growing rise of chaos. It worked perfectly, given the fact everyone was miserable here. All they needed was a little shove, which is exactly what I did to the guard who passed by me. He landed on a table, and the prisoners dragged him off, throwing him into the tussle.

Taotl shouted, pushing more guards to join the fray. As soon as his back was turned, I attacked. My fist connected with his face, and he stumbled, dazed. He touched his jaw and smiled, but it only lasted a second. I grabbed the rail behind me and, using it for leverage, kicked him down the stairs.

He lay in a crumpled heap, groaning in pain. I jumped down after him and checked to make sure no one was behind me. My claws emerged from my fingertips, and I punctured his shoulder, dragging him into the dark bowels of the prison. His hands reached out, scrabbling for purchase, but it was too late.

I exited the lower levels so much taller than I was accustomed to. I adjusted the silk garbs around my shoulder and watched the chaos as the fighting continued. Samkiel helped a prisoner off the floor, the man's eyes swollen shut. He was leading him out of the melee when he paused and focused on me as if he sensed I'd come back into the room. I nodded once, and he returned the gesture before leading the man he was supporting toward the exit. I strode through the crowd, pushing prisoners out of my way and heading for the stairs.

A shout followed after me, and it took me a moment to remember what form I wore. "Taotl," he called. "We need reinforcements. They have gone mad."

"I'll go get them," I called.

This morning, I watched Taotl wave his wrist to unlock the door. I pulled my sleeve up and tried to look like I knew what I was doing, pressing my wrist against the metal. The door hissed open, and I breathed a sigh of relief. I stepped through, and it closed behind me. I inhaled deeply, the air so much fresher, this level less oppressive. When I looked up, I saw why. High above, a circular grate allowed in the bright morning sun and a fresh breeze.

I made my way up the stairs and to the left, working my way to the top. I glanced around a couple of times, wondering why I hadn't seen any more rooms or cells or why I didn't hear anything other than my hooves on the stairs. All thoughts died when I reached the room and heard a single heartbeat inside. I calmed my breathing, ready to play my part, and opened the door.

I froze, and time stopped.

"I fucked up," I said, my heart thundering as I dropped the facade and returned to my natural form.

Samkiel pulled me further into their cell, and Orym closed the gate. The chaos erupting outside had forced the guards to shove everyone into their cells early. Once I returned and restored order, all the fighting had stopped. The guards gathered the wounded, and I ordered them to their chambers, making it clear that no one was allowed out until early morning.

"Slow down," Samkiel said, grabbing my arms to ground me with his touch. "Talk to me. What happened? What did you see? Did you find the weapon?"

I nodded, hating what I was about to say. "Yes, but I don't know how to tell you this. I ate Taotl, but my blooddreams haven't worked since Rashearim. They didn't return when I got my powers back. I didn't see this, Samkiel."

"What? Just tell me, Dianna."

"The weapon . . ." I swallowed. "It's not a thing. It's a person. It's Logan."

XXXVI

Logan

An hour earlier

The door swung open. My body didn't move, but within the prison of my mind, I looked up. I preferred the harrowing darkness over the bloodletting they forced on me, but I had to admit I got bored. That damned commander was back, and I was expecting him to unload a tirade once more, but he just stood there. He didn't move toward his desk or the room behind me. He just stood and stared.

I couldn't decipher his expression and had no idea what was happening. Perhaps he had no use for me any longer. Perhaps I'd be shipped off, and they would take me even further away from Nev. Either way, this was Iassulyn, and I had truly suffered.

Taotl took one step closer, then another, as if he had forgotten how to breathe. As he neared, a familiar swirling mass of dark mist engulfed his form, and I lost my breath, too. Her piercing red eyes stared as if she could see into my soul.

Dianna.

I know that name! I know her! My friend. Our friend. Our queen.

"Are you in there, buddy?" Her words filled the dark, empty expanse of my mind, echoing through my memories.

"Yes!" I screamed. I yelled. I fought, but my mouth did not move. My legs, arms, and body remained still and motionless.

"Logan, if you can hear me, know that Samkiel is alive. We will not stop fighting for you and the rest of our family. We will bring you home, okay?"

My heart thudded. I felt it, even if it was only for a second, and I wanted to hold on to it. I wanted to latch myself to it and force my body to move, make anything move.

Her eyes searched my face, and I wanted to yell that I was there but nothing came.

Dianna sighed and placed a hand on my shoulder. I couldn't feel a damn thing. Her form grew and thickened, returning to that of the ugly commander. I watched as she took one last look at me, and then she was gone.

I curled inward again, wishing I could be free of this damned mind prison and lay upon the cold empty floor of my mind. Dianna had said that Samkiel was alive and that gave me hope, especially if she was with him. I would cling to that because I had seen what they were capable of when they worked together. I closed my eyes tightly and tried to think of something, anything, but the empty void I was existing in.

More of the celestials filled the hall as that chime rang out loud and clear. I knew most studied after hours, wanting to impress the gods and goddesses to stay their yeyras. I was looking for just one.

A group of female celestials piled out of the building, giggling about something. They held their books close, their long, flowy garbs dancing around their feet. They stopped and stared in my direction, their eyes widening in shock. I should have changed out of my armor before coming to see her, but I knew she would dart away the second she could.

"Is this why you snuck away the second we landed?"

Now it made sense why the females had stopped and why they were headed in our direction. Samkiel placed his arm on my shoulder, but I shrugged it off.

He took a step forward, taking up my peripheral. His damned silver armor was a beacon, and it was currently grabbing the attention of anything with a pulse in a mile radius.

"You followed me?" I glared at him.

He shrugged. "I was curious why you wanted to leave the briefing so soon, and now I see it's to gawk at the junior celestials. Or maybe just a certain one in particular?"

I didn't get a chance to answer because the female I was looking for finally exited the large study room. Her long, dark hair was tied back in a mass of twisted braids held together by a small ribbon at the bottom. She wore the same flowy white gowns as the others, but on her, she put every goddess I'd ever met to shame.

She smiled at the instructor walking beside her, speaking animatedly about runes. When she looked up and saw me, her smile turned into a sneer.

"Oh, I don't think she likes you," Samkiel said right as the group of celestials stopped before us.

It was all the distraction I needed. They swarmed, talking and flirting with Samkiel long enough to let me slide away. I darted past a few huddled groups, following Neverra as she practically sprinted away. She was fast. I was faster.

I stopped in front of her, cutting her off from the massive stone stairs that lead out of the auditorium and to the garden terrace floor below.

"Why are you avoiding me?" The words spilled from my lips.

She huffed and gripped her books tighter. "Why are you following me?"

"Why aren't you talking to me anymore?"

"Are we going to play a questions game, or can I leave?"

She moved to step around me, and I blocked her again. "Logan."

"Oh, so you do *remember my name."*

That got another frustrated huff out of her. "What do you want me to say?"

"Anything, really. I thought we had fun at the gathering. Then you acted weird, and now you are avoiding me."

"Because I know who you are."

My head jerked back in shock as someone asked to step around us. I moved a fraction of an inch, letting them pass, but not her. "Who I am?"

"Yes, you're Samkiel's kingsguard, and we have heard all about you and him." She tried to step around me again but stopped and let out a deep sigh when I countered.

"That seems almost insulting," Samkiel said from behind her. "Do you always speak of your future king in such a tone?"

Oh gods, Cameron was right about the ego. We'd never survive.

She half-turned, keeping her gaze lowered. "My apologies, my future liege. If you'd be so kind as to have your kingsguard move, I really do need to be on my way."

"No." He shook his head, and I nearly lost mine. Neverra's gaze widened slightly, realizing she may have just insulted the Prince of Rashearim.

"I truly did not mean any ill intention, my future liege. It's just that—"

"If you wish to make up for your grievances, there will be a ball in three moons. Accompany my kingsguard, and all will be forgiven."

Her jaw went tight, but she merely forced a smile. "Yes, my prince. If that's what you wish."

Samkiel's smile was downright venomous. "It is."

"Then so it shall be." She turned back to me with rage and hate in her eyes. "I shall see you then."

I didn't stop her this time, letting her walk past me. She didn't look back, but I felt the slight shove against my shoulder as she passed, and Samkiel caught it, too.

"What was that?" I sneered at him.

"You were taking too long to ask her. I was merely helping."

"With all due respect, prince," I said, dragging the last word out. "I don't need your help."

"She's fun," Samkiel said, ignoring me. "I need fun." My skin practically vibrated as I glared at him.

He barked out a laugh. "Calm down," he said, slapping my shoulder. "I wasn't talking about her."

"Good," I said as we turned back toward the exit. "And don't you have enough fun as it is? How much more fun do you need?"

Samkiel was quiet for a second. "Having fun and having a distraction or three are very different things. I have distractions, Logan. Never forget that. I do not have fun."

As we walked out of the auditorium, I wondered just how much of himself he buried that none of us were aware of.

XXXVII

Imogen

Isaiah spoke to Kaden in those damned hushed whispers. A line of generals passed by, their golden swords and shields held tightly to their sides. We had not been called, so why were soldiers moving?

My thoughts died as Isaiah looked at me, his hand stroking his jaw as Kaden continued to talk. If I had control over my body, my heart would have leaped into my throat when Isaiah's eyes met mine. It was cursed and damned and wrong, but the only time I didn't feel like an empty shell was when he was near me or looking at me. Gods above, I didn't know how to explain that, and a part of me absolutely hated it, hated him, even if he did keep me safe. No one even dared look at me now, much less touch me. Not even Nismera questioned it.

Even stuck in my head, I at least knew my body was safe with him. I didn't sleep in this state, not like I had before. But Isaiah gave me his bed, said the words that made me lay down, and he slept on the floor. I stared at the ceiling and wondered why he did it until sunlight filled the room and the day repeated. He never tried to touch me. It was quite the opposite, as if he were afraid to, and I didn't mind one bit. It was strange to feel peace when I could feel nothing at all.

Kaden nodded once before turning and disappearing from view. Isaiah strode toward me, stopping and folding one massive arm over the other before sighing. He whispered the command, and I followed once more, a part of me wondering if I would follow him even without the words.

XXVIII

Samkiel

Doors screeched across the stone floor as guards went by, opening cells for breakfast. Orym groaned and rolled out of bed, shuffling around a bit before leaving the cell. Dianna shifted beside me, and I sighed, resting my head atop hers. I hadn't slept much, and I did not feel like eating, not when Logan was so close. Questions circled through my mind. How long had he been here? What had he made him do? Then there was the one that made my heart ache. Was he still in there?

Dianna had snuck me up to the upper levels the night after the brawl, and seeing Logan damn near made me weep. I hugged him and hated that he did not hug me back. He stared at me, no flicker of emotions or life, just emptiness, and I hated it.

Dianna's arms wrapped around me and pulled me close as if she felt my apprehension. She nestled her face against my throat and inhaled deeply. "You didn't sleep last night. I'm pretty sure I have a bruise on my leg where you kicked me." Her breath tickled my neck as she spoke.

"Sorry," I replied.

She pulled back to look at me. "It's because I took you to see Logan?"

"I think it's a combination of everything, truly," I said, brushing a kiss to her nose.

"I just wanted you to see him. I'm sorry."

I pulled back a fraction to look at her. "I know. It's not that. It's . . . I had this hope that if I found them, maybe if they saw me and knew I had come for them, it would help break whatever trance they were in. But when I saw him, held him . . ." I shook my head. The swell of emotions and pure heartbreak were almost crippling. "He didn't even flinch or respond. What if—"

Her lips slanted over mine, stopping me mid-sentence. My body relaxed, the taste of her warmth driving the cold, dead feeling from my heart. Her mouth teased mine, moving over it in a way that sent my heart racing and my blood pumping.

She pushed at my chest, rolling me onto my back. "We will save him, save all of them, okay? Don't give up hope."

"How can you be so sure?" I asked the one question that had been gnawing at my gut all night.

"Because I am always right." She flicked my nose with her finger.

Another sick emotion welled up in my gut. My eyes burned with the one truth I had buried since I woke up and saw I wasn't in Rashearim any longer. "It's my fault. Even with those runes on me, I should have fought harder."

She raised up on her elbow above me, her eyes holding nothing but pure, unrelenting strength. "Do not place this blame on yourself, Samkiel. I will kick your ass. I swear it. You were tricked and lied to. They were more than ready to subdue you, and they did. You fought, you always do for them, for me." I turned my head away from her as a tear rolled down my cheek. Her grip was tight on my chin as she forced me to look at her again. "I know how that magnificent brain works, and you're wrong. You are enough."

This time, when my chest ached, it wasn't just because I lost them but because of the strong-willed woman currently staring at me who could read my thoughts without even trying.

I nodded. "Even if we get them back, I know nothing of the words Azrael used. The book is gone, and I don't know what its magic or lasting effects of the spell are. Some chemicals can alter the brain so much that nothing is left once that chemical is removed. Logically—"

"Stop." Dianna pressed her body close and kissed me again. "We are going to find a way to fix all of it, and we are going to save them. Together. Even if I have to rip the world to pieces for you, for them, I'll do it. We will fix this." She ran a hand through the dark curls that swept over my brow, brushing it back from my face. "Okay?"

I nodded because what choice did I have? She was determined. I forced a smile. "With you at my side, how could I lose?"

Shadows darkened her eyes, but she kissed me again before I could question it. However, this time, she did not pull away as quickly. Her mouth slanted over mine as she turned her head, deepening the kiss. Her tongue ran across my lower lip, demanding access, and I gave it to her. Dianna broke the kiss, her hand roaming across my chest. I groaned as she pressed kisses down my throat, her fingers teasing and dipping lower.

"What are you doing?" I asked, my breath catching.

"Taking your mind off things." She lifted the edge of my shirt and scraped her nails over my lower abdomen in a way that had my blood running away from my brain. Slipping her hand into my pants, she covered my mouth again, kissing me deeply as she gripped my cock, swallowing my moan. I hissed and let my head fall back as she stroked me, my length growing harder in her hand with every slow pass.

"What if someone walks by?" I groaned as she lowered her head toward my neck. I felt her tongue snake across my skin, sending another jolt of pleasure to my cock.

"I'll kill them," she whispered, nipping my ear.

My abdomen flexed as her palm curved around my tip, spreading the moisture there down the shaft, pausing to squeeze the base.

"Does it feel good?"

"Fuck yes," I gasped and nodded.

She slid her fingers lightly over my balls before tenderly cupping and massaging them. My cock twitched at her delicate torture.

"I like this. Having you in the palm of my hand." She squeezed ever so lightly, smiling at me.

"You're a cruel, evil woman," I whispered.

I groaned when she released my balls and wrapped her fingers back around my shaft. She squeezed and, in a slow, torturous slide, moved her hand toward the head. She licked her lips, watching her hand work my cock. "You think so?" she asked, tracing along the underside with her thumb, just beneath the head.

A sharp nod was all I could manage. I slid my fingers into her hair and pulled her toward me, capturing her mouth in another slow, deep kiss. Her strokes turned harder, every twist and pull pushing me closer to the edge. Gods, how long had it been? I felt like an untried youth when it came to Dianna. No matter what we did or how often she touched me, I still craved her. If I had my way, I'd take her every damn day, multiple times a day if I could, and that frightened me. I'd never been so consumed or obsessed with another. Dianna was not just a want but a pure, blinding need.

My pulse quickened, both from the adrenaline of being caught and the pleasure that rippled through my veins. I knew if a guard walked by, I'd ruin our entire cover in a heartbeat and slaughter them. My lips pressed together almost painfully as I tried to stifle the moan bubbling in my throat. I'd taught her too much of what I enjoyed.

Dianna twisted her hand as she stroked up, closing her palm over my tip and squeezing. I damn near erupted. She owned me, mind, body, and fucking soul. Her eyes flicked to mine, and she smiled at my untethered response. It wasn't my fault everything she did felt so fucking good. My hips thrust up, sliding my cock through her grip.

"Look how hard you are for me." She licked at my chin before nipping it. "Is this mine?"

"Yes, akrai. Yours." I nodded as she fisted my cock a fraction harder. "Everything I am is yours." Her smile was downright devious as she glanced at the cell door before adjusting and slipping down my body.

I half sat up, leaning on my elbows. "What are you doing?" I hissed. "Someone could see."

A hand job was fairly easy to hide if someone walked by, but her head bobbing between my legs would end everything. I'd level the place if anyone dared to see her like that. She smiled at me and pulled her hair back, the hunger in her eyes damn near making me come. "You better come quickly, then."

Dianna licked her lips, settling between my thighs. She tugged the waistband of my pants over my hips, fully freeing my cock. I had a few seconds to protest before she took me into her mouth, and then I just didn't care. I couldn't stop the groan that the feel of her warm, wet mouth forced from me, and I damn sure couldn't help but curse when her tongue swiped across the underside of the head of my cock.

"*Fuck,* baby." I gripped her by her hair as she worked my cock, directing her head as I thrust up into her mouth. She swallowed me deep, her lips stretched around my girth, and my eyes rolled back. "You are a goddess, akrai."

I felt her smile around my cock before she took me deeper. Her hands wrapped around the shaft at the base, matching her pace as she moved up and down. She looked up at me and swirled her tongue over the swollen crown before releasing my cock. My balls tightened and ached as she laid her tongue flat against my shaft, sliding her open mouth up and down my length. My abdomen flexed at the sight, and a blistering ball of pleasure built at the base of my spine. I knew I was seconds away from coming. With another flick of her tongue and a twist of her hand, I was done.

Dianna felt the first pulse and wrapped her mouth around the head, sucking hard. Unable to stop myself, I pushed up, forcing more of my cock into her mouth. She moaned, her hips shifting restlessly as I spilled into her mouth, and she swallowed every last drop. My hand clasped around the back of her head, and I rode that feeling of pure blinding pleasure.

My body shook, remnants of my orgasm rippling through me. I pushed up onto my elbows, panting, but my head fell back with a moan as her tongue darted out. She licked around the base of my cock and lapped up the shaft before she swirled her tongue around the head, licking up every bit I'd spilled out.

Gods, I would die for this woman.

I forced another spoonful of the mush they served here into my mouth and hunched my shoulders, trying to appear smaller than what I was. I just wished to draw less attention after the brawl. A man to our right yelled and launched himself across the table, punching another prisoner in the face. Guards rushed forward and separated them. The guards were not gentle, taking out their anger on the prisoners while the rest of the room tried and failed to mind their business. No one wanted a rehash of before. Some were still bruised and battered, while others just wished to stay in their cells.

"I still think it's a waste of time," Orym said, shifting next to me.

"We cannot leave them here," I said, taking another bite.

"I still can't believe it."

"I can," I remarked.

Just like on the trail here, other prisoners had started sitting with us. Many of the guards were still pissed about the fight, and I think they thought I'd protect them. I'd saved and helped as many as possible while maintaining the diversion itself. I just hadn't wanted anyone to get killed in the process, which was why our table was now full.

They spoke amongst themselves, not paying Orym and me any attention, just as we told them to. Dianna had formed a new plan, and gods, I loved her for it. After seeing the files she'd snuck down to us last night, we'd learned this prison was more of a holding cell with limited capacity. Only the prisoners Nismera truly wanted stayed alive, which was us here on this lower level. The others were killed the day they arrived and then tossed outside the castle walls to keep the creatures who stalked these mountains fed and away.

I stopped eating and lowered my spoon, my eyes drawn toward the upper levels. Taotl walked down the row, no one else noticing who really lay under that skin. A small smile crept over my face to see the nearly seven-foot commander with a tail tipped in dark fur dragging behind him. He glanced toward me with a flash of red eyes. The gleam was so quick that I would have missed it if I hadn't been looking right at him. It didn't matter what form she wore. I could spot her out of a crowd of millions. It was as if my soul was drawn to her, seeking the connection. I adjusted myself in my seat, the memory of this morning making me hard.

It had been weeks since the woods, and I hated every second I couldn't be inside her, and from the look she shot my way, I knew she felt it, too. Whether she wore a suit of armor or the form of vermin, she was always watching me, never too far away. Gods above, I loved her more for it.

I'd never been one who needed protection. I was always the one running headfirst into any battle. It was just another thing we had in common. She and I were the same. Both of us had been given far too many responsibilities at a young age, forced to care for those around us and keep monsters at bay. Only hers were more physical than mine. I was the one the kingdom depended on. Sure, I had The Hand, but I was still alone. With Dianna, I did not have a single worry or fear that she wouldn't completely have my back. My only fear was for her, never of her.

"Are you listening?" Orym nudged me.

I pulled my gaze from her and looked at him. "Did you say something?"

"Yes, your plan? I heard you and her whispering last night."

I glanced back toward the spiraling rails, but she was gone. I raised my spoon to my mouth, speaking around it. "She found a map of the prison layout," I said.

"Even with that information, you run a risk. The beasts that stalk these cliffs are evil. They have talons the size of my head or yours, and they scour the skies, waiting to snatch us up and kill us. Why do you think they waited for so long to come here? They had flown north for a season, and now they're back and out of food, I might add," the dwarf, Ozean, said, pointing his spoon at us.

"I have a plan for that," I said, pretending to laugh at what one prisoner near me said. The others followed suit, acting as if we weren't plotting to leave this place.

I nodded toward the back, and Orym stood.

We walked out the back of the dining hall, heading toward the cells. We walked down the curving rocky steps, guards standing in every hall. It wasn't until we reached our floor and passed the guard on that level that I spoke.

"I plan to form a tunnel to get everyone here out," I said, checking to make sure we were not being followed or overheard. I ducked into our dug-out cavern cell and sat on my small cot. Orym sat down across from me, leaning his elbows on his knees.

I reached under the cot, grabbed the map Dianna had stolen, and unfolded it. A long spiraling tunnel took up the top page, showing the tip sticking out of the top of the mountain. Exits were clearly marked, and it was easy to find the main gate we'd entered through. I flipped the page to one that showed the layout of the cells and how they all curved around the central structure. I placed it between us, pointing to what I needed.

"This portion of the prison is the most vacant. I think they used it once as a storage unit for something, but Dianna went there the other night, scoping it out as she said, and it's empty."

"Empty?" Orym's gaze flicked up.

I nodded. "If I can make an escape tunnel that leads up, I can connect it through the lowest levels near Savees's cell," I said, tracing the path I wanted to take.

"If you do that, it will come out at the bottom of the mountain, straight at the river's edge. Away from those treacherous creatures that fly high above the mountains."

"Exactly."

His eyes scanned mine as if I were crazy. "I mean no disrespect with this. I know your name and what you're capable of, but with that," he pointed to my midsection, "I know your power has not fully returned. They still speak of it burning in the sky. Digging a tunnel of that length will take—"

"Power," a voice said from the doorway.

We both turned as Dianna dropped the illusion, her lean form replacing that of the ghastly male commander as she stepped inside. She placed her hand on Orym's shoulder, patting it as she sat down.

"Don't worry about the tunnels. I got started on them while you all were sleeping the last few nights."

"You did?" I asked.

Her eyes raked over me. "Yeah, just to get a head start. I couldn't sleep. Plus, I put Savees to work, so that helped."

Her gaze locked on mine, the air between us feeling thicker. I hadn't slept much either since being here. Everywhere I lay was uncomfortable, and with her new disguise, I couldn't hold her every night. The nights when I could, I was on alert, making sure that one of the passing guards didn't see her.

Orym cleared his throat. "Explains why the humidity has increased."

Dianna shrugged. "Sorry about that, but at least we have made some progress."

"How far did you get?" I asked.

She glanced back at the doorway, making sure no one was walking by. "Deep enough you can hear the river a few miles up, and you can't smell the stench of this place."

"Pretty deep, then."

She nodded, folding her arms. "Yeah, we still have a ways to go, but it is large enough for everyone to fit through without bumping their heads. I'll make a rule that the guards stay away from the sleeping cells at night. They may actually like that. We can also get some of the other prisoners to help us."

I watched Dianna hungrily as she spoke and noticed a spot of red, smaller than a fingernail, on the edge of her collarbone. Unease settled into my gut, and I inhaled deeply, catching a whiff of blood. It was small, but enough to know she'd been feeding and apparently cleaning up after herself, only this time she missed a spot.

Orym and Dianna continued to discuss the size and dimensions we'd need to fit as many people as possible. We planned and plotted for a while longer before Dianna stood and got ready to leave. I joined her at the door as Orym made his cot.

Everyone was being summoned back to their cells, and it was busy with people moving back and forth. I stopped at the entrance with Dianna, and she glanced around the corner and back. She leaned forward, her lips grazing mine for a mere second before she stepped back.

"I'll be back in a bit. I need to go check on Logan."

I nodded, grabbing her arm and stopping her before she transformed. "You've been feeding?"

Something flashed in her eyes, and I knew she was about to lie to me, but then I saw her think better of it. "Yes. Keeping this form and everything has been draining me."

"Who?"

Her head reeled back before a smile slowly curved her lips, and I realized how I sounded. "Just a random guard. Trust me. I know how to be careful. They're none the wiser and wake up with just an itchy throat."

"Okay." My lips formed a thin line. "And you're all right?"

Her smile lit up her face. "I'm fine, Sami. Perfect. Let's just work out your master save-the-world plan and get out of here."

"The food they serve here isn't helping. I just assumed you'd let me know if you needed blood."

"What are you going to do? Knock out a guard to feed me?" she asked with a smile, but I saw a flicker of something in her eyes.

"If I need to."

She cupped my cheek and brushed a kiss to my lips. "You're sweet, but I'm fine. I don't take much."

"It's not that," I said.

"Okay," she said, "what is it then?"

I thought about how to word what I was going to say next without starting a fight. "I wish for you to rely on me more, is all. You're no longer alone. If you're hungry or need something, I want you to ask me. Let me help."

Her gaze softened, even if a hint of apprehension remained. "Okay."

"Okay." I scanned her face before nodding. "Be careful."

"Pinky promise." She raised her hand toward mine, and I took it, wrapping my small finger around hers.

She pulled away, and her form grew taller than mine as she again donned the commander's armor and appearance. One last look, and she ducked her head out of the cell and left. I watched until her form disappeared around the corner, and more inmates flooded in, heading toward their cells. I returned to my cot and tucked the maps away before settling in. It wasn't until lights-out and a hush fell across the prison that I knew Dianna had lied to me.

XXXIX

Cameron

I pulled at the collar of the dragonbane armor, trying to stretch it away from my neck. The way I had poked my damn chin on these fucking spikes just added to my already massive headache. I pushed the door open to my room, yanking at the clasps on the side of the chest plate. Finally getting it loose, I ripped it off and threw it to the floor. I let out a sigh of relief, the soft leather underarmor so much more comfortable than those damn spikes. Impatiently, I stripped off the leather and pulled my shirt up, freezing with it halfway over my head. "Are all celestials built like you?" a soft feminine voice purred.

I pulled my shirt the rest of the way off and tossed it over the chair. "I swear, what's the point of having a room if everyone enters whenever the fuck they want?" I asked, looking at the beautiful elf woman draped across my bed.

Her tail swished, the mauve skin glistening against the setting sun. She wore the same relaxed silk dresses that Nismera gave everyone here. I swore that woman did not know what cheap was. Even the ones she hated here wore garments that made me take a second glance. I blamed it on her prestigious upbringing. Maybe she was afraid for anyone to see her and the ones who lived in her palace as less than perfect.

"I've seen you a few times before," I said. "Usually, that cute nose is right up Isaiah's ass."

She scooted off the bed, her pointed ears twitching. "Yeah, well, he seems to have moved on to your sister." She smiled, the tips of her canines gleaming. "Isn't that what you called each other? Family?"

"Get out," I said, my tone cold.

"Don't you want to find them, though?"

My shoulders dropped. "Like I'd trust one of Nismera's right-hand commanders."

She shrugged and stepped around me, her tail sliding over the bare skin of my chest. She headed toward the small corner table and poured herself a drink. "You have to trust someone in this wretched world, or you won't survive."

I folded my arms across my chest. "And you expect me to trust someone who rolls around with Isaiah?"

She sipped her drink, grinning at me over the rim. "I don't sleep with him because of the power or to gain favors. I do it because I like sex, and I need information. Trust me, my loyalties are not to this place, just like yours aren't."

The elf winked at me and downed the last of her drink. She strolled across the room, trailing her fingers over the bed. Stopping in front of the window, she tossed the curtains back and reached up to release the lock on the frame. She pushed it open and sat on the ledge.

"Do you miss the sunlight? Freedom?" She closed her eyes, tilting her head out the window, the wind cutting a breeze through the room. "I do. We had cliffs as high as the sky itself where I lived. The forests were not green but a shade of blue."

I nodded, curling my lower lip in my mouth. "This is great bonding, but I don't really feel like it."

And I didn't. I was hungry again, and now that Kaden was up my ass about the let's-feed-less-on-people-so-we-don't-murder-them tirade. I had a stash of blood bags he had taken from the kitchen. It helped quench my thirst, but not by much.

"I know you're a liar, Cameron."

She turned to me, and her eyes looked eternal as if she was a part of the world and not.

"I don't know what you're talking about."

She smiled again. "I know you found something at River Bend. I know you've been lying to Kaden, and I know you lied to Nismera."

My breath caught, but I said nothing.

"You got that promotion by telling her of the Toruk going north, only it didn't. It went west with a man and child on its back."

"What do you want?"

She turned, fully facing me and crossing one leg over the other. "Don't be afraid. I won't tell. I'm on your side."

"My trust in others is a little on the lacking side."

The elf lifted her hand, and a small wisp flew through the open window. It landed on her palm, and she held it close to her ear, then smiled at me. "I have connections everywhere, and even though you were trying to help her, you set Nismera on a course that will lead her right to Dianna."

"No," I said, taking a step forward.

"Don't worry. I fixed it for now, but we need to work together because you snooping around in realms that are loyal to her will have you dead before you ever find Dianna."

She stood, the wisp fluttering away as she walked past me toward the door.

"Wait. What's your name?" I asked.

She looked at me over her shoulder. "Veruka."

"Do you know how to find Dianna?"

Her hand froze on the door. "I think the real question you should be asking is why is Nismera so concerned about making such strong weapons?"

My lips turned downward. "That's easy. She fears Dianna."

Her eyes went dark, but she held my gaze. "Nismera fears The Eye. So ask yourself, what makes a goddess afraid?"

Veruka opened the door and walked out. I stared after her, wondering just exactly what would scare Nismera.

XL

Dianna

Night fell, and I headed back to Samkiel and Orym's cell. The guards loved having time off after ensuring everyone was locked down for the night. Our plan had worked surprisingly well over the last few days. Every night we worked on the tunnel, the physical release a welcome one and a way to burn off the frustrations of being here.

The attitude had changed around the prison. All the prisoners were excited and had a glimmer of hope now that they knew who Samkiel was. The possibility of freedom was apparently all they needed to want to help. I passed a few cells, the prisoners inside fast asleep, and headed toward Samkiel. One glance inside told me he wasn't there. Only Orym slept in his cot. He would be downstairs.

I wondered if he would ever actually sleep now that Logan was here. He was even more determined to save everyone. I remembered the look on his face when I'd taken him to see Logan, and anxiety bit at me. He'd assumed Logan would see him and immediately remember him, returning to the friend he so desperately missed. But when Logan had not so much as blinked at him, Samkiel's mood had soured tremendously.

My chest still burned with the rage I'd felt the next morning when Samkiel had cried with the agony of losing his friend all over again. It made me want to kill something. He didn't deserve everything this miserable realm threw at him. I knew he was beyond scared, and I wanted to wipe that look from his face.

I skipped down the stairs to the lowest level. This was my fear and why I didn't want him finding them just yet, but this was another stark reminder that I couldn't protect him from everything.

I passed Savees's old cell. I hated that they'd kept him down here with no lights and rotting corpses. So, I'd suggested he stay up top when night fell, and now he slept in our cell. He was more than happy with the arrangement, not even wanting to share the blanket Orym tried to give him.

I rounded the corner and heard the chipping of rocks. A massive dug-out tunnel stretched into a darkness so complete that not even the lights I had stolen from upstairs touched it. Even with my enhanced vision, I couldn't see Samkiel. I stepped inside, the noise of metal against stone growing louder the deeper I went. A soft glow came from up ahead, and I walked a bit quicker, eager to see him. One more turn, and I saw Samkiel, something in me easing at just the sight of him. He grunted as he shifted another large rock and wiped the sweat from his brow. I stopped and leaned against the roughly hewn stone wall, taking in the view.

Samkiel tossed another massive stone, his biceps bulging. He raised an ablaze ax and slammed it against the stone. I always thought Samkiel was beautiful. I mean, who didn't? It was written in every textbook about him, but dirty, sweaty Samkiel might be my favorite. He had removed the top part of his prison garbs, and it hung loosely at his waist. Every dip and line of muscle flexed as he raised the ax, chopping against stone. Silver light sparked with every hit, and the rocks fell away like butter.

"Maybe I should have had you digging out this damn tunnel sooner if I knew you'd do it like this," I joked.

Samkiel's ax stilled for a moment, but he didn't turn toward me. Hmm. Weird. Usually, my little jokes or puns got a response. Maybe he was just tired and focused.

"I've been stealing as much information as I can, sending Reggie the maps and books they have here," I said, and yet he didn't flinch at my voice, just kept chipping at the wall.

"Good," he said.

He dropped the ax and tossed a few of the larger pieces he'd broken off further into the tunnel, but he didn't even turn around.

"Logan is still the same, but he stays close to me." I sighed. "I've tried to make him eat or drink water, but nothing. I assume they don't need it while in this state, but I'll keep looking in those files. Maybe they can tell us something more."

He picked up the ax again. "All right."

I pushed off the wall in a huff. "Okay, are you going back to one-word answers again, or are you going to tell me what's wrong? Besides being in this sweaty underground death trap."

Silence.

"Sami."

His shoulders slumped, and he lowered the ax, placing it against the neighboring wall. He turned to face me, his arms folded, bunching the corded muscles across his shoulders and chest. "I know there is a lot going on right now, but when are you going to tell me?"

My heart dropped.

"Tell you what?"

No, there's no way he knows. My heart thudded, a cold wave of terror slithering down my back.

"Don't play coy. You think I don't notice everything about you? As if I don't pay attention. I noticed in Jade City but waited for you to say something, but you didn't. I know a lot has changed since Onuna, since the remains of Rashearim, but I thought you'd tell me."

I didn't say anything. A part of me was confused about exactly what he knew, the other hating myself for having told so many lies that I couldn't tell which one he meant. My eyes bore into his. He had no idea how right he was. So much had changed. So much about me had changed. And then it hit me. Every time he looked at me these last few weeks, he wasn't just stealing longing glances. No, he was worried about me. A fraction of my black heart cracked so hard that it outweighed the hunger in my gut.

"I know you haven't been eating the food here, not that it's the best, but I also don't remember you eating while we were in Jade City," he said. "So my next question is, how many did you feed on there?"

Relief washed over me, chasing away the bloodied, broken image of him dead in my arms, of my tear-soaked face, begging for him to stay with me. He didn't know of my plea for help and that I'd threatened the whole universe. I wouldn't have to face the disappointment and fear in his eyes because I'd scared Death with promises of hate-fueled revenge and destruction. He was worried about my feeding.

"Just one," I whispered, giving him the one truth I could offer him. "It was Killie. I was still full from my trip to Tarr. I don't know why I'm so hungry or why blood is the only thing I can keep down. It is the only thing I crave." I shrugged. "It just is, and we have more important things to worry about than a problem that neither of us has any idea how to fix."

"Dianna." He dropped his arms. "I don't know how much clearer I can be when I tell you that *you* are important to me. So yes, regardless of what's happening, *this* is important."

I peered at the ground, begging it to swallow me whole, anything to escape the look he was currently giving me.

"Is that what happened to the wildcats here? They didn't flee because of you, did they?"

I kicked a small rock. "I only ate a few of them. The others fled, to be fair."

"And how many guards have you been feeding on here?"

"All of them," I said before holding up my hands in defense. "But not to the point of death. I can erase their memories of it. They just end up really sleepy."

Samkiel chewed the inside of his cheek and glanced away, nodding. He didn't say anything for a moment before raising his hand and summoning an ablaze dagger. My entire body tensed, and my heart raced, my blood pounding in my ears.

"What are you doing?"

Samkiel took a step toward me but stopped short. "We can do this one of two ways. It's your choice, but you will feed here and now from me."

My mouth watered, and heat pooled in my core at the prospect. "Sami." I swallowed. "You don't know what you're asking."

His brows furrowed. "Yes, I do."

He turned his wrist so I could see it clearly. "Do you see this?" He pointed with his blade. They were hard to see, but there were two indentations on his wrist. My lust-clouded brain raged, thinking another had marked him, but then I realized.

"Wait." My gaze shot to his. "Was that from Ecleon?"

Samkiel nodded. "Yes, there, but also before."

Warmth spread through my chest. "Before?"

"Yes, after your run-in with your friend who was not your friend."

A snort left my lips as I remembered Sophie, the witch who shot me in the chest. I remembered him bursting the door into a million pieces, pulling those spikes from my chest, and saving me. I also remembered the blooddreams after, and now I know why. I assumed he had bled into a cup and made me drink back then. We could barely stand the sight of one another, but he had let me feed from his wrist. He'd offered his flesh to his mortal enemy.

I couldn't stop the moisture that threatened to blind me as I looked at him. "You fed me then?"

He shook his head as if it was no inconvenience. "Well, I most certainly couldn't let you die."

"I thought you hated me back then, and here you are, shoving your wrist in my mouth." I choked on a laugh.

"My feelings for you have been a lot of things, mostly confusing back then, but never hate. Never you."

"Same," I said before standing on my tiptoes, kissing him once before pulling back. My hand slid over the necklace I'd given him and rested on his chest, that steady, rhythmic beat against my palm.

"I'm sorry. I just didn't want to hurt you, and I don't know what's wrong with me right now. I'm beyond ravenous."

His finger rested under my chin, lifting it ever so slightly. "Dianna, I care about you tremendously, and I mean this with no disrespect, but stop coddling me like a child. I am not frail or fragile. You cannot hurt or break me, not when you feed from me and not when you fuck me. I need you to stop treating me like I am made of glass. I have fought monsters that could swallow this prison whole with my arm hanging on by tendons. You can't hurt me. I only hurt when you hurt. Your burdens are mine, such as your pain is. That's what you said. Did you not?"

I nodded. "Yes. Yes, I did."

"All right then. I know my limits, and you haven't even come close to touching them yet." He tipped my chin once before angling his wrist toward me. "Now, let me take care of you."

He held his wrist to my lips, his words ricocheting through my chest. My gaze raked over him as I cupped his hand and forearm. I stepped into his embrace, and he enclosed me in his arms, turning me so my back was pressed against his chest. My tongue slid over his pulse, and I couldn't tell if it was him or me that moaned as my fangs pierced his skin. His blood filled my mouth, and my eyes rolled to the back of my head.

The taste of him was damn near orgasmic. His blood was like the sweetest wine and chocolate mixed into one. I pressed close, fitting the soft curves of my body to the harder planes of his. Samkiel swept his hand across my head as I fed, whispering in my ear how much he wanted and needed me. I gripped his arm tighter and latched on deeper, my every sense overwhelmed with him.

I injected a tad more venom into my bite, and Samkiel groaned, but not in pain. The adyin lines on his body glowed brightly, casting a silvery glow all around us. I sucked, pulling more into my mouth, answering his groan with a soft moan. I was so lost in the taste and feel of him that I didn't realize he had walked us toward the wall. His body jerked when his back collided with the stone, and with how his cock was pressing into my back, I could tell just how much he was enjoying this. I pulled my fangs from his wrist and slid my tongue over the puncture wounds before spinning toward him.

"Why did you stop?" he asked, his eyes dark with hot need.

I yanked at the waistband of his pants. "Because I am craving something else now."

He didn't hesitate, grabbing me and spinning me until my back hit the cavern wall. His hands moved quicker than mine, stripping me bare. He dropped to his knees before I could lean in for a kiss. I didn't have a second even to process what was happening before he tossed one leg over his shoulder.

My nails dug into his scalp as he ran his tongue up and down my center, and I realized maybe I wasn't the only one starving. My hips thrust against his face as he devoured me, my moans echoing off the cavern walls. Every flick and swirl of his tongue had my knees threatening to buckle with pleasure. Need coiled tight and low in my abdomen. It had been so long for me. My fear of losing control if he touched me had kept me from allowing things to go too far. Now, he had barely been between my legs for a minute, and I was already on the verge of coming.

"Sami." I pulled at his hair, feeling the rising heat in my core. He groaned against my flesh in denial, and my back lifted from the wall, chasing that vibration. "Wait, Sami, please."

He pulled back and licked his lips, watching me as if all it would take was one word or demand from me, and he'd do it. It was the most erotic thing in the world to see the realm's most powerful man kneeling between my legs.

"Take me," I demanded.

His smile was brilliant, happy I wasn't telling him to stop, but instead of standing up, he blew a breath over my heated flesh. "Come on my mouth first. I need to taste you. I've missed it so godsdamn much."

My moan was a strangled cry as he lowered his mouth to my clit and sucked. Hard. I arched my back, clasping his head and grinding against his mouth. The rocks cut into my shoulders, but I didn't even feel the sharp pain. He licked and fucked me with his tongue until I came so hard I was damn near dizzy with it.

I didn't even have time to come down from my high before his hands clasped my thighs, and he lifted me in one solid motion. I was still panting and tingling when he positioned his cock at my entrance, and I jolted, teetering on the edge of another orgasm.

My nails bit into his shoulders as he slid in slowly, my pussy aching with the stretch to fit his girth. It had been weeks for me, weeks of nothing, not even touching myself, and it took me a moment to adjust to him once more.

Samkiel's gaze locked on to mine as he shifted until both of my legs were draped over his bent forearms. He pressed his hands to the stone wall, spreading me wide, opening me so he could press deeper.

"I want you to fuck me like you mean it," he rasped out, his voice nearly a growl.

I clenched around him at his words, both of us moaning from the intense pleasure. I nodded and gasped out, "Yes, my king."

Samkiel leaned in, sliding his lips along my neck, his breath a hot wash over my ear as he said, "I want you to bite me while I fuck you. Truly bite me."

The words echoed through my chest, and the Ig'Morruthen in me raised her massive horned head. If she could smile, the bitch would. I saw him through her eyes from where she rested in the darkest part of me. She rose, scales and wings and claws shifting to just beneath the surface. What he said finally touched the last part of us we were afraid to share with him.

His smile was downright satisfied. "There's my red-eyed girl."

It was all he said before he slammed deep, driving the air from my lungs. As he fucked me, something shifted inside of me, something I was afraid of for so damn long. He wasn't afraid of me. The last part of my walls crumbled. He saw everything, wanted everything, and by the way he sought to push deeper into me with every thrust, I knew he craved me just as much as I craved him, claws and all.

The rising hunger hit me once more, but I was not scared this time, and I allowed my fangs to descend. Samkiel watched with lustfilled eyes and bared his throat to me. I groaned at the offer, and it was all I needed. I leaned forward and brushed a kiss over his pounding pulse before tracing the adyin line that swirled over the side of his neck with my tongue. My fangs pierced his skin, only I wasn't rough with him, not mean or hurtful. My bite was not to kill but loving, giving, and gentle. It brought down the final layer separating us. He accepted every part of me, and I reveled in it.

Samkiel's thrusts turned punishing as I fed, blood pooling in my mouth as heated liquid bathed his cock. The sounds of our bodies coming together, the soft gasps of pleasure, moans of ecstasy, and his grunts of exertion all echoed in the half-carved tunnel.

"Gods . . . Dianna!" he cried out. "*Fuck, fuck, fuck.*"

Bits of stone rained down on us, and I realized maybe we both had been holding back. This was more than just sex. This was a claiming. I was lucky he had dug so much of this tunnel, or they would have heard us throughout the entire prison.

Samkiel shifted me in his arms, cupping my ass and angling my hips. The new position somehow allowed him to get even deeper. The angle and the way he forged into me had his cock hitting that spot at the very depth of my core, and I saw stars. I extracted my fangs and threw my head back on a cry.

It was too much, too good.

I raked my nails down his back, trying and failing to regain some control of my body. So, instead, I gave in to the beast that was now fully awake and begged, "Harder!"

He delivered on my words with one punishing thrust after the other. I lowered my mouth to his throat and sank my teeth deep, needing to ground myself in him. Pure, white-hot bliss filled my mouth, and with every pull, he fucked me further into oblivion. This was what I wanted, what I needed so damn badly.

His moans turned into desperate grunts that sent me over the edge. My orgasm ripped through me, and waves of pleasure shuddered through my body. My core spasmed, and juices dripped from around his cock. I couldn't tell if I was begging or whimpering or if the words that fell from my lips were even coherent, just that my body clenched around him so tight it ripped another orgasm from me. His mouth covered mine, eating up every scream and noise I made.

"That's it, baby. Again." He angled his strokes just right so that my clit rubbed against him with every thrust. "Come for me. Come for me. Come for me."

Samkiel didn't stop as I squeezed around him. He felt so far buried in me that I swore I could feel him in my stomach. My body shook as he talked me through it, and I came apart again and again and again. The need and hunger that had built up over the last weeks spilled out of me with every dirty word, every thrust. I was sure his thighs were coated in a mix of us both.

My body jerked as my orgasms burned through me. Every nerve ending unbearably hot as pleasure so intense it bordered on pain raced from my core to my toes and back. My whole body flushed with blistering desire.

It wasn't until I was a whimpering, sobbing mess and my last orgasm had faded to small ripples that he finally spilled deep inside me. His cock twitched, and his fingers dug deep into my hips. He pulled me down hard and buried himself to the hilt inside me, his balls pressing against my ass. Shoving me against the wall, he held me there and gave two more powerful thrusts. He moaned low and deep, the sound seemingly torn from his soul, his body shuddering.

Maybe this was what we both needed: to cross that final line between us. One where he allowed me to be my true self and reveled in it, and one where I didn't hold back so he could unleash himself fully, as well.

I licked over the bite marks I left on his throat, cleaning the remaining blood, and for once, I didn't feel that aching yawning pit in my chest. I was fully and thoroughly satiated.

He held me close and buried his face against my throat. I ran my hand along the hairs at the base of his neck, panting wildly.

"Do you think we could fuck a mountain down?"

Samkiel laughed. "Probably."

"I'd suggest not."

Samkiel and I yanked our heads toward that familiar voice. Reggie stood with his hands behind his back and Orym at his side. Samkiel turned us and lifted me off his cock before placing me on my feet. He was careful to block their view of me with his body as I leaned over to grab my shirt and pants as he pulled his up. Once I was dressed, he turned, allowing me to stand beside him.

"Roccurem, when did you get here?" Samkiel asked, his voice hard like stone.

Orym held his hand up as if sensing tension. "To be fair, I did call both of your names in advance, but . . ."

Reggie did not lower his gaze, and the look he gave me made my blood run cold. "I had a vision. Scattered but there. Nismera's legion is on its way. They believe Dianna is here, and they are coming in force. You are out of time."

XLI

Camilla

Hilma hissed, another fragment burning her skin as we tried and failed to force it back together.

"Hey, instead of you two idiots standing over there snickering all day, come help," Hilma snapped to the two witches giggling at the corner table where they were mashing herbs. They stopped what they were doing and scurried over.

"Sorry, sorry," they said in unison, and I wondered how much power Hilma had here.

"It's fine." I rubbed my brow. "Let's take a break, huh?"

Hilma looked at me like that was out of the question, but we had been at this for hours, and these damn pieces refused to mend. I wish I knew what power kept them apart. Whatever it was, it was very strong, and just the thought of it made my skin prickle. Then, there was another part of me that whispered it didn't matter.

"Okay," Hilma said. "Quick bathroom break, but we have to finish this."

"Why the rush?" I asked. "Hasn't she been trying to fix this for years? I don't think we will get it anytime soon."

Hilma stared at me, and then a small smile formed on her lips. She nodded. "Yeah, you're right. Okay, I'm going to go eat. Wanna join?"

I shook my head. I already had plans. "No, I'm okay."

She shrugged. "Suit yourself."

I waved as the two other witches ran out, hand in hand, Hilma following them. My guards entered the room, waiting to escort me out. I had to admit I much preferred when Vincent escorted me everywhere, but once again, he was busy.

The guards escorted me out of the room, and I slipped my hand into the pocket of the silk pants Nismera made us all wear, tapping the item in my pocket to make sure it was still there. We walked in silence as they led me back to my room, and I even pretended to give them a curt smile as I slipped inside. The door closed tightly behind me, and I ran toward my dresser. Moving a few garments aside, I dug my necklace out of its hiding place and clasped it around my neck. I knew what I felt. It was the same power I had felt when I fled my burning mansion, that unmistakable power that flowed through my woods after Kaden had sent those beasts and they attacked my island.

Oblivion.

A quick chant and I slipped out my door and down the hall. It was so easy to move when you couldn't be seen. No one even glanced my way, and I prayed to the old gods, thanking them for giving me as much magic as they had. Otherwise, I would be a dead woman.

I reached the end of the wing, raising my hands as my magic whipped out, drawn to that power trail. I hurried through winding hallways and far too many stairs. The further I went, the fewer people I saw, only a handful of guards, and even then, they were few and far between.

Silence followed me through this wing of the palace, and an uneasy feeling met my every step. Images were carved into the shimmering, pale stone of the walls, depicting ancient battles between gods and monsters. I paused before a statue of a huge masculine form with jagged horns growing from his shoulders. His head was bent, obscuring his face, and he appeared to be holding a spear. I glanced closer at the words etched deep into the plinth. The curves and slashes of the words predated even my knowledge of language. I studied the muscled figure, drawn to it for some reason. The way the artist had sculpted the face, body, and pose, it was obvious that whoever this man was, he'd been deeply loved.

"That won't do," a voice said behind me, and I nearly jumped. I turned around to see Tara and Tessa coming toward me.

"It has to. We are running out of test subjects as it is," Tessa said.

I stayed still as they approached, their long silk robes dancing across the floor as they walked hand in hand.

"She will imprison innocents at this rate. Damn, maybe even her own citizens, to get this to work," Tara said.

Tessa raised Tara's hand to her lips and pressed a kiss to it. Tara blushed. "You are safe with me. We both are. Just do what she says, remember? Besides, the guards started to talk, so I think she's backing off them."

I followed the girls, passing the large statue and heading toward the stairs. What were they doing down here? What did Nismera have them doing? They continued down the steps and turned a corner, still lost in conversation. I tried to process all they said. Use her citizens? She had to mean those bodies Kaden and I found downstairs. Bile hit my stomach.

They pushed open a large door, and voices spilled out. Machines whirled as workers, small and large, shouted to each other. Several tiny winged creatures carried pieces of trash away from the area, snapping at each other in a language I didn't know.

"Any progress, Quill?" Nismera's voice had me backing into the nearest wall.

She strode toward the center of the room, her black gown flowing behind her. The feathers of some beast lined the neckline, dipping low enough to reveal the inner curves of her breasts. A crown made of sharp edges and spikes jutted from her head. When she turned, I realized it wasn't a gown but more a coat. Her lower half was covered in golden armor, stained with what I could only assume was blood. She must have just returned.

A man, or something close enough to it, walked toward her and bowed. He wore an apron covered in grime and glasses over his three eyes, the middle piece larger than the other two.

"Yes, I have the gauntlet almost ready as well."

Gauntlet? I took a step out of the shadows.

Quill turned away, and she followed. They moved past a few pieces of giant machinery and headed toward the back. I trailed behind, making sure I remained undetected. My heart thudded as we rounded a corner and entered a room that was a perfect circle. There were symbols worked into the stone on the floor, matching the ones on the giant device above us.

The runes lit up as Nismera entered, her power activating them. Quill and she stopped in the middle of the room, and I joined them, careful not to draw too close. She lifted her arm, and the walls enclosed us, glowing runes spinning. We moved forward and then what felt like down before the wall slid away. Quill stepped out first, and we followed.

I gasped and quickly covered my mouth, muffling the sound as we entered the massive stone room. Several people lay bound on the floor, their hands tied and mouths gagged. A few looked no more than twenty years of age, covered in dirt and grime. These must have been the recent shipment of prisoners one of her legions had collected.

Windows, three stories high, made up the walls, and I wondered what the view was like from here. I wanted to go look, but the large pillar in the center of the room pulled at my magic. Whatever was there both beckoned and repelled me. Quill turned his shoulder, giving me a clear view, and my blood ran cold. On the raised pedestal, encased in glass, was the ring of Oblivion.

Nismera walked toward it, her long nails grazing over the clear box, the runes on it lighting up. It was infused with godly magic to keep the ring stable. Oh gods. My magic jerked away, remembering only a fraction of the power belonging to the man who used to wield it. I took a step back, then another and another, speaking words to calm my magic. We were not in danger.

Nismera tapped on the box as if it weren't holding a weapon of mass destruction. "Anything new?" she asked.

"No, my liege, but we may try again."

She nodded, and with a flick of her wrist, a spear made of gold appeared. Runes lined the shaft, and power sang from it, dark, twisted power, made from blood and not just anyone's, but Dianna's.

I knew it, felt it in my skin. Ig'Morruthen and celestial. The perfect weapon made into a death spear. This was the one that killed Samkiel.

The prophecy Reggie spoke of was not wrong. They were destined to kill one another, and they had. My heart lurched. I knew she felt that now. She probably hated herself for it, and I didn't blame her one bit for wishing to burn the world for it.

"Let's try again, shall we?" Nismera asked. Quill took several steps back, moving to the side.

The people in front of her began to tremble as she lifted the lid off the case containing Oblivion. The portal activated behind me, and I turned as Tessa and Tara walked out.

"You're late." Nismera eyed them sternly.

Tara's blush deepened. "My apologies, my king." She bowed slightly, but Tessa couldn't care less. She just stood, playing with the ends of her blonde hair.

Nismera did not berate them. Instead, she turned her focus back toward the Oblivion ring.

"Tessa. Tara," Nismera said without looking at the witches. "Secure the area, will you?"

Both girls giggled before raising their hands. Magic burst forward, and a bubble formed over us, blocking out the area, and my ears ached. Their specialty was shield magic, and I had never felt a force field so strong. Quill tried to shift further away, a bead of sweat rolling down his leathery skin.

Nismera carefully plucked the ring from the pedestal and placed it on her finger. My eyes widened as her godly adyin marks lit up, and I wondered if she could actually wield Oblivion since Samkiel was her brother. Were they alike in that aspect? She gripped the spear with the same hand and turned toward the group of people on the floor. A crackling stream of light burst from the spear, arcing from person to person. Their bodies glowed and then exploded, one by one. Blood and gore coated the outside of the bubble, dripping down its surface in thick rivulets.

Nismera cursed as we all stood staring at the mess. Quill's mouth gaped open, and he turned to look at Nismera. Two quick strides, and she was in front of him, his apron gripped in her free hand.

"Why is it not working?" she hissed.

Quill stumbled. "I'm not sure, Your Majesty. It should work in all aspects. The ring is made from her amata. The spear holds her blood. They should bind as they would have."

My heart rammed itself into my throat. That was what she wanted. Oblivion. She thought she could bind it to the spear. Gods, that weapon in Nismera's hands would end everything.

She dropped Quill and slipped the ring off. "Take the remains back to the lab. Have them checked for even the slightest sign of oblivion."

Quill nodded and carefully locked the ring back up. Nismera called the spear back before stepping into the portal, Tessa and Tara following behind.

My feet barely touched the ground as I raced back upstairs. I didn't think, and I didn't remember taking a breath until I heard voices in the cafeteria as I came through the doors. Guards and generals filled the tables, cracking jokes over food as they ate. They were none the wiser of the psychotic goddess to whom they pledged their lives. Or maybe they did know. I glanced around, searching for Kaden, but didn't see him or his brother. I left, heading toward the war room. Guards stood outside, meaning someone was in there. It was mid-afternoon, and everyone was usually on break at this time. I had no problem moving past the guards and bursting through the door.

"Kaden."

Several heads whipped toward me, Kaden's included, and I froze. Okay, perhaps there was a meeting. The being made of ice and hate glared at me, even the touch of his gaze frigid. Ittshare. That was his name. He was a King of Yejedin and one strong enough to damn near control winter itself. He towered over Kaden, and half of his body was covered in the same dragonbane armor. His right arm and shoulder were exposed but covered in sharp spikes of ice.

"What is the meaning of this?" Leviathan snapped from his seat. He had papers folded in front of him, and they all seemed to be discussing battle plans.

I swallowed, realizing there were a lot of soldiers and council members in here, even if Nismera was not.

"Sorry to interrupt," I said, hating myself for what I was about to say. I scratched at the back of my head. "I was on my lunch break and wanted to see you for a moment . . . or two." My face heated as every eye in this damned place stared at me.

The smile that formed on Kaden's face made me want to rip his head off. He folded his arms. "See me? Go on, Camilla, use your words."

I expected steam to burst from my ears at this point, but I steeled my spine. This wasn't just a joke. I had finally figured out what his evil sister was up to, and I needed to tell him. If that meant playing into his ruse, so be it. "Do you want a quick fuck or not?"

His smile dropped. He was clearly already bored with this little game, and I heard Leviathan groan as he placed a weary hand over his face. Ittshare cocked his brow, and Isaiah snickered but covered it quickly before looking at his brother. The other guards, thank fuck, avoided eye contact, but it was Elianna's response that made me stumble. She glanced between us, hurt in her eyes. She recovered quickly and shifted in her seat, suddenly concerned with the tassels on the sleeve of her gown.

"I'll pass," Kaden said. "Maybe later."

My teeth were about to grind to dust, but I forced a thin smile. "Either come tonight or not at all."

I stormed from the room and back to my workstation, hoping to keep the last shred of my dignity. Gods above and below, this place would be the death of me.

I had worked until my nose bled, and Hilma decided it was a good stopping point. I cast several glances toward Tessa and Tara as they helped us, needing to keep an eye on them. If shield magic was their strong suit, then maybe this medallion I had been working on was more powerful than I thought. If they were here to keep damage to a minimum, I truly worried about what I was helping put back together. The only positive was that they didn't know I had been there. I wondered just how many working here held Nismera's secrets.

I made it back to my room well past dusk, and as soon as the guards left, I stripped and headed to my washroom. This was one of my favorite parts of my day. I'd managed to make a soap that helped ease my mind, a fine mist spreading across the room when it hit the water. It eased away all the stresses of the day, and the warm bath soothed my tired and sore muscles. My magic loved it, recharging my power after they had nearly drained me.

I sighed and leaned back. Vincent hadn't come back today, and I wondered what she had him doing this time. He had left with another legion member earlier. I had only seen him once, when Vincent had dropped me off at my workstation. He was tall and lined with muscles. The helmet he wore was all sharp angles and had wings that fanned out around his head. When he turned, I saw the thick, massive wings held close to his back. I asked Hilma who he was, but she just mumbled something about him being a brother to a powerful queen and shushed me back to work.

I dipped my head beneath the water one final time before standing and grabbing a towel. The floor was cool against my feet when I stepped out and dried myself off. I walked into my bedroom and screamed, scrambling to wrap the towel around myself.

Kaden lay on the bed, his hands behind his head and gazing at my ceiling. "Excessive, don't you think?"

"How—" I stammered. "Actually, what are you doing here? I'm naked."

He turned his head and looked me up and down. "I see that," he said before sighing deeply and turning back to his perusal of the ceiling. "I promise your virtue is safe with me. Besides, it's nothing I haven't seen before. It's not that appealing."

I grabbed the first thing I touched off my vanity and turned to chuck it at him. He caught my wrist and squeezed hard enough to crack the fragile bones. I gasped, and my hairbrush fell to the floor with a clatter.

"Now, now, there is no need for violence." He let go and stepped back, placing his hands in his pockets. "What was so urgent you had to burst into a council meeting?"

I held my wrist, willing my magic to the tender spot, sighing with relief as it healed. Turning, I grabbed the dark nightgown on my chair and threw it on, the hem swinging around my knees.

"I found something," I said.

His head whipped toward me, and his eyes flared with interest. "Dianna?"

So that's what he cared about above all. That's what got the attention of the cold-hearted, mean bastard in front of me. Dianna and Isaiah seemed to be the only things he truly cared for.

To be honest, I wasn't shocked. I'd always known he had the most lethal obsession with Dianna. His eyes followed her every move and expression. I was surprised he ever let her out of his sight. Although, I would bet that even when he pretended not to care, all those times when she left to be with her sister, he kept an eye on her. What was more surprising was that he tolerated my relationship with her, but even then, I knew he used it as a cover for his true feelings. I didn't know why he did it, but now it was all clear. He could still be with her without Nismera or the others breathing down his back.

"No," I said, watching as his shoulders slumped slightly. "I may or may not have snuck out during lunch and found another part of your sister's lair."

Kaden tipped his head, waiting. "Okay. Go on."

I took a shuddering breath, hating this part next. "I don't trust this place or its residents, so I'd rather show you."

"Very well." Kaden sighed. "Show me." He seemed so bored.

I stepped forward, my lips slanting over his as I showed him every part of what I'd seen down in the east wing. His grip tightened on my waist, his mouth pressing harder against mine, the kiss deepening as he saw that golden spear. He pushed back after Nismera killed her prisoners, his eyes scanning mine.

"That's it?"

I nodded, taking a step back.

A look of pure bewilderment crossed his face. "So Nismera wants to harness Oblivion?"

"Looks like it," I said a little too breathlessly. It wasn't from kissing Kaden. I had zero sexual feelings toward the man. It was just that I hadn't been kissed in a very, very long time, and I missed it. My mind drifted to a certain tall, broody celestial, and I quickly extinguished that thought. "Now, we also know why she had all those remains. I think she's trying to see if she can even use Oblivion. So, no creepy experiments, it seems. Although it doesn't explain the ones that were diced."

Kaden was silent for a moment as he paced, and then he glanced at me. "If it's not working, that would explain why she needed Samkiel's blood, even Isaiah's."

"How?"

"Isaiah has power over blood in general. She's probably just working on a way to stabilize Oblivion."

"Oh." I paused. "Okay, so how do we stop her?"

Kaden looked at me as if I had grown horns. "Stop her? From what?"

"She's killing innocent people to make that weapon, and if she succeeds, she will own this realm and every realm in between."

His dark brow rose. "And? Let her have it."

I was quiet for far too long, and he caught it. He laughed a small chuckle that had my magic screaming for me to run. He took a step, then another, until I had to tip my head back to look at him. His fingers gripped my chin in a painful embrace. "Have you forgotten who I am? You think I care about innocent fucking people? My sister already rules these realms, and she will have them forever. No one defies Nismera. You'll learn that here. And if you try, you will learn that Nismera is not the worst thing in this wretched world."

I said nothing as Kaden used his free hand to reach forward, moving a strand of my hair.

"I don't care for much in this world. I never have, but I do care for Isaiah. He's still easily swayed and impressionable, just as he's always been. He's the reason we were cursed to that damned prison dimension.

His hubris gets the best of him, but I promised eons ago I'd never let anything happen to him, and I meant it. If she's using his blood to bind a weapon, then so be it as long as he is not hurt."

"You don't know that for sure. How can you trust her so blindly?" I said.

The laugh that left his lips was unnerving, and I flinched. "You think I should care about you? Camilla, you are and have always been a means to an end. Gods damn, are you all this simple in any realm? You think soft kisses and whispered words make me a nice man, that I want to help *innocents*? I only love two people in this entire wretched world, and you are not one of them."

"That is a position I would never want to claim," I snapped.

"This ends now. No more snooping around this palace. If I catch you, I'll send you to her myself. How much magic can you do with no hands, hmm?"

I tried to jerk my chin from his grip, but he held tight. "Let go of me!"

A cold chill went up my spine as he held me there. In a serious lapse of judgment, I had forgotten he was a predator, an apex of his species, just like Dianna. He could rip my throat open if he wished, tear my head from my body, and right now, as he looked at me, I had a sinking feeling he just might.

XLII
Vincent

I stood in the massive refinery, a large building off the west wing of Nismera's palace. At times, I admired her reasoning. She had everything she could possibly need in one place. I shuffled on my feet and stared out the window, watching the sun lower. It had been another failed hunt for Dianna and her fate, and I had barely made it back in time.

It was a study in frustration, following breadcrumbs that led nowhere. I was surprised she had not told her brothers what she had me doing, but I didn't care too much. I would do what she asked like I always had. There was no choice in the matter. I blew out a slow breath, sorry I'd missed lunch. Dammit.

"Need to be somewhere?" she purred behind me.

Her hand ran along my shoulder plate, but I stayed still beneath her touch. "No, my liege. It's just smoldering in here."

It was only half a lie. It was blistering hot in here, her workers working away at whatever device she was building, but it was true I had plans. Camilla and I had lunch every day at the same time atop the fortress. It was the only time either of us knew peace, and I enjoyed it. She laughed the other day over a stupid remark I'd made, sending my blood boiling. It was so easy with her. It always had been. I had visited her on the remains of Rashearim for the same reasons. When I was with her, I could just relax and be anything but myself, just existing in her presence. She asked nothing of me but that.

I was in way over my head when it came to her. I knew it now, and I'd known it hundreds of years ago, yet I couldn't help myself even if I wanted to. She was like a magnet, drawing me in, and I was helpless to resist her pull.

"Don't worry, we won't be here long." Nismera dropped her hand, offering me a coy smile. It did nothing for me, and it hadn't in a very long time. I remembered those days back on Rashearim, and how I'd hung on every word she spoke, every move she made. I thought I loved her then, and she loved me, but like a flower unattended, that love wilted. I saw the signs too late, promising myself to her in an unbreakable bond, and now I was stuck. Until death.

Sometimes, I wished she'd struck out in anger toward me, wished she would free me from her servitude, but it never came. So, I did what she said and lied, manipulated, and hurt because I had no choice. Her will was my will.

My thigh still burned from the memory of when she stuck me, binding my will to hers. No longer was I just a celestial under her guard, but as she put it, her pet. I couldn't break a command of hers even if I dared. She had tricked me then, claiming love, and I believed it so fiercely. I wanted love like any breathing fool. A part of me still craved it. But now all I thought of was how sick and twisted it was, how it could bring the greatest to their knees, and I hated it.

My heart thudded as I remembered how she had taken me away from Rashearim for what I thought was a night of passion, only it soon turned into a living nightmare. She rode me until I was blind with bliss, then stabbed me as a hundred witches descended on us. I still dreamed of the chanting and the burn of that binding spell. In my nightmares, I remember begging her to make it stop, but she didn't listen. She never did. I hated it, hated her.

Machines screeched to a halt, yanking me from the memory. I shook my head, thinking of the one witch who only ever touched me with care. She was my salvation, my peace.

Quill approached, shuffling his feet. He was covered head to toe in grease as he kneeled before Nismera. "It is done, my liege."

Nismera squealed, clapping her hands. "Excellent, Quill. Let me see my new toy."

"Yes, yes." Quill turned, motioning to his staff, and they pushed a cart toward us. On top sat what appeared to be a piece of armor wrapped in cloth.

"What is it?" I asked.

Nismera stepped forward and yanked the cloth off of it, revealing a shiny steel gauntlet. She picked it up, turning toward me.

"It's for you, pet."

"Me?"

She nodded hopefully. "Hold out your arm."

I swallowed the bit of apprehension I felt and did as she commanded, just as I always did. She slid the gauntlet into place, and my skin tingled as raw power ripped up my arm.

I grunted as the sensation became nearly unbearable before it eased. "What was that?"

Her smile made me afraid to know more as she clapped her hands together. "I received word that a certain prisoner reached Flagerun."

"The prison in the mountains?"

She nodded. "Yes, the fate is there. He was captured in Jade City before it fell. With the way she has been tirelessly looking for him, I'm assuming he is her new lover. I need him dead, and you're the one I trust the most to get the job done."

I shook my head. "You have the Kings of Yejedin, Kaden, and Isaiah. They are much stronger."

She placed a hand under my chin, forcing me to meet her gaze. "You dismantled and destroyed my greatest enemy. Not them. You can do this, and I made the perfect weapon to help."

"It can kill a fate?" I asked, flexing my fingers in the gauntlet.

"It can kill anything." Nismera stood on her tiptoes, placing a kiss on my lips, but I felt nothing, no spark of lust or pleasure, just her lips on mine. She pulled away, and I nodded, forcing a smile to match hers.

I didn't know what expression was on my face, but everyone made way for me as I headed to my quarters, giving me a wide berth. The sun had already set, which meant I knew where she was. The guards outside her door saw me and bowed their heads before removing their helmets and striding away. Their shift was over once I was back in my room.

I was in front of her door the moment they turned the corner, my knuckles dancing across the wood.

"One second," she called.

I heard her footsteps, but a heavier tread accompanied them. My brow furrowed, and I didn't wait before turning the knob. I pushed the door open and froze in the doorway.

Kaden stood near her bed, his hands in his pocket as she adjusted the sides of her nightgown. A gown I thought was too sheer for her to wear around company, especially his. The scrunched look on her face and the slowly fading mark under her chin made me see red, and I was across the room without remembering how I got there. My fist cracked the side of Kaden's face, his cheek splitting under the gauntlet. Kaden laughed, his eyes flaring red as he reached for me. I lunged for him. One moment, we had our hands on each other, and the next, we were on opposite sides of the room.

"Vincent!" Camilla snapped, her emerald magic holding us like a vise.

Kaden snarled, exposing his fangs. "Could you be any more obvious?" he spat.

I couldn't hide my hate. "Don't touch her! Don't *ever* touch her."

His teeth snapped at me, fangs elongated and sharp. "Don't worry. I had my fill of witch. Wasn't anything to write home about."

I writhed within the grip of her magic, grunting with the effort to free myself so I could rip his face off, but her hold was too strong.

"Both of you!" Camilla snapped. "Stop before the guards end up in here."

Kaden stopped growling, and I lowered my lip, concealing my teeth. No matter how much I hated him, I wouldn't risk anything happening to Camilla. She nodded as we both agreed in our own way, then she let us go. Kaden scoffed before running his hand across his healing cheek, and I froze.

"If you say anything . . ." I said, pointing a finger at Kaden. Camilla placed a calming hand on my arm.

"You'll what? You couldn't take me on my worst day. I could beat you with both arms tied behind my back," Kaden taunted.

"Seriously." Camilla tossed her hands up. "Fine, fight, get us all killed, or worse."

I didn't want Nismera here, neither did she, and he knew it.

"You're both pathetic." Kaden chuckled and shook his head. "Don't worry, lap dog. I was just leaving," Kaden said, walking past with a shove to my shoulder.

"Oh, and make sure my sister doesn't know you are sneaking into witches' chambers late at night. I'm sure she'd hate that." Kaden strolled out and shut the door quietly behind him, leaving Camilla and me alone.

"He won't tell," Camilla said. "I know that much."

I ignored her, gently cupping her face. I swore I'd seen the bruise, but now nothing remained.

She rolled her eyes. "Vincent." She placed her hand over mine. "I'm fine."

"I hate him," I hissed.

"Who doesn't?" She smiled.

"Since when do you trust him?"

She shrugged. "Since I have something over him."

"I don't like it." The words left my lips before I could tell my brain to shut up. Thoughts and words like that usually stayed in my head, but I was too wound up from imagining Kaden and Camilla together.

Her lips turned up slightly. "I didn't know you cared."

I took a step back, then another, allowing both of us some breathing room. "That's a lie."

Camilla shook her head. "Not really. I haven't seen you in days."

I took a shuddering breath, knowing I couldn't tell her where I was or what I was doing, all because of Nismera's will.

"What does he have you looking for, anyway?" I asked, scratching the side of my head.

"In simple terms, Dianna."

Her name still made my skin crawl. Regardless of any good Samkiel had seen in her, she was still Ig'Morruthen and pure fucking destruction. She was like Kaden. Their attitudes changed so fast, whipping out and killing without a second thought. I hated her, too.

"Do you let him touch you?"

Her gaze widened a fraction, just as surprised as I was. I had no idea where this was coming from, the words, or why I was acting out of control, but it seemed I couldn't help it, not with her.

"Careful, Vincent. It almost sounds like you are jealous." She tilted her head ever so slightly.

She adjusted the strap on the thin, black camisole nightgown that cupped her curves so well the sight could bring any being to their knees. My body heated, and I envied that damn fabric. I envied it so much because I knew my hands could never touch the spots it did.

Maybe it was how she looked now, the half-tousled look as if she'd just climbed out of bed. Half of her hair was tied back, other parts escaping their entrapment. Was this what she looked like after sex? I wondered if her lips would have the after-kiss puff when they had been thoroughly and properly kissed. Would her cheeks turn a shade darker if I said filthy things to her? I grew hard at the mere thought and turned away from her.

"I wanted to check on you," I said, hoping there wasn't any hint of how I truly felt in my voice. "I had planned for us to eat lunch together again this afternoon, but I was busy."

"It's okay." She sighed, and I turned toward her. "I assume Nismera took you for some mission. I know you always have to choose her."

I'd choose you! I wanted to say it, to scream it, but my voice wouldn't allow it.

"Speaking of missions." I raised my hand, showing the gauntlet. "This is what she showed me, what she had made."

Camilla's eyes widened as she took a step forward. "Oh my. Well, at least we know it's strong enough to cut Ig'Morruthen skin."

I couldn't help but grin when I looked at her. Not that it seemed I wanted to.

Camilla reached out, her fingertips just grazing the metal before she yanked her hand back.

"Are you all right?"

She nodded, placing her thumb in her mouth and sucking slightly as if the gauntlet had burned her. Her lips wrapped tightly over the pad of her thumb, and I fought back a shudder of desire, trying to keep my cock under control. I took a deep breath and forced myself to focus.

"Let me see," I said, able to hear the roughness of my voice.

I nearly groaned when Camilla's thumb left her mouth with a wet pop. She held up her hand to show me she was okay. "I'm fine. That thing just has a shit ton of magic on it. What's it for?"

I started to tell her it was to slay a fate, but I remembered how she spoke of Roccurem and how she liked him. So, I lied to her once more.

"A mission. It's classified."

Her smile was short-lived. "How long will you be gone? Do I need to plan new lunch dates with different guards?"

A smug smile pulled at my lips. "As if they would be better company."

Her smile damn near crippled me. It was so genuine, so bright as if the sun itself would hide from it.

"Was that humor?" she asked, her eyes sparkling up at me.

I said nothing, but hope flared in my gut at her words. They sounded like she'd missed me, and no one had missed me in so long. I had hurt my family, destroyed them for Nismera, and I knew they would welcome my absence.

"It's late," I said.

She nodded, glancing toward the door. "It is."

Silence fell, the spike of tension between us jagged, sharp, and deadly. I swore if I moved just a fraction closer, it would spear us both. Her eyes widened again, and she licked her lips, a blush touching her cheeks.

"Wait," she said, breaking the tension between us.

I tried my best, I truly did, to not watch her walk away, but that thin material outlined the most perfect backside I had ever seen. My eyes were a helpless slave to its movement. When she turned, I had forced my hands behind my back, and my eyes were back on hers as if I hadn't just been ogling her ass.

"Here," she said, holding out a circular disk. It had small shapes carved into it and swirled with her magic.

I slid my finger over the cool surface, and the power in it flickered, licking against my skin as if tasting me, leaving a tingle in its wake. It settled again, but I felt a thin thread of connection to it now. "What is this?" I asked, staring at it.

She shrugged, her smile a little shy. "I made it. My family and I have made these for ages. I used what I had here, but it shouldn't affect how it works. Think of it as a tool to absorb bad dreams or things of that nature. It will protect the one who owns it."

I cradled it in my palm. "You made this for me?"

She fidgeted with her thumb as she spoke. "I know you have nightmares. I don't know if it will work, especially when you're gone on those gods awful missions she sends you on."

A thousand and one words were stuck in my throat. "Thanks." It was all I could say as I wrapped my fingers around the metal disk in my hand. I needed to leave, but I didn't want to.

"You're welcome."

"I hope I won't be gone too long. Try not to replace me." I smiled, and she returned it.

"As if I could." She half turned, raising her thumb toward her bed. "I'm tired. It's been a long day. Can you just say bye to me tomorrow before you leave?"

"Of course."

She nodded, placing her hand on my armored arm. A fine tremor ran through me. Her touch wasn't cold and lifeless like Nismera's but warm with the offer of succor. She was comfort, and she felt like home. "Goodnight, Vincent."

"Don't let Kaden be alone with you anymore, Camilla. I don't trust him."

Her eyes were soft as she looked at me, and she nodded. "I don't trust him either."

I left her room, making sure the door snapped closed behind me, but I didn't go to mine for a long, long while. Instead, I did what I had on Rashearim and sat outside her door, listening to her sleep. I slid my thumb over the disk she gave me, enjoying how her magic nipped at my fingers with green sparks, and for once, I felt peace.

XLII
Kaden

"Another?"

My eyes snapped up. The bartender's spiked hair stuck out to one side, his pointed ears riddled with rings and chains. I nodded and looked around the loud bar. It was crowded, filled with laughter and a mix of beings, but the seats on either side of me remained empty.

I glanced at the door just as the bartender set the glass in front of me. I nodded my thanks and picked it up, bringing it to my cheek. The ice-cold glass dulled the ache from that damn gauntlet. Maybe I should go back and gut Vincent, but I knew Mera would have a fit if I did.

Mera. I sighed. Camilla was right about one thing. She wanted power, she always had, but they saw her as a monster, not like Isaiah or me.

A door slammed nearby, the sound echoing through my soul and stirring up memories best left in the past.

"You can't do this!" I screamed, but his power was far too strong. "You can't lock us in this prison."

"You do not tell me what I can and cannot do. You knew better, both of you did, yet here I am, cleaning up a mess that will result in war," Unir snapped back.

"Then let us help fix it," I said. "This is not a solution."

Unir held no remorse as he squared his shoulders and gave Isaiah and me a firm, blank stare. "To show mercy to one would be to show it to all. In this, I cannot."

I ran forward but was stopped by a barrier and slammed back. "Father!" But it was too late. Unir pushed his hands forward, and runes formed of silver light flared to life on the floor and ceiling.

"You do this, and I will make you suffer," I vowed, my voice as broken as my heart.

"That is an idle threat. You will never leave this place to follow through," Unir said. His eyes glowed silver, and a misshapen rock slid into place, its jagged pieces fitting against the edges of the cell like a lock. With one final snap, it closed, sealing us in. I stayed there banging on it for hours, days, months. I didn't remember. Isaiah cried at my side, blaming himself.

I picked him up by his arm. "Hey, look at me." He didn't, and I shook him. "Look at me, Isaiah!" His bloodshot eyes met mine. "This is not your fault. He is a cruel, cold man, okay? None of this is your fault."

I pulled him into an embrace as he sobbed. "You don't hate me too?"

I shook my head. "No, never."

He'd locked us in the realm we used to run with vile beasts and creatures he deemed beneath him. Like them, we were nothing but inconveniences to him. So, we had built our own home from the ground up in that prison realm, and it had turned our hearts as jagged and brutal as the landscape. He never came back, never checked on us. I knew he had replaced us with that squealing runt of a child that had been born.

Unir had never cared and had used us as weapons until we'd outlived our usefulness. Once we were no longer needed, he'd tossed us aside without an ounce of care. That was when hate bloomed in my heart and the moment I had grown into a man. I sat on that throne in Yejedin, vowing, above all else, to make him suffer in ways he'd only dreamed of.

I spent years with Isaiah, training the prisoners we could, readying them for the war I craved. It wasn't until the world shook and fractured that I knew beyond a shadow of a doubt that one of our siblings loved us. She had cared enough to punch her way through our prison to save us. Nismera made it possible. She cared, and she would have our loyalty until we were ashes and the realms burned.

The seat next to me creaked as Isaiah sat. The bar had gone deathly quiet. He and his lethal reputation were well known here, and it didn't help he was wearing that damn dragonbane armor, either.

The bartender stepped forward, and I could smell the fear leaking from him. "Would you like the same, sir?"

Isaiah smiled and nodded before turning to me. "I was looking for you. Elianna said you stormed into the city, and I thought of this place."

"Hmm, it seems Elianna is paying far too much attention to me."

"What happened to your face?" he asked.

I groaned and waved off his question. "Doesn't matter. Learned anything else?"

The bartender brought his drink back and then scurried away. Isaiah took a sip before placing his glass down. "Only that Vincent and a small unit are heading to one of her prisons to collect more prisoners, it seems. Nothing else. The Eye has been quiet."

"Everyone is terrified of Nismera," I said, lowering my glass back to the bar and running my thumb along the rim.

"Yeah." Isaiah leaned forward. "They just don't know her as we do."

I scoffed. "They praise Unir as a hero, but he locked his very sons away for centuries, tossing us aside when that fucking brat was born. Nismera was the only one who gave a shit. She saved us. She broke through a realm for us, yet . . ." I stopped, raising the glass to my lips and taking a drink. "I hope she burns this world of the old gods. I hope no one even remembers their godsdamn names."

"Is that what's bothering you?" Isaiah asked. "I knew being back would stir old memories, Brother, but we're not there anymore. We're free."

He'd hit far too close to a nerve that still felt exposed and raw. Isaiah spoke of freedom, but my mind and soul still felt trapped there.

Even though fresh air filled my lungs and heat did not mar my skin, a part of me was still waiting to be saved.

"You know I will protect you no matter what, right?" I said, lowering my glass. I didn't look at him, but I felt his eyes on me.

His hand clasped my shoulder tightly. "I know, you always have."

"War is coming, Isaiah. We need to be prepared."

XLIV

Cameron

I tilted my head back, the bitter liquor hitting the back of my throat with nothing more than a slight sting. It stopped burning a while ago.

The stars above shimmered through the silver energy that swirled through the sky.

I raised my bottle high in a salute. "That's all that's left of you now, isn't it, buddy?" I said to the light show above. I stared at the remnants of Samkiel, and my heart clenched, my vision clouding with tears. I'd lost him, my family, and Xavier.

"Okay, hear me out." My feet shuffled as I tried to keep up with him. His armored boots were stained with red dirt. I knew he'd just returned from whatever assignment Unir had given him, but I couldn't wait to ask.

"Another ill request for permanent room service and your own castle on a hill?" Logan said, shaking his head, his armor filthy.

"That was one time!" I snapped back, drawing a laugh out of Samkiel's most trusted. "This is about The Hand."

Samkiel's dark braid bounced against his back with each step, his dented helmet held under one arm. The sash with the three-headed beast strained around one biceps. He turned and came to a stop, his guards nearly stumbling as they came to an abrupt halt.

"Cameron, for the last time, I merely mentioned tryouts. I haven't had time to breathe, let alone think of when they would start."

I pointed a finger at him. "Well, first of all, that's a lie. You seemed to be breathing fine with the few nymphs who ran out of your bedchamber last—"

Samkiel rubbed his hand across his face and nearly growled, "Cameron."

"Oh, right, that's a secret and not the point. The point is, I've been scouring around for the best, and I have a few I think would be amazing."

"Is that so?" Samkiel asked, adjusting the armor helmet in his grip to fold his arms.

"Yes. I've become friends with one of Kryella's yeyras."

"Cameron."

I held up my hands, and Logan snickered. "I know you two have a weird relationship, which is also not the point, but he's fast, smart, and a hell of a blade wielder. Dual actually. Just give him a chance."

Logan and Samkiel exchanged a look I couldn't decipher before he turned back to me.

"Very well. I will be with my father for the next two moons on another prolonged damned council trip. When I return, we will have tryouts."

"Yes." I clenched my fist and punched the air in triumph.

A smile broke across Samkiel's face. "For a price."

"What do you want?"

"You have to try out, too."

"Me?" I croaked. "Listen, I'm good being with Athos. She—"

"Lets you get away with anything?" He cocked a brow.

"Okay, fair." I sighed, placing my hands on my hips. "I'll try out. Just disqualify me early or whatever."

Logan chuckled, and Samkiel looked at him. "Why are you laughing? You're trying out, too."

Logan's face went slack. "Me? Why?"

Samkiel sighed and shook his head. "You two shouldn't question your future king so much. It's disrespectful."

My eyes rolled so far back in my head that I swore I saw my brain. "Oh, gods, now I definitely don't want to be under you." Logan *chuckled again. I turned to walk away, but I couldn't resist and called back with a wave of my hand, "Unlike the nymphs."*

"Cameron!" I heard him snap, and the energy around him built. I picked up my pace and was safely away before it reached me.

I practically ran out of the palace, skipping past guards and celestials alike until I made it to the center of the city. Voices buzzed, and people laughed. Shops thrived, customers carrying bags ladened with goods. Children gathered before a stand selling tangy melted creams, shouting about a new flavor. I placed my hands behind my back, pretending I hadn't run half a mile to get here, and pursed my lips. A small whistle floated through the air, a tune all its own. I stilled and waited for a response.

A sharp tune came from my right, and I turned to see Xavier leaning against a wooden post near a shop a few paces away.

"Well?" he asked as I walked toward him. "What did he say?"

"You know you can talk to him, right?" I asked, folding my arms. "He just looks really big and scary, but on the inside, he's softer than the frozen cream they sell here in the market district."

Xavier shook his head, making the dreads he wrapped in a topknot shake.

"He kind of scares me."

"Why? He saved you."

"Yeah, and did you see the planet after he left?"

I shrugged. "He was just making sure none of those damned creatures lived after . . ." My voice trailed off, seeing that haunted glaze fill his eyes. "But yes, I talked to him."

I reached forward, placing my arm around his shoulders and pulling him close. We walked side by side through the market, heading for the frozen cream stall.

"He has one of those all-important godly meetings for the next two moons. When he's back, tryouts begin."

"Great." Xavier all but beamed.

"And lucky you," I said as we got in line behind the children. "He's making me do it with you."

"Really?" His growing excitement was nearly palpable, and I couldn't help but smile.

"If I didn't know better, I'd say you're happy about that," I said, bumping my shoulder against his.

"Only a little. You're my only friend since the accident."

He grew quiet again, and I cursed every damned ghost that haunted him.

"Well," I slapped his back hard enough to bring him back to me. "You better love me for this because I hate following orders, and Samkiel has an ego the size of the sun, but I think I can get out of most of it if I get Imogen to join, too. That will distract him."

"That's your plan."

"Gods above, yes. It's always good to have a master one, buddy. Don't worry, I'll teach you."

He tipped his head back and laughed as the line moved forward.

I was happy to get him a family, a new one, even if a part of me was doing it out of guilt.

Tears pricked my eyes, and I took another swig, gripping the railing. The city below did not sing or rejoice. They moved as if one wrong step could be their death. Once the sun set, only guards patrolled the streets below. Nismera was a tyrant, always had been, and now she owned the cosmos. Peace, love, and joy did not exist under her rule, and now I feared there was no hope.

"What am I supposed to do without you?" I whispered to the wind.

XLV

Vincent

The portal whirled before opening to the snow-capped mountains of Flagerun. A chill wind sent snow flurries spinning into the air, casting the area in shades of white and gray. Armored hooves stomped around me as my legion rode in two lines on either side of me, spears at their sides.

The huroehe we rode were thick six-legged beasts. They were strong, adaptable, and deadly. Nismera had equipped them with their own armor, designed to protect them in battle. The addition of spikes along the breastplate, leg guards, and head meant they were able to slash and kill even if their rider could not. My favorite thing about them was they feared nothing and didn't spook. They were much more likely to run into trouble than away from it, which was invaluable in a time when Nismera had us venturing into other realms.

I pressed a spot on my left gauntlet, and a light flashed beneath my finger as the portal behind us closed. Quill had outdone himself with the gauntlet, and he had accomplished it in very little time. It made me wonder what else he was capable of. How had he achieved such quick results? The stench of blood and death permeated his lab. Was he brilliant? Did he use blood magic? Or was it a combination of both? I made a mental note to dig a bit deeper into his past.

"It's quiet." Abbie trotted up next to me, her beast stopping when she pulled on the reins. "Too quiet."

I glanced toward her through the slit of my helmet, and even past her own armor, I could see the apprehension.

"It's Flagerun," I answered. "Nothing but mountains and skyrippers."

A few of the soldiers nervously glanced up as if searching for the damned feathered beasts. I knew the risk in coming and so did Nismera. Skyrippers had adapted to the harsh climate, eating every bit of their prey, including bone, to survive. They were driven by hunger and mean as fuck. We would be relatively safe once we made it inside the prison, at least from them. I wanted to get in, do what we came to do, and leave.

The skyrippers were why Nismera had sent damn near a hundred soldiers with me, but I wasn't going to tell my legion that. If the beasts were starved, a hundred might not be enough. Nismera said she wished for me to return but was not too concerned about the others. I would have rejoiced in her care at one time, but now I knew it was hollow. It wasn't like when Camilla spoke to me or looked at me. I didn't feel that warmth in my chest. After years of having friends and family, I knew what true love and care felt like now.

I shook my head, trying to clear it of the witch who was probably pacing her floor until her magic burned it, waiting for me to return. Despite every horrible thing I'd done, she still cared about me. I didn't deserve it, but I would accept her care and friendship.

"Move out!" I shouted, pointing toward the rising cliff above. Snow crunched under hooves as we began the climb.

"It's too quiet," Abbie said again as we trotted up the mountainside. The soldiers had been nearly silent, keeping their eyes on the sky.

"You keep saying that," I answered.

"We would usually hear a skyripper by now, especially with us getting closer."

I shrugged, holding my reins as we turned onto a path that hugged the steep cliff, grateful for the rolling clouds that offered a reprieve from the bright sun. "Perhaps they are well fed."

"Or perhaps something far worse is here," she said, her eyes scanning restlessly.

"Does Nismera know you fear the sounds of small animals?" I asked her.

Her eyes cut to mine. "It is better to know all of your surroundings than not."

The cliffside opened as we leveled out, the wide trees coated in fresh snow. Abbie was correct, even if I did not say it. I didn't hear any skyrippers, and we were well enough up the mountain to be in their territory, but we held our pace. The trail continued between the cliff face and snow-capped rocks as we neared the prison.

The ground leveled out, and I held up my hand. Every soldier behind me came to an abrupt stop, our breath forming clouds in the cold air. I folded my reins and hopped off, my legion doing the same. Abbie approached and stood at my side.

"Where is the prison?" Abbie asked.

I raised a finger, pointing to the edge of the mountainside. "There."

She cleared her throat. "Sir, there is nothing there."

"Exactly," I said through gritted teeth.

The wooden bridge that led to the prison was gone, along with half the mountainside. I raised my hand again, telling my legion to stay where they were.

I walked to the edge of the clearing and looked over the cliff. There was nothing left but jagged rock and rubble. The prison had been destroyed. It looked as if a force of nature had hit it hard, reducing it to dust and stone.

"The prison is no more," I said loud enough that they could all hear. "We're leaving."

Murmurs started between the soldiers, and I felt a spike of fear from them.

Abbie shook her head, shushing the ones behind her as the second in command before turning back to me. "Gone? No skyripper invasion could do that. What has the power to take down an entire prison?"

I shook my head and turned around, scanning the area. What had I missed? At the side of the clearing, snow fell off the massive rock formation, and an eyelid blinked open. I stared into a single crimson eye, my heart thudding as if it would burst from my chest. This was a trap.

The dark, misshapen stone moved again, and I realized that those were not jagged edges but spikes. Dianna's Ig'Morruthen form had grown tremendously. It was my last thought before I yelled for the legion to move back. She raised her massive scaled head, opened her mouth, and set the mountains of Flagerun ablaze.

XLVI
Dianna

The mountains of Flagerun were no longer covered in snow. Instead, flames licked at them, forming rivers of molten rock. Behind me, the forest cracked and trees snapped. Embers floated on the air, the sparks funneling toward the sky in a plume of smoke. I ripped the head off a soldier and tossed his body into the fray. Others screamed as they tried to escape the fire by running down the slope, but the flames caught them, turning them to ash.

His voice rose above the sounds of battle, broken and cracked, ordering someone to leave. I hopped atop the rock separating us and grabbed the person he was speaking to. Wrenching her head to the side, I sank my fangs deep and drank. I tossed her drained body at his feet, her bloodstained helmet making an odd clanking sound when it hit the rock. I braced my feet and slowly clapped. "Well, would you look at that? A golden prick army led by the biggest prick of all."

Flames hissed against the snow, sending steam into the air. Vincent stared at me, a myriad of emotions flashing through his eyes. I saw shock, fear, rage, and something that looked like despair. My smile deepened when I noticed he hadn't escaped from the fire unscathed. His skin was burned and pink along his neck, face, and left arm.

"Surprised to see me?" I asked, tipping my head to the side.

This changed everything. Luckily for me, I had a plan.

"Dianna." He spoke my name behind gritted teeth. "I have to say I am. You were halfway across the realms last I heard."

"Well, you heard wrong, but I'm not surprised, given your sources."

Vincent crossed his arms over his chest and nodded once. "So it's true then? You are protecting Reggie. Isn't that what you called him? Honestly, I thought you'd mourn longer, but you did fuck anything that moved after your sister died. Guess it's a pattern."

My smile never faltered. He expected me to lash out, to charge him. I saw the way he pressed his foot into the ground, readying for the attack. He wanted me unhinged and out of control. I tilted my head. "How do you want this to go? Do you want me to send your ashes back to Nismera? Do you think she will care?"

I jumped from my rock and landed in a crouch, grinning when I saw him flinch. Placing my boot on the chest of a soldier's corpse, I yanked a spear from his side. "I don't think she will," I said, spinning the weapon between us. "I don't think anyone will care about the celestial who was too weak to stand up to a god for his family. Who would care about a warrior who didn't even try to stop her? A man who was too weak to save the people who loved him the most, even when he didn't deserve it? I think you're just a sad little boy who hides behind his weird mommy issues, draping himself in armor and blades to feel good about himself. Who would love that? Love you? That's why it really hurts, isn't it? That, no matter what cruel thing I did, Samkiel loved me. Your family loved me. But you? We both know they will never forgive you, never love you again. So I don't think anyone is going to miss you. What do you think?"

"I think you're the same raging bitch," Vincent spat, his celestial adyin glowing a bright blue.

"No." I smiled. "I'm worse, actually." And then I charged.

He wasn't aware of my feedings. He didn't know how much power I had been harboring, how much rage, hate, and anger I had honed to a fine-tipped blade, readying it to pierce the very hearts who ripped mine out. But he and the realms were about to find out just how much of a hateful bitch I could be.

Steel rang against steel, echoing through the mountains of Flagerun. Every hit I made, he parried or blocked. We darted around each other, both of us glaring and filled with hate. It was a dance we were destined for since the day we met. I hated Vincent, and he hated me. Vincent's blade sliced through the air with a whistle, aiming to slice my head off. I ducked and spun. Using a move Samkiel had taught me, I raised my spear and slashed across his face. I smirked, glad I had managed to get that stupid helmet off his head in the first moments of the fight. Vincent stumbled back and touched the cut on his cheek. He pulled his hand away and looked at the bright blue celestial blood coating his fingertips.

Vincent smiled at me, his eyes cold and calculating. "Spinning uppercut. Samkiel actually taught you something. With how the two of you were going at it, I didn't think he would take time away from fucking you to train you."

"Careful, Vincent, you sound jealous."

"The only thing I am jealous of is that you will find peace when I kill you in the next few minutes."

He charged, aiming for my midsection. I hopped back, blocking his downward strike, my blade taking the brunt of the hit.

"You know," I huffed, pushing him back, "I actually feel sorry for you. I always wanted a family and a home, and here you are, tossing it away for some washed-up, old hag who wants to be a ruler."

Vincent braced his back foot on the slick stone and swiped his spear up. I spun away and rolled, snow and ice sizzling against the burning rocks.

"You're even more of a fool than I thought if you think Nismera doesn't already own these realms."

"Yeah?" I said, stepping back once more. I had a plan, and like a puppy, he was following me right into my trap. "Couldn't tell. Especially when she sends her lackeys to do the hard work."

He scoffed and advanced. "You wouldn't last a second against her. No one can. If Nismera ever shows up, it's not for capture. It's for death."

"Gods." A sick laugh left my lips, and I took another step back. "You really have a hard-on for her."

His grip tightened on his spear, and he lunged forward, slashing at me again. I shifted to the side, and he slipped, slamming into the rock I pressed against. His spear hit the stone and fractured from the force. Vincent growled and tossed it to the side. I took advantage of his momentary distraction and jabbed him with mine. He bent back, dodging my blows, one after another. I'd be a liar if I said Vincent wasn't a good fighter. He was part of The Hand, and Samkiel had trained them to be the deadliest warriors in this realm or the next. They were designed to fight beings like me or worse, but where he excelled at fighting, I was born from blood-thirsty rage. It was in my very makeup.

I spun the spear over my head, and he stepped in, his fist coming at me. I rammed the tip into the ground between us. Vincent moved back, and I smiled.

"You missed." He smiled, sliding his foot further from where the spear stuck deep into the ground.

"Did I?" I asked, tipping my head as a crack formed around the spear tip and spread toward the rocks surrounding us. The boulder at my back let out a horrific groan and split. I pushed him toward it and stepped back. Vincent's eyes widened as he stumbled. The rock came down on top of him, the force of it collapsing the cliff edge. We fell, rocks and boulders tumbling around us.

Wings erupted from my arms, just a partial shift to get me back to the top of the jagged cliff. I landed and dusted my hands off before willing the leathery appendages away.

A piercing pain ripped through my abdomen, forcing a gasp from me. I glanced down to see the tip of a silver sword protruding from my body. He ripped it out and slammed it back in. I screamed, my body lifted into the air and tossed aside.

I coughed, blood stinging my mouth. I tried to push up but slipped, pain igniting through every nerve in my body. There, in the snow with a blade dripping with my blood, stood Vincent, unscathed, unarmed, and with a weapon made by the gods themselves.

"You have all the makings of a goddess, you know?" Vincent slung my blood across the snow and took a step closer. "Your hubris will be your downfall. You are arrogant and cocky, rude and unskilled, and above all, just fucking annoying." He kicked me onto my back, and darkness edged my vision, my body shuddering with pain.

"How?" I rasped. "How can you have that?"

Vincent shrugged, looking at the blade. Its shine was almost the same as Samkiel's and far brighter than anything the celestials could wield. Celestials could not wield godly weapons. They were far too powerful and could burn them alive. My gaze snagged on the gauntlet he wore and where it connected with the sword. I didn't have to guess who had given him that protection. Fuck. The Ig'Morruthen in me snapped and hissed, knowing that regardless of form, a godly weapon could kill me.

"Nismera made this." He nodded and kneeled before me. "Strong enough to kill a fate, which is what I was here for, but your death will bring me so much joy."

"I suck with swords," I said, punching him in the face. "I'm better with teeth and claws."

Vincent tumbled back onto his ass, and I struggled to get up. He screamed in frustration and launched himself to his feet, wiping the bright blue blood from his face. I had just managed to get upright, clutching at my abdomen, when he swung that sword at me. I ducked, landing another punch to his gut. He stumbled back, and I placed my hand on the rock for leverage before kicking out, slamming my foot upside his head. He shook his head but didn't stop coming at me, aiming for my legs, my arms, my head, any part he could reach. I wouldn't lie. He was quick, and I felt his sword get close to my skin so many times.

Ignoring the pain in my gut, I tried to figure out how to disarm him as we danced around each other. I rolled behind a thick fallen log, and that sword came down, splitting it in half. I had an idea. It was a stupid idea, and I would have to be quick. Samkiel would be out of that tunnel soon, and he would come straight here after he saw what I'd done.

I rolled again, dodging as he slammed the blade down after me over and over again, and then I saw it. I felt the breeze as it lifted along the cliff. The edge beckoned me, and I jumped to my feet, grabbing his arm with one hand and head-butting him hard enough to throw him off balance. He stumbled, and I followed, kicking and punching as we went. He thrust the sword toward me, and I caught his arm against my body as he tried to slice me, the sharp edges and spikes of his armor cutting into my skin.

I lifted my leg and slammed my foot into his groin. Even with the armor, the kick was powerful enough to double him over in pain. I twisted his arm, flipping him over as I shuffled back a few feet, the rocks slipping beneath me. Vincent raised up, snarling at me as he pushed to his feet. He took a running start and raised his weapon. I grounded my feet, and when the blade came down, I grabbed his wrist and snapped it. His cry was sharp, but not as sharp as when I twisted the sword around and rammed it through his heart.

I jabbed the blade further into him, his eyes flickering cobalt blue, then dull as he grasped it, blood coating his lips. "This is for Samkiel, for Logan and Neverra, and Imogen. For Xavier, for Cameron, and everyone else you've ever hurt, you traitorous bastard," I snarled, fire erupting in my palm. I slammed my hand against his face, smirking as my flames danced over his skin and slid beneath his armor.

His jaw went slack in a silent scream of agony as he stared down at me.

"I'll meet you in Iassulyn," I snarled, yanking the blade free and tossing his burning body off the mountain.

As he tumbled, I heard him gasp one word: a name. My knees met the ground before I could process what he'd said. I held my midsection, blood dripping past my fingers. The wound burned like it had been doused in acid, and I hadn't realized how much blood I'd already lost until Vincent disappeared. I pulled my hand away and looked down. What a mess. Fucking godly weapons. Fuck.

A flashing streak of silver split the glowing sky, and the air curled around me, each hot breath a harsh contrast against the cold world. The ground shook with his landing, and his silver boots had barely touched the ground before Samkiel was at my side. He caught me before I landed face-first in the icy snow. My vision blurred as I looked up at the silver king kneeling before me. His hands were warm as he lifted me, and I hissed in pain when he held me close. My knight, my savior.

His hand hovered over the wound in my abdomen, and worry creased his brow before he lifted and surveyed the area with murderous intent, looking for the one who had hurt me.

"I killed Vincent."

Samkiel's head whipped to me, worry pulling his brows together. I stared at his face, my head falling back against his arm. No blue light raced toward the sky, but my last thought before I fell unconscious was how I killed Vincent, and with his last dying breath, I thought I heard him whisper Camilla's name.

XLVII

Camilla

My hand rested on my stomach as a wave of nausea hit me. I groaned and stepped back from the table, bracing my hands on the sides.

"You all right?" Hilma asked.

I nodded and stood upright. That was weird. A rush of cold air danced over my skin, and I suddenly felt totally fine.

"Yeah." I shook my head. "I am okay. I must just be reaching the end of my magic for the day."

"Here, let's try one more time, and if you feel sick again, we will stop."

I nodded.

Hilma steadied the piece of the medallion and swiped a layer of metallic sap along its edge as I held the other fragment.

"Did she move a lot of soldiers out last night?"

Hilma glanced at me, one of her brows raised. "I mean, she usually does. They are always off doing gods know what."

I nodded as she brought the piece closer and cleared my throat.

"Did Vincent go?"

A wave of energy pushed the piece away from my hand hard enough to make her yelp and drop it on the table between us. She placed her finger in her mouth, sucking lightly as her skin healed from the small burn.

"One, why are you asking about her High Guard, and two, ouch, that hurt. Can you try to concentrate?"

I tried to plaster an unconcerned smile on my face. "I'm not worried about him." That was a lie. "I just assume if she sends her most precious guard, something big is going on."

Hilma wiped her hands along the curves of her dress before picking up the piece again. She grabbed her brush and dipped it in the sap. The medallion was so close to being done. It was a dark gray X-shaped stone, and we only had a few large pieces and a few tiny remaining.

"Well, I guess that's right. Yes, he left, but only he and his legion. I think Kaden and Isaiah are on another mission. You know, The Eye has been trying to regain a hold on the realms since those portals opened. My theory is they are headed to the Otherworld to stop Nismera from gaining any strong allies."

That piqued my interest.

"There are strong allies in the Otherworld?"

Hilma wiped another long sweep of that sap along her piece. "Oh, very strong and very pissed after being locked up and all. But they would follow Nismera over The Eye in a second."

I held my piece firmly. "Really? Why?"

She gave me the look that told me I was asking far too many personal questions.

"How about we focus on this?"

I pursed my lips into a thin line. "Okay."

She pushed her piece back toward me as I braced myself. That same force vibrated both pieces as we forced them together. I held fast as it shook. Hilma and I swirled our free hands, emerald magic weaving through our fingers. The pieces vibrated as if fighting. They wanted to stay separated.

"Madam?"

Hilma and I glanced toward the door, still holding the pieces.

"Not now, Lucielle," Hilma snapped, turning back with a look of pure determination crossing her features.

"I apologize. I was supposed to stop by sooner and drop this off, but I had to help heal an amputated leg."

Lucielle walked forward, dropping a small tied bag near us. The aroma of spiced meats and stew wafted from it, making my mouth water.

"The High Guard of the First Legion suggested this for you, Camilla. I believe the note reads: To help do your job properly."

A zing spiked through my chest. He knew he wouldn't make it here for lunch, and he didn't want me to eat with the other guards. My magic flared at the images that flooded my brain, and the pieces we were holding snapped into place. A slow hum filled the room and then died the next second.

Lucielle jumped back, her eyes as large as saucers. I grinned in triumph, holding up the solid piece.

"We did it." I smiled at Hilma, who was looking at the small bag between us.

Something flickered in her eyes, but it was there and gone too quickly for me to process it. She smiled at me and said, "No, you did it. My magic stopped the second Lucielle started talking." She shot the girl a glance that had her squeaking before fleeing the room. Hilma watched her go with narrowed eyes before grinning at me. "You really are one of the strongest witches we've come across, or maybe you just needed encouragement." Her eyes darted to the small bag and note again.

I placed the piece of carved stone down and cleared my throat. "No, I think we just make a great team." I tried to cover up the uneasiness in my voice but failed completely.

"Sure we do." She reached for another piece. "Ready to try a few more?"

I nodded, not daring to look at the gift left for me. We tried and failed eight more times before we left. We could only get the one piece together, but at least it was progress.

I took the bag with me when we finished for the night, but I waited until I was in my room with the door closed and locked before I glanced at the note. I read the note repeatedly until the moon crested, and a wave of uneasiness filled my chest.

XLVIII

Dianna

I groaned and pried my eyes open, smiling at the sight of the beautiful, large man sitting beside me.

"Black is definitely your color." My voice cracked as I ran my fingers over his biceps. The heavy muscles flexed beneath my touch, straining his long-sleeve shirt. "Oh, you also smell nice, and you cut your hair again and trimmed your beard."

"You've been asleep for four days, and the first thing you do when you wake is flirt with me?"

I snickered and stretched. I might have arched my back a bit, allowing the tops of my breasts to stretch the tank I wore.

"I'm hungry," I purred, keeping my arms above my head. "Feed me."

A slow, sensual smile curved his lips as he leaned over me. The same damn flutters I always got when he was near went into overdrive. I nuzzled at his neck, but he just grabbed something off the nightstand beside the bed and sat back up. He held a cup toward me, the contents the color of dark mud.

I pouted. "That's not what I meant."

"I know it's not, but we're also in a small tavern off the edge of Crustinaple with about thirty people below us."

"So?"

"So, I am still not used to the feeling when you take from me, and I do not wish for a group of people to storm the room when you start screaming for me. So," Samkiel said, shoving the cup toward my face, "this will suffice for now."

I huffed and sat up, grabbing the cup from his hand. "So proper."

"At times." He smiled at me as I took a sip.

Blood a little sweeter than I liked hit my tongue, but I swallowed. My stomach cooled, no longer yelling at me, and while it would soothe my hunger for a little while, I craved something else. I didn't tell him how much I actually preferred drinking from the vein. I savored the feel of my fangs piercing skin and the body heat of another living being as I fed. A part of me was afraid he would learn one secret too many about me and look at me differently. That would destroy me. I licked my lips and crossed my legs, setting the cup in my lap.

"Good?" he asked, reaching out and tucking back a lock of hair that had fallen across my face.

"It will do. What is it anyway?" I asked.

"There is no translation for it in your world, but think of it as a stag from there."

"You gave me animal blood?"

He dropped his hand, leaning slightly back as he regarded me. "Yes, I thought it peculiar for me to ask a stranger to borrow some."

That made me giggle as I took another sip. "Fair point. I thought you were just insanely jealous and preferred I tasted no one else."

He shook his head. "Gods don't get jealous. We can have anyone we wish."

"Oh." I leaned over and placed the cup on the end table before throwing back the blankets and scooting to the edge of the bed. "Well, in that case, I'm done with animal blood. I'm going to go see if someone is drunk enough to forget if I get a nighttime snack."

My feet barely touched the floor before his arms were around me. He tossed me onto the small bed, and I laughed as he pinned my hands above my head.

"Be careful. I'm mortally wounded," I said.

Samkiel released my hands and shifted his weight off me to lean on one elbow. His big hand skimmed the edge of my tank before pulling it up, exposing my abdomen.

"No, I checked. I made sure . . ." His words died when he saw nothing but toned skin. He glared at me. "You're not funny."

I grinned and held my thumb and forefinger just a little apart as he lowered my shirt. "I'm a little funny."

"Minute, if even." His fingers slipped just under my top, rubbing at the sensitive skin of my belly. "What happened at the prison?"

My mind flashed to Vincent and the rocky mountainside, watching his body fall to the water rushing below. I'd waited for that damn blue light to shoot across the sky, but it never came. I forced a smile as he regarded me.

"It's been forever since I've lain on a bed that was actually soft. I missed it," I said, opening my legs and sliding my knee along his side. "Do you want to use it?"

His hand wrapped around my thigh and pressed it flat against the bed. "I understand how weaker men would immediately fall for your wicked ways, but don't try to distract me with sex. Especially when I'm trying to have a conversation with you."

My lips pursed. He was so different from anyone I'd ever been with, and that was another reason I wanted to skip this conversation. I slipped out from beneath his touch and sat up. I felt the bed shift as I stood.

"Dianna." His hand reached out, stopping me.

"I want to take a bath," I said.

His thumb ran across my wrist as he turned me to him. "You killed Vincent. That's what you said before you passed out from blood loss."

I didn't respond, keeping my eyes focused on his feet. I wished the world would open up and swallow me whole.

"Do you feel bad?" he asked.

My head whipped up. My gaze met his, and I knew he saw not an ounce of remorse in my eyes. "No, and that's the problem. I feel nothing but relief about it. And I don't want to talk about it with you because regardless of what he did, he was your friend, and you loved him, and I killed him."

Samkiel nodded, his thumb drawing circles across my wrist. "Vincent is a complicated subject for me. I remember the man who twitched at loud sounds or when someone moved too fast. I remember the wounded version of him. The one I wanted to help and protect. I want to believe he was manipulated. A part of me screams it is far more than it seems. I had lived with all of them for hundreds of years. I saw how he was with the others, and I knew him. Or I thought I did. Then he turned The Hand into something I cannot comprehend. He hurt them. He hurt you and tried to kill you. So it's complicated. I want to feel hurt that he is gone and feel sad, but I don't. I'm more upset you are hurt, more upset I haven't found the rest of my family, and more upset I couldn't do more to help."

My chest tightened at his words. I stepped between his open legs and wrapped my arms around his head. He rested his cheek against my breasts and hugged me close, holding me as I held him. "I'm sorry."

He said nothing.

"Not for killing him," I added. "But for what you have lost."

He only nodded, but I felt his arms tighten around me. I slid my fingers through his hair, aching to soothe and care for him however I could.

"Samkiel, you're allowed to mourn," I said, pressing my lips to his hair. "You are allowed to grieve the friend you lost and your perception of him. You're allowed to mourn what has happened to your family."

Samkiel nodded, and I tightened my grip on him, letting him know he was not alone. Never again would I let him be alone.

"I've never had anyone like you before," he said.

"What? Someone as bloodthirsty and attractive?"

"That, but no." He laughed, his breath hot against me. "Someone who just . . . understands. I don't have to say anything. You just understand."

"I think one thing we can definitely do is relate to each other," I said, laying my head atop his.

"How did he wound you so?" he asked, his voice rough and deep.

"Well," I said, my fingers playing at the short hairs near his ear. "Hypothetically, could your deranged evil sister make a godly weapon?"

Samkiel's brows knitted together, and he pulled back a fraction to look up at me. "It's possible. I was unsure what my father taught her. The gods made godly weapons, but it required a magnitude of power and the right environment to create and sustain such weapons. With the wrong ingredient or slip of the hand, it could destroy entire worlds. For that reason, my father long ago built a facility on a desolate moon."

"Do you think she could be using that moon?" I asked.

Samkiel shrugged one shoulder. "Perhaps. We can check it out, but not now." He ran his hand over my stomach, where that weapon had already sliced me apart. "And I say this with every ounce of ego and pride I have, but I am not ready. And you were impaled by a godly weapon."

"It's not the first time."

A look of clear bewilderment raced across his face. "When were you . . . Dianna."

He shook his head as he realized what I was referring to, and my grin widened. "Regardless, I do not have my full power, and I barely survived her when I did. If we go there, I need to be at full strength. My focus right now must be on reclaiming my power from the sky."

"Can you do that?"

"It's possible," he said, dipping his hands to the back of my thighs. "It is mine, after all."

"I guess we can add that to our list of goals, then. Try to suck your power out of the sky."

Samkiel just nodded. I leaned back, trying to shift out of his embrace, but made it nowhere. His arms tightened around me, holding me to him.

"Another thing," he said, his brows lowered and the muscles in his jaw tight.

"Uh oh." I smiled weakly. "I know that look."

His lips pursed into a thin line. "You shouldn't have blocked the tunnel nor dropped the prison below the ground, either." I protested, but he raised a hand, silencing me. "I'm not done. You said you'd be right behind me, and you did the opposite. Had you planned that all along?"

"To be fair, I'd planned to close it behind you and the survivors. I was going to buy time for you all to escape and then meet up with you when I was done. I didn't expect the battle to last long or Vincent to be the one that showed up or the godly weapon, so I'm sorry."

He nodded, but I knew by the tension holding his muscles tight that he was still furious. "We're supposed to be a team, Dianna. We have to work together, which means you can't decide what we will do and then carry out those plans on your own. Especially now that we have a hint of what she is capable of making."

I nodded, feeling the slightest edge of guilt. We're a team, and all I've been doing is keeping secrets and lying. I still couldn't tell him what really happened in that tunnel. My heart clenched in my chest. Here he was, offering every piece of himself, and I couldn't cough up a fraction of myself. He was everything I had wanted and hoped for. Someone who would be there for me, someone who wanted me and would fight for me. He was offering me the promise of never again being alone, and right now, I felt so very lonely because there were things I was still too afraid to tell him. So my lies and secrets built higher, cutting me off from him like a godsdamned fortress.

"You're right." My smile was small. "I promise no more secret plans."

He glanced down, fiddling with the hem of my tank top. "I know you are strong and capable. I am not saying that to undermine you, but I worry for you. You don't have to do everything by yourself."

"I know." I nodded, reaching forward and clasping his hand in mine. "It's hard for me to remember sometimes, if I'm honest, but I'm working on it."

He lifted my hand and held my gaze as he placed a kiss to my knuckles. "We can work on it together."

"Together sounds lovely."

Liar! My damned heart screamed. *You're a liar!*

It was true. If it came to him and his safety, I would defy the very heavens themselves to keep him whole. More than anything, I feared that when he looked at me so lovingly, he saw the girl promised to him. She was a celestial being filled with love and hope and goodness, but she had died in a desert far away from her home world. She had been carved up and spit out by the most brutal creature and then reborn into something far more cruel than her predecessor.

Her edges were ripped, jagged, torn, and bloody, but she built herself back up the best she could. She enclosed herself in unbreakable and impenetrable walls that would take decades to breach. I hoped that when he looked at me and saw this new version of that girl, he would recognize that parts of her still existed. I hoped he cared enough to want me, and he could see that every bit of good I had salvaged from that girl was now his. These were hopes I clung to.

"Did you get the gauntlet?" I asked.

"Yes, I have it contained. I need to find us a safe place before I try to figure out how it works, just in case it is volatile. I don't know if it was one of your father's creations, but he was far craftier at making weapons than any of us, and it was always risky tampering with them."

I groaned involuntarily at the mention of Azrael, but Samkiel went on.

"I have a place on an abandoned planet in mind, but I need to verify it's safe enough before we go there."

"Oh? What's it like?"

He glanced out the window toward the stars and the part of him that still painted the sky in silver streaks.

"You'd love it if it's still the same. Towering mountains, rolling wooded hills, deep ravines, and waterfalls as beautiful as the ones on Rashearim. Your other form would enjoy exploring there."

"Maybe we can make it a new Rashearim if it's still pretty."

That brought a smile to his face that damn near made my heart stop.

"What?" I managed to get out, feeling breathless.

A smile still bloomed on his devastatingly beautiful face. The haunted shadows that had taken up residence in his eyes when he talked about Vincent had been banished. He no longer ached with thoughts of the man he'd called a friend and his betrayal. I loved that I could drive away his demons so effortlessly as he had done mine.

"Nothing," he said. "It's just . . . I'd like that. A lot."

"What of the other prisoners?" I asked. "Did everyone make it out okay?"

Samkiel nodded. "Yes. Most have also showered and changed clothes. I believe they have found places to stay around this city. I cleaned Logan up and left him with Roccurem. The remaining prisoners are probably at the neighboring tavern."

"I'm surprised they didn't all flee."

His fingers flexed on the back of my thighs. "Most will. I know a few are worried about the home they left behind. I do not fault them if they don't choose to stay."

"Even Savees left?"

His eyebrow flicked at my question, his annoyance palpable. "Am I going to have to hide you from every Otherworld being there is?"

I playfully hit his shoulder. "Stop it. That's not why I'm asking. Like you said, he's formidable and would make a great ally."

Samkiel's lip curved up. "I hope you speak of me so well in the presence of others."

I laughed before leaning forward and kissing him. "Sami, baby. You are the textbook definition of jealous."

"Hmm," was all he said before sighing. "No, he did not leave. Although now I'd prefer he did and immediately. I changed my mind about alliances."

"You're impossible." I smiled softly, running my hand along the side of his head. "Enough about alliances. You know what I'd like?"

Heat flared within his storm-colored eyes. "I am already thinking of seven things you are going to say, but please enlighten me."

I placed my hands on his shoulders. "I want a shower or a bath, whichever they have here."

"That can be arranged."

I leaned forward and whispered, "And you can come with me."

"That cannot be arranged." He smirked and gave my ass a couple of pats.

"Why?"

"Akrai," he practically groaned. "You are not the quietest, nor are we the most . . . gentle. Do you wish to cave in an entire tavern full of . . ."

Samkiel's words trailed off as I raised my shirt and placed it over his head. He moaned, and the heat of his breath washed over my bare breasts, making my nipples tighten.

"This is cheating." I felt his lips brush the sensitive skin between my breasts.

I giggled as I pressed his face between my breasts. "I never said I played fair."

"This is coercion," was his muffled response, and I knew I'd won.

Samkiel pulled my tank top off and grinned at me before he gripped my thighs and stood, tossing me over his shoulder. I squealed and was sure the whole tavern heard. He chuckled devilishly and swatted my upturned ass as he strode toward the bathroom.

"Quiet, Dianna. Or I will have to put something in your mouth to make you quiet."

Oh, my man was in a mood, and I loved it.

XLIX
Roccurem

Another squeal came from above, followed by the splash of water hitting the floor. Logan's cobalt gaze remained fixed on a spot across the room. Seeing them up close, I was utterly aware of how wrong Dianna was that they no longer contained any spark of life. I felt it as a small drum sounded in a vast valley. It was a whispered call for help, so far out of reach.

"Are they always like this?" the elf Orym from Flagerun asked as he entered the study.

I turned from the window and regarded him, slowly sipping my tea. His hands were in the pockets of the smooth, black attire Samkiel had acquired for all of them—a new set of clothes for his wayward allies. Orym's tail swished, and he glanced toward the ceiling.

"The lack of their mark forms a hollow ache. It is a desire to be completed. Mated pairs usually settle after the mark has sealed, but until then, they tend to mate furiously. It's natural. Nature demands its completion and seeks to seal their souls."

Orym's gaze landed on me with a flash of pain. I placed the teacup on the small coaster Miska had found. "You think of your lost mate, yes? That emptiness as well. It's not jealousy that marks your words, but pain."

He sat with a huff, placing one long leg across the arm of the chair. "You really are a fate."

"That I am." I nodded and gave him a small smile, hoping to put him at ease. "You should enjoy their copulation."

His face turned up in disgust. "Excuse me?"

"It is far better than what they used to do. What the universe demands."

Orym's death glare eased as he glanced up, the sounds from above gaining in intensity. His tail swished from side to side.

"And what did they used to do?"

"Try to destroy each other."

He huffed a laugh. "Sorry, that seems hard to believe. Since I've met them, they can barely keep their hands off each other."

A grunt echoed from above, followed by more water sloshing. This time, a dark spot formed on the ceiling.

"It wasn't always such. There was even a period of time I assumed she would win."

"Win? Kill him?" Orym's throat bobbed. "You think she could beat him? The actual World Ender?"

I raised one leg, crossing it over the other. "Absolutely. Dianna's power stems from a part of her she gained from a complete loss of control. It is angry and dark and the definition of wrath. She could burn the very stars from the heavens if she wished. Her power is old, very old, and so is her anger. At times, it is evil."

The room grew thick with tension and unease. I saw the knowledge in Orym's eyes and knew my words were only a confirmation of what he had already sensed.

"Why doesn't she? Could save us all from this war."

"Do you believe that to kill a fire, it is appropriate to add more flames or extinguish it?"

"I just mean, why hasn't she? Especially if you make it seem as if they were enemies."

A blissful giggle filtered through the ceiling, and a slow drip of water fell onto Orym's leather pants. He sighed and flicked it away.

"Because of love. Only her sister reached that celestial part of her, and now he does. He is order. She is chaos. One cannot exist without the other, and if she were to lose that, war would be the least of our problems."

Orym's eyes softened. "She had a sister."

"And she damned near destroyed the world when she lost her. Imagine what she would do for him."

Orym glanced up as the sounds of their coitus continued.

I reached for the tea Miska had crafted for me, my headache roaring back to the front of my eyes, and took a sip. The pain subsided, and I sighed in relief. "He finds peace in her, even before he knew what she was to him. It is something he has never found with another. I watched it from above. How that heart he'd encased in ice began to slowly beat once more."

A grunt came from the hall and not one of pleasure, like those from above. Savees leaned in the doorway, taking up the entire frame with his bulk. His ears twitched as he glared at the ceiling.

"They don't sound as though they hate each other now," he snarled. "I hate Otherworldly hearing."

"I assume it is treacherous for a Q'vineck."

Orym jumped from his chair, nearly toppling it as he scurried to the other side of the room. Savees just rolled his eyes, those twin tails flicking in annoyance.

"You were with me for weeks, and now you fear me?"

Orym's chest heaved. "You lot are supposed to be extinct."

Savees's teeth flashed, the white stripes along his neck darkening. "Don't worry. We are now."

I sipped at the calming liquid in my cup and regarded him. "I was surprised to see Nismera attempt to capture you. Your kind are a ferocious, rebellious bunch. I'm surprised she wished to claim you."

His smile held no humor. "Claim is not the right word."

"What?"

Savees cut a glance to Orym. "Whatever she needs creatures for, it is not for an army. I fear it's much worse."

"I think your concerns are an accurate assessment."

Savees ran a hand behind his ear and glanced up again. "Samkiel needs to be careful with her."

Orym snorted. "I think she can handle it. Trust me, I've been around them for weeks."

Savees's tail twisted in irritation. "That was not what I meant. She is power, power the Otherworld is raising its head toward. They will come for her. If they haven't tried to already."

"They will taste Samkiel's steel if they even try," Orym said.

Savees nodded in agreement before reaching behind him and pulling the thick hood over his head. He shifted his cloak, hiding his tail as it wrapped around him and secured the clasp at his neck. "When they finish, tell them where I went, won't you, fate? I have a few people who I think will join the World Ender," he said and strode from the room without waiting for a reply. Orym visibly relaxed once he was gone.

"You fear the Q'vineck?" I asked.

The noises above reached their crescendo, and Orym shifted his feet.

"I've heard stories of the giant beast they turn into. Fangs sharper than steel with claws to match. Their ferociousness in battle rivals even the Ig'Morruthen's, and I'd prefer all my limbs stay attached."

I turned toward the lost Elvian prince, who was completely unaware of his heritage or fate, and smiled. "I would not worry about the Q'vineck."

His eyes caught mine, questions burning in them. "Who should I worry about?"

The ceiling groaned as wood split. With a crash, Samkiel and Dianna fell from above. Water sloshed from the tub, and the beams beneath the floor cracked with the weight and force of the fall. Samkiel held tight to the edges of the bathtub, and Dianna's wide smile faded as she lowered herself under her king, her cheeks staining pink with a mix of pleasure and embarrassment. "Sorry."

L

Camilla

I woke with a jolt, sweat drenching the side of my head as my hair clung to my skin. I felt hot and then cold, my hand clutching at the fabric over my chest as I took one breath, then another. The sounds of hurried footsteps and shuffling out in the hall assaulted my ears, all my senses overly sensitive. I felt tension seep through the air like a heavy fog, the palace buzzing. The sky cracked. I jumped from my bed, quickly throwing on a dress and shoes before leaving my room. No guards stood outside, and when I checked Vincent's room, he wasn't there either.

I ran down the steps, the palace a bustle of whispers and murmurs.

What was going on?

"Camilla," Hilma yelled from behind me. I spun as she charged forward. "Oh, good, you're awake."

"As if anyone could sleep through this. What's happening?"

"You didn't hear?" Her eyes were like saucers.

"Hear what?"

"An Ig'Morruthen destroyed Nismera's entire legion. The mountainside of Flagerun is just gone, along with the prison. They are still bringing back remains, and I don't know if Vincent is one of them or . . ."

She kept talking, but the world had gone silent for me.

I couldn't find him, not at all. I laced my fingers through my necklace and hurried to Nismera's war room. She would know where he was. I walked close behind the generals speaking to Nismera, a shadow unable to be detected. One general turned as if he could feel me, the one next to him elbowing him to stay in formation.

He ran a golden armored hand across the back of his neck as he whispered, "I thought I felt something behind me."

We turned a corner into the long, overly decorated hall that led to the war room. Two guards opened the large, gaudy door, and Nismera walked in. I snuck past and went to the darkened corner. She tossed silver energy toward the hanging metal protrusions on the wall, illuminating the massive room.

"Leviathan," she said to the tall, lanky member of The Order as he bowed his head, "give me some good news, please."

"I wish I could, Your Highest, but I am afraid I only have the opposite."

She sighed as one guard held out her seat, the long sheer sleeves of her jeweled gown swaying as she sat. "The prison?"

"Demolished." Leviathan sat. "The remains are rubble along with the mountainside."

She steepled her fingers and leaned across the table. "And the member of The Hand?"

"Stolen, my liege. There were no reports of cerulean lights darting through the sky."

Member of The Hand? Stolen? Did she mean Vincent? Is that why I couldn't find him?

She ran a hand across her face before her fist slammed onto the table, the lightning beneath its surface skittering away in fear.

"The Eye will see this as rebellion, another foothold they think they have when they do not." Nismera met Leviathan's eyes. "She is becoming a problem."

"She has been for a while."

Nismera let a breath loose. "I should have killed her in her mother's womb when I had the chance. Now she's disrupting my plans once more."

"Do not fear, my highest. Let Kaden follow through with his plan, and then you shall have what you always wished."

Her nails tapped against the table. "Perhaps."

"If the fate is with her, she may still be one step ahead of us."

"I tried to have the fate killed, and Vincent came back an absolute waste."

My heart lurched. He was here? But I had checked the medical wing and everything.

"He returned from the infirmary in Pike's Bay a few minutes ago. We had the guards escort him to his chambers. I am afraid he is still in rough shape. We have not had the opportunity to seek out new healers since she destroyed Jade City."

She waved her hand, staring out the window of her war room. "He is nothing but a sentient weapon. He is not my concern. These realms are my concern. My rule will be challenged if I am even suspected of weakness. Losing that prison is weakness, having my legion decimated is weakness, having my general near death is weakness."

My chest tightened for him. Vincent had betrayed his family and was damn near on his deathbed for her, yet she spoke about him as if he meant nothing. He was nothing to her. I struggled to hold back the anger that bubbled in my throat. I hated her.

"You are not dealing with a simple rebel, my king. She was, for all intents and purposes, the Queen of Rashearim. She was meant to rule everything. Therefore, her—" Leviathan's head exploded, blood and brain matter spraying everywhere.

Elianna yelped and grabbed her notes. The other council members froze, none daring to speak.

Nismera's eyes returned to their normal color, the silver power that had burned in their depths receding.

"Rolluse," she said. The man sitting to the left of Leviathan's corpse stood, his hair, face, and clothes splattered with gore. "You are now the leader of The Order. Please don't be like Leviathan."

"Yes, my liege." Rolluse bowed, a slight tremor shaking his body.

"And there will be no further talk of rulers. I am your king. Your only. Understood?"

Every head in the war room bobbed, even the guards.

"What's our next step?"

Rolluse swallowed, reaching for the folder in front of Leviathan's chair. He opened it and cleared his throat before speaking. "The King of Quinural still requests to see you in five days for the resale. I suppose he wants to gift you the murrak and offer a display of power."

"He's only pissing in his boots because The Eye is growing close to his territory. Otherwise, he would have pledged his loyalty sooner." Nismera waved her hand.

"Regardless, a murrak is a rare creature. You can add it to the plethora of others you have collected and stored."

Collected? How many monsters did she have under this damn city? And what was she storing them for?

She sighed. "I suppose. Even with my ryphors, I do not have the time to fly there to retrieve it myself. We need to prepare for the coronation. I cannot prepare a legion to join me if I'm not here. What commander is stationed closest? Maybe they can pick it up for me?"

Elianna flipped through several pages before half raising her hand. "The closest would be Enit, but his calvary is too small. Send Illain."

I didn't stay to hear the rest, needing to check on Vincent. Sneaking out of the war room, I hurried toward my chambers, taking the wide stone steps two at a time. The hall was clear, but I heard the low murmur of voices and paused before turning the last corner. I carefully stepped into the corridor and pressed against the wall to listen.

"The infirmary did a terrible job," a tall woman said, her face and hands completely covered.

The short, stout man next to her nodded. "They are all we have now that Jade City is ash."

They hurried past me, continuing to talk and none the wiser. I didn't hesitate, nearly running to Vincent's door and pushing it open. I snuck in and spoke the enchantment, dropping the veil of invisibility as the door closed behind me.

Vincent's feet, raw and burned, were the first things I saw. He lay atop his bed, covered in gauze. My horror grew the closer I got. His entire body was covered in horrific burns. He seemed to be resting, but then I saw the tonic on his bedside table and knew they had sedated him for the pain.

My hand went to my mouth, and tears filled my eyes. Not a single hair remained on his head. Even his brows and lashes were gone. How bad had he been before the infirmary got to him? Near death, at least. I knew the true power of Ig'Morruthen flames and had seen what Dianna could do. She could have made this quick, but she had done this to make him suffer before he died.

"Stupid, stupid idiot," I whispered, wiping tears from my cheek. I kneeled beside his bed. "Why would you even go after her? You know it's suicide. How dare you try to leave me here alone! I can't do this without you. I can't be alone." It was true. He was the only friend I had in this wretched, wretched world.

My head dropped to my arms along the side of his bed as my body shook. Tears spilled as the stress of this damned place finally broke like a dam. If Vincent died, I would be alone, truly, utterly alone. A wet sob left my lips before I covered it, lifting my head. I refused to leave him like this. There was no telling how long it would take for his celestial blood to heal him.

I knew for a fact Nismera did not care one single bit, nor would she even venture here to visit him. He was a weapon to her but not to me. The tears dried on my face, resolve replacing despair. I stood in one solid motion and cast my illusion once more before leaving the room.

I stormed through the maze of halls, my magic raging around me. I didn't even care about the chaos I left in my wake. An emerald ball of power formed in my hand, and I blew Kaden's door off its hinges.

He lunged out of bed, his chest bare, dark slacks slung low around his hips, the twin lines of muscle on each side disappearing beneath them. His eyes were burning, and he snarled at me, baring his fangs, ready to end my life.

I lifted my hand and clenched it into a tight fist. Magic swirled around his throat, cutting off his air. He fell to his knees, his hands grabbing at his neck. Kaden glared at me, but I didn't release my hold. I paused in front of him, my hand still raised.

"You did this," I snapped. "All of this, everything, is your fault. You will fix it."

I spun my magic into a leash and dragged Kaden from his room.

"You drag me out of my room to witness the death of this?" Kaden pointed toward Vincent's body.

"He is not dead," I snapped from where I stood at the edge of his bed.

"Pretty damn close," Kaden murmured. "Dianna did this?"

I nodded. "Yes. Yes, she did."

Kaden leaned a fraction over as his lips turned down. "Impressive."

"I'm glad you think him being burned alive is impressive, you piece of shit."

Kaden glared at me. "I'm talking about the reset bone they did and also that gash on his chest. It went straight through his heart, yet he breathes."

"What?" I asked, scanning Vincent's body. I hadn't even seen that when I was in here before. I'd been too concerned with the burns. But there it was, a small red blotch that seemed to still be leaking right where his heart should be.

"What did you do?" Kaden asked me.

"I didn't do anything." I sneered at him. "But you're about to."

"And what does that mean?"

I raised my hand, my magic swirling over his torso, binding his arms, legs, and throat. His muscles bulged as he tried to break it, and if I didn't hurry, he just might.

"Relax," I said. "I only need to borrow a fraction of your life force to heal him, then I promise I will let you go, okay?"

His upper lip curled back, exposing his fangs.

I carefully kneeled on the bed beside Vincent and hovered my free hand above him. Magic swirled against my palm before breaking free to land atop him. The vibrant green ropes tightened around his body, just as they did Kaden's. I blew out a breath, stabilizing my mind and spirit before beginning to chant.

"Viti rucku mocharum."

A window slammed open.

"Viti rucku mocharum."

A cold wind curved through the air.

"Viti rucku mocharum."

A soft groan came from my right.

"Viti rucku mocharum."

I pulled on every bit of Kaden and myself. That secret part of me twisted and unlocked. I felt moisture coat my eyes and a familiar tug in my chest. It grew and pulsed, contained within the grip of my magic. I took a deep breath and released it, the power whipping out of me. It darted to Kaden and then to Vincent. My eyes sprang open, and the room descended into darkness. Then came the screams. I ignored the hundred-and-one voices whispering into my ears.

"Viti rucku mocharum."

My eyes were open, but I did not see this room. I saw everything and nothing all at once, darkness and light intertwined. A voice rose from below the world, below the universe, far but close, and something turned toward me.

"Well, aren't you new?" it said.

I was yanked back to the present, myself, and Vincent's room. Kaden and I gasped. My magic, an iridescent green, rose like a wave before crashing into Vincent's form. His body bowed off the bed, and he groaned, skin knitting together. The burns healed, and hair sprouted from his head. He opened his eyes and looked at me.

"Camilla?" His voice was the last thing I heard before pain sliced through my head, and I fell to the floor.

LI

Dianna

"How do you say go fuck yourself in Fivvern?" I asked, flipping another page.

Samkiel had stacked so many books on this desk that I swore my eyes would bleed before I read them all.

He chuckled, casting a glance at me. "Why must you only crave the bad words?"

I shrugged. "They come in handy far more than others."

"Perhaps." He leaned over another book and turned the page before sliding it toward me. "This would be helpful."

I groaned, slamming my head to the desk and the eight books surrounding me. "That's fine, add another. I barely learned the guard's language, and now you want me to memorize eight more?"

Samkiel snorted as I raised my head, placing my chin on my hands. "Technically, those are just volumes; there are about twenty-five languages in each."

I glared at him. "I truly hate you."

He smiled. "I promise it will get easier. We just need repetition, and you'll have it mastered."

"Easy for you to say." I sat up. "You studied for like a million years."

"Hey." He scoffed, leaning back in his chair.

I folded my arms and shrugged. "It's true. You're old."

"So are you."

"Pfft." I waved my hand. "Not as ancient as you are."

Samkiel narrowed his eyes at me, running his tongue along the inside of his cheek. "Okay."

That was my only warning before he jumped out of his seat and charged me. My eyes widened, and my chair went flying as I lunged to my feet. With a squeal, I ran to the other side of the table. Samkiel planted his hands on the tabletop across from me, watching me with a predator's gaze. He feinted to the right and then took off to the left. My laugh filled the small study as he chased me around the table. I darted past him and charged for the door, but he caught me around the waist and lifted me into the air. I kicked out right as the door opened, and I hit Orym square in the face.

"Ow!" he grunted, holding his nose.

Samkiel sat me on my feet at once, and I placed my hand over my mouth. "Oops."

Orym glared at me, cupping his nose before he glanced at Samkiel.

"We were just learning new languages."

"Uh-huh," Orym said, dropping his hand.

"Are you all right?" Samkiel asked.

Orym nodded. "Yes," he said, taking another step into the room.

Samkiel and I looked at each other as Orym walked by us. Samkiel grinned and reached for me again, but I sidestepped and shook my head. He pouted a bit, but we both turned toward Orym.

"Sorry to interrupt your learning, but I just received word about something you may be interested in."

"What is it?" Samkiel asked.

Orym pulled a small piece of parchment from his pocket, unfolding it before handing it to Samkiel.

"It's an invitation?" I asked, peering over Samkiel's arm.

Orym nodded. "Veruka could only sneak one. There seems to be a trade going down on the southeast side of the realms. A few big league players are involved, but whatever they are shipping and selling is causing quite a stir."

"All right. It will take us at least a day to reach there, and that's by cover of the night," Samkiel said, reading through the invitation again.

Orym nodded. "I can get us attire for it and a small area to stay in until then. The meeting is in three days."

"Perfect." Samkiel folded the paper and handed it back. "That's two more days for Dianna to perfect her Silmaun."

I groaned, and my shoulders slumped. Orym laughed.

LII
Dianna

I ran my hands down the sides of my dark blue dress. The corsetstyle top with the plunging neckline made my tits look bigger. I turned slightly, checking the back. The hem of the skirt sat high on my thighs, but everything would stay covered as long as I was careful. I blew out a slow breath and ran my hand along the long, sheer, puffy sleeves. It was so nice not to be covered in dirt or grime for once.

"Spin one more time," Samkiel said from the corner of our small room. He was watching me in the mirror, fixing his collar and looking closer to a street merchant than a god. I tossed a mischievous grin over my shoulder and did as he commanded.

We had made it to Veeq in the early morning and had spent our time learning the layout of the building, including every exit and entrance, before heading to the docks. We had spent hours watching the ships come in, but we hadn't seen anything unusual being unloaded. Samkiel worried Nismera would raid the Otherworld, stripping it of everything of use to her. I was just worried she would show up. Regardless of how arrogant I was, I wouldn't risk him.

"Do you like it?" I asked, twisting side to side.

"I do," Samkiel said, his eyes never leaving mine as he finished lacing his boots and strode toward me. His fingers cupped my chin and tipped my head back. He kissed my lips softly, careful not to mess up my dark lipstick. He traced the neckline of the dress with his free hand, teasing the sensitive inner curves of my breasts. "Even if it shows too much."

I snorted. "Please, it makes me look like I have boobs." I used my hands to push them together and even higher.

His eyes dropped to my cleavage, and he playfully swatted at my hands. "Stop that! You do have breasts."

"Yeah, but not big ones." I dropped my hands.

"Dianna, everything about you is perfect." He flicked my nose.

I smiled up at him. "It's been so long since I've dressed up and done my makeup. It's nice."

Samkiel studied me for a moment, but he only nodded and pressed a soft kiss to my forehead without saying anything. Stepping back, he grabbed one of the small bags he and Orym had filled with the weapons they'd bought earlier in the day. Samkiel started pulling out daggers and placing them in the hidden sheaths on the sides of his boots. I turned back toward the mirror and smoothed my hair. I'd left it loose, the natural waves flowing down my back. Even with the slight frizz, given the humidity here, it still looked nice.

Samkiel appeared behind me, and I smiled brightly at his reflection. He lifted his hands, watching me in the small, cracked mirror. His fingers brushed through my hair, and I fought a shiver as pleasure coursed through me. The corners of his lips turned upwards, and I knew he'd caught it. He separated my hair and twisted it in an elegant knot at the back of my head before sliding a long, slim, sheathed dagger into it to hold it in place.

"That's clever," I said.

He nodded and leaned over me, brushing his lips over my neck just below my ear. "You need weapons. There is no telling what she will have at that gallery, and since I can not be directly by your side, this will have to do."

I tipped my head, nuzzling the soft curve of my cheek against the rough stubble of his jaw. "You know I am made of fire, right?"

Samkiel smiled, kissing my cheek. "Indulge me. Please."

I nodded, then jumped slightly when his fingers teased my thighs just below the hem of my dress. "We don't have time for that."

I looked up at the mirror to find his eyes already on me, and my breath caught. His eyes had gone molten silver. Cool leather grazed my upper thigh, and a soft moan left my lips as he pulled it to the edge of my panties, his fingers scraping against my most sensitive area. His nostrils flared, and his smile was downright devilish as he caught my reaction. I widened my stance and leaned my head back against his shoulder. I held his gaze in the mirror, watching him through my lashes. My lips parted on small gasps, and I rocked my hips as he clasped the belt, making sure to roll his knuckles over my clit. He smirked and cupped my pussy, sliding a dagger into the sheath with his free hand before lowering my dress.

"Safety precaution," Samkiel said, and winked. It took every ounce of willpower I had not to toss him against the wall and make us extremely late to this stupid gallery, but Orym was across the hall, and I could only take so much attitude.

Samkiel steadied me on my feet and took a step back, his hand lightly grazing my ass. He lifted the bag, and I heard the crinkle inside.

I cleared my throat and smoothed my hair again. "What else do you have in there?"

Samkiel zipped it up. "A few extra things in case company shows up. I hope that won't happen, but it's better to always have a backup plan."

"Ah," I smirked, "I feel as though someone awful smart taught you that."

"Perhaps," he said, giving me a quick sideways glance.

Orym appeared at the door, wearing the same many layers of dark green fabric as Samkiel.

"How did you find even worse clothes than what they gave us at the prison?" Samkiel asked.

Orym walked in, carrying a small, smooth device, his lips twitching.

"I monitored the area when we arrived to determine what we needed to blend in as much as possible. The building where you'll be is far closer to the rowdy part of town. Samkiel and I will be outside, pretending to be loitering. That way, you can tell us what's happening inside."

I placed my hands on my hips. "And how am I going to do that? Scream really loud?"

Orym rolled his eyes. "No, with this."

He opened the smooth device and showed us what looked like beige marbles.

"What's that?"

"A way to communicate with each other without the screaming. It attaches to the ear canal, and we can communicate from miles away."

"So, like an earpiece?"

Orym looked confused, but Samkiel nodded in agreement.

"It's from her world."

"Ah," was all Orym said.

"Okay." I clapped my hands. "I get to wear the cool earpiece thing so you guys can talk to me."

Orym lifted the plug toward his ear, placing it and turning it on. Samkiel and I watched and then fitted ours. A scratchy tickle started deep in my ear, and my eyes widened as I looked at Orym.

"Orym," I said slowly. "Did my earpiece just move?"

He cast a glance at Samkiel, who tried to feign innocence. "It's just settling. It's not alive or anything."

I knew he was lying, knew Samkiel probably told him not to tell me because my safety was more important than my irrational fear of bugs, but I swore to every dead god if it moved again, they were shit out of luck.

"Okay, I am going to ignore that so I don't ruin this mission." I tapped my ear. "How does it work?" I asked and then heard my voice echo. I smiled. "Oh, that's fucking cool."

"Now that worry line across your forehead can rest," Orym said, patting Samkiel's shoulder.

Samkiel rubbed at his head. "I do not have a worry line."

I snickered. "I told him of that wrinkle, too."

Samkiel glared at both of us.

"Sami, you were worried about nothing. I feel so overdressed here," I said from behind my drink. "I'm glad you are outside. I've seen eight areolas, but on the plus side, no one is really looking at me."

"You can come outside, and I can show you what the dress does for me."

I nearly spit out the mouthful of my drink. I covered my mouth with my hand, turning from the crowd.

Orym groaned through the earpiece. "Can you two please not subject me to this today? I'm still burning my eyes out from the other day."

I snorted and pretended to look at the assortment of small, sweet cakes. It was true. He had caught us. Samkiel and I had decided to wander off for a training session that turned into me pressed against a tree again. "I'm sorry, but were you locked in a prison for weeks?"

"I was, but you don't see me with my pants down every five seconds."

I leaned down, looking closer at some of the sweet cakes as I spoke. "Honestly, maybe you should. I heard at the tavern that there is a small brothel nearby."

"Enough," Samkiel said, cutting us off. "Both of you."

I smiled and turned away from the cakes, weaving through the crowd. "Besides Orym's lack of fun, there has been nothing here out of the ordinary."

I passed an orange, fuzzy creature, my face scrunching in disgust as it spat at its glass cage. The crowd flowed through the gallery, laughing and drinking. Some moved in small groups, some clung to their dates, and others, like me, wandered alone.

"Unless she wants these small creatures, I don't see what Nismera could be after."

"That small creature you just described spits acid," Orym said. "I think that's right up her alley."

"Aw," I cooed and leaned closer. "But it's so cute."

I wiggled my finger at the glass, and a nictitating membrane flicked over the creature's wide, dark eyes. The hair on its body lay down as it watched me, and when I turned away, heading for another side of the gallery, I swore its eyes followed me.

I sighed as I passed couples laughing together or looking at enchanted weapons and paintings. If you ignored the fact this was an auction for one of the realm's worst living beings, they seemed to be having a great time. I missed that.

"I want to go on a date."

I heard Orym sigh.

"What do you mean, akrai?" Samkiel asked.

"I mean, minus the life-or-death situation, everyone here seems to be having fun. We haven't done that in forever. It's been one extreme mission after the other." I lifted the glass to my lips, spotting another creature in a glass container. This one was scaly. "Take me on a date."

"Let's get this done, and then you can have whatever you wish."

My lips curved against my glass. "Okay."

The hall I was following curved, and I found myself in a room empty except for a sword encased in glass. It stood in the middle of the room in a puddle of light. I tipped my head, able to feel the power like a soft hum in the air. I drew closer and leaned in a bit. The blade curved like a saber with a sharp tip, but its marbled, almost green color made it truly gorgeous. Tassels dripping with small jewels hung from the hilt.

"What a strange thing," a feminine voice said.

My back straightened. Completely mesmerized by the blade, I hadn't noticed anyone sneaking up on me. Either that or the woman before me had softer steps than she should.

"Excuse me?" I asked.

The woman smiled at the blade between us, tapping her short, dark nails on the case. "Something so rare and beautiful completely by itself."

My head reared back as Samkiel spoke in my ear. "Oh, please."

I raised my hand, turning the volume down a fraction, and smiled at the strange woman. She was a foot or so shorter than I. Her curly brown hair was clipped close to her head, with finger waves framing her face. A dark wing swooped from the edges of her smokey painted eyes, giving them a sensual curve, her full lips stained a matching black. Her dress fit her like a glove, the cutouts along the sides revealing a line of lean bronze muscle. Voices chattered in my ear, but I ignored them.

"Does that line usually work?" I asked with a flick of a brow as I sipped my drink.

Her smile was wide and vibrant as she stalked around the glass. Even her steps seemed premeditated. "You tell me."

I offered her a soft smile in return. "I'm sorry, but I'm taken."

"Damn right you are," Samkiel grunted in my earpiece. I raised my hand, turning the volume down even more, disguising the movement by tucking the short hairs behind my ear.

Her eyes glanced at my hand. "I don't see a mark or even a ring to signify that you are taken."

More chatter erupted in my ear, and I smiled. "Do I need a mark?"

She looked me over, her perusal slow and heated. "In this world, yes. It would make you less desirable to others. Right now, you are nothing but a rare gem, begging to be claimed."

Another grumble in my ear, and I cautiously rubbed at it.

"Have you been watching me?" I asked.

She leaned forward, her perfectly manicured nail pointing. "I have, and so has he." I looked, and a man near the door quickly turned away. "And her." A tall, aristocratic female wearing a dress with a high collar chatted with a group of men dressed in black, each of them hanging on her every word. She saw me looking her way and tipped her glass toward me in a silent salute. "And them." This time, she pointed to a couple who smiled at me and waved. "So, really, I'm doing you a favor."

She looped her arm through mine and pulled me along with her. I let her, and the eyes that watched me soon turned away as if being on her arm meant I was no longer an option.

"I thought this gallery was to sell deadly weapons, not people."

Her laugh was smooth as she patted my hand. "You'll learn everything can be bought, even flesh."

My gaze darted toward her, and I unwound my arm from hers. Saving me or not, I wasn't about to overstep a line, even as harmless as that. I wouldn't hurt Samkiel. Besides, I'd burn anyone alive who attempted the same with him.

Her smile brightened, but she did not attempt to grab my arm again. "Don't worry. I will not overstep since you're a taken woman, but I refuse to do this event alone."

"Why are you here alone?" I asked as she led me toward the long bar in the corner of the room.

She turned toward me. "Why are you?"

"I'm from Tiv," I said, using the cover Samkiel, Orym, and I had come up with. "I brought an old battle ax for her highest. Given how low my city is on wheat this year, I hope it will suffice."

She nodded and leaned against the bar. She raised her hand, and two glasses filled with the same alcohol I'd been drinking earlier slid toward us. I wondered how long she had been watching me. "I'm sorry about that, and I can relate. My home has not had rain in ages. All of our reservoirs are drying up. Our people are dying of thirst, and help is few and far between, so I also brought a few things, hoping for the goddess's favor."

"I haven't met a nice goddess yet, so good luck."

She only smiled before taking a sip. "My name is Faye, by the way. What's yours?"

"Xio." I smiled, using the name I'd claimed in Jade City.

"Ah, a beautiful name for a beautiful woman."

"No flirting." I raised my brow.

"It was simply an observation."

The lights in the room dimmed, and I looked around. A bright light formed toward the back of the gallery, and Faye tilted her head toward it in question. I nodded, and we started working our way through the crowd, leaving my drink behind.

"Gather around and witness a creature from your worst fears," a deep voice boomed over the speakers. "A legendary being from the deepest, darkest parts of the Otherworld."

Faye and I drew near as the crowd gathered. They whispered and beamed, excited as they watched the man on the bright rectangular stage. The hairs along my neck prickled, and I turned. There, through the crowd, I caught the shine of those damn golden soldiers.

Faye followed my gaze. "Seems she sent a legion to pick up her supplies."

I swallowed and watched the commander of her legion step through the crowd. His pointed helmet was tipped with reddish fur, and he proudly wore her banner across his shoulder. He had the same overdone armor that they all wore.

Well, at least we knew they were here, and it wasn't anyone Samkiel and I couldn't handle. That calmed my nerves a little.

"Now," the voice echoed once more over the speaker. "For your once-in-a-lifetime viewing pleasure . . . the murrak!" he called, raising his hand.

My earpiece buzzed as if Samkiel and Orym were both speaking at once, but I ignored it. The curtains behind him parted, and a massive glass cage was pushed onto the stage. People gasped, and I had to shift to see around a tall being in front of me. I took one look and wished I hadn't.

A hundred or more crystallized, opaque legs tapped on the glass, dancing around the giant shell like an exoskeleton. Its entire body was a shimmering mass of white so pure it was almost transparent. My stomach curled as it writhed. Bugs. I hated bugs, especially giant ones.

Antennae, the same white color, flicked as the murrak raised its giant head and hissed toward the crowd. They gasped and stepped back. Runes appeared on the glass, and nervous laughter rippled through the room when everyone realized the creature was securely contained. I wondered if everything here was contained the same way, even all these weapons. It hissed, pressing against the glass as it tried to push itself out. The runes flared, and it blinked, the cover of its eyes the same opaque color.

"The bidding will start at—"

The murrak raised its thick-plated head, its antennae moving as it sniffed the air. It looked right at me, locking onto my presence. Its body uncoiled, rising in its large clear cage, rows and rows of legs twitching. The pincers along its mouth opened, and an ear-splitting scream emerged, shattering every bit of glass in the room. Lights burst overhead, and everyone screamed because not only had it broken the sound barrier, it broke free of the only thing keeping us separate from it.

LIII

Dianna

Broken glass pierced my hands as I pushed myself up, screams erupting from all directions. I huffed and leaned against the bar, the rank stench of acid filling my nose. The guards had scattered, presumably to get what they could for Nismera. A wave of acid shot through the air, followed by more screams. I grabbed a tray and placed it over my head before ducking behind the bar. It seemed my furry little friend was wreaking havoc. Using my tray as a shield, I slowly rose to see people being tossed aside by a horned little creature as it ran for the door. There was a giant hole punched in the wall behind the stage where that fucking bug creature had escaped.

A woman ran through the room, glancing my way. Faye's face was covered in blood, and I saw the sword she was holding. It was the same enchanted blade that had compelled me earlier. Faye wasn't just a seller; she was a thief. She flashed me a crooked smile and took off running.

What if she was one of Nismera's guards? I needed to find out. Lights flashed overhead, leading deeper into the building. I looked toward the front door and the mob attempting to flee. Samkiel wouldn't be here in time, and Faye just snuck off to the back with that golden sword.

Fuck.

I pressed my earpiece, raising the volume, but all I heard were shouts of people running for their lives.

"If you guys can hear me, I'm heading below."

There were more screams, and I cringed. I pulled the damn thing out of my ear and tossed it away before going after Faye.

Lights strobed across the smooth, cream-colored walls. A trail of blood led the way, and I assumed one of those creatures had made off with someone. I walked slowly, trying to be as quiet as I could in my heels. I passed a few empty rooms that resembled cells, and my blood ran cold. How many creatures did she have here, and how many were now free? Another cacophony of screams rent the air, and I turned, making sure nothing was following me.

I felt the air shift. It was not a conscious decision, but I ducked, more sensing the attack than seeing it. A crunch followed as Faye lodged the ancient, cursed sword in the wall where my head was.

"No hard feelings, cutie, but if you work for her, you're dead."

I hopped up. "Work for her? For Nismera?"

Faye yanked the sword free, screaming as she tried to cut me again. I jumped back, avoiding her slashes as we danced in this small hall. Cracks formed in the stone walls with every hit, and the next time the sword lodged in the wall and she struggled to free it, my fist connected with her face. She yelped and stumbled back, wiping her nose.

"Damn, you hit hard."

I shrugged and yanked the sword from the wall. "You should see my kicks."

"I can't let you take that sword to her." Faye reached under her dress, taking out two blades.

I swung the sword in a looping circle, warming up my wrist and testing its weight and balance. "Oh, this old thing? Why not?"

Faye charged again, quicker this time. I dodged, using the sword as leverage, and blocked her blades. She was quick and highly trained, that was for damn sure. She dropped to the ground and kicked at my legs. I jumped and swung the sword above her head. She blocked the strike with both blades and lunged to her feet, pushing me back against the wall.

"I don't work for Nismera."

Faye gritted her teeth. "Sure, you're just here for a good time."

"Well, actually," I pushed back, sending her sailing across the room, "I was looking for whatever the hell she was interested in, and I think you just showed me."

The wall crumbled where she hit. She smirked at me and sat up, reaching under her dress again. Did she have an entire arsenal under there? She pulled out a small black circle and tossed it onto the floor between us. Smoke poured from the device, burning my eyes. I started to cough and felt a fist slam across my face. She yanked the sword from my hand, and I heard her run down the hall.

I coughed and blinked, trying to clear my eyes. As the smoke dissipated, I heard another set of footsteps coming down the hall. I looked up and saw a blurry, tall, muscular figure coming toward me. My heart thudded as the room changed, and I found myself back in the bone graveyard. I watched that figure come closer through tear-filled eyes, his powerful feet beating against the ground. He crouched, the thick plates on his shoulders shifting as he reached for me. I lashed out.

The room melted back to the hall and the flashing lights.

Orym held my fist. "Dianna, it's me," he said. "You're okay."

I nodded as he helped me up. I wiped my eyes again. "Where's Sami?"

"Out front, the whole place is in chaos. He's on his way. He stopped to help some people that were trampled, and he had to stop that acid-spitting creature."

I coughed again and nodded. "Okay, we have to go after her."

"After who?"

I turned and sprinted down the hall, waving Orym with me. "This way. She has some ancient sword that's imbued with power. I can't explain it, but I felt it. I don't know why she wants it, but we need to get it back."

We charged down the sleek hall, passing even more empty cells. Deactivated wards, the color of coal, were etched into the floor outside of each one. I didn't see any guards. It seemed they must have taken what they could and ran.

"I can feel you, ancient one," a voice called from further down the hall.

I turned to Orym to see if he had heard it, too. His brow rose, and he slid a blade out of its sheath. I reached for the one on my thigh and nodded, leading the way down the hall.

"A mighty beast has returned from the land of the dead and will leave thunder and ash in its wake, but this beast feels . . . different. Wrong."

I glanced at Orym, but he just shrugged. Neither of us understood what was going on.

"Ah, I see now. The old blood runs through you."

My lips curled at the sight before us. A pale woman was chained to the wall. She wore robes tied around her in several layers, her hair a tangled mess, but it was her eyes that made me pause. Or lack thereof. There were healed scratches and scars around the raw, hollow sockets, and I wondered if she had clawed them out herself. As Orym and I stopped in front of the cell, her head whipped toward me.

"The old ones have returned to the plane of gods, but you . . ."

"What is she?" I asked Orym.

"An oracle, but I thought the last of them had died when Nismera took the throne," Orym said grimly.

"The others are gone." She choked on a disembodied sob that seemed to echo within the room. "Everything will be gone. All is lost. From one, all will rise."

"Okay." I shook my head. "She's batshit crazy. Let's go. We have a mystery woman and an ancient sword to catch."

"You," she spat at me. "You are *empty*."

"Excuse me?"

Her body swayed as she bent around her chains. A smile curved her lips, her teeth dark, uneven, and cracked as if she chewed on bones.

Orym grabbed my arm. "Ignore her. The madness has set in."

"Madness?"

"Their power is unstable like Roccurem's or the other fates'. If they try to see too far, it can rip their brain apart. It seems they used her for just that until nothing was left."

"Why?" I asked, looking at her as she laughed and sobbed on the floor.

"Gods have tried to collect fates for eons. Samkiel's father was the only one who could until Nismera. But others wanted glimpses into their futures, so they took and used oracles for their own selfish purposes until none were left."

My lip curled. "That's terrible."

"This world has been for a very long time," Orym said as the oracle sobbed. "Let's go."

We turned to leave, and in a surprising surge of energy, she jumped to her feet, the chains groaning.

"An empty, empty shell," the oracle barked and laughed, slumping in the chains. "Hollow. Void."

I took a step back. "Okay, well, this was lovely. We're going to leave now and let you ramble on." I turned toward Orym, mouthing the words, *What's her deal?*

"Come on." Orym nudged.

"I wouldn't follow her, headless boy, or you'll have a twin to match." She laughed, the sound a sick, wet thing.

Orym froze. "What did you say?"

The oracle pulled on her chains. "You're both fools to think you can stop what's coming. Fools to think you'll make a difference. Chaos wants this world again, and chaos *will have it*."

"I prefer Reggie's ramblings over yours, just to be clear."

Orym tugged on my shoulder. "She mentioned my twin. Maybe she knows something. We should take her back with us."

"If you think I'm carrying the dirty, crazy lady back to . . ." My words trailed off. I stepped closer to him and lowered my voice so she couldn't overhear. "Back to them. You're more insane than she is."

"She mentioned my twin," Orym pleaded.

"Your twin is fine. You just talked to her."

Orym's eyes searched mine, his tail swishing in agitation, but he nodded. "You're right. You're right."

"Yes." I rubbed a gentle hand on his arm. "Now, mystery woman and sword that we have to catch."

The tips of his canines showed as he smiled, but he obliged, turning on his heel.

"You do not trust me, but trust the one who defies nature," the oracle spat. "She is destruction, boy. No one will be safe with her. No one ever is." She laughed, and I felt my nails turn to claws. I dropped Orym's arm, careful not to hurt him. My blood chilled at her words, and this time, Orym stopped.

"Dianna." Whatever was on my face scared him, and I knew my eyes bled red.

"Do you think you can touch death, girl, and it not take something from you?"

"Shut up." The words left my lips on a hiss. I turned toward her, and the oracle grinned.

"He watches you now." She swayed on her feet, a chaotic laugh leaving as she tilted her head up. "You will be his new favorite toy. No one gets close to his kingdom without . . . without . . . without." Her words died on another sob as whatever she was remembering or seeing crippled her.

"What is she talking about?" Orym whispered, but I said nothing, standing as if my feet were suddenly stuck to the floor. I felt it again, the cold chill that had been with me since the tunnels, as if a part of me had never left there or something had followed. Was that the man I saw at River Bend watching me? Or was it the shadows I kept seeing out of the corner of my eye? Was I being followed? My heart raced in my chest, and I knew what she meant.

". . . ianna!" Orym turned me toward him, jerking me out of my fear-induced paralysis. I remembered to breathe, and with every gulp of air I took in, determination set in a bit deeper.

"We need to leave," I said, steeling my shoulders.

Saliva dripped from her mouth as she pulled on her chains. "Ask her, headless boy. Ask her what she begged the stars for and what lives now. Ask her what she ripped from the very heavens. And then ask her if she cares. The old blood runs through her veins. The first Ig'Morruthen. He did not care either."

"Orym, let's go." I tried and failed to pull him away, and he brushed my hands off of him.

"No," he snapped. "What is she talking about?"

The oracle smiled far too wildly to be anything other than Otherworldly. "If Nismera is cruel, then you, Ayla, are evil."

"I am not," I snapped far too quickly.

"Ayla?" Orym asked.

"It's my real name. Or the one my father gave me. It's a long story." I raised my hand toward the oracle. "Just shut up."

"He does not know your father? The Celestial of Death. The one who carved weapons for the gods."

Orym's head nearly twisted off with how fast he looked at me. "Azrael? *Azrael* your father? What have you not been telling me?"

"Not now," I snapped.

"Yes, now." He bared his teeth. "You treated me as if I couldn't be trusted when it's been you this whole time."

"It's not like that."

The oracle went on. "You think the universe has not seen the blood you've shed and how you bathed in it? The vile and vicious things you've done and how you slept like a babe? Tell the doomed elf how you feed on life but are absent of it. Do you think the stars will reward you with love now? That you will know peace? You are *doomed*."

Orym's eyes narrowed on me. "What are you talking about? Tell me."

"Orym, stop," I responded far quicker than I intended. I pointed toward her. "You said it yourself. The oracles went mad."

"Ask her what she brought back," the oracle sneered. "Ask her what she threatened and why death itself paused."

"Shut up, or I'll permanently shut you up," I growled at her.

Orym's eyes widened as he stared at me. "Brought back?"

"Ask her," the oracle begged.

"No." I interrupted. "Look, we have to go. If that woman gets away with the sword—"

Orym stepped away from me. "I don't care about the sword. What is she talking about? What did you do?"

"Ask her what she carved from the universe and then ask her how," the oracle spat, and my talons grew.

"Dianna, what did you bring back?"

The oracle's laughter burst through the room, and Orym's eyes held so much fear that I knew I didn't have to speak the words.

He knew.

"The most powerful being in the entire realm is not the World Ender, but the one who protects the World Ender. The one who brought him back from the *dead*," the oracle purred.

I was in the room within the next second. Orym snapped at me to stop as I rammed my fist through her skull.

LIV

Dianna

I scrubbed at the dark blood staining my cuticles until the water in the sink turned from brown to clear. My mind flashed back to Onuna and how many times I had to shower the blood from my hands and mouth.

"If you breathe a word of this, I'll make sure her headless boy comment comes true."

Orym strode in, his hands in his pockets. Neither of us had changed. He still wore his dirty suit, and my blue dress was covered in debris.

"Samkiel will be up soon. He did a last sweep of the area for any missing murderous creatures or mysterious women with magical swords."

I nodded. I was so glad Samkiel showed up right after I killed the oracle. Orym said nothing, claiming she threatened him, and that was that. Samkiel was mostly concerned about me and whether I was hurt.

Orym leaned against the counter as I scrubbed and scrubbed.

"Did he find anything?"

"No." Orym sighed. "We assume most creatures are fleeing back to the Otherworld, and there was no sign of the mystery woman."

The stupid spot in that damn cuticle wouldn't leave.

"You didn't tell him. I guess you can live another day."

"You're going to have to eventually," Orym said.

"I know. I just . . ." I scrubbed my nails a fraction harder.

Calloused hands took mine, his mauve skin dotted with small bloody splotches. I knew when the chaos had erupted, he and Samkiel had helped as many as they could. Both were far nicer than me. He grabbed a dry cloth off the counter and gently patted my raw hands dry. "I think you got all the oracle off."

"Maybe."

"Do you want to talk about it?"

My eyes burned. "The oracle wasn't wrong about anything. I do feel hollow. Since it happened, I've felt different . . . wrong. It's like something is missing, and I can't find it. The only time I feel like myself is when he is near me."

Orym didn't say anything, just held my hands as I found the words.

"I had a sister." My voice was barely a whisper. "Who I loved very much. She is the reason I am what I am. I gave up my life to keep her heart beating, and then she was taken from me. I couldn't save her. Then Samkiel . . . I couldn't lose him, too. I refused to, so I threatened to burn all the realms in those tunnels, and I meant it. I would destroy everything, and I was prepared to do just that. Then . . ."

Orym squeezed my hands, grounding me. "And then?"

I nodded toward my finger. "It went away. Our mark had formed. It burned and sealed and went away. I lost us our mark. That was my price. He's not mine anymore."

Orym's eyes softened with pain as he looked at me. "That's not your price, Dianna, trust me. I've lived with you both and heard the way he speaks about you when you aren't even around. Gods, the way he looks at you. It's as if you have hung the stars themselves. He's tied to you now, Dianna. Trust me when I say that you don't need the mark."

The crack in my heart I'd refused to acknowledge seemed to heal at his words. I had been so scared that losing our mark meant we would lose *us*, and he'd leave me. That I had ruined us like I had ruined so much in my life. I glanced up at Orym, who was still gently patting my hands. "You think so?"

"There's no way you could have brought your amata back from the dead without being tethered in some deeper way." He smiled at me, attempting to cheer me up. "It would have been utterly impossible."

"Maybe."

"But the universe does not give you anything without paying for it. There always has to be balance." Orym's eyes burned into mine. "Dianna, I'm sorry you had to watch him die. I've been there, and I wish I were as strong as you. I would have paid the same price to keep her."

"You lost your amata." Everything made sense now. "That's what you lost."

I heard a throat clear from the doorway a moment before I felt his power encompass me.

"Am I interrupting something?" Samkiel asked.

I pulled my hands back, brushing a strand of hair from my face. The moment we were no longer touching, Orym stumbled back, pushed by Samkiel's power.

"No, I was just checking on Dianna."

"After I punched a hole in an oracle's face," I added.

Samkiel kept his gaze pinned on Orym, and I swore I saw sweat forming on Orym's brow.

"I believe I am pretty capable of taking care of her," Samkiel said, folding his arms across his chest.

I guessed from an outside perspective it had looked intimate and secretive. It was made worse because Orym couldn't tell him what we were talking about. So, instead, Orym cleared his throat and made his way out of the bathroom in a hurry.

I smirked, leaning on the sink. "I thought gods don't get jealous?"

Samkiel kept his eyes on the door until we heard Orym head downstairs, his arms folded so tightly that his shirt was straining over his biceps, shoulders, and chest. Then he dropped his arms and strode toward me, his lips pressed into a hard line, and a muscle in his jaw twitched. Watching him walk toward me seemed to ease my soul.

"You know I was joking, right? If I thought he was even slightly interested, I'd boil him from the inside out." He raised his hand and tugged at the strap of my dress. "Besides, you were gone all night in a lovely dress, spending time with another who all but tossed herself at you, and then you came back smelling of her. Now, I find you holding hands and whispering with Orym in our bathroom. I am feeling . . . territorial."

I studied his face, every line and beloved feature transcribed in my brain. Samkiel truly had no idea the lengths I would go for him and only him. I understood his jealousy. I had left him before at my lowest and had been with others to push him away. Even with all his power and self-confidence, a part of him would always worry. I regretted putting that doubt in his eyes. I cupped his face and forced a smile. "There is nothing more important to me than you."

His eyes softened, and that haunted look disappeared. He dipped his head and kissed my palm, his storm-colored eyes holding my gaze. "I know the feeling."

I smiled, this time not having to force it, and leaned forward to kiss his lips before stepping out of his embrace. He felt the hesitation there, the lack of me, I suppose. But I was still shaken by the oracle and all she'd said. I turned my back to him.

"Can you help me?"

He slid his fingers across the exposed skin of my back, undoing one small button at a time.

"I want a bath," I said softly. "And I want to go to bed."

"Anything you wish, akrai."

I looked at him over my shoulder. "Can you just hold me tonight?"

Worry creased his brow, not because he minded but because I never asked for that. My need for affection usually resulted in us both screaming with pleasure, never the soft, delicate moments he loved so much. Those moments scared me more than I wished to admit. I didn't know how to deal with the emotions those tiny moments gave me. I could fuck him until his legs refused to work, but I'd never truly had that level of intimacy.

Samkiel finished the last button, and I held the dress against my breasts to keep it from falling. He sat on the edge of the tub and twisted the chain-style knobs, running his hand under the water to check the temperature.

"Do you wish to tell me why you were crying, or shall I ask Orym?"

I knew when he said ask, he meant in a non-friendly way. Samkiel seemed to be more erratic than ever when it came to me.

"It was nothing," I whispered, and his brows rose in question. "The oracle said some things that upset me, that is all."

"Said what?"

He moved his hand to his lap, satisfied with the temperature as the tub filled.

"Said things that made me think of Gabby."

His brows pinched together in empathy. "Oh, akrai. Do you wish for me to go kill her twice?"

A snort left my lips even as my eyes filled with unshed tears. "You're cute when you're homicidal."

He smiled at me and stood up, pulling his shirt off.

"We will not both fit in this bathtub," I said, knowing that was exactly what he wanted, and he wasn't expecting sex. The one thing I'd learned from Samkiel was that he craved to touch me. Every chance he got, he held my hand, pressed a knee to mine, or even a foot. He especially loved bathing or showering with me. Samkiel wanted to do everything with me, and the knowledge healed a fraction of my cold, bruised, damaged heart.

"You know me," he tapped my nose, "I'll make it fit."

I couldn't help the small laugh that burst from me, even though I knew he hadn't said it on purpose.

"There she is. There's my Dianna." A soft smile graced his lips, proud that he could chase some of the darkness away from me. He held out his hand once more, waiting.

I dropped my dress, and he led me to the tub. It was not a good fit despite his confidence, but we made it work. Samkiel wrapped his big body around mine and held me close. He whispered to me, doing everything he could to make me laugh. The harrowing tension that had gripped me melted away.

After our bath, Samkiel headed across the hall to brief Orym on his plan. They talked for a while as I lay on the small bed, gazing out the window. A caw sounded on the wind, a dark bird with wings the color of midnight coasting by, its medium-sized body darting past the window. I moved my hands under my head, watching the silver of Samkiel's power burn in the night sky, and I made up my mind to tell him. I couldn't hide it anymore, and I had to tell him what the oracle had said. It wasn't fair to him, even if he would be mad at me.

The door creaked open, and Samkiel padded in. "Sorry, that took a little while. I also filled Roccurem in on what happened."

I nodded and rested my head on my hands. "What's the plan?"

Samkiel grabbed a throw off the chair and moved around to the other side of the bed. It dipped and creaked beneath his weight as he settled and spread the blanket over us. He wrapped his arms around me and pulled me close. Fitting my body to his, he rested his face in the crook of my neck.

"We need to wait until I find the murrak. That's my main goal."

"Not the girl with the sword?" I asked.

"No," he said. "The murrak is not to be trifled with, and I need to make sure it is no longer in the city."

I turned in his embrace. "What is it?"

His eyes held mine. "There are princes in the Otherworld, seven to be exact. Each carries a totem from their mother, Icnima. She birthed monsters as the fables go. The murrak is one of seven ancient creatures still in existence, a gift to her son, Umemri."

I recalled its massive form, the legs, and how it moved. Even its skin seemed Otherworldly. "It looks gross. You know I hate bugs. Why couldn't she get them something nicer?"

His smile made my heart do that stupid flip. "Yes, I suppose she could have, and it does resemble the insects from your world, but I am afraid it is far worse than anything Onuna has to offer."

"So, is your goal to capture it? Since it belongs to one of them."

Samkiel sighed deeply. "That's my goal. I would like not to elicit the wrath of the Otherworld. I am already fighting one war."

"It's tough being the hero?" I teased.

"Tremendously."

I nodded, another question waiting on the tip of my tongue. "Do you think I'm evil?" I blurted, not sure why I asked or why it slipped out. It was something the oracle said, and it had stuck in my brain. I was too afraid to look at him. Instead, I studied my hands, where they rested against his chest. I didn't know what I would do if I were to see a flicker or change in his eyes that told me even some part of him believed I was. Even if he didn't think I was evil, I was not good. Not like him.

"Is that what she said?"

"More or less." I shrugged. "I just want to be what you and Gabby see in me. Not what he made me."

A gentle, calloused finger touched my chin, lifting my gaze to his. No secret emotion hung in his eyes, no lingering doubt or question, just pure, raw . . . love.

"Dianna, you are perfect the way you are. There is nothing I would ever change about you. Fangs and all."

"I guess she just got under my skin." I leaned forward, brushing a quick kiss against his lips.

"You know what I think?" he asked. "I think there are a lot of people, beings, who see you, see your power, and fear it. They are used to being abused by such power, and meeting or even hearing of you frightens them. But that has nothing to do with you and everything to do with them. You are not evil and never have been. There is no question in my mind, body, or soul."

I felt my eyes burn. "I mean, not even a little bit of a question?"

"I have seen evil. I have fought evil gods, monsters, and beings for longer than I care to admit, but when I look at you, I see . . . hope."

My head jerked back. "Hope?"

He nodded, wrapping his arm around me a fraction tighter. "Hope. Because I know you have the power to change worlds, and you'd do that for the people you love. Love, Dianna. It doesn't make you weak.

It offers strength to anyone who experiences it, but with how intensely and completely you love, it makes you nearly invincible. I saw it in how ferociously you protected your sister and me. I have seen your heart, physically held it, and I have never met an evil being who loves as you do. So no, you're not evil."

I didn't even know I had started to cry until his thumb brushed away a stray tear. "That's sweet."

"We all have flaws. Such is living, but evil? You? Not even on your worst day."

I leaned forward, my forehead touching his. Never in my whole life had I felt as whole as I did when I was with him. I had never felt so alive. I never . . . felt. His breath mingled with mine, his scent alone, making my heart race.

He pulled back and glanced at me. His hand ran lazily up and down my back. "I will say it is peculiar, though."

"What?" I asked.

"Oracles, while boisterous, I suppose, are not usually confrontational."

"Well, maybe she lost it. No telling what she was subjected to. And let's not forget she dug her own eyes out. I mean, how many ancient beings are out there that speak in riddles?"

Samkiel chuckled. "Far too many."

"Sorry, I killed some ancient, powerful thing."

He shook his head. "Don't be. From what you said, I believe she knew your temper and what buttons to push, so you'd react as you did."

"Why would she do that?"

His gaze held mine, the light of the moon spilling into our dark room and making the gray a fraction more Otherworldly. "Fear of Nismera. Yours would be a quick death. Nismera has the entire realm terrified because her cruelty knows no bounds. Sometimes death is not the worst option and offers peace in place of suffering."

My stomach lurched at his words.

Ask her what she ripped from the very heavens.

I wondered if he'd felt the peace of death when he died, even for a second. Had he felt the rupture when I'd begged death to steal that from him? Would he hate me when he knew what I'd done? Would he leave? I knew in my heart that I could have never done that to Gabby, even though her being here would bring me so much happiness and comfort. I could never strip her of the peace she so desperately deserved. Even if I could have her with me, I wouldn't. But for Samkiel? In a heartbeat. I'd burn worlds, erase empires, and turn stars to ash if I had to.

The oracle was right. I was evil.

I ran my thumb across his cheek, my heart burning with one simple truth. "I am extremely selfish when it comes to you."

He smiled, placing a kiss on my palm. "I know the feeling."

I curled up next to him, listening to his heartbeat as sleep eventually took him. His hand stilled on my back, but I didn't sleep that night. I stared at the sky, watching the silver wave of his power ebb and flow across the night sky, barely noticing the bird made of midnight as it flew by again.

LV
Isaiah

Veruka finished braiding Imogen's hair and sighed. "How long are you going to keep her?" she asked, placing the braid across Imogen's shoulder.

I chewed on the pad of my thumb. "I am not *keeping* her. I'm protecting her."

"That's not what the other soldiers say. They think you've made her into your own personal sex doll," Veruka said, her hand on her hip and her tail thrashing behind her.

I snorted. "We both know that's not what I like."

Her mauve cheeks darkened with desire, but the memories of us together did nothing for me. Nothing did anymore.

"Well, if you're not using her, I—"

"No." I straightened and blew out a breath. "Don't you have a shipment to help unload?"

She made a disgruntled noise but left nonetheless. I walked to Imogen and checked her face over once more. No blood speckled her cheeks, and her hair was tidy, yet I couldn't stop myself from reaching out to touch her. I cursed myself and dropped my hand.

"Sorry about the whole . . ." I made an explosion noise, mimicking it with my hands. "I thought they would surrender, to be honest. The rebels have grown braver."

She said nothing, her gaze focusing through me. I wondered if it had scared her to see their heads blow off their bodies, knowing I did it without even so much as moving a muscle. My gut rolled at the thought of her fearing me, but I didn't understand why it made me uneasy.

"I'd never hurt you. You know that, right?"

No response. There was never a response.

A knock came from the door, and I turned as Kaden entered. He wasn't wearing his armor, just a loose-fitting shirt and matching dark pants.

"You look comfortable," I said.

He shrugged, placing his hands in his pockets. "Not on sister duty today. You?"

I smiled. "Just got back."

Kaden glanced behind himself before lifting his hands, the door clicking closed behind him. His eyes darted toward Imogen.

"She can't repeat anything you are about to say, remember? You brainwashed them all."

He watched me as I strode toward my bureau. I reached for the buckle on my shoulder and opened it, my armored chest plate falling to the ground.

"You seem upset about that. Growing comfortable with the celestial, Brother?"

I rummaged around for a shirt. "Why does everyone think I would fuck someone who wouldn't enjoy it?"

Kaden snorted. "I never insinuated that. I've just noticed you seem to have an attachment."

"I turned the ones who tried to touch her without her permission into a soup worse than the one Frigg thinks he cooks so well."

Kaden chuckled and sat on my bed. "My point exactly. Attachment."

I didn't rebuke his claim. I had no idea why, but from the moment I'd first laid eyes on Imogen, she was all I thought about. It was becoming a problem. Even when I closed my eyes at night, she was all I dreamed of. An attachment was an understatement.

I had been looking for a way to reverse what my brother did and free her. There had to be a way. I took Imogen with me on every assignment

Mera sent me on, and when I found a shaman or a healer, I would take her to see them. They all said that there was no cure. Usually, my temper would rise in response, and they lost their heads afterward. But at least I was trying.

"Is that why you've come? To give me a hard time?" I asked, folding my arms across my chest.

Kaden shook his head. "No, that's not why I'm here."

"What's wrong?"

"Remember when we were younger? We made a pact to keep what we knew of each other and our powers between us."

I nodded. "Yeah, is this another one of those times? Is this about Nismera's witch? You know I never judge. If you say you love Dianna, I believe it. But I know better than anyone that sometimes, especially in this world, you have to blow off some steam."

Kaden forced a smile as he stood, clasping his hands behind his back. It had been so long since I had been around him that I had forgotten how much power he contained beneath his skin.

"It's not about her. It's about you."

I folded my arms and frowned. "Me? Why?"

"Why does Nismera have your blood?"

My brows furrowed. "My blood?" Then it hit me. "Oh yes, she asked, and I gave. I didn't question it, to be honest."

Kaden's head tilted as I strode by, heading toward the bathroom. "At all?"

I shrugged. "Why? It's Mera. The only one who gave a shit about us when Unir locked us away. The only one who rescued us and gave a damn when the world didn't. If she asked for my liver, I'd give it. No questions. Wouldn't you?"

Something passed through Kaden's eyes, and he glanced away. I gripped his shoulder. "Just like I would you. You're still my favorite sibling."

Kaden smiled even if it bared no teeth. "As you are mine."

"Why the questions? Also, how did you even find out about that?"

Kaden took a step back. "You should clean up. Nismera is happy she got a few of her relics and Otherworld creatures, even if she didn't get the murrak. I think she wants a dinner set tonight."

"Are you okay?"

Kaden said nothing as he turned and headed for the door.

"Hey," I called out, and he stopped, his hand hovering over the knob. "You mean the world to me, Kaden. You never gave up on me, even when you were locked behind the realms. Nismera told me how often she spoke to you when I couldn't and how desperate you were to get back to me. You've always cared for and protected me, and I love you, but it's Mera, Kaden, not another monster."

He glanced at me over his shoulder and gave me another forced smile before he left the room, the door clicking closed behind him.

LVI

Dianna

Our shoes squeaked as we headed up the small steps to the inn. Orym, Samkiel, and I were covered in mud from our toes to our eyebrows. We stopped before entering, and Samkiel shook the caked mud from his sword before calling it back into his ring. Orym folded his daggers and tucked them back into their sheaths.

"Well, that was fun. Sign me up never again," I said, squeezing muddy water from my hair.

"Sorry," Samkiel said, scratching the back of his head and flinging dirt in all directions. "The murrak are known for being underground dwellers. I thought if it were still here, that's where it would be."

Orym shrugged. "Well, we checked every cave system here. I think it's safe to say it has gone with Nismera."

"Which is another big cause for worry," I said.

Samkiel nodded, placing his hands on his hips. "If she has the murrak, I fear what she may use it for."

"We need to let Roccurem know. I know he is still in touch with Savees. See if he has heard anything."

"Sounds good."

"And I'll check with Veruka," Orym added. "See if it made it there."

"Okay." I sighed. "So we headed back then?"

"No," Samkiel interjected, and both Orym and I looked at him. "Orym, you head back and let Roccurem know, but I want to show Dianna something."

Orym rolled his eyes and scoffed in disgust but nodded. "I'll let you know if I find anything, and I'll be sure to knock very loudly."

Samkiel glared at him in annoyance and lifted his hand. A small portal opened to the library where Reggie usually stayed. Orym waved before stepping inside and leaving us alone.

My smile was soft and warm, unlike how I felt last night. "What did you want to show me?"

Samkiel's head tilted ever so slightly. "It's a surprise."

"A flower for my lady." Samkiel held the stem of a beautiful white flower, the center a bright yellow. I smiled as the lady selling them beamed at us. She had been standing out here without a single customer until we walked up. Samkiel had bought them all, yelling for the patrons nearby to come. A small crowd soon formed, and they collected the beautiful blooms one by one. I didn't say anything as he handed her enough coins that she almost burst into tears.

I feigned a gasp. "Thank you ever so kindly." I toss a lock of my hair behind my shoulders. "How will I ever repay you?"

Samkiel's grin was pure joy. "I'm sure you'll think of something." He stepped closer, placing the stem behind my ear, the flower resting against the side of my head. "Let's hurry. I don't want you to miss it."

I nodded, and he grabbed my hand. Samkiel's smile was downright smug as we walked down the narrow stone road at the edge of town. I kept catching him looking at me, his eyes drawn to my dress with off-the-shoulder sleeves and a wide-flowing skirt that ended a little above my knees. It wasn't lust that burned in his eyes but pure astonishment. For once, I wasn't wearing black or red but a soft white.

"I would never in my wildest dreams have thought to see you in such a dress," he said, sweeping his gaze over me again.

My smile widened as I walked beside him. "I have to keep you on your toes. Never let you know my next move, you know?"

His laugh was infectious. "That you do."

We walked hand in hand as we neared the lower part of town, a display of affection I was still unfamiliar with. A few lights hung from branches, leading away from the buildings and toward the source of the laughter floating through the air. It seemed that after the events of the auction and all the chaos that followed, the city wished to forget and have some fun.

"Besides, you said something cute for tonight, and I couldn't resist."

His hand squeezed mine. "I am not complaining in the slightest. You simply surprised me, akrai."

Samkiel let go of my hand as we approached a small dock. He placed his hand at the small of my back, and we got in line behind a few other couples. A lean man stood near a tall barrel, handing out what looked like thin sticks. After each person received their stick, they took them to the end of the dock. Long, thin boats pulled up, and another couple got out, making way for those waiting. I watched the exchange as we moved up in line, excitement bubbling inside me.

We reached the man handing out the sticks, and he spoke to Samkiel in a language I hadn't learned yet. They exchanged smiles and money before Samkiel was handed two. He passed one to me.

"What is this?" I asked.

"You'll see."

"So mysterious," I joked as his hand splayed on my lower back and urged me forward. A boat landed near the dock, and a man helped the couple out. They were all giggles and sweet smiles as they passed us.

Another man held onto the boat, speaking to Samkiel. He nodded and gave us a brilliant smile before walking away. Samkiel stepped into the rocky boat, placing his feet wide to stabilize it before he held his hand out to me. I grasped it without hesitation, and he helped me in. I giggled as we wobbled and quickly sat on the small wooden bench, wrapping my dress under me.

Samkiel pushed us away from the dock and sat, grabbing the oars. I watched as he steered us into deeper water, the powerful muscles on his arms and chest bunching beneath his shirt. I tipped my head back, enjoying the cool breeze on my skin. The branches of the trees dipped and draped in ringlets, teasing at the surface of the lake. Small glowing bugs darted between the tall grasses along the shore before we entered a far more open space. Several boats were spread out on the water, separated by a few feet. Samkiel maneuvered us into an open space, and we came to a stop.

I watched a girl lift her stick thing and press it against her partner's. They sparked and started to glow, both of them burning at the ends. The lake lit up as more couples did the same, and I turned toward Samkiel, who was already waiting. He was always waiting for me.

I raised mine, touching the ends together. Sparks flew between us, a wash of gold illuminating our faces.

"You said you wanted a date amongst all the chaos, so I thought this would suffice." Samkiel smiled. "Here, look."

He leaned closer to the side of the boat, holding the sparkler out over the water. I shifted closer to him, leaning my stick against the side, letting it bounce next to his.

"What are we looking for?"

"So impatient." He smiled. "Just wait."

So I did. The water was a clear, shimmering blue, and I could see the bottom even in the dark. Then I saw movement between the thick oval rocks at the bottom. I held my sparking stick a bit closer to the water, hoping to see better. They weren't overly large, about the size of my foot, and strangely wispy. The pair rose from below, swimming toward the surface. They had no eyes from what I could see, just beautiful scales of cream and pink. Their diaphanous tails trailed behind them in sweeping paths as they twined around their partners. They followed the lights, Samkiel showing me how to move them. I smiled and followed his lead, watching mesmerized as the small water creatures danced.

"They are called moonkrest, and they are very rare. Only two planets in the whole universe have them, and they mate for life."

He shot me a glance, and I smiled. "Terrible decision for them, really."

Samkiel shook his head, his smile deepening. "They are nocturnal.

The moon is usually their guide as they swim up from the bottom to dance and feed all night beneath the light."

"They're beautiful."

"They are. The only problem is the moon only shows once a month here lately. An explosion not too far off in the cosmos pushed it a tad off course, so the locals found a new way to save the creatures. The lights we provide attract the little bugs that feed them," Samkiel explained, still moving his sparkler in a slow back-and-forth motion. "But being the enterprising folk they are, they expanded the effort into an attraction and the new hottest dating spot in the area."

"Smart move on their part."

He chuckled. "I agree."

I leaned over a bit more, watching the moonkrest twirl and dance around each other.

"Do you wish to know a secret?"

I let my sparkler sway as I glanced his way. "From you? Always."

"I was actually nervous about bringing you here."

"What? Why?"

He swallowed, his throat bobbing as his nervousness became apparent. "I know this will be hard to believe, but I have never planned a date in the history of my long existence."

I leaned back, a hand on my chest as I fake gasped. "You don't say."

"Ha ha, very funny." He rolled his eyes. "I'm being serious. I hoped you wouldn't hate it or think it was stupid. This is the part where I would ask Logan for his advice, and he would tell me if I was doing it right. He has far more experience with dates than I."

I leaned back over the edge of the boat, watching him. He didn't even realize the haunted look that swept over his face at the mention of his friend. I scooted closer to him, bumping his shoulder with mine.

"I think you did fantastic," I whispered. "Best date ever, truly."

"Mm-hmm." He snickered. "Don't mock me."

"I will admit, it is funny to think that you, the great and powerful World Ender, everyone's favorite—"

"Okay, okay." He nudged back. "I get it. I guess I just never needed to, nor was there anyone I wished to spend time with like this."

"Well, I am honored to be your first." I grinned at him.

"The festival was actually my first date."

The sparklers danced between us, and the fish continued to dance, but at the moment, we were far more invested in the conversation at hand.

"The festival was not a date." I snorted as the moonkrest snapped a bug from the surface of the lake and traveled to its mate to share its catch.

"It wasn't?" His head whipped to mine.

"No." A small chuckle left my lips as I cast a glance at him. "It was a fun distraction while we waited for that lead. Besides, you didn't even like me then."

His lips turned downwards, a single brow raising. "Oh, I didn't?"

"No." I playfully pushed him. "It was mild toleration at that point."

"That's not true."

My head tipped. "Oh?" I stared at him, waiting for him to continue.

"I felt something then, although I was completely unaware of what it was. I think you woke something up inside me then, and I've never been the same since." He shrugged as if he hadn't just altered my whole world. "I also counted every single person who looked at you that night."

My head tipped back on a laugh. "No, you didn't! Did you?"

Samkiel nodded. "I still do. I blamed it on my hyper-awareness and my need to protect you. All of which stemmed from my feelings for you. It seems I'm still like that, if not worse."

"Definitely worse." I leaned forward and kissed his cheek. "But I think you're perfect."

He smiled smugly. "I know."

My free hand whipped out, popping him playfully on the shoulder, and he laughed. Sparks flew into the water, and the fish swam a tad faster before looping back.

"So yes, that was our first date. I count it since it was the first time I had fun. I never had fun growing up on Rashearim, but then I met you, and well . . . you're fun."

Something sparked behind his eyes at that word, as if he had been searching for that for a while.

I smiled back. "Well, I am glad I can entertain you, my king."

He clicked his teeth, closing his eyes briefly before smirking at me. "Don't do that. I do not plan for our date to end just yet."

The laugh that left my lips had a few other couples looking toward us before I covered my mouth. "Okay, fine, that's our first." I nodded. "And ice skating is our second."

"Oh, yes. That one is definitely my favorite."

I lifted one brow. "Oh, because of how many times you fell on the ice?"

"Definitely." He cast a glance at me that was pure heat, and I knew he meant what happened after the ice skating.

The sparks between us burned brighter. The light illuminated Samkiel's tanned skin and dazzling smile, casting shadows across the planes of his arms and shoulders. I was completely enraptured by him. Against all odds and despite what the universe had taken from me, here he was, caring for me. He had pulled me back from the harrowing edge of despair more than once, and here he was again, offering me a slice of peace once more, and gods, I fell all over again.

Unable to verbalize everything I was feeling, I just said, "You give me the best memories."

"Good," he said with a smile before leaning over and placing a kiss on my lips.

The sparks between us fizzled as he kissed me again. Lazy, slow, and perfect. I could get drunk off his kisses and the different varieties he showered me with. I'd never memorize them all, but I hoped we had eternity for me to try. My hand cupped his face before sliding back to run my fingers through the short hair at the nape of his neck. The lake grew dark as everyone's sparklers went out one by one. His hand splayed across my back as he deepened the kiss, our boat rocking at the movement.

No force in this world or the next could pull us apart. I knew that more than ever in that moment.

It wasn't until the lake went silent, the forest with it, that we heard the screams.

LVII
Dianna

The sky was gleaming a thick orange by the time we made it back to the pier. Samkiel jumped out first and then reached down to lift me from the boat. We raced toward the city, crackling flames spreading from one tavern to the next as people flooded the streets.

"Nismera?" I asked.

Samkiel shook his head, his face grim. "No, they are screaming about monsters."

Splintered pieces of wood burst into the air. We darted forward while everyone scrambled past us in the opposite direction. One building split, then another farther down, a massive beast charging through them like they were made of paper.

"How many monsters are there?" I asked. A familiar aching screech resonated through the air, and I knew it wasn't many but one. One giant, creepy, crawling bug. "The murrak."

Samkiel slipped his rings on his fingers, his eyes burning silver. His armor flowed over his skin, covering him from head to toe.

"Sami," I placed my hand on his arm, "what if she shows?"

He didn't even glance at me. "It's heading toward the lower part of town where the families are. Sleeping families."

"Children." I finished for him.

"I need you to help me block it from the lower part of the city. I have to save as many as I can. Give me a head start, but whatever you do, do not engage with it." The lower part of his helmet flowed away from his lips and jaw. He cupped the back of my head and pulled me close, kissing me deeply. "Be careful."

I licked my lips and nodded. Samkiel took off at a run, and I shifted and lunged for the sky.

Flames burst from my throat as I circled high above, my wings beating in powerful sweeps. From my aerial view, I could see the path the murrak had taken in its hunt for food. It had demolished the town where the businesses were. Thank the gods, most of the citizens preferred to be home at this time of night.

I spat a controlled fireball, blocking it from the end of town where Samkiel was working. I glanced toward his small silver figure. He was going door to door, ushering families out of their homes and toward the safety of the tree line.

I swept lower, scorching another line through town, trying to contain the murrak. A screech, loud and damning, filled the air, and I knew the beast had figured out what Samkiel was doing. It doubled its efforts to get to him but kept running into my fire. It reared up and roared a challenge into the sky.

Great, now I was on a bug's hit list.

I cut through the rising smoke, scouring the ground below, but I didn't see the creature. I turned to make another pass. Fuck, had I lost it? A splash caught my ear, and I flew that way. My eyes widened when I saw the murrak burst through the water at the village's edge. Fuck, it had gone to the water to avoid my flames. I pivoted and tucked my wings in tight, diving toward the ground. My form shifted, and I landed in a squat. The smoke was thick here, the wind swirling it in eddies along the shore.

Screams rang through the air as the murrak made it to the village. I sprinted, pieces of stone crunching beneath my shoes. The murrak moved through the homes Samkiel hadn't reached. As people ran outside, it grabbed one woman and held her to its face, its pinchers opening. She screamed and went rigid, a clear translucent form of herself parting from her body and falling into the creature's jaws.

The murrak fed and tossed her body to the side. It rolled to a stop, her eyes white and unseeing, her skin ashen. Oh, gods. It didn't eat meat. It ate souls.

"Come on, we have to move now." I heard Samkiel say, but so did the murrak. It lifted its antennae and turned toward him.

Samkiel was bent, completely unaware of the creature looking at him as he lifted a man and his family out of the rubble. If the murrak could smile, it did so as it focused on him. Those hundred legs shot out, racing toward him. I had only a second to think about what to do, a second to save the one person I couldn't live without, so I reacted.

I sprinted forward, forcing myself to go faster, my legs burning with the effort. Samkiel looked up as the family near him ran. He saw me, then looked to his side as the murrak charged. My palms hit him square in the chest, sending him flying through the wall of the neighboring house, and the murrak grabbed me.

LVIII
Dianna

Rubble, sharp and jagged, hit my shoulder and face as we landed in a nearby house. A woman and her child screamed as I pushed the debris from my body and stood up. She held her baby to her chest as she wailed. I heard the rubble shift behind me, and the woman's eyes went wide with terror.

"Run," I said, pointing toward the back door. "Now would be nice."

She wasted no time, springing to her feet and running out the door with her baby clutched close.

Goosebumps ran rampant along my skin as I heard the murrak slinking behind me. I turned to face it and looked up . . . and up. It towered over me, dirt, wood, and stone falling from its exoskeleton. Its pincers opened and closed as it glared down at me. The creature's large, crystalline body whipped toward me, wrapping around me, binding my arms, and immobilizing me completely. I grunted, struggling against the strangling grip. The creature's assortment of legs dug into the ground. It opened its twin pincers, and a scream made of death burst across my face. Tendrils of white light emerged from its mouth, slithering disgustingly against me, looking for something to latch on to. My body tensed in anticipation, except . . . I felt nothing. There was no pain, no stretching as it tried to consume my soul.

It stopped and closed its jaws, rearing its massive head back in surprise. The antennae atop its skull flicked as if trying to get a read on me, its black-as-night eyes widening.

"Void," it said in a gasping voice before it dropped me.

I landed in a crouch, confusion furrowing my brow as the murrak backed up. I wasn't sure, but I thought it looked at me as if I was the terrifying one. "What?"

A bolt of silver flashed before my eyes, and the creature's blood sprayed, covering my face. The head of the murrak dropped to the ground, and its body followed. I stood, watching the disgusting legs twitch, that word repeating over and over again in my head. Every damned beast here had seen me and said the same thing.

Void.

Hollow.

Empty.

The way the oracle had laughed echoed in my head.

"Do you think you can touch death, girl, and it not take something from you?"

Samkiel gently gripped my elbow and turned me to him. His eyes blazed with worry as he looked me over. I was frozen solid, couldn't think, couldn't breathe, and not from that damned bug, but because I had finally figured it out.

". . .anna?" His voice brought the world back to me, my ears ringing. "Dianna, look at me. Are you hurt? How do you feel?" He grabbed my chin, forcing me to look up at him. "Do you feel—"

"The cost of resurrection," I said, my voice cracking.

His brows furrowed. "What?"

"You said." I swallowed the thick lump in my throat. "They all said."

It explained why my hunger was never satisfied, why nothing eased the gaping hole in my chest, why I struggled to feel for anyone except him.

"Dianna, what are you talking about?"

"You died," I blurted out.

He looked at me like I had slapped him, but I continued.

"In that tunnel, you died." My heart hammered, and my breathing turned ragged. "You don't remember it. I think because it happened so fast, but you died, and I held you, and I hated everything. So I begged and pleaded for a way, and Reggie gave me one. I made a promise in that tunnel, in that damn cold tunnel, that if they didn't return you to me, I'd rip the universe to atoms. I meant it. Our mark formed, burned on my finger, and then disappeared. You breathed and—and—and . . ."

I was shaking. Everything that had happened over the last few months came tumbling out. I had been so fucking stupid never to question it, to think I got out free with no consequences. The words just kept coming, spilling out of me, and I could not stop them.

"Resurrection has a cost, and this is mine. Every single Otherworld creature has said it to me, but I didn't get it, didn't understand. It," I pointed to the corpse of the murrak, "said it too. Void."

"Your soul. The cost of saving me was your soul," Samkiel said, and I flinched. His jaw clenched, and his hands fisted. The pure, blistering anger in his eyes nearly obscured the soul-deep sorrow.

LIX

Dianna

Samkiel turned on me the moment we stepped into the makeshift study, and the door slammed shut behind us.

"You've been lying to me. For months."

"Yes."

"Months, Dianna."

"I know." My voice cracked, the lie finally out.

He turned away from me, pacing feverishly, his boots thumping heavily against the carpet. His armor still hugged his form, gray ash dulling the brilliant shine. He'd discarded his helmet to rake his fingers through his hair, toweling the sweat-damp strands.

"Did you know? In the tunnels, when you asked? Did you know the cost then?" His gaze flicked to mine.

I lifted one shoulder, unable to bear his stare for too long. I twisted my fingers in front of me. "I didn't ask."

"You didn't ask?" he damn near yelled. "Dianna, do you have any idea what you could have done? To yourself and the realms? There is a reason resurrection is forbidden, a reason it has not been done or attempted. You put yourself at enormous risk! You—"

"I don't care," I cut him off this time, meeting his gaze.

He stopped and raised a single brow before scoffing at me. "You don't care? You lied to me, have been lying to me for months, and you don't care?"

"No," I stumbled. "Well, yes, I care about that, just not the other part. The cost part."

"Dianna." His face held nothing but pain and anger. "Your soul, Dianna. You gave up your soul for me. I would never ask such a thing. You have given up so much for others. I would never ask you to shred yet another part of yourself. Never. I want you alive and well and happy, even if I am not."

"I am," I said. "I am all of those as long as you are with me."

No matter how true they were, my words did not quell his rage. They only seemed to twist the dagger I had placed in his heart further.

"You gave up your soul, Dianna. We have no idea what that even means. Logically. You don't think! You just act and damn the consequences when it comes to your own safety."

"So I did something irrational." I tossed my hands in the air. "When have I not?"

"This isn't funny," he snapped. "You cannot make a cute joke or quip to get out of this."

"I know, I know. Listen, I wasn't trying to hurt you, okay? I just needed time to figure it out, honestly. Roccurem said—"

Samkiel stared at me, his eyes blazing now. It felt as if his building rage was sucking all the air from the room. "That's right," a harsh, bitter laugh left his lips, "Roccurem knows. Why would he not?"

"It's not like that," I corrected.

"It is exactly like that, Dianna! Because you confide in another instead of me. What other secrets do you two have that I know nothing about?"

I knew what he was thinking and how he was feeling. I had hurt him so badly before by giving myself to others, but it was the farthest thing from the truth.

I hurried to his side, placing my hand on his arm. I shook my head. "It's not like that. He was there and—"

He pulled away from me, and I felt that yawning crack form between us all over again. Panic, quick and frightening, had me reaching for him again. "There's no excuse. You have had months to tell me. I laid every piece of me at your feet, and you cannot even give me a fraction of you."

"I do," I said, hearing the plea in my voice. "I have. Look, I'm sorry, okay? I am."

He shook his head. "You keep saying that word, but I don't think you know what it means. You cannot say you're sorry and keep hurting someone, Dianna. It means nothing after that."

"I don't know what else to say." I shifted closer, but he avoided my gaze. "This. Us. A relationship is all new to me. Everything is new to me."

He finally met my gaze, and the pain darkening his eyes made my breath catch. "It's new to me, too, but I know for a fact that keeping secrets, big or small, is no way to start. Especially about resurrection. How can we have an ounce of anything without trust?"

My head reared back, agony piercing my heart, and I wasn't sure if it was my emotions or his that were affecting me so strongly. "You don't trust me?"

His face twisted with pain, and I hated myself.

"How can I when you kept this from me? When you don't trust me enough to tell me about something like this? Something that affects me just as much, if not more, than you. When you trust others above me? When you don't trust in my commitment to us enough even to tell me about our mark!"

It was true. From his perspective, it was the truth. I confided in others over him. Everyone knew but him. In my head, I was protecting him, but in reality, I was protecting myself.

"You're right. I did confide in others. Roccurem knows. Orym found out when we were in that tunnel with the oracle. Gods, even Miska knows. Do you know why it was easy to tell them? Why it means nothing with them but everything with you?" I waved a hand toward him. "Because of this. Because I don't care how they look at me or how they judge me, I could live a hundred more years and never care. I was scared, okay? Afraid of what it meant and of what you'd say."

Samkiel ran his hand over his head in agitation, pacing back and forth in long strides. "Of what I'd say?"

"That this isn't real. That maybe by bringing you back, it changed you. I am afraid that you won't want me anymore. Losing our bond terrifies me because what if that means I've lost you? I am selfish and cruel, and gods above, I am evil if I need to be for you. I would do anything for what you gave me, for what you showed me, and even the thought of losing it, losing you, makes me sick with terror. So yeah, I'm sorry I kept it from you, but I couldn't lose you again!"

The way he looked at me scared me more than anything I'd faced before. I wondered if I had finally found his line. Was this the thing he couldn't get past?

"I'm sorry that I hurt you, but I am not, nor will I ever be, sorry for what I did, for what I will do for you. I never claimed to be good or decent. You knew what I was, who I was, and you decided to be with me all the same."

"Dianna—"

"No!" I felt tears prickle my eyes, the darkness swallowing me whole. "Do you know what it feels like to have your soul cleaved in two? To have it ripped from you? That's what it felt like when you died in my arms. Pure, blinding pain that I don't think this world or the next has a word for. So don't stand there scolding me like a fucking child. You are not my father. I killed him to get to you, and I still wasn't in time. I would burn the world for you, Samkiel, and I would happily hand over my soul so that you may live. I would do it all again if it meant you existed."

He wiped his hand across his face. My words setting in and growing roots.

"How would I know what you go through?" he asked. "You lock yourself away behind walls I cannot breach. I've tried, Dianna. I've really tried, but you keep me at arm's length."

I said nothing but crossed my arms over my torso, trying to keep myself from falling into pieces.

"Admit it," he begged. "No matter how close I am to you or how I touch you, there is still a part of you that you will always keep from me."

I felt my chest crack and split wide open. This was what I was afraid of. He saw too much, and he wanted it all. I didn't know if I could give it to him.

"I'm trying," I said, no longer able to keep my voice steady.

"Try harder because I will not have half of you. I will not love only half of you. Sharing your body with me is not enough," he said, and I swore my heart broke. "It may have been to others in your past, but it's not enough for me."

I had never seen him so utterly broken. This was it for him. I had tried for months after Gabby died to find his limit to push him away, and it wasn't until now, when the thought of losing him threatened to rip me in half, that I found it. I'd rather be stabbed, burned, and beaten than experience the pain of seeing that look in his eyes.

I closed the distance between us, unable to tolerate it any longer. My hands went to his face. "Sami."

He gripped my wrists, not painfully, but with enough force to keep me from touching him. "Your lies and secrets will tear us apart far quicker than any force in this world or the next, Dianna."

Samkiel released me, and I let my hands drop to my side, and I prayed to the old gods and the new to have the floor open and swallow me whole. His eyes blazed into mine, and I shivered from the power in them, but I couldn't ignore the pain that darkened the silver. It was as sharp as any blade, and I was the one who had thrust it through his chest.

He lifted his hand, and I thought it was to stroke my face as he had done so many times before. Instead, he held it out over my head, and a rush of air whipped my hair forward as a swirling portal opened behind me. I turned and saw Reggie's all too familiar study back on Youl.

"I need you to go," he said.

I turned back to him, my eyes burning before the tears fell, staining my cheeks. "Is this . . . Are you . . . Do you not want to be with me?"

His eyes held mine, and I realized the only thing I feared in this world or the next was happening. I had my heart ripped out of my body on Onuna, and this pain was worse.

"I need to rebuild the city," he said. "And I need . . . time."

Time. He didn't say the other part, but I knew he meant time away from me. Samkiel never wanted to be away from me. The last time . . . my throat tightened, my vision blurring.

"For how long?" My voice was a trembling mess.

My question was met with silence. My heart broke, fractured, cracked into a thousand tiny pieces. They felt raw and bloody, and I never wanted to touch them again.

"I love you." It was a whisper, a plea, and the gods' honest truth.

His face crumpled, and he took a step back from me. It was just a step, but it felt like a gap so fucking wide I wished it was real so I could throw myself into it. Samkiel never pushed away from me, no matter what I did or said, but this? This was it. This was his final straw.

"Go."

My shoulders slumped, and I turned and walked through the portal. It closed behind me, and Miska, Orym, and Reggie all looked at me with pity. They had heard that last bit.

"Dianna?" Reggie said my name as a question.

I shut my eyes, and I think I felt my hand lift to ward Reggie off. The tears finally slid down my face, but at that point, I only felt the ache in my chest. I may not have had a soul any longer, but Samkiel had just ripped my heart out. That was okay. It was his anyway. I wiped my face and stormed from the room that was suddenly too small, too cold, and too empty.

LX
Camilla

I flexed my hands at my sides, studying the remaining fragments of the medallion.

"It looks like a stone should go here." I pointed to the hollow grooves of a couple of pieces.

Hilma's lips turned up. "Oh? Hmm, I've never noticed before, but then again, we never got this far."

My instincts blared a warning, but I forced a smile. I didn't trust Hilma. I didn't really trust anyone here, but spending so much time with her made her feel like more of a threat.

"Listen, why don't we call it a night, okay? You managed to get a few more pieces back together, and I don't need you burning out for days again."

I nodded. I had told them that my magic was depleted from being overworked. There was no way I would tell them I had cast a healing spell to damn near bring someone back from the edge of death. I'd slept for three days, drifting in and out of consciousness. I remembered Vincent checking on me, every part of him whole and unscathed. Once I'd seen that, I rested easy.

We hadn't spoken about what I'd done or how he had ended up so hurt. He had grasped my hand on the way to breakfast the first morning I had made it out of bed, and I knew that was the only thank you I would receive. Nismera didn't care either way. She thought the infirmary had done its job quite well, and she was back to sending him on more missions.

"You're right. I am tired."

She smiled, calling for Tessa and Tara to clean up after us. The girls groaned and rolled their eyes but set to work. I said goodnight to Hilma and was escorted to my room. For the second night in a row, there was no Vincent.

It was well past midnight when I heard armored boots against the stone of the palace floor. I tossed the book I was reading aside and padded to the door. When I stepped out, the guards just outside my room turned to look at me. I knew they were about to tell me again how I couldn't leave. I held up my hand to forestall the conversation we were all tired of having. They had repeated that same message for the last two days. I was stuck in my room unless my damn bodyguard was around, and Vincent had abandoned me for two days.

"Is he back?" I asked, pinning the closest guard with my glare.

He opened his mouth to answer. I was sure he was about to repeat how he couldn't tell me anything, but then Vincent came up the steps.

My anger faded as I watched him limp up the stairs. He held his helmet at his side, Nismera's war tassels not swinging like they usually did. His face and armor were covered in grime, his hair matted with sweat. I could smell the scent of blood from here, and I hoped that none of it was his. Vincent gave the guards a pointed look, and without a word, they nodded and left their stations. They didn't even look at him as they hurried past him and down the stairs, probably thrilled to be rid of my constant bickering and demands to know about his latest mission.

"What happened to you?" I asked, folding my arms and leaning against my door frame. "Why does she have you going back out so soon after what happened?"

"I don't ask questions. I just do what I'm told." He grimaced at me before heading to his room across the hall. I knew he didn't want to talk about it and planned to go into his room and shut the door, but hell if I was going to let him ignore me. He swung the door closed, but I lifted my hand and made a fist, my emerald magic curling around the frame to stop it.

Vincent spun and then grabbed his side with a hiss. He straightened slowly, his face ashen.

I stalked forward, still holding the door open. I didn't want to fight, even though it felt like that was all we had done for weeks. For as long as I had known him, there had always been a push and pull between us. Vincent had always been the silent type, but I often caught him watching me.

"Don't think you can shut the door on me and lock me out," I said, stepping inside his room.

"Quiet down, would you?" he said, glancing at the door behind me.

I slammed the door, the walls rumbling from the force of my magic. Vincent's eyes burned into mine.

"I was worried about you. I may have healed the outside parts of you, but you still need time to heal."

"I'm tired, Camilla. Can you yell at me tomorrow?" He turned and dropped his helmet on the floor. I saw it then. The claw marks ran from his neck all the way down his back. The armor had stopped the claws from digging in, but I could still see the bruises spreading over his back.

"What happened?" I asked against my better judgment.

"Can you ask me that tomorrow, too?" he asked, pausing near the bathing room. "Unless you want to stay and talk about it, but I am about to get naked, take a bath, and get into bed."

"Nismera isn't coming in for her nightly rounds, then?"

He made a face at me, one I didn't know him well enough to read, and reached for the collar of his armor. A latch moved, then another before it fell, landing on the floor with a dull metal thud that reminded me of a drum. Scars formed patterns over his muscled bare chest, but it was the fresh cuts and bruises on his midsection that drew my attention right now. I didn't think that wherever he had been was just a routine mission.

I turned away as he reached for his pants. "I'll be right back."

I heard him snort before more armor thudded onto the floor. I left his room and hurried across the hall to mine. I grabbed a few things and headed back. Armor littered the floor, all spikes and sharp edges. I wondered if that was truly what Nismera looked like on the inside. Her outward beauty made even me pause the first time I saw her. The long, silver-blonde hair swept behind her in waves. Her frame, while small, held power so immense that it wafted off of her like a perfume. But it was her eyes that told the truth of her nature. They seemed to soften around her brothers, but something dark and hateful lurked behind every emotion. It was something my magic acknowledged and reacted to. Every time I was near her, I felt it retreat, wanting to hide so deep within me I feared I would never get it out again.

I stopped as I entered the bathing room, my heart lodging in my throat at the sight of him. He was standing in the glass-enclosed shower, water pouring down on him from the ceiling. Even with the steam filling the room, I could see his heavily muscled chest and tapered waist, leading to . . . I placed the few items I'd brought on the counter, setting them down hard enough for him to hear me.

"That was fast," he said. "What did you do? Run?"

I sighed. "Our rooms are only a few steps from each other."

He made a noise, and I heard a rattling from the shower. I straightened my shoulders, staring at the potions and salves I'd laid out on the counter.

"Anyway, I brought you things," I said, watching his reflection in the mirror but careful to keep my gaze above his waist. Things? Holy gods, Camilla. I mentally slapped myself. What was wrong with me?

He nodded and wiped a hand across his face, the water clumping a few of his eyelashes together in a way I wouldn't think about. I was a super powerful, world-shattering witch. He had no power over me. I turned around decisively and leaned against the counter.

Vincent turned off the shower, and I squared my shoulders, proving I wasn't affected by his nakedness in the slightest. He grabbed a towel and wrapped it around his waist before stepping out, and I realized how much of a liar I was. Vincent was always so well put together that I had no idea he had muscles on top of muscles under all that self-righteousness of his.

"What is that?" he asked, nodding toward the few small jars I had with me.

"Come. I'll show you," I said, gathering the bottles and walking into his room.

He sighed and followed, setting the salves on his bedside table. I heard shuffling behind me and turned just enough to see the towel on the floor and Vincent pulling up a pair of loose pants. I waved for him to sit, and he did with a huff.

"What are you doing?" he asked, watching as I settled behind him.

"Helping you," I said, opening a single jar. "You know, again? I should probably charge you at this rate."

His lips turned up in a smile, and I hated that it made my breath hitch.

"Be still." I rubbed the liquid in my hands. "This may be cold."

"What?" Anything else he might have said died on a sigh and a deep groan as I rubbed the salve over his shoulder and down his arm. The muscles tensed beneath my touch, but I saw the knots ease and the small bruises beneath disappear. "That is . . . amazing."

I tried and failed to ignore the sounds he made as I moved across his back to his other shoulder, but I knew they would be burned into my brain like a brand. I also tried to deny the way my lower belly clenched, but I knew I'd probably touch myself while thinking about it when I bathed tonight.

"Camilla?"

"Hmm?" I asked, shaking away the illicit thoughts.

"I said, what is that?" He half turned toward me.

"Oh," I said, "it's a homemade salve I made from an herb I had. I found a few plants that are similar to the ones on Onuna. It heals through your pores and nerves . . . and I'm rambling."

"You're fine." He chuckled softly. "You really are one of the smartest, strongest witches."

I felt my face burn. "My family would proudly disagree."

"Your family? You never talk about them." He tipped his head forward, stretching his muscles as I rubbed my hand down his spine. His wet hair clung to his shoulder, inky black and heavy. He arched, the sound he was making more in pain than anything, and I wondered how much damage he'd done to his spine.

"You never talk about yours."

I saw his jaw set in a hard line and felt the tension beneath my fingers. I knew he was about to shut down, so I went on.

"There isn't much to say about mine. I grew up in a big home with a few siblings. We all competed for the head of the coven once we hit eighteen. That's when our powers surge the brightest. I was considered the weakest of my siblings."

"How many siblings did you have?"

"Just my older brother and sister."

"What happened to them?"

I swallowed hard, my touch faltering. Leaning forward, I grabbed more salve, rubbing it between my palms before sliding them over his back. "I told you we competed. It was normal then. Most covens only had one child who would inherit their family's powers, but all three of us inherited from my mom's side. I wasn't as popular growing up and was often bullied. My siblings were the cool kids, I guess. It wasn't until I hit puberty that anyone even paid attention to me."

Vincent grinned a very male grin and glanced over his shoulder at my breasts. "I can see why."

I pressed a tad bit harder into his back, and he yelped. "Hey, I'm trying to tell you a story here. Pay attention!"

"I'm sorry." He smiled softly, and I knew he wasn't truly sorry. "You just looked sad for a second. That's all."

My hands paused on his shoulder before I pressed deeper into the muscle. "It's not a happy childhood, but when do we villains have one?"

"You're not a villain, Camilla. I have you beat by a mile."

"Is that how you see yourself?"

He nodded. "Keep going with your story."

I swallowed, returning to his aching muscles and a past I hated. "As I said, most covens only give power to one child, not three. In each generation, the families compete for control. Whoever is left standing is head of the covens until the next fifty years or so."

"They made you fight each other?"

"It's tradition," I whispered. "It happened on El Donuma. The first trial separates us in the deep forest. We have to rely on magic to find our way to the main temple. You would think that whoever collects the gem would win, right? Wrong. You have to transport the gem all the way back to your family without using magic. That's where it gets bloody. The contestants cheat, of course, but whoever makes it wins." I paused, remembering the sounds of crackling bushes and screams rending the night. It had rained so hard, and I was soaked and muddy, trudging through that damn forest.

"We don't have to talk about it—"

"Aguiniga," I whispered. "That was his last name. His power rivaled mine and my family's, and he knew it. The ones he allied with knew it, too. They planned to take us out first. I remember running with my siblings at my side, that damn jewel clutched in my hand, but he cheated, used magic, and not just any magic. He used a death curse. The ones they don't teach us. I remember trying to give that damn jewel to my sister or my brother. They were stronger than me, more loved. They were needed, not me, but they refused. I used to think they hated me, you know? Like most siblings do, but . . ."

I didn't realize I had stopped touching him, my hands resting in my lap as the memories took me. The lights flickered in the room, Vincent's head whipping toward them.

"We almost made it back in time. I heard a shout, then a thud, and they lay at my feet when I turned around. He had caught up to us. He had aimed for me, and they jumped in the way. I remember kneeling in the mud, dropping the jewel as I reached for them, and then I remember . . . power. I flattened the entire continent in an instant. There was nothing left. Not even me, I guess. Everything was different after that. I wandered the ruined forest for days before I heard a helicopter overhead. It was Santiago's father who found me. They took me in, and the rest is weird history."

"If that . . . Why let everyone think Santiago was stronger than you?"

I shrugged. "It was a good cover story. I got to live a semi-normal life after. Only a handful of covens remained after that, and we all just pretended it was a freak accident. A trial that was too brutal. They never had them again."

"Camilla." He glanced at me as if seeing me for the first time. "I'm so sorry."

"Don't be. It was barbaric to begin with. I blamed my family for the longest time for what we lost, but I guess I got my revenge. This is also why I hated what Kaden made me a part of. It's also why I kept Gabby's body. I never got to bury my siblings, and I knew if Dianna was coming to kill me, at least she could have her sister back. How could I ever blame her for wanting vengeance? I did the same."

Vincent was quiet for a moment. I knew that talking about what happened on the remains of Rashearim made him withdraw into himself.

"You know I don't think you're the villain either."

He huffed. "How so?"

"You don't gloat or brag about what you've done. You avoid the ones you hurt and pretend your pain doesn't exist. I've worked with villains my whole life. You don't make me feel that way."

"Well, you worked with Dianna, who nearly destroyed the world, so I'd say your judgment of character is off by a lot."

"What is it with her?" I said a bit too firmly. "Why do you hate her so much? I used to think it was a weird crush. I mean, I know she's gorgeous—"

Vincent let out a bitter laugh. "That is the furthest from the truth."

"Okay, so what is the truth? You share a bed with Nismera, who is far worse than Dianna, yet you hear her name and . . ."

"Just drop it, Camilla. It's late. I think we're both exhausted." He rubbed a hand across his face.

"No, tell me. I just told you my family's secrets. I deserve this. After everything."

Vincent shifted on the bed so he could look at me without twisting his back. His eyes held none of their remote coldness. Instead, all I saw was a weird sense of . . . longing.

"It was when Kaden first held . . . I guess the word would be auditions, for his sept. He wanted only the strongest for what Nismera had planned. He asked me to be a witness but to stay back. I was a secret, and there were those in his sept that he didn't fully trust. It was fall in Onuna, and the leaves had just turned golden brown. I flew in under the cover of night, arriving late. Vampires, werewolves, witches, and every Otherworld creature in the realm attended the briefing, mingling and chatting, some even dancing. I hadn't realized it was to be a party, but it worked perfectly. Everyone was so distracted that they did not notice me watching from the shadows. Kaden stood with me, wanting to talk about the potentials he had gathered, but I wasn't listening. I'd spotted you through the crowd. You wore a dress of ivory and satin that spilled to the floor, and your hair was pulled back, part of it draping over your shoulders. Then you laughed, and I thought you were the most beautiful woman in the entire world."

I remembered that day. My breath hitched, recalling the event in vivid detail. I'd been so nervous. I had tried on seven dresses before finally landing on that one. My heart thudded in my chest. No one had ever called me the most beautiful woman in the world or remembered me in such detail, especially after hundreds of years.

"Why didn't you approach me, talk to me?"

Vincent snorted, a portion of his cold demeanor returning as he sat up and pulled away from me. "Because I may have been watching you, but you were watching Dianna."

My gut rolled. Yes, that's who I was laughing with that night, who I'd befriended first.

"That was so long ago . . ."

Vincent shrugged. "It doesn't matter. She got to you first."

Fool, I thought, cursing him. It did matter. This whole time, I'd assumed he hated her for her power and what she could do. But he hated her because she had me. I couldn't breathe, my heart racing.

"Vincent."

"Camilla. It's fine. Everyone seems drawn to her. I still don't see why, but I just wanted you to know." He offered a soft smile. "No matter what happened in your past or who made you feel less than, you are, and have always been, special. No magic required."

My hands dropped to my lap, tears prickling my eyes. No one had ever said such a thing, yet here he was, memorizing what I had looked like on one of the most nerve-racking nights of my life.

Vincent groaned and stretched, rotating his shoulder. "I think your magic salve worked. I don't feel as though my shoulder is being ripped off."

He started to stand, but I was quicker. I lurched forward, my hand cupping the back of his head as my lips slanted across his. Vincent froze, or maybe time itself did. I wasn't sure, but I swept my tongue across his lips, pleading for entrance. A sound escaped his lips before he grabbed my arms, pushing me back.

"What are you doing?"

I blinked a few times. "I don't know."

His eyes scanned mine, something ancient and powerful there before his eyes darted to my lips and back. "Do it again."

And so I did.

LXI
Roccurem

The small town was quiet, clouds gathering in the sky. I walked toward the small building, the sounds inside telling me I was in the right place. The smell of sweat and alcohol filled my nose as I walked in.

A short man shook his head and tossed a bar towel over his shoulder. "Listen, if you're here to hit on her, one of my guys just left with his balls on fire."

I forced the smile Dianna had taught me to wear so as not to scare others. She said that being too stoic made others uncomfortable, and they retreated into themselves in my presence. But at least now I knew I was in the right place. I said nothing, walking past him and heading to the small cut-out door.

"Your funeral, buddy," he tossed over his shoulder, and my lips pressed into a thin line, knowing his funeral was a hundred and twelve days from now. He would die in an attempted robbery.

I found the stairs to the lower level, the stone walls and steps chipped. Punches rang out, and I heard her grunt. The space was a large open gym, hanging bags made from materials able to withstand a berserker's rage swung from the ceiling.

Dianna's fist shot out again, the muscles bunching across her shoulders and sweat soaking the small garment she called a top. Her foot swung out next, hitting the bag hard enough to send it swinging to the right from the force. A part of the ceiling chipped, and a whispered murmur came from the back by the wired gates. Several burly onlookers gathered there, talking amongst themselves about the dark-haired beauty who could throw a punch.

She left the first day after their squabble, not from the tavern but somewhere in between. It was as if her sadness had carved a slit in the darkness, and she let it devour her. I wondered if her grief was the epitome of darkness. Without Samkiel acting as her light, darkness was all that remained. The second day, she came back to the house looking for him. When she saw he had not returned, something cold and angry replaced the sadness.

Samkiel was all she had left in this world, even if she did not speak the words aloud. Granted, The Hand and others filled a fraction of that void, but only Gabriella and Samkiel had ever been close enough to truly know her. They were the only two who had ever been able to reach her. Gabriella had been her heart. Samkiel was her soul.

"I've looked for you," I said, stopping beside her but well out of range of her rage.

Dianna punched the bag again but didn't respond. She moved so quickly, her strikes precise and even, just like her World Ender.

"What do you want, Reggie?" she said, still hammering away.

"It's been days."

"I can count." She spit the last part, and I knew the anger she felt was an echo from their fight.

"If I may, my future queen?"

Her head whipped toward me, her eyes flashing red as she caught the bag in her hands, steadying it. "Don't call me that."

I persisted. "If I may, it is very common that in times of great pain or feelings of betrayal, others will say things they do not mean. They often act in certain ways, but it is just a reflection of hurt. That is all."

"It doesn't matter." She barely lifted her shoulders in a desultory shrug before tossing another punch. "We're done."

I shook my head. "It was a minor derailment, yet you assume the end so quickly."

She scoffed. "Derailment? Did you hear us? I lied about a lot, Reggie. I kept so much from him."

"You should have told him."

"You don't think I know that?" A low growl reverberated from her throat, her fists hitting not once but twice. "I do. But I didn't, okay? I couldn't, and I could give you and him a million fucking reasons I didn't, but it doesn't matter because I hurt him. Again. I lied to him. Again."

"You had your reasons, even if I wished you would have spoken sooner to avoid this."

"My reasons." She huffed and landed another punch before resting her hands on the waistband of her dark pants. "I can blame it on the hundreds of years I was with someone who didn't care about my feelings. I could blame it on how I lock everything away. But the truth is I lied because I was afraid. I was afraid if the mark left, that meant my price was him, and I guess that turned out to be true. It's not like we're mates now. I was just delusional."

"I think you are wrong about that."

She held up her hand. "Do you see a mark? No."

"You are truly a fool if you think that man would ever stop loving you, Dianna."

She turned away from me. "You weren't there. You didn't see him. He's never acted that way with me, never pulled away so quickly, even with what happened on Onuna. So maybe with the mark gone, my soul gone, we don't have that connection anymore. Maybe he sees the real me now."

"If I may—"

Dianna spun, her foot shooting out. The bag snapped from the ceiling, small parts of brick raining down as it sailed across the room, landing in a heap. "It doesn't matter, nor do I want to sit around wallowing in self-pity, either. He can hate me. He can leave me. I don't care, but I will be the one to keep him alive. The world needs him, even if he doesn't need me."

Murmurs erupted behind us as her onlookers left, wide-eyed and whispering, but it was the short man from upstairs who yelled down, "You will have to pay for that!"

We watched him grumble and walk back upstairs. As soon as he was gone, Dianna turned back to me.

"He just needs time, my queen. He deserves that." My head throbbed as a vision tried to press into my consciousness, but it faded quickly. I rubbed at my temples, watching her.

A single sweat-drenched brow lifted. "Whose side are you on, anyway?"

I forced a smile. "Yours, but I warned you about withholding precious information."

"You know what my new theory is?" She didn't wait for me to answer. "My new theory is we were destined to kill each other, not fall in love. So maybe it was never meant to last."

"You cannot truly believe that. After everything."

She spun, unwrapping the beige cloth from around her knuckles as she headed out of the room. "What I believe is that I will not let The Hand suffer just because he and I cannot work out our differences. I know I fucked up. I can't change that, but I refuse to let them rot under her control. So he and I can work together or not, but I won't leave them with her. After they are safe and sane, I'll burn her and her godsdamn city to ash, and then . . ." She paused, taking a deep breath, and turned to me. "I don't know what I'll do then."

She headed up the stairs back to our safe house as I rubbed my brow and sighed deeply. "You two are the most stubborn creatures I have ever encountered in this universe or the next."

LXII

Dianna

After showering and washing off the sweat from my workout, I stood in the center of our . . . no, *my* small room. I hadn't touched the bed since we fought, wanting proof he had come back so we could talk. But he hadn't returned. I felt my eyes prickle with tears again and shook my head, storming to the small bag on the floor. I dressed before quickly leaving the room, no longer wishing to be there.

"Miska!" I called out.

I heard the shuffle of small feet from down the hall. Her door opened, and she poked her sleep-tousled head out. "Yes?"

"I'm hungry," I said, placing my hands on my hips. "Let's go upstairs and have breakfast."

"What are we eating?" A sleepy, deep groan came from my right as another door opened.

"Orym. You're awake. Great. Come on, family breakfast meeting," I said, walking toward the worn wooden stairs leading up to the tavern.

"Samkiel gave direct orders that you are to stay here until his return. You are wanted by Nismera's legion, who happen to frequent the city," Reggie said, forming behind me.

"Oh yeah? Before or after he left?" I snapped as we all headed upstairs.

"He returned the other night when you went out to grab . . . things," Orym said, Reggie glaring at him.

A new ache bloomed in my chest as another piece of my heart fractured. He hadn't even tried to see me.

My jaw clenched, but I smothered the irritation and pain. "Okay, well, I think if he wants to give orders, he should be here to do it."

Reggie's sigh only lightened my mood. He clearly knew this was a fight he wouldn't win.

"What if he doesn't come back?" Miska asked, cutting a piece of meat. Reggie froze on my left, and Orym pretended to look anywhere else as he ate.

The tapping of my nails stilled on the bar.

"Did you guys break up?" Miska asked next.

"Miska." Orym's head whipped toward her as she glanced up at him and then back at me.

The people in the tavern kept chattering away, but I said nothing. I had no answers. I was unsure. There was only so much one person could take, and I had given Samkiel a lifetime of reasons not to want me. Because of me, we no longer had our mark or mate bond tethering us. By his customs and laws, nothing bound us together.

"What?" Miska asked, looking at Reggie now. "No one is talking about it, but we saw you that night. Then he closed the portal, leaving you with us, and then he came back, but it was a quick visit. Are you going to leave us next?"

I turned toward her, seeing the fear and shine of tears in her eyes. I finally realized she hadn't even touched her food, just picking at it this whole time.

"Why would you think that?"

"Why would you stay?" She glanced down at her food. "You only saved me to help him, and if he's gone, what if I'm of no use to you?"

My lips pursed. As much as I hated to admit it, there was some validity to her concern. Everyone knew I was selfish. I used and saved people mostly to help him, but I wasn't as I was before the realms opened. I wasn't that person any longer.

"I'm not leaving you. Any of you. We still have a family to put back together and a nasty bitch to kill." I pointed at Miska. "Don't repeat those last words."

A bright smile broke across her face, and she leaned forward, hugging me tightly. I froze, not returning the embrace, shocked by the contact. Orym raised a brow, a smile tugging at his lips as he took a drink.

I patted Miska's back once before pushing her back a little. "Okay, enough of that."

"Sorry," she said, sniffling as she sat back up. "What's our next plan? Where do we go without Samkiel?"

I snorted. "Without him? There is no without him. He'll come back, and if he doesn't, I will hunt him down and drag him back if I have to. Regardless of what's going on between us, we still have a lot of work to do. So we can be adults and work together. We've done it before . . ." The last part of my sentence trailed off because I knew it would never be as it was before.

Miska nodded proudly before turning back to her food and digging in. Orym continued to stare at me over her head.

"What?"

He shrugged and turned back to his food. "Nothing."

I sighed and leaned back, casting a glance toward Reggie. "I expected you to say something."

"I have nothing to add," Reggie said. "You are exactly where you are supposed to be."

A small snort left my lips. "Always cryptic."

Orym's glass clinked on the bar top as he snickered.

"Has Veruka had any new leads as of late?" I asked Orym.

He took another bite of his food and surveyed the room, ensuring no one was close enough to overhear us. "She has cut back on the raids, but that's all."

I nodded as Miska scarfed her food down. The tavern abruptly went quiet, and a whirring sound filled the silence. Outside, dust blew past the dirty windows, and the glasses on the counter vibrated. The liquid inside Miska's cup shook in time with a series of heavy thuds.

"Get downstairs," I said. "All of you."

Miska stared at the door. "What is it?"

I sighed. "Soldiers."

"No," Orym said, shaking his head, "that sound heralds a legion."

"Take Miska," I said.

Orym and Reggie stood, and Miska jumped up, plastering herself to Reggie's side.

"Stay below until I come for you, all right?"

They all nodded, though Reggie held my eyes a fraction longer. I watched as they disappeared through the door, and I heard the lock click. Voices picked up outside, and the patrons in the tavern hunkered down as if hoping if they made themselves small they wouldn't be bothered.

Standing, I grabbed the hood of my cloak and pulled it up. I headed to a small table off to the side, away from the door Reggie, Miska, and Orym went through. I pulled the wooden chair out and sat down, but I didn't have to wait long. The tavern door swung open, and the ground shook.

"Greetings, civilians of Youl. We are here searching for an escaped fugitive recently sighted in this area. We received reports of her being nearby."

I cursed. It was probably the guy whose balls I burnt when he tried to get handsy at that damn gym.

I didn't move, keeping my back turned toward them. Armored boots stomped across the floor, soldiers checking every patron. Everyone focused on the deep-voiced man, and I knew he had displayed an image of me when all eyes turned toward me.

Well, I hope it was at least a good picture.

I kept my eyes down, watching as numerous pairs of boots surrounded my small table. One soldier grumbled, and I knew this was about to get bloody. I heard heavy footfalls and felt someone stop behind me.

"I am Tedar, Commander of the Eighth Legion, and you are hereby detained under the rule of the highest."

I tapped my nails on the table and looked up at the two soldiers glaring at me from across the table. Sighing, I scooted my chair back and turned toward the commander, ignoring his flunkies. I nodded and crossed one leg over the other. "Oh, yeah? Who is the highest?"

Tedar laughed a full belly laugh before slamming his hand down on the table hard enough to crack it. "You're funny. Funny doesn't last long."

My nose scrunched. "Apparently, neither does soap."

Tedar's soldiers gulped. I doubted many beings spoke to their troll commander with such disregard.

Rage bloomed in his large eyes. "She will not mind if you come back a little bruised."

He pulled back his arm, his massive fist aiming for my head. I spun and picked up the chair I was sitting in, slamming it across his thick, armored arm. Tedar laughed as it broke into pieces.

"Was that supposed to hurt, girl?" He laughed, looking at his guards.

"No," I said, "but this will."

I twirled the broken chair leg in my hand before sending it sailing toward him. It hit him square in the center of his forehead with a loud thunk. His smile dropped as his eyes crossed. He raised one hand and touched his head before falling like a felled tree.

I dusted my hands off and casually turned to face the soldiers. They all stood gaping at me, gripping their weapons.

"Come on," I said. "You're actually doing me a favor. I've had a shitty few days."

LXIII
Samkiel

I had worked for three days straight, carving pieces off that damn mountain and rebuilding. I glanced at my hands. They were all healed now, the silver rings gleaming under the moonlight. My entire body still ached, but I deserved it. I'd felt her cry after I sent her away, and I hated myself for it. I would rather rip my heart from my chest and shred it myself than ever hurt her, but I was so . . . My resolve reasserted itself. I needed to get this taken care of. Then, the emotions could come.

My boots slapped against the small puddles that accumulated along the cobblestones, the rain coming down in sheets. People ran past me, seeking shelter. It was a universal truth that most beings hated the rain and would hide, giving me the perfect coverage. Water soaked my hooded cloak, but I barely noticed as I strode forward.

Lights sparked from the safety of their intricate metal lanterns, blue and white smoke floating skyward. I carefully descended the half-broken steps and wove through the streets, staying in the shadows in this rundown part of town.

I slipped my hand into my pocket, finding the small stone and rubbing my fingers over it. That had been my first stop, and this was the second. I turned down a dark alley. Barrels, overflowing with discarded animal flesh and bone from the nearby restaurants, reeked of rot. A few eight-legged creatures scurried to the sides as I approached. They raised their double tails and hissed at me, warning me off their trash trove.

Music flooded the end of the alley, and the sound of voices grew louder. A sign hung over the door, the letters from the old language carved into the rusted metal. *Brothel.* Two towering figures stopped when they saw me approaching. A curl of smoke left one's lips as the other gave me a toothy grin, displaying his serrated teeth. I gazed at them steadily and looked away as I passed.

I paused before the weathered gray door, praying to the old gods he was here. Gathering information while trying to keep a low profile turned out to be harder than I expected. Everything had changed since Nismera took these realms. So many beautiful places were nothing more than rubble now, and it seemed that brothels had become the places that everyone ran to, both to forget and conduct business. Criminals and businessmen alike turned a blind eye to each other here. They were worn down like all the realms she ruled over, tired, hungry, and ruined.

I sighed and squared my shoulders before pushing the door open. Carnal sounds of pleasure could be heard above the music, but that was not why I was there. The outside of this building was an illusion. Inside, it was a massive column, the center open space with rooms lining the floors both above and below.

I moved past a topless waitress, balancing a tray on her feathered tail. She handed glasses out to a group of men. Moans and grunts of pleasure filled the air, some from behind closed doors, some tucked into the darkened alcoves.

I paused in front of one of the viewing rooms. A woman was suspended upside down while a male wrapped his arms around her middle and buried his face between her legs. Their sounds of pleasure and need had me licking my lips, imagining Dianna spread before me like that. I wondered how long it would take Dianna to forgive me for leaving before she let me attempt that maneuver.

"Are you looking for something in particular, gorgeous?" a voice purred from behind me.

Pulled from the erotic thoughts of having Dianna at my mercy, I turned. I smiled and nodded at the harpy. She wore a teal dress that hung loosely on her. Each strand of her hair ended in a fine blue and white feather, matching the bigger ones that grew along the sides of her arms. Talons, thick and sharp, tipped her fingers and toes.

"Actually, I am," I said. "I'm looking for Killium."

Her eyes dilated for a mere second before she covered it up with a soft smile. She shook her head and cocked her hip, acting coy. It was an obvious display, trying to avoid my question. But I was in love with the only woman who could ever do such a thing to me. "Sorry, I don't know that name. Maybe I can find you—"

My smile was pleasant, even if my mood was not. "You do, and I know he's here. Tell him Donumete wants to see him."

Her nostrils flared. "I'll see what I can do," she said before stepping back.

I watched as she turned down a hall, disappearing out of sight. I leaned against the railing to wait, watching the movement on the levels beneath me. The realms were so different now. I knew when I locked myself away that things would change, but seeing the utter desolation of so many of the realms made my heart hurt.

"I thought sealing the realms, the plan you had always intended, would have left them in peace. Instead, we trapped them here with a monster," I whispered to the ghost of my past as if my father could hear me even now.

A burst of laughter filled the air, ripping me from my thoughts. There had to be at least a hundred people here. I didn't see any soldiers in gold and black armor, but I kept my cloak pulled tight, regardless.

I leaned my elbows against the railing, clasping my hands in front of me. My gaze snagged on my bare finger where our mark should have been, or was, I suppose. She had lied to me for months. I wanted to stay mad, to feel as hurt as I should, but a part of me knew why she'd done it. I knew Dianna, and even if I didn't agree with her actions at times, I understood her reasoning. She held everything she loved close, afraid it'd break or be taken from her, and that was exactly what I'd done. I broke. I died. That part still hadn't sunk in. I remembered little other than falling asleep as she held me. Everything seemed so blurry, mashes of memories that made no sense.

"I love you."

Her voice echoed in my head. I would have stayed if I had not opened that portal right then. She'd finally spoken the words I so desperately craved, and it felt as if my soul had ignited when they fell from her lips. My legs had stilled, my body refusing to move, and I'd wanted nothing more than to stay. She'd given up the very fabric of her being for me. I would never be worthy of her, of that kind of love, but I would be a godsdamn liar if I said I wouldn't try to be.

I wanted to make her promise that we'd never keep things from one another, but I had something I needed to do first. Fear had taken root in my gut, mocking me. I had a throne to reclaim, a crown to take back, and a war to win, but my greatest fear was that I could not protect the one I couldn't live without.

"Donumete, Killium will see you now."

I straightened and nodded at the harpy. I followed her around the floor toward the back of the building. As we stepped through a doorway, I noticed the same men from outside standing against the wall. So, they were not just patrons but guards.

The two large creatures smiled their toothy grins. One lifted an artistic picture with a webbed hand and pressed the hidden button behind it. I watched as a part of a wall slid to the side, revealing a small elevator.

The harpy smiled at me as she waved a feathered arm, gesturing me in. I stepped in, the harpy and the guards shuffling in behind me. None of us spoke as the wall closed behind us. A dull, blue light ran around the perimeter of the car before the door sealed shut, and the elevator jerked.

The two guards flanked me, and the harpy was at my back. The guards placed their hands in front of them, seemingly at ease, but I caught the slight twitch of the slightly taller one.

I sighed. "Is this really necessary?"

"I'm afraid so," the harpy said, and I heard her unsheathe the blade she carried at her side. "Given that Donumete is dead."

I'd learned far too young all the dirty tricks in fighting. Most went for a weak part, and when facing a taller opponent, that usually meant the knee or groin. Distraction was also a valuable tactic. When fighting in a team, usually one went high, the other low, which in most cases worked. In this case, not so much.

I heard the air curve around her blade as she struck low, and I jumped, avoiding the blade aimed at the back of my knees. I landed in a crouch, the second strike slashing the air right above my head. The taller guard rushed forward as I stood, a blade as sharp as his teeth aimed for my gut. I twisted and grabbed his wrist, using his momentum to slam him against the harpy behind me. They let out a grunt as they hit the wall and slumped to the floor, feathers flying around the elevator.

The second guard snarled, his tail whipping out of his coat, the tip curled around a dagger. He fisted two more and charged. My fist shot out, connecting with bone. It cracked with the contact right as the elevator doors opened. The guard fell into the small room, landing with a dull thud. I reached back and dragged the harpy and the other guard out with me, tossing them to the floor.

"That's a hell of a greeting."

I took a deep breath and straightened my cloak before entering the room. A small device chirped, alerting the creature currently crouched over its desk. He turned toward me, his three large eyes squinting behind the circular glasses he wore. I removed my hood. The item he held clattered to the floor as he stood, his long snout gaping.

"May the old gods damn my soul. Samkiel. It is you."

The drowsy guards in the room practically jumped out of their skin at the mention of my name.

"Samkiel?" A woman emerged from behind a door. Dark gray ringlets fell to her shoulders as she wiped her hands on her apron.

"Jaski," I said.

Her smile deepened the wrinkles in her cheeks, and a shine of green flickered in her eyes as she looked at me. "My eyes don't deceive me. You truly are alive, but . . . different."

Killium pushed past his cluttered desk and limped toward me, the wiry hairs on his back raised in greeting. His leg bore mechanics he hadn't had the last time I'd seen him. I met him halfway and bent to hug him.

"You were dead. I swore it. We all did. The sky carries your power. I see it every day. Nismera, she—"

I raised my hand. "I know, old friend, we have a lot to discuss. Can we?" I nodded toward the back room.

"Of course, of course." He waved me on, and I threw a tendril of power behind me, closing and sealing the elevator.

LXIV
Samkiel

Jaski placed a plate heaped with soft baked goods between Killium and me. He smiled at her in thanks, and she hummed softly as she took a seat. Their love was nearly a physical bond. It was inspiring and comforting.

I forced a quick smile. "I am glad to see you two are still together."

Jaski smiled at Killium. Her eyes were so filled with love that it felt as if I were intruding.

Killium smiled as he nodded. "Almost two thousand years, give or take."

"I remember," I said with a grin. "Jaski made you work for it."

Jaski laughed, the sound filling the room with warmth. "It was good for him, and I was worth it."

Killium squeezed her hand, but he looked at me, his expression growing serious. "I still cannot believe it, Samkiel," he said, swirling the green liquid in his glass. "The sky does not lie, and neither do the realms. You died, or so we all thought."

Jaski leaned forward, magic swirling in her eyes. "It is truly remarkable. You are here, whole, but different. I cannot tell what has changed, but you seem fully resurrected."

Killium let out a brief whistle. "So many will be envious should they learn you have managed this."

"Correct," Jaski said. "Necromancy is forbidden. It is illegal in all the realms because of the effects. Not a single soul has been brought back from the Otherside that did not come back wrong."

My pulse quickened. I knew that. I knew the stories. It was another reason I was so upset when I learned what had happened, but it had been months since my return, and I still felt the same. I ran my hand over my side, that dull ache still present. Perhaps not all the same, but I hadn't come back wrong.

"Well, I can tell you now, I am not craving brains."

They shared a glance before bursting into laughter. I sipped my drink and watched them.

My fingers tapped against the glass I held, combating my nerves and erratic thoughts. I couldn't tell them the truth. I couldn't tell anyone. If the wrong people found out that Dianna had brought me back to life, she would be hunted for the rest of her life. What she'd done was unprecedented. No one in my long life or before had succeeded, and those who tried were destroyed.

All those previously resurrected came back as barely more than corpses, flesh-eating monsters, or the really dangerous ones who hungered for brains. I just couldn't tell them. Dianna and I were going through something, but she would always be my first priority. Instead of saving the realms, I would level each of them if it meant keeping her safe.

"So tell me," Jaski prodded, "what powerful witch or warlock loved you enough to attempt something so deadly?"

Killium chuckled. "Now, now, Jaski, you know Samkiel. Why would you assume love?"

She smiled as she leaned her chin on her fist. "Only love would make someone do something so absolutely reckless."

Heat flared across my chest as I remembered Dianna saying those three little words. I sat up a bit straighter and cleared my throat. "No witches or warlocks. The spear meant to kill me . . . well, it missed. I assume I was close enough to death that the spell broke."

They stared at me and then my abdomen as if they could see the wound. I hoped it worked. I hoped they didn't know I was lying.

"Well, I can tell you that Nismera does not know—"

"And it has to stay that way." I made sure every word I said had power behind it. I would not risk Dianna.

"Of course," Jaski answered, touching my arm. "Your secrets are always safe with us."

"You should seek out The Eye, though," Killium said. "They are dying to get an upper hand over her."

"I will." I smiled. "Also, I will not lie to either of you. There is someone in my life who is very special to me, special enough that I need your help."

Both of them perked up at my words.

"There is?" Jaski beamed. "Tell us everything."

"I will, but first." I dug in my pocket and pulled out the stone, placing it on the table between us. Killium's eyes widened. I knew as soon as he saw it, he'd know what it was. Jaski let out a low whistle, her hand running across the bristles on Killium's shoulder.

"Gods, Samkiel, you traveled very far for that."

I nodded. "That and one other thing."

Killium laughed and slammed his drink back. He grabbed the bottle and refilled my glass before pouring more of the sluggish fluid into his cup. I rubbed my hand over my face and sighed before telling him where I had been, what had been going on, why I was back, and of her.

"I'll need a few things added. I need a very sturdy weapon."

"This is wonderful." Jaski clapped her hands and leaned forward. "Have no fear. We can do just that. I'll need to stabilize it first."

"I can't believe it," Killium said. "The last time you rushed to me in a fuss, you needed a pregnancy test for a maiden. You couldn't even remember her name, and now you show me this."

I lifted a brow and took a deep gulp of my drink. It eased my nerves, my muscles, everything. I sighed and placed the glass down.

"Yeah, that was a long time ago, and I was very, very young. A lot has changed. Plus, you helped tremendously. I got the procedure done shortly after. The Hand did, too."

The room grew silent.

"I'll do what I can. For you both." Jaski stood and picked up the stone before walking out of the room.

Killium filled his glass, his face turning grim. "I'm sorry about that. I heard what happened to them. How Nismera sold them all to the most ruthless."

Killium slid the bottle toward me, and I poured myself another. "I plan to retrieve them, but there is something I need to do first. It's imperative."

"I'll do it. It's been a while since I made any, honestly. These realms require a different form of magic."

I nodded and tipped my glass toward him before taking a sip.

Killium leaned back, the glasses atop his head glimmering under the kitchen light. "So she is the one?"

"My one and only," I said, finishing my drink and setting my glass down. I met his gaze.

"I hear the mark works wonders for those lucky enough to have it," Killium said. "I'm sorry you never received it, but this is good news."

I nodded, spinning the glass on the table. I couldn't tell him Dianna was my amata. Then he'd ask about the mark and why it wasn't there. I couldn't tell him what she gave up so I could live no matter how much I trusted him. Dianna's life and safety would always be my top priority, and if Killium ever threatened her, I'd slay him.

"Yes, a very good thing indeed." I glanced up at him. "You know me well. I grew up knowing my amata was dead, and I wanted no one like that ever. Then she showed up and dropped a building on me as if it were nothing. I think it started then. Definitely not lust or love, but intrigue nonetheless. Maybe it was my ego, but no one had ever challenged me as she did."

He chuckled behind his glass. "That's what you need."

My brows flicked up in agreement. "We didn't get along at first, but we were forced to work together. So I spent time with her every day, and whatever intrigue I felt for her grew like an ember until it burned me from the inside out. She is so fierce and brave and courageous. She knew who I was, knew the stories, and didn't care. Her loyalty knows no bounds, and she risked everything for her sister. Only a fool would not love a person that astounding. She drives me absolutely insane. Sometimes in a wonderful way, other times she's downright maddening."

Killium reared back, laughing. "That, my boy, is love." He took another gulp of his drink. "I'd love to meet the being who finally tamed the great Samkiel."

"One day, everyone will know who she is," I said, the corner of my lips quirking. "Speaking of great love, how have you and Jaski been?"

Killium cleared his throat, the guards behind me shuffling. "We almost didn't make it past the Clearing."

"Clearing?" I asked.

Killium nodded and reached for that bottle once more. "It's what we called it when Nismera first took over. She went from world to world, eliminating all who followed you. Clearing the world of you, some said. If they did not bend to her will, she wiped them out. Hundreds turned to ash with that damned light. She knew about me and my tinkerings."

Tinkerings. He said it so casually, as if he hadn't helped the gods craft some deadly things. Killium was an elemental, and the power he bore beneath his skin to shape and wield the elements was unparalleled. Put him and Azrael together, and we could supply all the realms ten times over. It was just a shame their ideals did not match. Killium built weapons for peace, Azrael for the highest bidder.

"She found you?"

He chugged another glass before slamming it down. "We were the first on her list since we were the ones that showed you all how to make the rings. Once Azrael fell, I knew we had to flee, but she found us. Jaski almost died getting us to safety. Her magic has been unpredictable and difficult for her to call forth ever since. She used too much too fast and for too long. It fucked with her." He motioned toward his leg, the steel around it reflecting in the dim lights. "And Nismera left me with this."

I crossed my arms, leaning back a tad. "I'm sorry I wasn't there to help."

"Still got that shining self-righteousness, I see. Thinking you can save all the realms, boy?"

"Someone has to try." I tipped my head toward the guards. "So, is that why you are hiding beneath a brothel with mercenaries?"

The said mercenaries' eyes widened, and they avoided my gaze.

He chuckled. "Not just a brothel, a meeting place for those looking to rebel. The ones with the same symbol on the side of their head as yours. Although, yours isn't quite right."

"Smart." I nodded, my lips turning down. "You need better protection, though."

I thought back to when I'd entered and wondered just how many rooms weren't being used for their intended purposes.

He coughed a laugh. "Those are N'vuil mercenaries you're talking about."

I focused on them, and the three of them looked as if they wished to be anywhere other than near me. "Shitty mercenaries. If I can disarm them that quickly, they won't be able to survive Nismera if she finds you."

Killium clicked his tongue. "No mercenary could stand up to you, Samkiel. You are the untouchable king. You will cause a stir, given you're the only one who has ever come close to wounding or killing Nismera."

"I don't plan to cause a stir just yet. I still have some things I need to do first, which is why I'm here."

He nodded. "Yes, yes. I don't know where the Everrine is. Last I saw, she was in the Zelaji realm, and it has since been destroyed and cultivated by a rather nasty infestation."

"I'll start there then."

"Did you bring what you need for this weapon?"

"Yes, and I can help if you need a bit of power. I don't want to hurt Jaski."

"Always so kind. I knew I liked you better than the old gods." Killium stood, and his mercenaries came to attention. "With your power, I'll only need an hour to craft it."

An hour wasn't bad. I'd assumed he would need longer. It was good news, to say the least. I feared for the tavern I'd left her in and all the beings in it if I were gone too long. But I couldn't talk to her yet. I needed to make sure this was done first. Then, we would have a discussion. It wasn't fair to her, and I knew it. My absence would only cause those demons she so desperately guarded against to come roaring back, but I needed time to think and plan.

We left his small kitchen, heading back into Killium's shop. He had gadgets and items stacked everywhere. Jaski placed a helmet over her head and moved at lightning speed, her arms going so fast she looked like she had six. Green magic clung to her slight form, and sparks flew in every direction. Smoke curled against the ceiling, and the vent above her buzzed. Above the noise, I could hear her humming contentedly. I stepped around another table, lightly tapping on one circular hanging contraption. It buzzed ominously, and I pulled back.

"That's a new project for a Prince in Sundunne," Killium said.

I turned toward him, a single brow raising. "Are you supplying weaponry to rebels, Killium?"

He only smiled at me as Jaski flipped back the face guard of her helmet and turned to hand him the dust fragments she had made. She said nothing as she walked back to her station. Killium grabbed a few metals before settling at his table. He leaned forward, dragging a complex piece of machinery close, adjusting some dials and flipping a switch. It whirled to life as he placed his goggles on his face. Sparks flew into the air as he worked, both of them set on their separate tasks.

I grabbed a seat next to Killium, telling him exactly how I wished for it to look and what I needed it to do. An hour turned to three before he was done, but it was still much better than I expected. I stood and stretched before pulling my cloak back on. I took the package he handed me and tucked it securely into my pocket. His mercenaries had watched us the whole time and now pretended to have more interest in the items around Killium's shop than me.

Jaski wiped at the sweat on her brow and grinned at me, leaning into Killium's side.

I fastened the last thick button on my side, the cloak hanging to the back of my thighs. "When I rebuild this world anew, I will return for you, friend. As long as I live, you will always have a home and business."

"Even if it is mildly illegal activities?" Killium asked, wrapping his arm around Jaski's shoulders to support her.

I smirked, placing the hood over my head. "We will work on that."

He nodded, his eyes shining with unshed tears. Jaski patted his chest. "You were always one of the good ones. You and your father. I am glad you are back. Maybe there is hope after all."

LXV
Samkiel

The portal behind me hissed as it closed, and my hand dropped to clutch at my side. I'd spent so much energy the last few days, and the expenditure had my wound feeling as if it had ripped open. I took a breath, then another, but I was accustomed to this pain. Straightening my shoulders, I pushed my hood back and strolled down the dark alleyway. I heard raised voices, followed by banging and cursing. Beyond the mouth of the alleyway, the small city glowed with orange flames, smoke clogging the air as shadows darted back and forth.

A pair of smoldering red eyes suddenly burned from the shadows, making the hair at the back of my neck prickle. Before I could even get a word out, my back hit the wall, a cool blade pressing against my throat. Dianna held me firmly in her grip, her crimson eyes blazing at me.

"You left me for *three fucking days. Again.*"

"I can explain."

She tipped her head to the side, the blade pressing harder into my throat. "Oh, look at that. You can actually hear me when I talk to you."

I swallowed, the blade scraping at my neck. I deserved that since I'd made her leave when we spoke last. It hadn't been in anger. I'd left in determination, but she didn't know that.

"Traveling realms takes time. I apologize."

Her nostrils flared, inhaling deeply to take in my scent. Her lip curled, and the red in her eyes flared into flames.

"Wait, it's not what you think," I said quickly, knowing she could smell where I had been.

Dianna stepped back, all heat and pure rage as she lifted her foot and spun. I didn't know why I thought I could block that kick. It just made it hurt more. I flew through the wall into the neighboring room and landed hard. I groaned and arched, my back aching. Dust floated through the air as she stepped through the crumbling hole she'd made in the stone wall with my body.

"Okay, you're mad. I understand, but that's no reason to burn a city."

She flipped the dagger in her hand. "Oh, I didn't do that. That was your sister's legion who showed up."

I was on my feet the next second. "Are you okay?"

Her fist shot out, but I caught it, wrapping my fingers around her entire hand.

"You care? Since when? You sneak in and leave without so much as acknowledging my presence and then come back smelling like a sex house!"

"Dianna."

She yanked her fist away and came at me again. I clasped her wrist and took her to the ground. I used my body weight to hold her, pinning her hands above her head as she thrashed. She shoved into me, tossing her hips up, which had the opposite effect of what she was going for. I took advantage of the position and maneuvered my hips between her thighs, pressing harder against her.

"I should cut your balls off and feed them to you," she snarled, her bared canines gleaming in the darkness. The crowd outside, shoveling and fixing their ruined buildings, didn't even notice the two most powerful beings in the universe fighting a few feet away. Even the shop she'd tossed me in was abandoned.

I risked getting close to those teeth and leaned into her space. "You'd miss them too much."

She growled and thrashed but to no avail. "Get off of me!"

"Promise you won't try to stab me."

She stared at me, her eyes still blazing with that glorious red, but she eventually let the blade in her hand clatter to the floor above us. Knowing how fast she was, I rose swiftly and extended my hand. She scowled and hit it away from her as she stood.

"I'll ask you again. Are you hurt?" My hand rubbed across my throat. I was a little surprised to find she had not even scratched me.

She adjusted the hem of her dark shirt. "Not by them."

I lowered my gaze. There was still so much to talk about, so much to say. It didn't surprise me in the least that she'd managed not only to kill one of Nismera's commanders but also take half of his fleet. She was brutally efficient when protecting those she loved, making every fiber of my being burn brighter and hotter for her.

"Where is everyone?"

Her eyes never wavered. "You would know if you'd been here, but you weren't, and from the smell of it . . . You know what? No. I'm not doing this with you. I've already done it with your brother."

Glass crunched on her boots as she tried to storm past me. My hand whipped out, grabbing her arm before she could go anywhere. "Dianna. I did not do what you are accusing me of, nor would I ever hurt you like he did."

"No," she said, her lip curling even as her eyes shone. "You're worse. Now let me go."

I did, and she stepped back, creating distance between us. She glared up at me as if I were a threat, and it gutted me. I realized how thoroughly I'd fucked up. I should have stayed and talked instead of leaving her, but I had a reason, a purpose, and something I needed to collect before we moved forward.

"I apologize for sending you away. A lot happened and . . ." I stopped. I couldn't tell her, not here, not like this. "Just come with me. Please. There is something I need your help with."

She folded her arms tight to her body. "No."

"No?" My brow lifted.

"No. I'm taking a play out of your book. Maybe I should disappear for a few days. Maybe visit a sex house too? I hear threesomes are great for heartbreak. Oh, wait. I can't because the fucking universe is hunting me, and what—"

Her words died as soon as I advanced on her. I crouched, wrapped my arms around her thighs, and tossed her over my shoulder. She yelped, her hands digging into my back as she thrashed.

"Put me down." She tried to kick her legs, but I tightened my hold on them.

"No."

"You smell like rancid wine and sex," she hissed, punching at my shoulder. "What, did you leave to get drunk and get your cock sucked?"

"To be quite clear, I was at a brothel."

"I knew it!" Her scream was damn near demonic as she clawed at my shoulder. "Put me down! I'm going to kill you. You won't have to worry about Nismera finding you."

"Would you stop biting me?" I adjusted her on my shoulder. "It was not for sex. I went to visit an old friend who is in hiding. He can make . . . things."

She removed her teeth from my back. "What the fuck does that mean?"

"You'll see."

I moved my arm in a slight circle, my side aching as I pulled on my power. The air split on a whisper, sending dust and trash skipping over the ground. Dianna grumbled and bit me again, but we were already in the portal and gone.

LXVI
Dianna

My feet hit the ground as Samkiel lowered me from his shoulder. I stepped away from him without saying anything. The swirling portal closed behind us, and I looked around. We were in what looked like an abandoned city. Half-destroyed buildings and crumbling infrastructure rose from the center, and a large, cathedral-style structure glared at us from a few miles up.

Samkiel stepped past me, staring at the skyline and the ground as if listening for something. The cobblestone road was fractured, parts of stone standing up in jagged patterns as if something beneath it had moved so fast it busted the infrastructure below.

"What are we doing here? What is this place?"

Samkiel stopped and glared down a narrow street, but I only saw more abandoned and destroyed buildings. "An old place where we once gathered for ceremonies. It was at the center of the Netherworld. Great kings and queens would travel from all over. It doesn't look like much now after Nismera's rule, but it once was beautiful."

I looked out over the dark, empty city but couldn't see it, not with how worn down it was. "Oh? Did you come to a lot of ceremonies here?"

Samkiel stopped and motioned for me to be quiet. I rolled my eyes but didn't speak. He continued down the road, and I followed him with a sigh.

"Are we not going to talk about anything?" I asked, my tone irritated.

He spun toward me, placing his finger to his lips.

I threw up my arms. "There isn't anything here. I didn't even hear a heartbeat besides ours."

"Dianna," he hissed, crouching to peek around a corner before tossing me a glance. "Hush."

My lips formed a thin line, and I shook my head. I crossed my arms and stood behind him, tapping my foot. He rose to his full height before dipping through a low doorway. I followed him into the small half-collapsed building, not needing to duck. A small web hit me in the face, and I spun, ripping at it as I grew more frustrated. My hands scratched at each other as I tossed the slick material to the ground.

Samkiel's eyes blazed into mine. "Dianna. Shush."

Fire lit my hands, the blaze hot enough to burn steel as I glared at him. "I swear to gods Samkiel, if you shush me one more time . . ."

His eyes widened a fraction, and his gaze focused behind me. I heard the chattering and spun, every hair on my body standing on end. A mummified body was attached to the wall, wrapped in white webbing. A beast of many legs and protected by a dark shell looked at me with all twelve of its eyes. It opened its mouth to scream, its orange and black spotted wings fanning out. A whoosh flew past me, and a silver ablaze dagger hit it square in the head. Its wings went slack and its body limp, skewered to the wall by its head.

The flames died in my hands, and the room grew dark once more. "Okay, something tells me this city isn't abandoned but overrun with giant flesh-eating bugs, and now we have to kill them all. Great. Did I ever tell you how much I hate bugs?"

The creature's body twitched, and I shivered. My stomach turned, and it wasn't just because of the giant bug embedded in the wall. I was still hurt. He brought me here for this? After everything? We didn't even talk about what happened. He just assumed we would jump into our next mission, and I couldn't. I threw my arms up in frustration.

"Samkiel, I can't do this. I can't just act like nothing happened between us. You left and—"

I turned and froze, every muscle in my body seizing. It wasn't in fear of the hundreds of flying bugs that probably infested this city, but because Samkiel, World Ender, Destruction Incarnate, and the legendary God King throughout all twelve realms, was kneeling before me. His hand was raised, and he held a shimmering silver ring that held a rhombus-cut, clear jewel. The band gleamed in the low light, and the main stone and the four smaller gems surrounding it sparkled like starlight. Power wafted from it, pure blinding power that I could nearly taste.

"W-what?" The word left my mouth in a whisper as I glanced between him and the ring. My body flushed with heat, and my heart pounded. I took a step back.

"I wanted to do this differently, but I am afraid that creature signaled more to come. There is no perfect place to do this. No place would be perfect enough for you, but anywhere you are is perfect for me."

My brain stopped completely, unable to comprehend what was happening. The ground shook beneath us, or maybe it was me, my entire world tilting.

"This is how it is done on Onuna, yes? They get down on one knee and confess their undying love." Worry creased his brow. "Am I doing this wrong?"

I couldn't breathe, couldn't think. Every form of language emptied from my brain at the sight of Samkiel kneeling before me, holding that ring out. My heart thudded in my chest, and my throat went dry.

"What is this? What's happening?" I managed to gasp.

"Well, I believe this is the part where I ask." His smile was so soft and so sweet. It broke my heart. "Dianna, will you—"

"No."

Samkiel's brows furrowed, and he stood. I backed away from the ring he held like he was offering me poison. "No?"

I shook my head. "No."

He opened his mouth, undoubtedly to say some pretty words that I would believe, but I could not let him say them. There was too much between us, too much still not talked about, reasonings, answers, and questions. Even more than the fight, there was the fact that I hurt everyone I loved. I'd hurt him, and I refused to do it again.

"Why would you ask me this?"

He flinched as if I'd slapped him. "Because I love you."

Love. He said that word so effortlessly as if the last few days hadn't happened. He loved me. I'd known that since the tunnel, yet hearing it now only twisted my gut. He loved me, and I was the worst thing for him.

"How?" My voice was nothing but a whisper.

"How can I love you?" His face drew tight.

"Yes. After everything I've done, everything I put you through? Especially recently?"

Samkiel looked at me in utter disbelief as if I had said the stupidest thing in the world. The ground shook once more, a rumbling I felt more than heard.

"Don't look at me like that." I shook my head. "I lied to you."

Samkiel nodded. "I know."

"I hurt you." My voice cracked. "Like I hurt her."

My chest split wide open, and I wondered if he could see the dark, damaged heart beneath. The one that was still bruised and bloody no matter how many words or soft smiles he tossed my way. No matter how hard he tried to fix me, I was still a broken, violent thing. I'd realized as we fought that I was never going to change. I had spent eons surviving alone, being brutal in a brutal world. He required a pure, safe love, and all I could offer was a vengeful inferno of it. Nothing soft or delicate, my love cut, but I refused to make him bleed for me any longer. That was not a healthy love. Even I knew that.

"Dianna."

"No." I was firm, and I meant it. I took a step back, my boots echoing on the rotten, wooden floorboards, waving my hand toward that damn ring he held on his palm. "Samkiel, I will not stick you with a horrible life as I did her. I will not hurt you as I did her. I refuse."

Heat flared in his gaze as he took a step forward, sunlight casting a glow across his face from where it spilled in through the missing half of the building. He was sunlight, pure and radiant, but as he stepped closer to me, he drew farther into the darkness. *I* was that darkness. It couldn't have represented what I was trying to keep from happening better.

"I have told you a thousand times before that there is no horrible life with you, only without." His voice was strong and unwavering. Samkiel was a warrior, first and foremost, and this was a fight I knew he would not back down from. "Yes, we fought. People who love each other deeply do that. Yes, you hurt me by lying to me, but I know where that comes from."

"Stop." I raised my hands. "Stop making excuses for me. We both know the truth. I am not good for you. We are no good together. My entire existence, ours, is to kill one another."

"I know what you're doing, and I hate it." He stepped forward, and I took another back, maintaining the space between us because I had to. I needed to. He watched it, caught the movement, and his eyes burned hotter than any flame I could summon. "Don't do that. Don't you dare shut me out again, not like on Rashearim, not now, not ever."

"Says the one who shut me out three days ago. You sent me away because you needed *time*."

"Yes, because you *hurt* me." His voice raised a fraction. "You hurt me, Dianna. I needed time to think, not because I planned on leaving you. I needed time to process and make this for you," Samkiel said, holding out the ring again.

"Well, I don't want it." I spun from him and stormed out of the crumbling building, away from our crumbling future.

"You're being a coward!" he shouted after me.

My feet stopped abruptly, and I turned back to him. "What?"

"You heard me. You're a coward. You are afraid of this, and what it means, so you're doing what you always do. Shutting down, protecting yourself because you think I'll hurt you. You're running because this scares you." He stomped out of the ruined building, the dirt kicking up around his feet. "And you don't get to run away when you get scared. You don't get to abandon me when it's tough, Dianna. Never again."

My heart hammered in my chest, every word he said breaking down the mountain of steel doors I used to protect the most vulnerable parts of me. He just slammed them all wide open.

"That's not what I'm doing." And I was a liar, a godsdamn liar, but Samkiel saw right through all my bullshit with pinpoint precision. "Listen, you were right to send me away, okay? There's too much between us. We—"

He reached me then and grabbed my arm, dissolving the space I had made between us in an instant. "You promised not to do this. When we were on that damn balcony, you promised that you'd stay no matter what. You promised you'd never abandon me again."

I pulled away from him, tears in both our eyes. "You ask too much of me, and I don't know if I can give it."

Samkiel didn't back down. "So removing your actual soul is alright, but *this*? Marriage? Is it too much for you?"

I said nothing, but my breathing turned ragged. The necklace I'd given him on that night shone in the sunlight. He was right. He was always right, but this . . . It was just another proof of his devotion, and I was so fucking afraid. Monsters did not scare me, the dark didn't send a chill down my spine, and gods, even bugs were not as terrifying as this. Samkiel offering me his whole godsdamn heart terrified me because I knew I'd eventually fuck up again. I'd break him, and I wouldn't be able to live with myself.

"This." He held the ring between us, its diamonds shimmering in the setting sun. "This is no matter what."

"I'll hurt you." My voice came out as small and damned as I felt.

"Then hurt me." Samkiel's eyes softened, and he stepped closer, his body almost flush with mine. "But don't leave me."

The world shook beneath my feet. A rumble so deep it made me stumble. Samkiel caught me, and we turned toward the half-fallen building as a horde of flying creatures erupted from it.

"What is that?"

"A hive," Samkiel whispered, "and they just woke up."

The ground split, and we stumbled apart. Fissures tore across the ground, spreading in our direction. Even here, even now, we were being torn apart. The universe was trying to right itself and restore balance. Then there was me, doing the only thing I knew how to do. Leave.

His eyes met mine, and the world shuddered again. The sky darkened, a thick cloud of those creatures blocking out the dying light. I watched in horror as the ground beneath his feet cracked and yawned open, swallowing him whole. And the universe, the hateful, cruel bitch, laughed.

LXVII
Dianna

A switch flipped in me as he disappeared beneath the ground. I felt it in my bones. A gaping, aching pit opened up inside me and threatened to consume everything. The world went silent. My form shifted, two legs turning to four. Thick, dark hair sprouted over my body. My jaws lengthened, filled with sharp teeth, and ended in a sensitive nose. My ears flattened against my head as a howl of rage ripped from my throat. I didn't hesitate to launch myself into the tunnel after him. My large paws beat against the ground, my claws digging into the dirt, propelling me faster.

I was stupid. Stupid, stupid, stupid, and beyond that, I was a gods-damned liar. I could pretend I knew what was best for us, pretend that leaving was better, but I was a liar to him and, above all, myself. The physical pain I'd felt when Samkiel disappeared into the ground in front of me was nearly as bad as when death ripped my soul in two. It threw me right back to that moment, to the anguish of holding him in my arms as he died.

I knew I'd burn oceans to mist, skies to dust, and worlds to rubble to keep him near. Love was too dull of a word for what I felt for him and one I hated to say. It meant nothing. I understood now why they had stories of losing an amata and why Logan was feral when he felt

Neverra in Yejedin. I understood now and knew the true loss of another's soulmate was one of the worst pains known in any realm.

It was not sharp or piercing but an agony that melted your bones, seared your flesh, and carved a hole so deep into you that you'd pray for a quick death to be with them. So no, it was not love. It was more necessary, like air in my lungs, blood in my veins. It wasn't just a nebulous emotion that came and went on a whim. This bond was a near-physical thing, tangible and constant.

I sprinted through the labyrinth of tunnels, ripping and tearing into every insect creature crawling or flying after me. Gore marred my jaws and teeth, but it only fueled my rage. I'd tear apart anything that got in my way without a second thought. I couldn't explain the feeling that burned in my chest and crawled through my being. There were no limits I would not breach for him. I had ripped him from death. These things would not take him from me.

Their exoskeletons crunched between my teeth, the sounds of their death cries filling my ears. I reveled in it. I'd make anything that touched him dead, and I'd enjoy it.

A scream echoed through the hive. It wasn't one of flying insects, but my tether to this world, thick, masculine, and in pain. I listened, focusing all my energy on locating him in this labyrinth. I heard the grunts of battle and the clang of steel ringing through the air. Glancing at a hole above me, I crouched, settling the power into my bones. I jumped, my hind legs propelling me through the hole and down another tunnel. The sounds of battle grew louder. I burst into a small cavern, the flutter of orange wings darting past me. I launched myself at the closest one, my jagged teeth sinking deep. My jowls dripped with blood as I ripped and shredded. These must have been headed toward Samkiel because they scattered quickly, not staying to engage me.

I spun, my ears lifting to points at the top of my head as I listened once more. The sounds of fighting came from my left, and then I heard him from my right. There was an echo that came from beneath me. Fuck, these holes acted as an amplifier. I inhaled deeply, information flooding me. I snarled and darted back through the tunnel. My feet skidded as I came to a stop at the edge of a massive hole in the middle of the tunnel, dust kicking up under my claws. One glance down, and I jumped.

I landed silently in a dark, empty cavern. Holes lined the ceiling and walls. Some opened into tunnels, and others were covered by crystallized webs. I squinted and moved closer to one of the covered holes, my hackles rising as I caught the smell of rotting flesh. It held a cocooned corpse. Fuck. There were hundreds of them here. I was in the center of the fucking hive.

Eerie chittering came from all around me. I turned in a slow circle, fangs bared, expecting to see something behind me, but it was just more empty darkness.

"Your eyes shine red, yet you slaughter my horde?" a voice echoed, the scratchiness of it making me shiver. "We are on the same side, you and I."

"Doubtful," I growled, my lips pulling back in a snarl. I hoped my words were clear enough. Then I paused. "How can I understand you?"

"You are Ro'Vikiin reborn."

I paced the cavern, hoping to track that voice. So it could hear me and understand me as I could it. It wasn't like the creatures I was used to dealing with. One thing I knew about bugs in a colony or hive like this was that they usually had a queen. I would be willing to bet she watched me now from her shadowy den.

"Why does everyone keep calling me that?" I snapped at the air, feeling something powerful and ancient circling me.

"Your blood screams it, and you protect a Lightbringer, just as he did. Why do you protect the Lightbringer so? They are a plague to our kind," it said, the chittering, scratchiness of its voice making my lips pull back in a silent snarl.

Lightbringer? My heart thudded in my chest, claws digging deeper into the dirt. Samkiel. "Where is he?" I snapped, my teeth echoing the sound.

Something scurried above me, and dust rained down on me. I jerked my head up, my ears pinned against my head.

"You are a disgrace. Filth. Betrayer. Like the one before you."

"I don't have time for riddles," I snarled.

I heard more movement above, and it grew a fraction darker. It was distracting me, covering the exits, taking away any fraction of light here to blind me further.

"No riddles. The cosmos were shrouded in darkness for eons before that damned light came into this world. It ripped us apart, separating us into different worlds. Light, how we hate it, yet you're covered in it. That smell. Such a disgrace."

My eyes closed as I focused, my ears twitching. I heard the legs on my right, but I stood still and listened. Far below me, I heard Samkiel grunt. I felt the pull of him like a tether, a string connecting us. It pulled tight as soon as I located him. My eyes snapped open, and I realized the cavern had gone still and deathly quiet.

"The light will end us all, and you will burn with it, just as Ro'Vikiin did," the voice called from above my head. If I could have smiled in this canine form, I would have.

"Oh yeah? You keep talking about burning. I'd probably choose my words wisely."

I tipped my head back just as those massive pinchers opened above me. Eight massive eyes glared at me, and eight eyes widened, reflecting the orange glow of my flames. Fire built at the base of my throat and tunneled its way out. She shrieked and flew to the other side of her nest. I sucked in another breath and released a torrent of flame that ripped through every web she had built. The cavern shook with her anger, and I continued to burn the place, looking for a tunnel that led down. A section of the web melted, and there it was. Perfect.

I ran, my claws digging in, feeling her leg scrape against my tail. I heard her thundering behind me and leaped, her body crashing against the floor, too big to follow. Her screeches made my ears ache, but I barely noticed as the dust settled from my landing and I had fallen into hell itself.

LXVIII
Dianna

There, in the center of the cave, surrounded by a swarm of those bugs, I glimpsed his silver armor. My feet ground to a halt as he swung his sword, chopping away limbs and slicing torsos in half. For a man of his size, Samkiel moved with elegance and grace. He was every bit a warrior trained to kill, and nothing stood in his way. One by one, they fell, and one by one more emerged from the surrounding holes.

Lightbringer.

That's what she had said. Samkiel was their target all along, and while he may be a fantastic swordsman, he was outnumbered and, by the looks of it, growing weary. His side ached, his power not fully his because it was still spread across the sky. Darkened mist danced around my form, and I was truly me again. Anger flared in my gut. These damned creatures were threatening to steal him from me.

I fought my way through to him and yanked the blade from his hand. He looked at me with bewilderment from behind his face shield as I spun it over my head, slicing two of the creatures in half.

"I'd die for you," I practically yelled at him over the chittering of the creatures.

A creature screeched, advancing on us as I stared at Samkiel. I twisted the blade in my hand, the hilt burning my palm, but I didn't care. I rammed the sword into the creature charging at my back, not breaking eye contact with him for a second. Samkiel watched me as I shook the gore from the blade.

He shook his head and flicked his wrist, summoning another sword. "And you think I wouldn't do the same for you?"

"I love you. You are it for me and have been for a very long time." My sword whipped over my head, blood spraying as I lopped the head off one of the bugs. Samkiel and I were fighting, yet our eyes were only on each other.

"Well, you're it for me," he yelled back, thrusting his blade to my side, impaling one of the creatures as it reached for me.

"I'm stupid." I kicked my foot out, stomping on the chomping head that neared me. "I was wrong. I would rather fight every day with you than be without you."

Samkiel raised his hand, light heating my cheek as it whizzed past my head. I felt the splatter of warm moisture as the creature charging at my back exploded. "As would I."

I spun around him, going back to back as the bugs chattered, wings flaring. "Good."

"Great," he huffed before we pushed off each other.

We cut and maimed, limbs and wings flying. Soon, the floor was covered in corpses and twitching legs. Samkiel's head lifted mid-strike. I heard it, too. More bugs scurried in from our left. The holes there, that's where they were coming from. That was the main port.

"Sami." I pointed toward the main opening. It was the largest, allowing them to swarm.

"On it," he answered.

He flicked his ring, returning his ablaze weapon to it. In the next heartbeat, a silver bow formed in his hand. Thick in the middle and curving up, it was nearly as tall as him. He pulled the string back, and an arrow made of light appeared. The creatures near the tunnel paused.

It was all he needed. Samkiel released, and the arrow hit right above the main entrance. The wall shook, and the stone split. Rocks fell, crushing the bugs that tried to scuttle back in. I stared at the twitching legs sticking out from between the boulders in disgust, listening to the deep rumble echo through the tunnels. For a moment, I worried the cavern would collapse, but it remained intact.

Samkiel stared at me, his eyes molten behind his face shield. The chill of battle had retreated, his eyes burning with the same heat I always saw in his gaze when he looked at me.

"You found me."

"You find me, I find you," I panted back, handing him his sword. It collapsed into his ring as soon as it touched his hand. "That's how we work."

His lips twitched in a barely there smile as he looked around. The scurrying in another section above us was a welcome distraction, our previous conversation a dead weight between us. "The hive is a labyrinth."

"Yeah, I gathered that much," I said.

"Don't take an ablaze weapon from me again," he said, nodding to my burned palm. "How's your hand?"

I raised it, the skin knitting together slowly. "Right as rain or whatever. I didn't hold it that long."

Samkiel nodded, his hand clenching as if he wanted to reach for me to check. His boots crunched over bug remains as he stepped forward. He didn't come to me, but around. He lifted his head, inspecting the cavern and the tunnels where the beasts had come in, making sure that all were clear. I knew what he was doing. He was avoiding eye contact and all contact in general.

Samkiel craned his head to the right, looking at a particularly wide hole. "This hive has to run through the entire city."

"It would make sense. I found cocoons back there with bodies. A lot of them." I moved to his side, and he deftly stepped around me.

"Her hive must have taken the city. They burrow as we have seen, but the last I knew, they stayed in the Otherworld. There is less sun exposure there. Someone must have brought them here. I don't see how they could get this far on their own. Maybe a transport or something."

"Hmm, that would make sense. I wonder who would bring them here, though, and why." I sighed, folding my arms.

"I don't know, but she's been nesting here a long time. There is no telling how many eggs have hatched. We need to find the queen. We kill her, and the horde dies. If we leave her alive, she will just rebuild and repopulate."

"Sami."

He turned, but pain filled his eyes, not hope. He held his hand up to stop me, but his fingers slowly collapsed into a fist. "Not here. Or now. We can talk about it once we leave, but we need to find—"

"Ask me again," I snapped, cutting him off.

Samkiel turned toward me, and his helmet rolled back, disappearing into the collar of his armor. Confusion marred his expression. "What?"

"Ask me again."

I stepped forward, my hands in front of me, fingers intertwined. We were both covered in guts and bile, and gods knew what else. There was nothing romantic about this, but I stared at him and felt nothing but warmth. He was the one person who never abandoned me, no matter how cruel, vicious, or mean I was.

Samkiel had been there for me after I'd lost one of the most important people in my life, pulling me out of one of the darkest times of my life. He never judged or faltered, his love and loyalty a constant. I didn't deserve him, and maybe he was right. A deep, dark part of me reveled in the fact I had finally done something to break us.

My fears were no longer present because they came true. The truth was he was too good for me, and I was more comfortable leaving. It was safer. I could protect my heart, my soul. The problem was, neither of them was mine any longer. They were his and had been for some time now. He had picked up the pieces, bit by jagged, broken bit, and put them back together. Somehow, he had healed them and made me whole. So even if my love was a dark, powerful, brutal thing, it was still just love.

"If I ask again, will you say no? Because I do not think I could stomach it."

"Do you want the truth?"

He nodded, neither of us caring we still had a queen to kill and several more entrances those damn things could get through.

"I thought it was painfully obvious," I said, blowing out a breath. "I'm an idiot."

His head reared back. "What? No. You're one of the smartest people I know. One of the smartest I've ever met."

I shook my head. "Not when it comes to you."

His eyes softened, his throat bobbing as if he'd swallowed whatever words he was about to speak.

"You're right about a lot of things. I run when things get hard. Sometimes, I lock my emotions down and everyone out. I think the absolute worst, so yes, you leaving made sense. When you sent me away, I thought you had finally realized how damaged and broken I was and decided you deserved better. So I was going to deal with it. I had made up my mind that no matter what, I would still help you get your family back and save this blasted realm you care so much for. Even if you hated me for lying to you and hurting you again and wanted nothing to do with me."

I paused, twisting my fingers together but refusing to look away from him. He deserved to hear this.

"So, when you asked, it scared me. It wasn't what I was expecting. Samkiel, you are not anything I could have ever expected. You prove my worst insecurities wrong at every turn and make me see how good some people are. You make me *feel*. At times, being in this relationship with you is hard for me because I care so much. I don't want to mess up, mess *us* up, and I don't know what I'm doing. So yes, you're right. I am a coward because quitting seemed safer. But then the ground split, and you disappeared. I was reminded once again that being without you is worse."

He folded his arms across the thick breastplate of his armor, and I marveled at him. He was every bit a white knight, and now he was glaring at me. I expected him to tell me I was wrong, maybe with soft words or a hug, but not the grin that slowly formed on his face. "You're right, too."

"About which part?" I asked.

"You are an idiot."

My hands dropped to my sides. "Hey!"

He took another step, this time not trying to stay away from me. "I want you to repeat in that glorious head of yours what you just said. How you'd help me save my family and the realms despite how you thought I no longer wanted you. You put yourself, your feelings, and your heart last again. And don't think for one second I deserve anyone better than you. There is no one better than you. There never has been. No one is more courageous or godsdamn selfless. You ran into a hive full of flesh-eating acidic insects—"

"Wait." I held up my hand, frowning in disgust. "Flesh-eating acid?"

"With no regard for yourself, to save me. So yes, you are an idiot."

"I just—"

Samkiel lightly grabbed my arms. "How could I not be completely and utterly in love with you?"

"You love me?" My heart melted.

"With everything I am and everything I ever will be."

My world stopped. It was fractured and remade with those words. They weren't just words but a promise, a declaration from two people who had been burned by the world. We had lost everything and never wished to share with another so deeply. He had offered me his heart, and in return, I'd give him the broken pieces of mine. It was more than love for us, and I knew now it always had been.

Tears blurred my vision, and I lurched forward, my lips slanting across his. His mouth moved over mine, deepening the kiss. We froze and broke the kiss, both of us grimacing in revulsion.

"A perfect moment ruined by bug guts." I swore, wiping and failing to remove the grime from my face.

Samkiel laughed as he did the same.

"Don't laugh." I glared. "It's not funny."

"Kinda funny." Samkiel's face scrunched as he wiped the bug grime at his mouth. "That was not well thought out."

"No," I agreed. "They taste just as bad as they look."

Samkiel made a face and lowered his hand. "I am sorry I left as I did. I had good intentions, even with how I was hurting at the time."

"I'm sorry I lied to you." I said, meaning every word. "Truly—"

"We'll talk about it later." He gave me a small smile. "First, we still need to leave this place."

"Right. Kill the mega queen."

"But first." He reached beneath his armor and pulled out the ring he'd wrapped in a piece of thin black material. "Dianna. Ayla. Akrai. My world. My life. My love. Will you marry me?"

"No."

His brows drew together so tightly I worried about his face freezing that way. My smile was so big it made my cheeks hurt. "I'm kidding. It's yes. It's a thousand times, yes."

The cavern trembled violently, almost knocking us over. A roar reverberated through the air, this one far too loud to be the creatures we'd been fighting. Samkiel grabbed me as the ground bucked beneath us, throwing us off balance.

We turned in mid-embrace, creatures emerging from tunnels on all sides, debris and dust raining down all around us. The queen was royally pissed and looking for blood.

"I hope that's a serious yes because we have an enormous problem now."

I gave him my hand, extending my finger. "It's a yes. Now give me my damned ring."

His smug, male smirk was adorable as he placed the ring on my finger. Heat coated my skin, a warm, tingly feeling washing over my body before fading away. He rubbed his thumb across the stone, and silver armor flowed over my body, covering me from head to toe. Samkiel did not just give me a ring. He offered me protection, too. I had so many questions, but the first wave of insects reached us, with the second horde right behind. My admiration and curiosity would have to wait.

LXIX

Dianna

My palm slapped into Samkiel's, and he hauled me from the hole in the ground. We both took a deep breath, fresh air filling our lungs. Samkiel bent and pulled at the clawed, severed leg still clinging to my armor, its grip still tight after death. He managed to work it free and dropped it to the ground, where it continued to twitch. I kicked it with my armored boot, and it fell back into the hole.

The silver armor wrapped around my body was identical to his but more feminine and exactly suited to my shape. I looked at him through the narrow slit across my eyes. His armor looked so intimidating, but now I knew it was easy to breathe and move in. It was like leather and spandex wrapped into one with a hardened shell on the outside, but so much lighter than I expected.

"You think that's all of them?" I asked, stepping over some rubble and further from the hole, just in case.

He shrugged one powerful shoulder. "It doesn't matter. The queen is dead, and the others will follow. They are made from the same chemical that floods through her. A new queen hasn't hatched, so the line has ended."

"You're so smart." I smiled at him, even though he couldn't see it.

He snorted. "Not by my own doing. Remember, I got in trouble frequently for my actions. My punishment was hours locked away studying, memorizing texts and languages, and . . . Well, you get it."

I nodded as he summoned his blade back into his ring. I dropped my gaze to my sword and rotated my wrist, spinning it in a figure eight between us.

"How come it doesn't burn me now?"

"As long as you wear this," he tapped my armored shoulder, "it won't. I made sure of it. Ablaze weapons kill almost everything. It's safer and keeps me from worrying about you."

"You know I breathe fire and become a giant, scaly beast, right?"

His brow flicked upwards behind his helmet. "Appease me, please."

"Fine." I chuckled and flicked mine like he did. Only my sword stayed. "How do I do the cool, flippy thing like you do to make it disappear?"

I couldn't see his smile through his helmet, but I saw the corners of his eyes crinkle. He grabbed my wrist and twisted it, flicking my ring against my knuckle. The blade disappeared in an instant.

"Just like that."

I glanced at him, forgetting he couldn't see my returning smile. "Thanks."

"Not an issue," he said, staring at me.

"What?"

He shook his head. "Nothing. It is just nice to have an equal in every way. You are perfect."

He looked at me, and a warmth rubbed across my subconscious, inviting and welcoming as an ocean breeze against the shore. It was lovely and peaceful, but as soon as it touched me, it was gone.

He couldn't see my smile, but it was there regardless. "Remember you said that when I say something annoying later."

"Absolutely." He nodded, not even trying to deny it.

"Or piss you off," I added.

"I'll keep a list," he said, humor lacing his words.

My hands fell to my hips. "So we have a major fight, argue, and three days later, you drag me out to an abandoned, broken city to propose to me and kill some infesting bug species?"

He nodded at the large cathedral-style building up ahead and started toward it. "Not just that. We are here to retrieve the last officiant in the realms that can perform the Ritual of Dhihsin."

"What?" I called, nearly tripping over my feet as I followed after him.

"Did I misspeak?" he asked, glancing back at me over his armored shoulder.

"No, it just sounds like you want to perform a ritual we can't actually do since I have no soul. We aren't super, special mates anymore, remember?"

"We are to me," he said, not missing a beat. "We can still perform it. The mark will not appear, but in all ways, you will be what you call in your world my wife."

This time, I did trip. I grabbed onto one of the half-destroyed buildings as we rounded a corner. "Wait, stop."

He did, turning to look at me.

"Are we getting married now? Here?" I asked, gesturing toward the demolished town that was filled with rubble and smelled like death.

"No, not here." He glanced to where I pointed, then back to me. "I have another place I found while I was away. I want to perform the ritual there."

"Sami." My heart lodged in my throat as another realization struck me. "You planned all this while you were gone?"

He looked at me as if I had grown horns. "Yes. If we cannot share the mark, I want the next best option. I want everyone who encounters us to know who we belong to. I want something that can protect you when I cannot. I thought I'd made my intentions very clear?"

"No. You did, and it's very romantic." My throat dried up at the thought and care he had put into all of this when I thought he wanted nothing more to do with me. "But . . ."

"But?"

I shrugged. "It's just in my world, couples plan weddings together. Family and friends are there, and it's a big celebration."

"It is for us as well, but our family is not with us right now. Also, given what we have learned about my resurrection and what you no longer have, I refuse to search for them or put either of us in harm's way until this is done."

I said nothing, but he caught the change in my posture.

"I swear to you, you will have the most extravagant ceremony when we all can be together once more. I'll move every star for that day." He closed the distance between us and grabbed my hands. "But right now, we don't know when or if we will have time for this again. Every time we get a brief bit of happiness, it is ripped from us. I refuse to wait anymore. I want you, all of you. I love you, all of you, and if I have to carve out time for this, for us, by the old gods and the new, I will do it."

The tension in my shoulders eased, and I took a deep breath. "Okay."

Samkiel ran a hand down the back of my armored neck before stepping back and tugging on my hand. The walk through the destroyed city was quiet aside from the sounds of our armored boots on cracked stone, and then another thought raced through my head.

"You know," I cast a glance at him as we walked hand in hand, "I don't have a dress."

He kept walking, my hand grasped firmly in his, and I struggled to keep up with his long strides. It was as if, now that he had my agreement, he was unwilling to wait any longer. We passed more abandoned houses, following the road toward a small hill.

"Yes, you do. I bought you one."

"You did?" I couldn't help my smile or the warmth that blossomed in my chest.

"Yes, in my tradition, it is part of the ceremony. The partner who proposes has three tasks they have to complete. One, they have to find a precious gem for their intended, and it has to be rare. That is a sign of how they view their intended. Your stone can only be found at the center of one very active and nasty lava pit. Two, they are to take care of the event itself. In doing so, they prove they are capable of taking care of their partner. Three, they handle the attire. If their partner doesn't like what they have chosen, it is said that they do not truly love or know their intended, and the ceremony is voided."

I shook my head in pure bewilderment. "That's actually really romantic."

"It is." He squeezed my hand a fraction tighter.

Stupid tears threatened to blur my vision. I had never been loved like this. I squeezed Samkiel's hand in return, unsure if he even felt it with our gauntlets. "So if I hate my dress, we call this whole thing off?"

Samkiel laughed. "Yes, but I am not worried in the least."

"Cocky." I bumped into him.

I was so foolish. The entire time he was gone, I had assumed the worst. The part of me still damaged thought he'd be like Kaden. Even though I knew Samkiel would never treat me as Kaden had, I still expected the absolute worst. I'd thought he had given up on us when I'd been the one threatening to pull back. I truly didn't deserve this man, but I no longer cared. He was mine, and I was keeping him.

I didn't have pretty words to offer him, and I sucked at revealing my emotions, so I did what I always did and said, "I am going to fuck you senseless."

His whole body went rigid, and he practically stumbled to a halt. Silver lined his eyes, and I didn't need to see his full expression to know how my words had affected him. This time, it was his turn to stumble over his words.

"Well . . . I mean . . . we technically could now. If you want? This entire place is abandoned."

I smirked beneath my helmet, dropping his hand as I walked past him, tapping his shoulder. "Ravage me after the ceremony."

We searched the upper levels of the old, broken structure before making our way downstairs.

"Are you sure they are still alive?"

Samkiel nodded and walked in front of me, ducking low to avoid the support beam above. "My sources say yes. The plus side is that she is similar to an air fae. The energy carried by the wind nourishes them so she would not starve. They are quite able to defend themselves and adept at hiding, but overall, they are usually docile. She would not feel the need to flee in fear of the creatures we so politely destroyed."

He held out his hand, and I took it. We walked down the rough-hewn stone steps, following them as they circled deeper.

Samkiel let go of my hand as he reached the landing. He twisted the knob of a wooden door, but it did not budge. His body stilled, and he tipped his head, listening.

"It is barricaded from the inside, and I can hear a heartbeat."

"Lovely," I said.

Samkiel leaned back and rammed the door with his shoulder. The door gave, and whatever was bracing it on the other side scratched against the stone with an ungodly sound. I flinched and covered my ears.

"Sorry," he whispered and summoned a ball of light into his hand before stepping toward the ruined door. Nothing stirred but a tiny, little creature hissing away from the light. We walked further inside, the room a complete disaster. Some crates were lodged to one side, half overturned and empty, while the others were in shards. Samkiel stopped in the center of the room, raising his hand as he looked around. He paused as his light found a hall in the far left corner, half hidden by a support beam.

"Wait here," he said. "Just in case."

"In case what?" I asked.

Samkiel didn't answer, but as he stepped closer to the hall, I heard running footsteps coming from my right. A battle cry tore through the air just before I was tackled from the side. I hit the ground with a clang, but the armor absorbed most of the impact. My hands rose instinctively, stopping the descent of the rusty spoon aimed at my face.

A woman with pale skin and swirling white markings on her face snarled at me, exposing conical-shaped teeth. One minute, she was staring daggers at me, and the next, Samkiel had her up on her feet. He yanked the spoon from her hand and tossed it aside.

"Everrine. Be calm." Samkiel's voice was infused with power.

Her sapphire eyes dulled, and her lower lip trembled. She tossed her arms around his neck and sobbed, the flowing white gown she wore dirty and ragged. She clung to him, speaking quickly. I was so glad Samkiel had taught me the common language, or I'd be lost.

"Samkiel," she wept, stepping back so she could look up at him. Her hands clasped the sides of his helmet, and she pulled him down, placing a kiss on each cheek.

I gripped her arm and pried her from him, ignoring her hiss as I pushed her back.

"Mine," I snapped, making sure my eyes flared a vivid red.

She took one look at me and bolted up the stairs, screaming with every step she took.

"Docile, huh?" I asked, folding my arms.

"They usually are." Samkiel rested his hand on my shoulder. "Sorry about that. I—"

"Just go get her before I burn her alive, and we have to do the ceremony ourselves."

"Yes, akrai."

LXX
Dianna

I emerged from the portal, my lungs rejoicing with the pure, sweet air as I took what felt like my first breath. I stepped forward and felt my eyes widen, my gaze flitting all around me, trying to make sense of the incredible beauty. Mountain ranges and narrow spires towered over the valleys, their peaks piercing the dazzling blue of the sky. Forests stretched far and wide, the greens and blues of the trees interspersed with pops of red and ribbons of silvery rivers. Small floating islands cast massive shadows. Waterfalls spilled from their edges and poured into crystalline lakes, adding a shimmery mist to the air that burst into rainbows where the sun shone through.

"What is this place?" I turned toward Samkiel as he dragged the officiant through the closing gate.

"It will be the new Rashearim."

"Here?"

He nodded.

Everrine dropped to her knees the second Samkiel released her. Raising her hands above her head, she bowed until her face was in the dirt. "Please forgive me, oh great future queen. I pledge my life to protect you and your kingdom's secrets. Please spare me from my mistake." She continued to ramble on.

"What is she doing?" I glanced at Samkiel. "What did you say to her?"

He shrugged. "I told her you are my future queen, and I want her to perform the ceremony. I assume she feels bad for touching me, even in gratitude. She is asking for forgiveness. Oh, and she also doesn't want you to eat her."

I rolled my eyes and stepped forward, grabbing her arm and pulling her up and off her feet. "Please, stop. I'm not going to kill you or eat you." She quieted, but her lower lip still trembled. "Unless you don't help us get married, then I might."

"No, no, I will. I swear it." She nodded. "My life is forever in your debt, Queen of Rashearim."

My heart thudded. "I'm not—"

"You will be," Samkiel cut off my denial, walking past us both. I dropped Everrine on her feet, and she straightened her gown, the arms and tail trailing behind her. "I know it doesn't look like much now, but this place is the most beautiful of all the realms."

"Fitting," I murmured, standing by his side. He caught my joke, remembering how I'd told him how beautiful he was the first time I'd met him.

"I plan for this to be our home and, eventually, the epicenter of New Rashearim. Once I have my powers fully back, that is."

"And we defeat your evil sister."

"That too," he agreed.

"And your evil brothers."

"Yes."

"And also rescue your family."

He chuckled. "Yes, yes, all of that."

Unable to take my eyes off the view before us, I nodded. I could see it, what Samkiel envisioned, but I worried he thought getting his powers back would be easy. Regardless, I'd help him any way I could.

"So, this is what you wanted to show me? Our future?" I said, smiling at him.

"Yes, but this," he held out his hand, his silver armor matching mine as I put my palm in his, "this is what I wanted you to see."

He led me toward the edge of the cliff and stepped behind me. His massive arm took up my vision as he pointed to the left.

There, carved into half the mountain, sat the largest castle I had ever seen.

"What?" I tipped my head back, gazing up at him in shock.

"This was the first place I went after our fight. I needed a place to keep the one person who I love the most safe. Nowhere we have been has been good enough, and when I remembered this realm, I needed to see if it still stood. It does, and it is also abandoned. I checked the entire place. They even left the furniture."

"You left me to go house hunting and wedding planning after we'd just had a major fight?"

He shrugged. "Well, when you say it like that, I suppose it does sound a bit strange."

There he was, once again proving that he was nothing like I'd ever expected. I had been miserable those days after we fought. Miserable and crying and depressed that I had ruined the best thing that had ever happened to me, yet he was quite literally building our future.

"I would burn the world for you," I whispered, meaning every godsdamn word. "Take your helmet off."

It disappeared in a flash, and he reached for my hand, flicking my ring so mine dropped next. His smile broadened, spreading across his face before he leaned forward to kiss me. Every worry I'd had over the last few days melted as his lips touched mine, neither of us caring about the gore that still covered us. I hadn't realized how utterly scared I was that I'd come so close to losing him.

"Can we just get inside before you start all that, please?" Everrine said from behind us.

Samkiel and I broke apart and turned. We'd forgotten she was even here.

She held herself stiffly, the wind whipping at her garments as she shivered.

"I do not have well-insulated armor, and I am freezing since we are so high up. Let me perform the ceremony, and you can kiss each other until you turn blue."

I followed Samkiel into the massive hall, taking in every inch of the estate, and *estate* was putting it lightly. Not only had he left me to fashion a wedding ring built to protect me, but he'd also found us a new home built for a queen.

My throat dried as he smiled and pushed open the twin double doors. The hinges creaked, stiff with disuse. He stepped aside, and I paused on the threshold, looking out at the room sprawled before me. I took a hesitant step inside and spun, taking in the towering ceiling and massive interior.

"This bedroom is bigger than the one we had on Rashearim."

He nodded, watching me with pleasure. "It is."

"They just left it all?" I asked, glancing around. A bed with four twisted wooden posts sat to my left, covered in an array of furs, but it was the mantle on the other side of the room that caught my attention. It stood sentinel above a fireplace that nearly took up half the wall.

"Yes, Nismera's reign is not one to be taken lightly. I am sure that with the realms locked down and Unir dying, they must have felt abandoned and left to her mercy. The problem is, she doesn't have any. The knowledge must have instilled the utmost fear and panic in them."

I could hear the soul-deep guilt in his voice, his crown weighing heavily today when he had to confront the realities these beings had faced without him to protect them.

"I wonder what happened to them."

"Probably captured or enslaved, or worse," he said before clearing his throat. "I already removed the relics from the castle so you won't see any pictures of them. There is still a lot of work I want to do in this place, but I thought we could do it together. I was only able to get a few of the most essential pieces from Rashearim."

I swallowed the growing lump in my throat and reached for the frame resting on the split wooden mantle. The image went blurry, but I lovingly traced my fingers over Gabby's smiling face. "The most essential," I managed to say, my voice clogged with tears.

"Yes," he said from behind me. "I want you to make this your new home . . . I want you to make this *our* new home. Fill it with laughter and joy like only you can. I want to fight with you here, love with you here, and fill it with our family. Only you can give me this, Dianna. I can give you the house, but only you can make it our home."

I spun, tossing my arms around his shoulders as I kissed him once, twice, three times. My hands curled in his hair as I moved away just a fraction, my nose running across his ever so slightly.

"You shouldn't have traveled back to Old Rashearim without me."

"I was safe," he whispered.

I sniffled, the overwhelming emotions threatening to take me. "I can't believe you did all this in three days."

He shrugged like it was nothing. "I didn't sleep."

Carefully, almost reverently, I pulled back and stepped out of his embrace. I turned, placing the picture back on the mantle and staring at the one next to it. Neverra and Imogen were making goofy faces. I remembered Neverra's insistence that I join in, and I'd ended up squished in the middle. I looked so different then, so sad. They had tried with everything they had to help bring me back into living and not just existing. I would do the same for them.

Inhaling, I turned toward Samkiel. "I already love our new home."

The joy that suffused his face took my breath away, and I knew my words meant more to him than a throne or crown. They were everything. This home would belong to all of us because I would carve our enemies into bloody ribbons to get our family back.

His fingers brushed a strand of hair from my face. "Miska, Orym, and Roccurem will be here as well."

"A full house then," I said, lifting one brow.

Samkiel nodded and lowered his hand, taking mine. "There is just one more thing."

He led me deeper into the suite and through another doorway. This room was smaller but spacious enough that a group of us could move freely. A large, half-dusted, freestanding mirror stood proudly to the right. What used to be an ornate dressing screen was sectioning off one corner. It had seen better days, tilting to the side, parts of it broken. A large, round dresser took up a good portion of the center of the room, a collection of drawers running up and down its surface.

"I know you adore large walk-in closets, and I thought this would be perfect once we fix it up." He smiled at me before dropping my hand. I watched him shift the broken divider to the side, revealing a long dress draped over a plush maroon chair.

My heart stuttered as he moved to the side, watching for my reaction with careful eyes.

"Is that . . .?" My words failed me.

He only nodded.

I stepped toward the dress almost hesitantly. Picking it up by the hanger, I walked to the mirror and held it in front of me, careful not to let it touch my gore-smeared armor. The contrast of the dirty metal against the pristine white fragility of the lace was nearly comical. The fabric looked so soft, and I longed to touch it but was hesitant, not wanting to mar its perfection.

Samkiel stepped behind me, and I met his eyes in the mirror. He was always behind me. I could face anything, knowing he stood at my back. He was my shield, my strength, and soon he would be my husband.

"I hate it," I said. "The wedding is off."

Samkiel's eyes shuttered for a fraction of a second before he saw my smile bloom across my face. He grinned and leaned forward, nipping at my ear. I squealed, lowering my head.

"Stop it," he growled against my cheek.

"It's beautiful," I said. "No, that's the wrong word. It is stunning, Samkiel."

He beamed and placed a kiss on my cheek. "Just as you are."

"You just knew I'd love lace?"

He smirked adorably, his lips quirking in smug pride. "I may have paid attention once or twice."

"Oh, yeah?" I grinned at the challenge. "What's my favorite color?"

"Black, even though I tell you it's not a color but the absence of one, and you roll your eyes and say I am being too literal."

"Okay." I chuckled. "That was easy. What about—"

"I know you broke your wrist when you were young, protecting your sister. You showed me where the scar was when we were in that small motel on Onuna, and you were trying to make me feel better about my outburst. I know the ocean is your favorite place, even if it still hurts you. When you were young, you lied and said that you and

Gabriella had the same birthday so that people would think you were twins. Pasta was the first thing you learned to cook, but baking is your favorite. You prefer silk over most fabrics, leather over rough jeans, and you think that one of the best perks of immortality is that you can wear heels for hours and your feet never hurt."

A small laugh escaped me at that last part, and I remembered bitching about that on one of our first long treks looking for Azrael's book.

His eyes shone a bit brighter, and he dipped his chin to press a kiss to the top of my head. "Did I pass?"

I pursed my lips and shrugged. "You did okay."

"I told you. I always listened, even when you thought I wasn't." He focused on the reflection of the dress. "But you do like it? Most I found were far too vibrant or fluffy. I thought this one was perfect for you. It is simple, yet elegant, and on you? It will be absolutely devastating."

"It's perfect." I smiled at him, no longer talking about the dress. I hung the dress almost reverently and turned in his arms, my eyes prickling. I pressed up on my tiptoes and leaned against him, brushing a tender kiss full of promises on his lips. "Absolutely perfect," I whispered before pulling back. "Now, get out of my room so I can get dressed."

He threw his head back and laughed before meeting my gaze and stepping away. "As you wish."

I turned back, staring at the dress again as he strode toward the door. "You know I can't wear panties with this, right?" I called out, grinning mischievously over my shoulder.

He paused at the door. His expression was calm and innocent, as if my words hadn't sent desire blazing through him. "Oops."

"I have never had anyone do my hair before." Miska fidgeted as she stared at herself in the mirror. She wore a champagne-colored dress, the hem dancing around her feet with her every movement. The fabric was light and smooth but shimmered softly at the smallest touch of light.

"Really?" I asked, twisting another strand and pinning up the side.

"Yeah, I always did it myself. Everyone avoided me in Jade City."

"Right."

"You're good at it." She grinned at me.

I smiled at her as I secured the last piece of her bun. "I used to do my sister's, and she did mine. She actually taught me how to braid my hair."

Miska's head turned to mine. "What's that?"

"I'll show you one day." I handed her a small mirror and turned her until her back was to the big one so she could see her hair. "What do you think?"

"Wow," she whispered, reaching up and lightly touching it. "I'm pretty."

"The prettiest." I smiled and stepped back. "Okay, I need to get dressed now."

Miska nodded and hopped off the stool before striding into the bedroom. I stared at the gown. It all seemed unreal, as if I should pinch myself to make sure I wasn't dreaming. I stripped off my robe and let it fall to the ground, carefully pulling the dress from the hanger.

The lace fabric was so soft. I was afraid it would rip if I moved too quickly. I unbuttoned the lower back before stepping into it. Slowly, I wiggled it over my hips and slid the straps over my shoulders. I reached behind me and buttoned up the low back before adjusting my breasts in the cups. The bodice had enough structure that I wouldn't spill out of it if I bent over.

I turned toward the mirror and stared. My lips curved in a soft smile as I ran my hand across the fabric over my abdomen. Beneath the white lace, a silky panel cut to mimic my hourglass shape was sewn into the dress from breast to mid-thigh. Another piece lined the back, molding lovingly to my ass. Together, they hid everything he didn't wish to share with the world. Along my sides, nothing but the sheer lace traced the curve of my breasts to the tuck of my waist and over the flare of my hips. It spilled to the floor and beyond in a breathtaking train. My back was bare, the edge of the dress starting just below the small of my back. I stared, marveling at my reflection.

"All done," I called out.

I heard the shuffle of small feet draw close.

"Your bedroom is so huge you could have fifty husbands in here," Miska said as she entered the dressing room and stopped. I saw her eyes widen in the mirror. "Wow."

I smiled. "You like?"

"You look like a goddess." Miska gaped. "No, you are way prettier."

I snickered, continuing to stare at myself in the mirror. "I knew there was a reason I kept you around."

"Wait, really?" she asked, something unsure darkening her eyes.

"No," I grinned at her, "that was a joke."

"Oh." Her coy smile brightened her face. She stepped closer, looking at the long train. "This castle is fit for a god and goddess. I wonder who lived here before."

I fiddled with my hair, trying and failing to decide what to do with it. I had used most of my pins on Miska's. Gathering the silky strands into various styles, I finally decided on a half-up, half-down, pinning it back just enough to keep it out of my face.

"Samkiel said it was one of many abandoned places during Nismera's conquest. This entire planet was just left," I said.

She smiled at me. "Well, I heard any place can be home if you make it. Maybe this can be that. A new start to a new era."

My eyes fell on her, a familiar sense washing over me. "A new era indeed."

I grabbed the veil off the edge of the vanity. "Now come on, we need my shoes."

Miska practically skipped out, and I gathered up the longest part of my dress before following her into the bedroom. Miska was right. It was massive. Sitting on the edge of the bed, I slipped on the shoes and buckled the straps around my ankles before standing.

"Okay, Miska, final touches," I said, turning toward the mirror. I tossed the long portion of the veil over my shoulder to hang down my back. Lifting it to my head, I slid the combs along the band into my hair, securing it. I tipped my head, studying my reflection in the mirror and adjusting the veil.

"I've only ever heard stories about amata ceremonies, the grand balls and parties that last for days. I've never participated in one before," Miska said, bending to grasp the edge of the veil. She gave it a shake, fanning it out to let it lay against my back.

"It's my first one, too. Hopefully, the last," I joked.

She smirked. "Thank you for letting me be a part of it."

"Well, you're kind of stuck with us now since I destroyed your home, but you're welcome."

She smiled at me. "You seem sad. Most pairs are so happy they can barely contain their excitement."

I looked down at my hands, twisting my ring. "Not sad, not really. I wish Neverra and Imogen were here. You'd like them, and they'd like you too. Plus, Logan, Cameron, and Xavier, I know they would be giving Samkiel a hard time, but he needs them, too. And I just wish . . . I just wish my sister was here. She loved giant celebrations and love and every mushy feeling you can think of." I half laughed, blinking back tears. "She would give me so much grief if she could see me now. I was the person who scoffed at the idea of love and forever mates, and here I am, in a castle, getting ready to marry the one person I cannot live without."

"Marry?"

I nodded. "It's what it's called in my world. Even there, it is sometimes a huge celebration. It depends on the person, really. Gabby always dreamed of a huge wedding. She'd been planning her own wedding since we were teens. She had a dress and cake, and everything picked out."

"Did you?"

I shook my head. "No, I dreamt of surviving and keeping her safe. I never thought that weddings, sweet words, and flowers from lovers were for me. This was her dream, and she isn't even here to give me shit about it now."

Miska's hands fell to her hips as she scolded me. "Who says she isn't? We heard stories growing up of how our most loved ones could watch over us from beyond. Even if we can't see them anymore."

A short laugh left my lips at her newfound attitude. I looked out the open window and into the night sky. Had she followed me into this new existence of mine?

"Maybe she is," I said as Miska continued to smooth and adjust the veil and my train.

We were silent for a moment before she stepped back and said, "All done."

I stared at myself in the mirror, not truly recognizing the woman looking back at me.

"I think you're lucky all the goddesses aren't here for this. They'd be so jealous of you."

"Me?" I laughed. "No, but you? In an old book I once read, there was a goddess of flowers and herbs, a healer. That's who you remind me of."

Color tinted her pink cheeks a darker hue as she smiled. She was so unused to receiving compliments it made me want to burn Jade City twice. "I'm not anything special. The others could heal better than me. They'd have your king completely well by now."

I stepped forward, the long end of my dress snagging under my heel as I placed my hands on her shoulders.

"Samkiel is broken because of the betrayal from those closest to him. Not you, okay?"

"I should have known about the poison. They were always so sneaky and kept me out of things."

"Miska." I smiled and crouched in front of her. "He is not mad at you. I am not. You saved him. You made an antidote."

Miska nodded. "Thank you for taking care of me and not making me work until my hands bleed."

"I want you to start over. You can be something this world doesn't stamp a label on. You have a home with us, Miska. Our family may be small right now and a little broken, but it's a family that will always stand by you."

Miska smiled and hugged me gently. A knock came from the doors, and she stepped back as I rose.

"You can't see me yet. I told you!" I snapped toward the closed doors.

"It is merely me." Reggie's voice filtered through the heavy wood.

"Oh." I headed toward the door, Miska giggling behind me. "Sorry, Samkiel was being insistent earlier, and I just assumed."

I opened the door, and Reggie paused, beaming with pride as he looked at me.

"What?"

He shook his head. "My apologies. I have seen this outcome in so many variations, but this one is my favorite. You look . . ." He paused, meeting my gaze, and I could have sworn the fate had tears in his eyes. "Like you have found your home."

A soft smile spread as I stepped to the side, allowing him to enter. "Well, you don't look too bad yourself."

He nodded before stepping fully into the room.

"I fixed her veil," Miska chimed in as the door closed.

Reggie gave her a grin in return. "It's quite lovely."

"So is your suit," I said. "He had time to get that too, I see."

Reggie nodded. "Yes, and a few other items. It is quite impressive given such a short time."

I picked up my dress and walked back to the bed. "I need a drink," I said, carefully sitting down.

They both looked at me.

"Not the blood kind. I need alcohol." I let out a shaky breath, my leg bouncing nervously.

"That's to be expected," Reggie said.

"Is this really happening?" I asked.

Reggie grinned widely. "Yes, yes, it is."

I stood again, wringing my hands as I paced. "You'd tell me, right? I don't think Dream Reggie would lie. What if he changes his mind?"

Reggie clasped his hands behind his back. "I can tell you with a hundred percent accuracy that there is no vision I have ever seen where he changes his mind about you."

I stopped, my hands dropping to my sides. "Okay, but don't realities change all the time? What if he is downstairs as we speak, plotting his escape? Gabby had seen this movie one time—"

Reggie reached into his pocket. "He is busy with the officiant and Orym, organizing the final details as we speak, so I stated I would bring this for you. It is the words you must speak when signaled."

"Oh. Words . . . words are good." My hands were suddenly shaking, but I gripped the paper and unfolded it, reading through the words. "I can't believe this is happening."

"I'll leave you for a few more minutes, then we shall begin," he said, striding toward the door.

"Wait!" I called out far too loudly. Reggie turned, waiting patiently as if whatever I had to say was the most important thing he had to hear. "Umm . . ."

I handed Miska the paper, and she looked at me as if I had grown horns while Reggie watched me expectantly. My tongue darted out of my mouth, running over my lower lip. I tugged at a loose strand of my hair, but Miska reached out and swatted my hand away. I pouted at her but took a step toward Reggie, determined to do this.

"On Onuna, a bride would usually have someone give her away. Typically, it was her father, but Gabby and I always agreed that when she got married, I would walk her, you know? And I don't have anyone." The words were so hard to say. "You have been closer than a friend to me for a while now. You're the closest thing I have to a father figure in that I-kidnapped-you-from-another-realm type way. You have been here guiding me, even on my worst days. So, Roccurem, would you walk me down the aisle?"

I met his gaze, a look I had never seen crossing his features. He smiled, joy lighting his eyes. "I did not see that coming."

My finger lifted, and I pointed at him. "Ah-ha! See, even fate doesn't know everything."

Reggie gave me a deadpan expression. "That does not change the outcome. Samkiel is not leaving you."

"Yeah, yeah," I said, dropping my hand. "So what do you say? My adopted father died with my adopted mom when Rashearim fell, and my real father sent me away, then was mind tortured and tried to kill me. So, do you want to be my stand-in daddy?"

"Never repeat those words." He rubbed his brow before dipping his head slightly. "But, yes. It would be my honor to escort you, Dianna."

I smiled so big my cheeks ached. Reggie left the room, and I turned to Miska. I took a shuddering breath and extended my hand. "Okay, hand it over."

She laughed brightly, the sound like tinkling bells, and handed me the small piece of paper.

"All right, let's memorize some words and get married."

LXXI

Vincent

The otherworldly screams of the last two fates echoed through the room. My jaw set as Nismera paced.

"Why won't they stop?" Tessa asked the blonde witch as she shook her hands. Tara held her hands up, keeping the screams from reaching the upper levels. Nismera and her illusions made sure all those above never suspected the horrors that existed in the depths of her palace.

"Tedar is dead," Nismera said.

"I heard."

"Slaughtered with his legion at that damn waste of a city."

I nodded, standing with my feet shoulder-width apart and my arms behind my back.

"I cannot have this, Vincent," she said. "I need every city with even a hint of rebel activity burned to the fucking ground."

"Yes, my liege."

"No survivors." She chewed on the pad of her thumb. "I need them to know if I even think they are up to something, it will result in ashes and blood."

"Yes, my liege."

"Take your legion to the East. Start there."

"Yes, my liege."

She nodded and cupped my cheek, her lips slanting over mine. I closed my eyes in what I knew she thought was appreciation. But I was imagining Camilla, trying to chase away the feel and taste of the bitch touching me. I thought of her laugh, the way she smelled, and how soft her lips were beneath mine. I imagined the taste of her lips when I'd press her against the nearest wall on the way to lunch just to steal a few kisses.

Nismera pulled away, and I tried to act as interested as I used to be all those many years ago.

"You are perfection, my pet," she whispered. "I'll meet you on the battlefield once I finish a few things."

My heart pounded frantically. Dianna had finally upset her enough that she felt her presence was needed. When Nismera joined us on the ground, she came to eradicate, not capture. A slick sweat formed over my skin, but I forced a smile her way.

The fates continued to repeat the same words, screaming them over and over again. The magic-imbued chains wrapped around them, holding them immobile.

I stared at the fates, and they finally fell silent. The sudden quiet was more disturbing than their screams. They were so unlike Roccurem. Their natural forms were in a constant state of change, but now they were stuck in horrific, disjointed figures. The rags Nismera forced them to wear stretched over their deformed bodies. They stared past me and into my soul, the voids that were their mouths gaping in a silent scream.

I knew why Nismera was pissed, why she had sent me on so many missions and kept me close when I was here. She was nervous, and when Nismera was nervous, it was detrimental to every single being in this realm and the next.

None of us said anything as we left the lower chamber. Tessa and Tara performed one last spell, sealing the room closed as the fates started their screaming again. The magic sank into the door in a flash of green, sealing it, and we all left.

On our way upstairs, Nismera told me to take my new legion and fly out that night. She told me to go to the East and shut down any rebellion, but we both knew she wanted Dianna. The next time we found Dianna, Nismera would show, and she would kill her. I wondered if she'd told Kaden. Did he know how much she detested Dianna and his plan? Dianna was a loose end, and regardless of what she told Kaden, Nismera would not allow her to live. No, I would do what Nismera asked without fail.

I donned my armor and left my room. I paused outside Camilla's room, pressing my hand against the door. With a deep sigh, I ducked my head and left.

The legion and I took the ryphors through the portal, going from city to city, burning, killing, and capturing. Through it all, the fates' warning was seared into my brain. The words they were screaming echoed through time and space.

Fear!

Fear!

Fear!

The Queen of Rashearim.

LXXII

Dianna

Reggie met me at my door, my nerves making me feel sick. I took his arm, and we headed downstairs. The castle was quiet, but as we drew near the main floor, the smell of mint and something floral filled my nose. My gasp was audible when I saw how the lower level had been changed. Everything was sparkling clean, and flowers in every shade clung to the walls as if they were growing from the stone. Long vines draped the banisters and doorways, delicate white blossoms scenting the air. A long, plush, cream runner led me to the main foyer, to him.

"He used his powers, didn't he?" I whispered to Reggie.

Reggie nodded. "He deemed it only appropriate, given the occasion."

My lips curved in a small smile. I knew it would have taken so much out of him with the still-healing wound on his side and him not sleeping for three days, but this meant so much. I just hoped he wasn't too tired.

Soft music and warm light flooded through the large double doors. The wooden flooring was gone, replaced with shining stone trimmed with gold lines tracing the walls. I kept my eyes down, letting Reggie lead me to the doors. I heard the music change, somehow becoming more intentional to herald my arrival.

My grip on Reggie's arm tightened, and I forced myself to look up as he paused at the threshold. My breath caught, unable to process what I was seeing. This wasn't the room we had passed through earlier. He had completely transformed it. The ceilings rose to dizzying heights, seeming to go on forever. Massive chandeliers hovered above, spilling warm light into the room and overflowing with flowers so beautiful they made me want to weep.

This was similar to something from Samkiel's old world, containing bits of the beauty I had seen in the blooddreams. These rooms were sacred and meant to celebrate gods and goddesses. This was what he wanted for me? My pulse quickened. Did he truly consider me worthy of all of this?

Reggie continued to guide me forward, and I finally gathered the courage to look toward the front of the room. My breath hitched. There, atop a raised dais, he waited.

Samkiel was breathtaking. Outside of the blooddreams and his council garbs, I had never seen him in a uniform, but he wore one today. The white brocade jacket was obviously custom-made, fitting his large frame perfectly, the gold buttons drawing the eye. His matching white pants fit snugly to his powerful thighs and were tucked into tall boots. A cape draped his left arm, leaving his right free to grab a weapon. The heavy material was embroidered with intricate gold designs and held in place by a thick dark leather strap that crossed his wide chest. It spilled off his powerful shoulders, the hem just sweeping the floor at his feet. Samkiel was royalty, and today, he displayed that fact. He was a king awaiting his intended queen.

My nerves melted away the moment our eyes locked. A smile that made my cheeks hurt spread across my face. He looked at me as if I were the most beautiful thing in the world. I hoped he saw the same adoration in my gaze. I didn't know how I'd ever looked at or touched another before him.

This was it. He was it. He was my everything.

My heart swelled as we walked toward him, and if Reggie wasn't holding my arm, I was sure my legs would have given out. The music slowly quieted as I reached the steps. The gold and white stone seemed to glow beneath my feet. We reached the top, and Reggie let go of my arm and stepped back, but I had no idea where he went. All I saw was Samkiel.

Everrine coughed discreetly, and we both jerked and turned toward her. We stood side by side as we had been since our first meeting. I tried and failed to hide the smile that refused to leave my face as Everrine began speaking. She held a bejeweled chalice in one hand. With the other, she drew a rune in the air before us and said something in a language I didn't know. The rune glowed for a moment before dissipating. She spoke another word and drew a different rune. It flared to life before fading.

Everrine placed the chalice down and held her hands out toward us, nodding. I glanced up at Samkiel and followed his lead as he offered her his hand, palm up. She clasped his first, drawing a blade with her free hand.

The growl that escaped my throat had her taking a step back, her eyes wide. I hadn't even realized I had moved, but I had stepped in front of Samkiel.

"It's okay." Samkiel smiled brightly. "It's a part of the ritual."

"You didn't tell her?" Everrine squeaked. "Oh, praise the old gods."

Ritual?

"Blood of my blood," I said, remembering what Reggie had told me in that tunnel.

"Exactly," he said, pulling me back to his side and nodding toward Everrine. "Continue, please."

I steadied my nerves. Apparently, I was more on edge than I'd thought.

Everrine kept an eye on me as she stepped back into place and tentatively reached for Samkiel's hand. I watched as she drew the blade across his palm, silver blood rising to meet the air. The Ig'Morruthen in me thrashed and ripped at me, wanting to burn her to ash for the slight alone. But I swallowed and fisted my hands, forcing myself to remain in place. He was fine. He was not in danger. He was alive. I repeated it like a mantra, even if my body didn't believe me. I wondered if my anxieties would ever calm when it came to threats to the ones I loved after watching both him and Gabby die. Or was this an overprotective side effect to our marks being gone?

She turned to me, asking for mine next. I held out my hand, palm up. My lip twitched as she dragged the blade across it, and I felt power encircle me like a vise. My eyes lifted, and I caught Samkiel watching me intently. I wondered if it was a struggle for him to see me bleed as well.

Everrine brought our hands together, and I eagerly pressed my palm to his.

"Blood to seal," Everrine said, picking up a silky length of ribbon the color of sunlight.

"A cloth of Dhihsin to symbolize two souls merging into one," she said, tying the ribbon around our hands.

"The Dhihsin?" I whispered to Samkiel.

Samkiel smirked and lifted a shoulder in a half-shrug. "Not really, but we had to improvise. Short notice and all."

Everrine glared at us, shushing us with a look that only made us smile harder.

She stepped back and raised her hand as if to give a grand speech, but my eyes were glued to Samkiel. He looked so good. I loved how his jacket and cape curved and draped over his broad shoulders and muscled arms. Those powerful arms had carried me despite every cruel or harsh thing I had done. He lifted me when all I wanted to do was fall.

Samkiel smiled at me as if he could read my mind. This was love. This was what it felt like. What it was supposed to feel like. I finally understood why others would go to war for it and clash or rage at its demise. I knew if I lost him and his love, the universe would quake at the mention of my name.

". . . now all who witness thee shall know the union is not to be forsaken."

She spoke to the room, but only the three of them stood near us.

"Now," she clasped her hands, "repeat after me."

"By my blood, I am made. In sickness and in health, I am by your side. Sworn to you and no others, I am forever yours. My heart remains yours for eternity and after. Forever awaits, and from today onward, you and I will be one in heart, body, and mind. These words, this oath, are engraved on my soul."

Laughter flooded the large room as Miska was spun from Reggie to Orym and back. Her smile almost touched her ears as she twirled, and I was sure mine matched. I grasped Reggie's hands as Samkiel spun me toward him, Miska taking my spot. Another twirl, and we switched once more. I heard her say something about using the bathroom as the other two talked about food. I leaned in, back in my husband's arms once more.

"What's that face?" Samkiel asked, his finger flicking under my chin.

"This?" I scrunched my nose. "This is my happy face."

"Ah. Do you wish to know a secret?"

I nodded.

He leaned down and whispered, "I'd sell the world to see it every day."

I pulled back with a fake gasp. "The entire world?"

He nodded. "The entire thing."

"That's not very heroic of you."

He shrugged with a smirk as he spun me. "I have my moments."

A small laugh left my lips as I turned back to him, clasping his hand and leaning forward, fitting my body to his. I rested my head on his chest, one arm outstretched, my hand cradled in his as we danced to a slow piano melody. A light mist swirled around our feet. I wasn't sure where it had come from, and I didn't care.

"It was almost perfect," I whispered. "I wish everyone else was here."

I felt him stiffen as if he had been thinking the same. "Me as well."

"Cameron would have already done something absolutely mischievous, Xavier at his side. I'm sure Logan and Neverra would have asked us to dance several times, Imogen would have several guards falling at her feet, and I'd make sure she didn't go home alone."

He rested his cheek on the top of my head as we continued our slow dance. "You know them so well."

"I want another big ceremony when we're all together again," I asked, leaning back.

His eyes searched mine, but his smile didn't reach them as he said, "Me too."

"I won't lie to you," I said, my throat bobbing. "Never again, but at first, I truly believed there was no hope for them."

"I know," he whispered. "I could always see the deflection in your eyes when I spoke of them. I also know that you'd never say it out loud because of how much I love them."

"I was wrong."

His head reared back. "What?"

"Back at the prison when we found Logan. He didn't respond when he saw me, so I brought you up top to see him. At first, I hated it because there was no reaction to you either, and I didn't want to disappoint you. But when you turned to leave, and I swear on Gabby's life, I swear I saw him blink. Just once."

Samkiel didn't say anything, but he slowed our dance.

"You did?" he asked. "Why didn't you say anything?"

"You were so sad the next morning. I just didn't want to give you false hope, but I did see it. We will get them back, Sami." My hand tightened on his arm. "I swear it."

"We will." His lips brushed my forehead as he spun me around. "Just dance with me tonight. We can talk about battle plans and schemes tomorrow."

"Okay." I grinned, and to chase away the dark clouds that had formed in his eyes, I said, "So, how do you feel about being called my husband?"

His face lit up. "So much better. I never have to hear you call me your friend again."

I threw my head back and laughed. When I looked at him, he was just staring at me, dumbstruck.

"What?" I asked.

"Nothing," he whispered roughly. "I just love you."

My smile slowly faded. He gave me those words so freely, and I knew he wanted nothing in return. There was no mission I had to complete. No artifact I had to return. No person I had to kill or maim. I didn't have to jump through hoops for affection from him or beg for attention. I never thought I would receive those words, so instead, I shut my heart down, grew claws and fangs, and loved myself. Samkiel gave them freely and wholeheartedly.

"I love you, Samkiel, and I don't need a soul to feel that."

His hand was a heavy weight on my lower back as we swayed, his fingers caressing the sensitive skin. It was every godsdamn magical moment I could only dream of, except this was real. I squeezed his shoulder and rested my head against his chest. One beat, then two, and even with the dazzling music, his heartbeat was my favorite song.

LXXIII
Dianna

Samkiel stood near the portal he'd opened, speaking to Orym, the small office waiting on the other side.

"Do you see this?" Miska asked, picking up a yellow-stemmed flower. "Humberry. I can make this into a salve that will heal my sore feet."

I snorted and tore my eyes away from Samkiel to look at her. "Well, I'm sure that will be effective sometimes."

She nodded before collecting more little flowers and petals to stuff into a small brown satchel.

"She is quite peculiar, yes?" Reggie asked, coming to my side.

"Indeed," I said. "But she may be right. Foot cream may come in handy depending on what is to come."

"She is important for what's to come." Reggie smiled. "And there are more like her you haven't found yet."

My brows furrowed. "Are you back to creepy messages again?"

Reggie shook his head, his hand going to his temple. "Did I say something?"

"Do you not remember?" I took a step forward, but Samkiel's voice had me turning away.

"Roccurem." Samkiel nodded toward the portal, where Miska showed Orym what she found as they stepped through.

Reggie placed his hand on my shoulder. "It was a lovely service."

I watched him walk away, concern niggling at me. I knew I'd heard him correctly, but I had no idea what he'd meant. His eyes didn't go white as they usually did when he saw the future, but he didn't seem to remember what he said. The portal closed behind them, worry coiling in my gut. Something was wrong.

Samkiel took the steps two at a time, his light touch on my arm bringing me back to reality. "Are you okay?"

I shook my head and smiled up at him. "Yes." I would figure out what was going on with Reggie another day. Today belonged to Samkiel and me.

"Can you believe it?" I said, leaning against him and holding my hand out, wiggling the finger with my wedding ring. "We're married."

He held his hand out next to mine, the thick silver band he wore gleaming back at me. I pulled his hand to me, looking closer at the stripe of crushed stone that ran down the middle of the ring, circling his whole finger. A shiver ran through me, my whole body reacting as his ring touched mine.

"Woah, what was that?" I asked.

He nodded to our hands and our rings resting side by side. "It's the magic settling into them now that mine is on. It's pretty potent but should stabilize in a few weeks."

I turned my hand, placing my palm against his so our rings connected. Another shiver rippled through my body. It was involuntary and quick, making my belly clench.

He smiled down at me, his eyes flaring with silver light. "Intense, right?"

"Very," I said breathlessly.

Intense wasn't the right word. It was more so a pressure that enveloped me like a warm blanket, encompassing me in safety and security as if I had been freezing before, and now he was wrapped around me. He was my missing piece, and he was finally where he belonged, utterly and completely with me. I finally understood why mates went insane, why they raged, and why they broke when they lost it. If it felt like this, then absence was beyond pain, beyond agony. I thought I was a rage-filled, damned beast before, but if someone took this from me, I'd make the leader of evil look like a saint. My eyes locked onto his as if I finally learned to breathe once more, and I wondered if it would feel even better during sex.

"It might."

My face went slack, and I pulled my hand back. "No fucking way. Did you just read my mind?"

"Another perk of the magic."

My eyes went wide, not with fear, but with a pulse of excitement. "How?"

Samkiel shrugged and glanced at his ring. "It's a spell crafted into the stone. Jaski, Killium's wife, can imbue objects with power. She was one of several pupils under Kryella, and she was able to wield arcane magic. It was quite a feat. I was very lucky she survived these years, but also why I smelled as I did when I returned. She and Killium have been hiding in some very unsafe places to stay out of Nismera's reach. Their magic makes them both valuable targets. My evil sister would love nothing more than to claim them, so they are in hiding."

My smile did not falter. They had done so much for me . . . for us. "You had her make them to mimic the mark?"

"As close as I could, yes." He nodded. "We still cannot share powers, unfortunately. That will forever be out of our reach without the true marks, but there are a few perks."

I stepped closer and took his hand in mine again, that shiver forming once more. He hadn't left because I'd hurt him. No, he left because, without the mark in this vast world, he'd never be able to truly keep me safe if we got separated again. He wanted the next best thing.

"I am sorry for lying to you. Truly, I am." I held his gaze. "You can feel that, right? With these?"

His eyes searched my face before he nodded slowly. "I feel your sadness, but I did not need the rings to know that." His thumb passed over my ring. "I did not mean what I said back then. I do trust you more than anyone. I was just hurt. My entire family has lied and kept things from me. I . . . you . . . I just wanted you to be different."

My hand cupped his face. "I swear that was the last epic secret I have. The only one. I just didn't want to hurt you again. In the end, I hurt you the most. I was just scared of what you'd say, of what it would mean. I wanted to pretend we were still this epic destined love, even if I'd ruined it."

His face softened as he placed a kiss on my palm. "You didn't ruin anything. Mark or not, you are all I see, all I want. Destiny be damned, right?"

"Destiny be damned."

I grasped his hands and wrapped them around me, placing them on my lower back. I twined my arms around his neck and pressed my breasts against his chest.

"You still want me?"

He bit at his bottom lip and lifted one brow. "Yes, why else would I marry you?"

My laugh turned to a squeal as he lifted me into his arms and strode toward the stairs.

Samkiel placed me on my feet outside our bedroom door and stepped in front of me. His grin was mischievous as he took my hand and opened the door.

"Why are you being so cryptic? I've already seen the . . ."

My words died as he led me in. Flickering lights and flowers were arranged on every surface, and a spicy floral scent hung heavy in the air. The thick curtains were pulled away from the large windows, moonlight illuminating the gorgeous landscape outside. The bed had been made up with fresh linens and blankets, both pulled back invitingly.

"Wow," I gasped, taking it all in. "When did you do this?"

"During the ceremony."

My brows shot up. Not only was Samkiel there, but he was also decorating the room above. I knew he could multitask, but that was . . . impressive.

He tossed me an impish grin over his shoulder. "I've been told I'm pretty impressive before."

My mouth formed into a pinched smile as I turned to him, still so unused to him being in my head. "What about arrogant?"

He laughed. "Maybe once or twice by a dark-haired beauty."

My brow rose. "I hope she keeps you humble."

"She does."

"It's beautiful," I said. "Beyond beautiful."

Samkiel smiled and walked to the fireplace on the far wall. "I wished to do more, but I have used so much power I'm starting to burn out."

"Sami." I shook my head. "This is beyond my wildest dreams, but you don't have to impress me, especially when the cost is that. Trust me. I am already impressed."

"I'm fine, and I'll sleep later." The way he said later had another shiver running across my body, and I wondered if it was my emotions or his I was feeling. He crouched and placed a couple of logs before snapping his fingers. A flame shimmered silver before catching and then burning a deep orange. A comfortable warmth slowly replaced the chill in the room. "Just wait until we have another ceremony when I'm fully restored, and everyone can be there. It will be even more extravagant than this."

I smiled, knowing he meant it, but this had been so much more than I could ever wish for. Today made me whole. "You know, on Onuna, usually the bride would have something scandalous underneath her dress to torment her husband with."

"Oh?" Samkiel said, wiping his hands as he stood and turned to look at me. He sauntered over, unbuttoning his jacket. He stopped right in front of me and ran his fingers along the strap of my dress. "You don't need that to torment me. All you have to do is look at me, and I get hard. Your mere existence does things to me."

"Does it?" I ran my hands up his chest to his thick, broad shoulders.

"But," Samkiel said, "I do quite enjoy the devilishly wicked things you find."

"Oh, yeah?" My smile was downright devious as I glanced up at him through my eyelashes. "I find certain things you wear rather enticing, too."

Samkiel chuckled. "You do? Like what?"

I stepped around him, dragging my hand down his arm as I headed toward the foot of the bed. I threw him a heated glance over my shoulder. My nipples tightened as I slipped the straps down my arms and turned to face him. I swore my breasts swelled beneath the touch of his hungry gaze.

He took a determined step toward me, but I raised my hand, stopping him. "We are married now, yes?"

Confusion flooded his eyes. "Yes."

"That means I am your queen, yes?"

The corners of his mouth lifted in satisfaction. "Yes."

"Therefore, you obey your queen, right?"

Heat flared in his eyes, and I was mesmerized as silver flooded his irises. "Yes."

"Good," I said, my hands going to the back of my dress, the movement lifting my breasts toward him. I slowly released the buttons at the small of my back. "Stay there until I tell you otherwise."

His hands flexed before turning into fists, and he clamped them behind his back. "What are you doing?"

"I told you I had fantasies, right?" My dress slid down my body in a soft susurration of sound to pool around my feet, leaving me completely bared to him. "Well, this fantasy occurred back on the remains of Rashearim when you wore your council garbs."

His adyin burst to life with silver light as he slowly lowered his hands. I saw the hard ridge of his cock thicken between his legs.

"Fantasy?" His throat bobbed. "Of me?"

I nodded and sat on the edge of the bed, scooting back just a fraction. I didn't need to see his arms to know the muscles beneath his clothes were strained as he watched me. Setting my heels on the edge of the mattress, I spread my legs wide for him. He took a shuddering breath, his eyes falling straight to my already slick sex.

"Do you want to see what I did one night while you were away? I couldn't sleep, and I'd grown frustrated with the on-again-off-again tension between us. So I slipped my hand like this."

Samkiel went rigid as my hand swept a pass over my sex. My fingers drew smooth, slow circles around my clit. Pleasure speared through me, and a moan parted my lips. I loved seeing the way he watched every stroke with feral, wild need.

"Dianna." His voice was a warning. "I am not this strong."

My smile turned devious. "You move, I stop."

He whimpered. Samkiel actually whimpered as his mouth formed into a thin line. I loved how much power I had over him, how absolutely wild I drove him without even touching him. I leaned further back, my free hand curving around to stroke and tug at my nipple.

"Fuck," Samkiel breathed as he watched me. Between his desperation and what I was doing, my need tore at me, and I moaned a fraction louder.

"You'd been gone for a few days." I shuddered. "I was in my room late at night, and all I could think about was you. All I pictured was you." My fingers dipped down and slipped inside. Tight, wet heat welcomed the intrusion as I watched him. "I wondered, what would happen if you came back and saw me utterly drenched at the thought of you?"

I withdrew my fingers and lifted them to my mouth, licking them clean. I swore lightning skittered across the ceiling in our room.

"Do you want to know?" His voice was husky, deep, and pissed. "What I would have done?"

I nodded. "Show me."

Before the words were completely out of my mouth, the crackling heat of his power wrapped around my wrists, forcing my arms wide.

"First, I would make sure you could no longer touch what is mine." Samkiel stalked, bearing down on me with that turbulent silver gaze. "Then I'd ask what you were thinking about that made you do something so wicked by yourself." His fingers curved under my chin, and he tilted my head up. His mouth lowered to mine, his tongue sliding across my lips before he claimed my mouth. He growled as I shared the lingering taste of my pleasure, stroking my tongue along his. He broke the kiss and said, "And you'd say?"

"You." The word left my lips breathlessly. "Always you."

"And then I'd get on my knees, lapping at every drenched bit of you, making you come over and over until you couldn't take it any longer and begged me to stop." He pushed my legs further apart before kneeling between them, and my heart skittered. "And after you thought you couldn't take anymore, I'd fuck you so hard that the next time you even thought of touching yourself without me, all you'd feel was the aching flesh of where I'd been."

His hand gripped my thighs, spreading me achingly wide, the cool air tickling my sensitive flesh. He watched me as he slowly and deliberately licked from my center to my clit.

The moan that escaped at the feel of his hot, wet tongue on my most sensitive flesh was loud and exhilarating all at once. My nerve endings pulsed, and my belly clenched as he did it again. I whimpered when he abandoned my pussy and licked and nipped at my inner thighs. I pulled against the power holding me in place, determined to put his mouth back where I needed it, but there was no give, and his hands held my hips right where he wanted them. His breath was teasing and hot, his tongue lapping along the crease of my thigh, driving me fucking wild.

Samkiel was following through on his promise, cleaning up anywhere I may have dripped from fingering myself. His mouth moved closer to my core, and I lifted my hips. His tongue made another pass, but this time, he started at the sensitive skin just below my entrance.

"Samkiel!" I cried out, my body trembling, needing him back at my clit. He didn't respond, but I felt a deep vibration against my flesh as he laughed. "Fuck," I whined, my hips writhing in his grip. I couldn't move anything else, his power holding me tight. "Sami, please suck me."

He gave another long, agonizing lick before his tongue speared into me. I groaned, my pussy clenching around him, the sensation so good, but at the same time I needed more. My hips rocked, riding his face, his nose pressing against my clit as he tongue fucked me, and gods above, I lost it. I didn't even feel the orgasm build before it ripped through me. Samkiel greedily drank my pleasure, savoring every shiver and tremble as I screamed his name.

I tried to move, trying to ride another wave of pleasure, but Samkiel held me tight. He moved his head from side to side, stimulating my already overly sensitive clit. My body shook as he worked it like a master, bringing me to the edge again and again but not letting me slip over. Then, I did the one thing he said I would.

I begged.

I begged as he continued to lick and tease me, begged as he finally sent me over, and then I begged as he released my hands. I needed more, his mouth and lips and tongue everywhere on me, and then I needed him to fill me.

Samkiel's eyes flicked toward me as if he'd heard my thoughts, and a slow, seductive smile spread across his face. His hands grasped my ass, his fingers damn near bruising as he pulled me closer.

"I need you," I whimpered, but he ignored me.

I watched as he tasted me again, his tongue pressing deep in a long, slow lick before he sucked my clit into his mouth. I saw stars, pure, blinding white stars.

"Fuck!" I screamed, throwing my head back. He was relentless, sucking and flicking my clit before his fingers dove deep, stretching me. My back lifted off the bed as he curled them inside me.

I couldn't watch anymore. I could barely breathe as rapture licked at my core, building into an inferno. Another pulsing need built with it, one unfamiliar as he tossed me into another orgasm. I screamed as he drew it out, drawing one whimpering pant after another from me.

"Sami." My words were breathless demands as I jerked and twisted in his hold. His fingers pressed on that spot deep inside me, massaging it greedily, and all I could do was whimper and squirm. "Baby, please, please, please."

Tears welled in my eyes from the complete rapture he sent me through. My body demanded more from his skillful mouth, even if it killed me.

"Oh, gods. Oh, gods." His fingers curved again, and my body bent. Heat ripped through me as another orgasm followed. I was going to die, here and now. I couldn't tell if the noises I was making were even words.

"That's my girl." I felt him smile against my soaked flesh. "Give me one more, okay?"

I moaned and shook my head, words escaping me. All I could manage were whimpers or screams with every flick or lash of his tongue, every thrust of his fingers. He hit that spot deep inside me, working it, and my body curved and bent, following his lead.

My hands reached, grabbing at the sides of his head, threading my fingers through his hair as I slammed myself down on his fingers and tongue. I clenched and quivered and broke. My head fell back, my mouth agape, and all I could do was hope I didn't crush him as my orgasm ripped through me. I released my grip on his head, my hand slapping on the sheets above me as my legs closed around his head. My body twisted as my fists balled into the sheets, riding through wave after wave of pleasure.

I was a panting mess as my body shook, no longer riding the waves of pleasure but drowning in them. Samkiel's grip on my hips eased, and my eyes snapped open. My quivering thighs tensed, loath to let him move away.

Samkiel pressed a kiss to my swollen clit and smiled up at me, his mouth glistening with my release. "That was for leaving you."

My heart squeezed, and then my lower belly clenched as he dragged a finger to his lips, licking the remnants of my orgasm from his face.

"Multiple orgasms for leaving me?" My laugh was hoarse and weak. "Leave me more often."

I didn't even realize I was crying until he leaned over me and wiped my cheeks. The tears that stained my face were not from pain but pure, poignant euphoria.

"And for also making you cry."

A choked sob left me. "I'm okay with it now."

His eyes darkened with lust mixed with . . . pain? "The only time I want to be responsible for your tears is when you're a sobbing, aching mess. When I've made you come so many times that you weep from bliss."

I grasped his jaw and pulled him to me. His lips slanted over mine before I heard him reach for his lapels. I sat up and grabbed his hands, shifting to my knees as he stood. My legs felt like jelly, but I needed him more. His smile faded as I grabbed his collar and pulled him to me once more, crushing his lips back to mine.

I may have initiated the kiss, but he was ravenous and quickly took control again. My hands slipped between us, and I ripped and tore at the fabric separating us. Buttons bounced against the floor, and his cape, jacket, and shirt followed. He groaned as my fingers pinched at his nipple. My hands slipped down over his abs and then lower to rip at his pants. I kissed him harder, and he sucked on my tongue but pulled back when I wrapped him in my hands. Samkiel threw his head back and gasped. I wasn't light or gentle as I pumped his thick length. His stomach flexed, and he leaned forward to rest his forehead against mine. He moaned, our breaths mingling.

Samkiel angled his head to kiss me again, but I urged him back and slipped off the bed. I dropped to my knees and took him into my mouth. He shouted, and his fingers slid into my hair, gripping the long strands. I fisted my hand around his base and tightened my lips around him. My tongue moved from side to side as I bobbed my head, moistening the length of him. I leaned in and grabbed his ass with my free hand, forcing more of him into my mouth until I felt the broad tip hit my throat.

"Fuck," he groaned, thrusting forward. "Yes, please, just like that, akrai."

I sank deeper onto my knees, adjusting to the thrust as he pushed into my throat. I glanced up at him through the veil of thick lashes and swallowed around him. His mouth fell open, and he used his grip on my hair to angle my head. He threw his head back in ecstasy, exposing the thick column of his throat.

"I love you. I love you. I love you."

I released him with a pop, continuing to stroke him as I looked up at him, drawing in deep gulps of air. He watched me, his eyes barely open, just a sliver of silver glowing behind his lashes. I thought he had said those words out loud, but his teeth were clenched tight, and I realized he hadn't said them. He had thought them. I traced the tip of my tongue along the adyin that glowed over his shaft before taking him back into my mouth. He pulsed against my tongue, his thighs trembling. Heat flared in me, and I felt my need dripping down my thighs as I took him deep and swallowed him once more. I gagged on him, my throat constricting around his cock. His head dropped back, the muscles in his forearms bunched as his grip tightened in my hair. His abs coiled and flexed, his hips thrusting instinctively, aching to get as deep as possible.

"Mine, mine, mine. MINE!"

Desperate need ripped at me, and I twisted my fist around the base of his shaft. I lovingly cupped and squeezed his balls. He moaned, and a shudder wracked his powerful body. Feeling the effect I had on him, tasting the precum spilling onto my tongue, and hearing his declarations through our rings sent me close to the edge. I knew one touch, and I would come again. I sucked and twirled my tongue against the sensitive underside of the head and felt him swell. Very lightly, I scraped my nails over his balls, and his groans echoed loudly in the room as his hips thrust forward.

"Akrai." He pulled my head back so his cock slipped out with a pop. "I'm going to come."

"Good." I panted, stroking up and down his glowing length and pulling against his hold, trying to take him back into my mouth.

"Not like this, not tonight," he groaned. "I need to be inside you. Now."

Samkiel lifted me and fell with me onto the bed. His lips slanted over mine, and he shifted us higher on the mattress before lowering his weight onto me. He ground his cock against me, rocking against the slickness between my thighs as if he couldn't help himself. My knees bent, and I slid them up his sides, opening further to him as he continued to kiss me, slow and passionate. He fisted the hair at the nape of my neck, pulling my head back so he could look at me. I licked my lips and waited, thinking he was about to say something filthy, but his eyes were soft and warm, filled with not only lust but—"I love you," he whispered.

I smiled up at him, sliding my thumb along his lower lip as if I might touch those words as well as hear them.

"I love you," I said, and even to my own ears, they sounded like a vow.

It was not just three little words for us. It never was. Whatever missing fractured pieces we'd lost so long ago seemed to come slamming back into place.

Samkiel's lips met mine in a slow, rhythmic dance. He shifted his hips and settled the head of his cock at my entrance. He pushed into me slowly, my body stretching tightly around him. I gasped and broke the kiss, locking my eyes with his as he rocked into me. His enormous body glowed, his godly adyin marks pulsing with each beat of his heart. His breath washed over my lips as he seated himself balls deep inside me. Fire erupted through my veins, and I clenched around him in sweet welcome.

He claimed my mouth again and began to move with slow, passionate strokes. Oh gods, I felt him everywhere, every move inside me, his hands on my thighs, his tongue in my mouth. If I had a soul, it would be screaming and melding into him with how deeply he seemed to touch me like this.

I had never felt this kind of intimacy, and I knew he felt it too. I could taste it in his kiss, feel it in how he worshiped my body with every stroke. The proof was in the litany of thoughts he didn't know how to say out loud.

Samkiel pressed his forehead to mine, our mouths only inches apart. Something felt like it was shifting between us again. No words were spoken, just this hungry, aching bond that for a moment felt sealed, felt complete. His hands cupped my ass, and he dragged his length in and out of me slowly, deliberately, as if this moment was so precious he didn't want it to end.

I loved this, but I needed more. I raked my nails down his back and bit his lower lip. "Sami, please."

His next thrust made me gasp. He pulled my leg higher on his hip and ground against me before pulling all the way out and slamming deep. I screamed and arched beneath him, forcing him deeper. His grip tightened on my ass, holding me still.

"Who do you belong to?" he growled, pulling out and thrusting deep again.

"You."

Another deep, powerful thrust that had me crying out and my body rippling around his cock.

"Again," he demanded. "Tell me again."

His hips snapped again, the brutal thrust hitting that spot inside me that had me damn near crying in pleasure.

"I'm yours! I'm yours! I'm yours! I'm yours!"

Only moans left my mouth, but I knew he heard the words by the way he pounded into me a fraction harder. His hand moved between us, his thumb pressing on my swollen clit, circling it. The noises leaving my throat weren't mortal or from any known language. My skin prickled with heat, and pleasure shot from my core to my toes. He dipped his head and bit down on my nipple hard enough to send jolts of electricity to my very center. I screamed and clenched around him as he slammed into me, his thumb pressing down on my clit. My body shuddered, and I came apart.

"Samkiel!"

He gripped my hips in both hands, holding tight, making sure I stayed on him as I shattered around him. He growled and pulled out, fighting my body's hold on him. Without pausing, he thrust back into me, so deep this time my belly clenched. Another orgasm washed over me, my body clamping down so hard on him he groaned. My name tore from his lips as I felt his cock twitch inside of me, but it was what I heard in my head that melted my heart.

"My akrai. My Dianna. My love."

LXXIV

Dianna

"Are you sure that food is even good?" I asked.

His laugh echoed inside the large ice box. I placed my hand under my chin, watching the muscles flex across his back and admiring the tiny red scratches marking his skin. He turned, his arms full, and bumped the door closed with his hip. My lips twitched when I saw that more scratches marred his chest, along with a scattered pattern of bite marks across his neck. An overwhelming sense of pride filled me. I'd marked him.

"Mine."

His eyes flicked to me, a soft smile playing on his lips.

"You read my mind?"

He didn't say anything as he set the assortment of fruits, vegetables, and greens on the table. They were so colorful, a few colors I'd never seen before. I sat back down on the wooden bench, wincing at the ache between my legs.

"Are you all right?" he asked, his eyes watchful.

"Yes." I smiled back. "Just a little sore, but good sore. Happy sore."

"Ah." Pure male satisfaction filled his eyes, and he smiled to himself. He flicked his wrist, and an ablaze dagger formed in his hand. I had never seen this one.

"Good sore," he repeated smugly.

I shook my head. But even I had to admit that he had a right to his cockiness. He had made good on his promise from earlier, and our wedding night had turned into our wedding morning, then afternoon and evening. Now here we were, finally in the kitchen after he'd fucked me into oblivion and back.

I rested my chin on my hand, watching him cut up the assortment of food. The long wooden table could host up to fifty, but it seemed more for serving or prep work. The kitchen was massive, but I knew it was nothing compared to the actual dining hall. A metal rack hung above a massive stove, dust-covered pots and pans hanging from it. Samkiel had said the place smelled rancid when he'd found it. He had cleaned up and gotten rid of the worst of it, but dust and debris still littered the floor.

"Did I tell you I forgive you for leaving me again?" I asked as he chopped and minced, placing the assortment in a different bowl.

"Yes." He smiled, glancing up at me. "But I promise I won't again."

I knew he wouldn't. It was strange but familiar, the bond between us finally being the closest it could be without the marks.

In between bouts of lovemaking, we had talked, and I told him everything. I felt his pain over the loss of our mark and the still-aching wounds my lies had created in his heart. I told him about seeing Gabby and how, even though I loved it, I knew it was the final time I would see her. He shared the burden of those bittersweet emotions, kissing away every tear I shed. Now, there were no more secrets between us, and I intended to keep it that way.

I smiled at him as he picked up the bowl and moved to the stove, continuing to make whatever it was he was making. I knew he was starving after our eventful two days. My eyes dropped to the healed bite mark on his left pectoral. I definitely wasn't hungry anymore.

I raised up on the bench slightly, watching him for a moment. "Samkiel, this place still isn't exactly clean. Are you sure that food is safe?"

He laughed, grabbing some green stalk thing and peeling it. "Yes, all fresh, all new."

I held my hands up in mock defense, the sleeves of his shirt sliding down my arms. "I'm just saying. You were poisoned before, and it's always good to be safe."

He finished preparing his food and tossed one leg, then the other, over the bench to sit next to me.

"What is that?" I asked as he dug his fork into his bowl and took a big bite.

He swallowed before moving it toward me. "You remember that dish you made for us on Rashearim?"

"During our three-day sexathon?" I said. "Yes."

He tipped his head almost bashfully. "It's the closest I could get, similar vegetables, more or less."

It looked lackluster at best, but his effort was adorable. My eyes cut to his. "I didn't know you liked it so much?"

He nodded and pulled the bowl toward him, taking another big bite.

"I'll have to make you more," I said as I watched him. "Without the cheese, you're missing a key component."

His eyes rolled dramatically, and he laughed. "Well, cheese was not on my list of things to get when I was away."

I stroked the short hairs at the base of his neck, that warmth in my chest spreading once more. No, it wasn't, but a home, a ring, and an entire marriage ceremony were.

"This is sad," I said.

"What?" he asked, his fork halfway to his mouth.

"You are never allowed to do the shopping, ever."

His laugh almost made him choke, and I rubbed my hand across his back. He shook his head at me before taking another bite. I rubbed small circles on his back, my gaze catching on my new ring.

"You know, when a couple gets married on Onuna, the wife often takes the husband's last name."

"Mm-hmm." His eyes cut to mine as he continued to eat.

I shifted, turning on the bench to face him and leaning my cheek against my hand. "So what's yours?"

He turned to look at me, the moonlight caressing his skin and glinting off his hair. Oh gods, this man was beautiful. I wondered if he would ever not take my breath away. "You don't want mine," he said, a small grin tipping his lips.

"I want your everything."

He shifted next to me, and I could see the love in his eyes. "Dianna Unirson? No."

"That's your last name?" I frowned. "Makes sense, I suppose, to carry on the legacy so forth and so on."

"Exactly," he said, digging his fork in once more. "So let's carry yours."

My head reared back as he continued to eat, as if he didn't just say something monumental.

"Mine?"

He nodded, stirring his food. "Yeah. What if I took your last name?"

"My last name isn't real," I said softly, even as my heart squeezed at his question.

His brows furrowed, and he lowered his fork. "Who told you that?"

I shrugged. "No one, but in case you forgot, Gabby picked those for us. My real name—"

"Your real name is what you choose," he said so sternly I thought I'd made him mad.

"I just meant . . ." I didn't know what I meant.

"Dianna. Gabby gave it to you, to herself. It's real to me." He lifted his hand, tucking back a long stray curl from the side of my face. "And I want it too. It carries a pretty strong legacy. A woman who defied all odds of survival and risked her life to keep that which she loved safe."

"One who failed," I added, my eyes beginning to burn.

"When?" He cocked his head. "Gabby lived three . . . no, four times her lifetime and loved every second with you. I had barely crossed over before you ripped me back to the land of the living."

I snorted and dropped my chin, but he caught it.

"I'd say a way better legacy than mine."

I leaned forward and placed a kiss on his lips. His words healed some still broken part of me. It was real, just as Gabby was to me, and he saw and respected it. Gods, I didn't think I could love him more, but here we were.

I smiled against his lips, and he ran a hand down my back.

"What's so funny?"

I shrugged. "Samkiel Martinez. It sounds funny."

"Mhmm." He shifted to straddle the bench, pulling me between his spread thighs and wrapping me in the warmth of his arms. "It sounds like I am yours, and you are mine."

Samkiel dipped his head to kiss me again, but a bright light tore through the kitchen, turning night to day. In unison, we jumped to our feet and hurried to the windows. Fear laced not just my veins but my mind as well, and I knew I was not the only one who felt it. Had Nismera found us? Her legion? But as we glanced up and watched the trail of light, I knew it was not her. Outside, what looked like a comet raced across the night sky.

"Wow, comets on this planet look so much prettier," I said, pushing up on my toes to peer around his shoulder.

Samkiel shook his head, and I felt his muscles bunch beneath my hand. "No, not a comet or a star."

I glanced at his face and saw that he had paled.

"Then what is it?"

"A casmirah. I have only ever read about them. They are rare, mythological creatures that only fly through the sky to herald a new ruler. One flew for my father, and now one flies . . ."

His words trailed off, his eyes darting from me to my hand, and we both stared at my ring.

"Oh."

LXXV
Roccurem

One day later

The small study was filled with slow music and Miska clapping her hands, but my attention was on the street corner below. A man I'd seen change his fate twelve times finally met his future wife by bumping into her on the corner below.

"They had this small music player that I asked for, and it was only three silver coins," Miska said. "Can you believe that?"

"Absolutely not," I responded.

She giggled. "Okay, it was five, but Orym helped."

Orym shook his head and said, "Miska, can you give us a moment, please?"

Her eyes widened as she looked between us. "Sure, but the music player is yours, Reggie. I always hear you humming at night, so now you have something to sing along with." Miska smiled once more before heading out and closing the door behind her.

"You hum?" Orym asked.

I merely shrugged. "Not that I am aware of."

"Are you aware of a lot recently?"

I gave the elf a soft smile before sitting at the small table in the center of the room. I took a sip of the tea Miska had made earlier, and the slow throbbing in my head subsided.

"I believe you have news, yes?"

Orym nodded and came to stand near me. "Nothing good."

I said nothing, waiting for him to go on.

"A casmirah was spotted last night shooting across the sky. I take it that you know its meaning?"

"Very well. I have seen only five in my existence. They are never wrong about their choices."

Orym scratched his brow. "Then you know the East is gone," he said, placing a small handwritten note on the table. "Veruka sent me an update. Everything is gone because of—"

"Dianna," I interjected, placing my tea down.

"That's what Veruka and I assume. The more Dianna challenges Nismera by killing her troops, the bolder and more hostile the rebels grow. The more they recruit and expand their numbers. Nismera is nervous."

"She has a right to be, yes."

"Well, Veruka says that Nismera now thinks that the casmirah appeared for her because she rid the world of Dianna and her beast, eliminating the threat."

"Hubris is a gift not only for gods, you know?" I said, adding one sugar cube to my tea and stirring.

Orym took a seat across from me. "What do you know? I mean, we're talking annihilation here, Roccurem, on a massive scale. There had to be at least fifty planets out there."

"She is a goddess created from destruction and fear. If those she rules no longer fear her, she loses her upper hand. Now, she thinks she has gained it back," I explained.

"And that does not frighten you?" Orym's panic only increased. "It's nothing but floating shards of rocks there now. What weapon does she have that can do that?"

"Many." I leaned back, taking another sip. "But what frightens me has not arrived yet."

"What does that mean?" Orym asked.

"You should get some sleep and spend at least one more day resting."

Orym's face paled as he stood. "We need to tell them."

"We will when they return."

Orym sighed and rubbed a hand over his face. "I'm going to send another message to Veruka. Maybe with more information, we can get ahead of her."

I said nothing as he headed for the door, nothing about his concerns or worries about what was to come and nothing about the harsh cold that followed him from the room.

LXXVI

Camilla

I sat at my vanity, clasping my earring and watching shadows coalesce behind me in the mirror. I rolled my eyes and blew out a long breath as Kaden stepped from them, adjusting the cufflink at his right wrist.

"Dramatic much?" I asked and stood to face him.

Kaden's brows shot upward as he regarded me.

"What?" I asked, gazing down at the sparkling gown that hugged my body.

"Nice tits."

My eyes closed at his crudeness, and I placed a hand on my brow.

"Do you plan to steal Vincent from my sister with that dress?"

I dropped my hand, my cheeks flushing as I turned from him. "I'm not stealing anything."

I didn't deny that I loved the dress that had been sent to my room. A part of me reveled in being able to dress up and wear something beautiful. Maybe I did hope he'd glance my way and not be able to look away. My magic thrummed happily at the thought.

"Speaking of outfits, what are you wearing? You look like a gothic vampire with that high collar," I asked, my eyes raking over his reflection as I reapplied my lipstick.

Kaden smirked but looked away, and I smiled. Tit for tat, you bitch. His suit was a mix of black and red. The shirt he wore beneath had a high collar but dipped to reveal the top of his pectorals. The suit did him justice, at least. Much like his brothers, Kaden was a truly beautiful man. Of course, once you got past that he was pure evil and would kill you without thinking twice.

"Where is your shadow?" I asked, referring to the brother who rarely left his side.

"Funny."

Kaden stepped closer and ran his fingers over the end of one of my makeup brushes. "You know, if Nismera finds out the two of you are fucking, she will kill you both."

"She thinks you and I have a thing. I doubt she will suspect there is anything between Vincent and me," I said, snatching the brush from him.

He lifted a brow and looked down his nose at me. "Trust me. You're doing me a favor."

I didn't ask what he meant, but I wondered if it had to do with the countless guards and witches that tried to frequent his bedchamber, and he turned away. Maybe he was using me for a cover as well.

"Besides, Vincent and I are not having sex," I snapped, cheeks flushing.

It wasn't a lie. Kissing and touching each other every chance we got? Well, that was a different story, even if that story wasn't all that interesting right now. He had avoided me for days, allowing the random run-of-the-mill guards to escort me.

I hadn't seen him since the day he had flown out with her and their legions atop the ryphors. When they came back that night, they were drenched in blood and gore. The next morning, the palace was weighed down with silence. Even the cafeteria was a ghost town. I knew then that the atrocities they had committed must have been horrific, and when Vincent hadn't sought me out, I knew he had participated. Apparently, slaying millions of beings together drew them closer because I had heard them together numerous times since they returned.

Once again, Nismera came first, and I was tossed aside.

"Close enough to it." He slipped his hands into his pockets.

"Why do you care, anyway?" I snapped, a little more defensive than I should have been. I was betraying way too much. "Don't you hate us both?"

"I don't hate either of you. I don't care enough to." His smile was pure venom. "Besides, you're the strongest witch on this side of the realms, Camilla. It'd be a shame to lose you."

I rolled my eyes, adjusting one final pin in my hair. "Strongest? Is that a compliment?"

Kaden grumbled.

My eyes cut toward him. "Hmm, the world is ending."

Thunder clapped above, and I glanced past him toward the large window. The sun was beaming, and I knew it must be more guests arriving for Nismera's coronation day.

"Are they really all flying here to pledge loyalty now that she's destroyed a quarter of the known universe?"

"It is more than that." Kaden stared out the window.

"So you admit your sister is a madwoman?"

"She prefers conqueror," Kaden corrected.

I shook my head, making sure the last clip in my hair was stable and secure. "Why this? Why now? Isn't your psychotic sister already queen or king or whatever title she has made up?"

Kaden finally looked at me. "You didn't see it last night?"

"See what?"

"The casmirah?"

My brows knitted together. I knew that word, or it at least tickled at a memory. He studied my look of confusion and rolled his eyes.

"It's a myth older than you and me combined. Casmirah fly through the sky when a new ruler is about to ascend. One blazed through the sky last night, and Nismera believes it is heralding her reign now that Samkiel is dead and she's eradicated the threat of Dianna's rebellion. She believes the rebels will back off after the power she displayed. Her brutality does seem to be working in her favor."

"If that's the case, why didn't—"

My door swung open, and I flung myself into Kaden's arms, pressing my lips to his.

"It's time," the guard spat impatiently. They hated me as much as I hated them. They very much resented being assigned babysitting duty when Vincent wasn't available to escort me everywhere. Nismera didn't trust me, and she had good reason. The second I had the chance, I'd make her pay for so godsdamned much.

I pulled back from Kaden with a smack, hoping our ruse worked. Everyone seemed to accept without question that the once-hated rivals had turned into lovers. So far, at least.

A second guard stepped in, careful to avoid eye contact completely, fear turning him quiet and timid. Kaden slowly removed his hand from my waist. "She's coming," Kaden said, more power behind his words than was needed. "In a moment."

The guards did not question him, bowing and leaving.

"We have to find a better cover," I said, wiping my lips.

Kaden ignored my comment, glancing toward the door. "Have you heard anything else?"

"No." I shook my head. "She's still doing her experiments, and that stupid talisman is driving me insane. I have it almost complete, but the last pieces are harder to mend, even with all my power. Hilma hasn't even remotely slipped up again. Why do you care anyway? I assumed you were done after I told you about Oblivion."

Kaden sighed deeply, ignoring my question before extending his arm. "Shall we?"

"Have you heard anything else about Dianna?"

His eyes flared a vibrant red for just a moment, but he smothered it as I laced my arm through his.

"Only a city demolished where a hive of revvers lived. I'm sending Cameron to check it out."

"How's he liking his new promotion?" I asked.

I knew they had made Cameron a legion commander with his own small unit because of the information he gave Nismera.

"He hates it, but it gets him one step closer to who he truly wants. You two can relate."

I tossed him a glare as we walked out the door, not the least bit surprised to see no guards waiting for us. They wanted to avoid Kaden if at all possible, and with him escorting me, they weren't needed.

We walked arm in arm toward the main gallery, following the sounds of voices and clinking glass. Massive vases overflowing with white flowers flanked the entryway. Artfully strung small lights cast an ethereal glow over the room. All of it was designed to present the illusion of welcome and peace, but Nismera was a blight on all of it. This was bait, and she was the predator laying in wait.

I sucked in a breath as we walked inside. There had to be at least a hundred or more beings here, all wearing outfits that sparkled or shined. Crowns rested upon the heads of kings and queens, proclaiming royal power. My hand squeezed Kaden's forearm as a path cleared before him. No one looked at or acknowledged him, but people instinctively moved out of his way.

"Who are these people?"

He reached for a passing wine glass, the liquid inside bubbling as he sipped before looking at me.

"Exactly who you think. They are neighboring royals here to pledge their allegiance to Nismera."

I smiled at him as if we were having a normal conversation, but no one paid us any mind. "There are so many?"

His smile met mine as he leaned close. "Did you assume there would be none left?"

My hand curled around his biceps, playing the part. "I've only heard of her power leaving wastelands in its wake. I never thought there would still be this many rulers left who did not challenge her."

"That's why there are wastelands, Camilla. Those who opposed her are nothing but dust on the wind. Besides, the realms are massive. You truly believe that none would bow to her rule rather than be annihilated? Only a fool would challenge Nismera with any hope of winning."

I nodded along, eager to ask more questions, but Isaiah joined us, clapping a hand on Kaden's back.

"Have you seen our lovely sister?" He glanced around, peering over the head of one tall being to the left.

Kaden shook his head. "No, but you know she likes to make an entrance. Give her time."

Isaiah smiled at Kaden, and I couldn't help but stare in wonder at just how messed up it was that the two deadliest High Guards Nismera had smiled at each other as if they couldn't tilt a world on its axis with their power alone. I wondered then just how much Kaden actually felt. He looked at Isaiah with great fondness, whereas others were lucky not to end up dead if they offended him. Kaden displayed an unseen side to him when it came to his brother. Isaiah may be the only being he truly loved, his odd obsession with Dianna aside.

A blonde ponytail swished near Isaiah's shoulder, and I took a small step around Kaden to see who it was. Imogen stood near Isaiah, her swords strapped to her back and still wearing armor.

"You brought Imogen here?" I hissed.

Isaiah looked at me as if I'd spoken out of turn but didn't respond. He slapped Kaden on the shoulder and promised to find him later before turning and leaving. Imogen followed, that heart-wrenching, empty expression still on her face.

I grabbed Kaden's arm a little harder than I meant to. "Why is he carrying her around like a doll? What is he—"

"Calm down." Kaden pulled away from me in a subtle movement. "My brother tends to latch on to things. I blame the way everything was taken from him."

"She is not a toy. If he wants one, I'm sure the elven girl staring daggers at him right now will be happy to volunteer."

Kaden followed my gaze to where she stood next to a table littered with an assortment of food and cakes. Her pointed ears were decorated with jewels that sparkled under the lights. She wore a swath of shining fabric that curved around her body, giving her mauve skin a shimmering glow. Her tail thrashed behind her as Isaiah passed, not wasting a glance toward her as he headed deeper into the crowd.

"Veruka?" Kaden scoffed. "A fuck buddy, if even that. You'll learn sex means very little to old, powerful immortals."

I glared at him. "Oh, yeah? Then why haven't you indulged?"

His eyes cut to mine. "Who says I haven't?"

"Everyone. The witches whisper about all who have tried, and all you turn away. Is it because of how Dianna reacted after all the years you treated her like second best? Afraid when you drag her back, she won't want you if she knows—"

Kaden gripped the back of my neck, the movement so fast and his hold so tight, I hissed in pain. He pulled my face closer to his, and I wrapped my hand around his wrist. To any onlooker, the way he held me made it seem as if we were two lovers who couldn't stand to part.

"Let's get one thing straight," Kaden hissed through a dazzling smile. "We're not friends or colleagues. You don't get to speak to me however you wish. I could rip your pretty little head off and not think twice about it."

"Then do it." I glared back. "Or admit that you are afraid."

His teeth ground so tightly together that I thought they would break.

"I hate to burst your bubble, but you deciding after years that she is *finally* good enough for you will not work. Even if you manage to drag her back after you murdered her sister and her actual love, she'll never touch you again, never love you again. You will never be Samkiel."

I expected him to snap my neck, to hurt me, anything but what he did. The anger in his eyes fizzled, his grip on the back of my head loosening. "I have a plan for that."

"A plan?"

He released me and blew out a long breath, clearly not wishing to share his plan. He turned away, and my gut clenched.

He slipped his hands into his pockets. "I know you want to think the worst of my brother, but Isaiah is the only thing keeping that girl out of the beds of any general who decides he wants a taste of The Hand. He keeps her close to keep her from being raped."

My brows furrowed. "What?"

"What do you think happened to the last unit that had her?" Kaden scoffed. "Half of these generals and commanders Nismera has recruited would make me seem like a sweet kitten. Imogen is lucky he got to her when he did."

I remembered Hilma telling me about it, but I only remembered parts. I tracked Isaiah and Imogen through the crowd. He stopped to speak to someone and looked up, his gaze locking with mine. Isaiah killed them all for her because they'd tried to touch her.

"I-I didn't know," I said, breaking eye contact with Isaiah.

"Exactly, you didn't. You, like so many others, know nothing of us." Kaden drained his glass, placing it on a passing waiter's tray.

"Saving someone from something that horrific doesn't make you a good guy. It makes you decent. It should be normal to be disgusted with that," I said. "I just didn't know you or him had any decent parts."

Kaden scoffed. "You think we are the cruelest monsters, but we're not even the worst in this realm."

I didn't say anything, but I did glance toward Isaiah again, watching as he disappeared into the crowd with Imogen obediently following.

A trumpet sounded behind us, startling the crowd, and we all stopped speaking at once. One by one, we turned, following the noise as the doors were pushed farther open. Kaden placed a hand on my elbow, moving us back into the masses that separated on two sides. He pushed me half behind him, and I peered around his massive frame.

"I can't see—"

He shushed me, and my brows furrowed. What the hell?

"Is it Nismera?"

He shook his head, watching the door. "No, worse."

As if on cue, soldiers marched through the door in twos. Their pearlescent armor was gorgeous, shimmering in the light. Intricate scrolling designs were engraved along the arms and legs, and a massive winged creature was emblazoned across the chest.

They looked like angels. Powerful, majestic angels. Their helmets were tall, sitting atop their heads in curving lines, with a pair of wings mimicking the flaring from their backs. Everyone watched as they filed into the room, all carrying boxes of various sizes. A few of the lids were half open, and I caught the gleam of jewels as they passed.

My hand tightened against Kaden's side as the crowd whispered. I caught the eye of a man across the way, his gaze blazing into mine. The ties and buttons across his jacket did nothing to hide the lean, muscled form beneath. Dark hair curled around his ears and fell across his forehead. I had the strangest sensation of familiarity as he stared at me. He smiled, and it was a beautiful contrast to the dark stubble covering his jaw. Another set of winged guards walked between us, and when they passed, the man was gone.

My gaze roamed, searching the crowd for him, but everything in me paused when a woman who would put the models of Onuna to shame entered with a man at her side, their wings tucked against their backs. I knew him. Well, I didn't know him, but I'd seen him here before. Ennis. Vincent had said he was the brother to a powerful sister. Only she wasn't just powerful. No, given the crown she wore, she was a queen. No one so much as whispered as they entered.

The crowd watched her as if afraid to look away. Her fitted white gown trailed behind her, the skirt split to allow her long pale legs to move freely. As she passed, the spell seemed to break, and everyone resumed their chattering and laughing.

I pushed past Kaden, intending to follow after her, but I only saw the tips of wings through the crowd as they strode toward the back of the massive room.

"Who was that?" I asked, returning to Kaden's side.

Kaden seemed relaxed as always, but I noticed that he, too, tracked their retreating forms. "The Queen of Trugarum. Her name is Milani."

"You say that as if it's a curse. She's beautiful. Her wings look so soft."

Kaden chuckled darkly. "Beautiful but deadly. I'd dare you to touch them. They may look like feathers, but they are sharper than any blade."

"Is she important? I didn't see anyone else enter like that."

"Very," Kaden whispered. "She owns the southern realm and all its territories. Her armada is one of Nismera's strongest forces."

"How?" I gaped at him. "I assumed Nismera wouldn't want anyone with equal power."

"Equal power alliances mean no one would ever dream of testing you," Kaden said.

My eyes widened as I glanced toward the corridor at the back of the room where they had disappeared.

Kaden and I mingled, making our way around the room. Tables were artfully arranged throughout, like small islands in the sea of people. Large sparkling chandeliers hung from every part of the grand ceiling, and I hadn't noticed until I glanced up how much they resembled starlight.

We reached another soaring doorway, and I paused, drawn by the sound of music. A man stood alone on a raised stage, swirling pale lines running over his exposed skin as he sang. They changed colors and patterns, keeping time with the music. His fingers flew over the strings of the instrument he held as he played a passionate ballad. The crowd gathered at his feet, mesmerized by his song. No one seemed to notice the silver chains wrapped around his ankles nor the guards stationed at the sides of the stage.

"He's a muse," Kaden whispered near my ear. "A gift from a neighboring queen as penance. In return, Nismera spared her kingdom."

"A muse?" I felt my face pale. "She would trade a muse for protection?"

"You'd be surprised. There is no being more depraved and heartless than a leader protecting the people they love."

I swallowed the uneasiness in my gut as I watched the muse. He had to be no more than twenty, beautiful in the way of the gods, with shaggy dark hair. He wasn't ghastly thin, which meant she kept him fed, but I could see the trapped pain in his soft brown eyes.

"I think he is the last left," Kaden said it so calmly as he placed his hand on my lower back and steered me away.

"His voice is—"

"Intoxicating? Mesmerizing? It should be. He inspires those feelings."

"No wonder the crowd has grown."

"Mm-hmm," he responded distractedly.

Kaden, who I hadn't seen grab another glass, sipped at a fiery red liquid, his gaze locked on a balcony high above. Looking at him, I wondered if he was nervous. The music changed tempo but quieted, and I heard someone clear their throat. I followed Kaden's gaze, hurt tightening my throat.

Silence rippled across the room, and everyone turned toward the large staircase. Now I knew why I hadn't been able to find Vincent. He was at her side. Jealousy made me chew the inside of my lip as he stared at her with a soft smile on his lips. I hadn't seen him in days, and the one time I'd heard him come back and stop near his door, I heard them together inside. Maybe kissing me made him realize how much he really missed her, and now that she had finally given him the time of day again, he was done with me. It seemed I'd only been a distraction.

I should have known. Why did I ever think I could change him? He wouldn't even change for his chosen family. I was nothing to him, to no one. My magic must have started to leak because Kaden dropped his hand to mine, interlacing our fingers. He took the brunt of my magic. He didn't react to the burn, but his touch grounded me. It was such a simple gesture, a kind one, and kindness was something I did not expect from Kaden. Maybe he was right. I knew nothing of him and Isaiah.

When I looked up again, I could have sworn Vincent's eyes were on us, but it was probably just my imagination. Guards in shiny golden armor surrounded them, and I realized she was expecting an attack. She held a single hand up, her magnificent black dress fitting her lithe form like a glove. Its neckline plunged nearly to her belly button, exposing the inside curves of her full breasts. The dark color of it was a stunning contrast to her flawless skin, but it was the crown on her head that garnered whispers. Silver prongs reached for the ceiling and branched off like sparkling sunlight. I had never seen anything so beautiful.

Kaden made a noise in the back of his throat, and I tipped my head toward him without looking away from Nismera. "What is it?"

"That crown." He kept his eyes straight ahead, speaking around his glass. "It was my father's."

Unir's crown.

Holy gods above and below.

My mouth grew dry as she started down the stairs, taking them one by one until she reached the bottom. Every single being in her presence went to their knees, including Kaden and I, because the crown she wore told everyone exactly what and who she was now.

King of the Gods.

Nismera instructed everyone to dance and mingle, the muse singing a slow melody. Maybe no one else could hear it, but I heard the sadness and fear underlying the song. I hated it, hated being here even as Kaden spun me. I caught glimpses of Vincent and Nismera through the throngs of people as they danced. This whole thing was as fake as the smile on her face.

Dead bodies lined the depths of her palace, and the screams of those she tortured with her experiments echoed off the walls below, yet she pretended to be this savior of peace and ruler of the realms she so kindly liberated. Did they not see the monster beneath her skin? Did they not feel its harrowing breath or its dead and rotted eyes? Her porcelain skin may seem perfect, her hair as light as golden sunlight, but a demon from the very pits of Iassulyn lived beneath her breast, and it would swallow us and the world whole.

"You're staring," Kaden whispered against my ear.

"No, I'm not," I said, even as I looked away.

"If it makes you feel any better, he is watching you, too." My breath hitched, and Kaden's chest rumbled with a deep chuckle. He knew it affected me.

Another breathless whisper near my ear made goosebumps rise on my arms and neck. "He looks every time you are not. You two should be careful. Nismera finds out you're plucking the strings of her favorite toy, and she will skin you both alive."

I pulled back, and Kaden's lips were mere inches from mine. The way his head was tilted, I wondered if he was pretending to kiss me just so Vincent felt a fraction of the hurt I did. It was not what I wanted, though. None of this was. My life and heart were not a game.

My chest hurt as my reality crashed down on me. I did not want to be in this castle of a prison with a demon of a ruler who pretended to be kind. I did not want to feel for a man who had betrayed all he claimed to love and now treated me as a passing distraction. I did not want to dance and fake a relationship with my arch-nemesis.

I couldn't do it, not anymore. A fine tremor went through my body, and my eyes burned. I had been strong for so long, but now I felt like I was going to break apart. I wasn't strong enough.

"I can't watch this, and I can't do this anymore."

Kaden's brows rose as if he'd read every thought I had. "You try to flee, Camilla, and they will hunt you down. You'll never escape this place."

I let go of Kaden's hand as I lifted the hem of my dress. Turning, I darted through the crowd and out of the ballroom. I ran past others, thinking of the crown she wore. She'd claimed it with the blood of the innocents she'd trampled. It was all too much.

Laughter beat at me, fake and forced. The sky bled silver with the power of the last true king. He would have ruled with kindness and fairness. I hurried past the tables of food prepared by beings forced to do so, whipped until they bled in service of her.

I ran up the staircase to the second level, excusing myself as I squeezed between kings and queens. I glanced behind me, but Kaden hadn't followed me. No one had. Maybe he'd run to tattle to Nismera about me.

I stumbled against someone and reached out to steady myself. A small prick of pain stung my hand, and I hissed, pulling back and rubbing at it. I turned and came face to face with the beautiful man from the foyer. A slender woman stood at his side, her short brown curls cut close to her head. Her dress was deep maroon and damn near transparent. She offered me a slow smile that was as seductive as she was.

"I'm so sorry." The man looked at my hand. "Did I hurt you? These stupid pins on my suit have come loose, and sharp edges, no matter how beautiful, still cut."

"I am fine. Thank you," I said, forcing a smile. He wore a small crown, its dips and swirls reminding me of the flow of wind. "It's my fault. I was not looking where I was going."

"Running away from the party?" his date purred.

"My feet hurt," I said, knowing it sounded ridiculous, but my head was still reeling.

He glanced down before flashing me another devilishly handsome smile. "They look fine to me."

"Yeah, well, looks can be deceiving," I said.

His smile faltered. "That they can, witch queen."

"What?" I asked.

His eyes flicked to something behind me at the same moment his date tapped his forearm. His pupils grew a fraction wider, and he stepped away from me before excusing himself. I glanced over my shoulder to see Vincent storming up the stairs. Fuck. I turned back, but my mysterious conversationalist had already left. I gathered my dress again, heading toward the corridor that led to the private rooms. Silence fell behind me, and I could feel the weight of Vincent's gaze on me.

"Where do you think you're going?" he snapped from behind me.

I cursed celestial speed, Kaden, and his big mouth.

I kept walking, not bothering to slow down. "To bed. You can keep the cheap party. I'll pass, and you can go fu—"

My words died on a yelp as he grabbed my arm, turning me away from my exit and down a hallway lined with paintings and statues.

LXXVII

Camilla

I hit at his hand as he dragged me further down the hall. "Let go of me."

Vincent ignored my struggles, his grip tightening to the point of pain. I thought about whipping out a string of magic and cutting his arm off at the elbow.

"Would you stop?" he scolded, leading me into a room and shutting the door behind us.

"Let me go."

"So you can run away? Do you really think you'd escape this place? That people have not tried?" he snapped at me.

"Fucking Kaden," I sneered. "Sorry he ruined your little date, but I just wanted to leave that stupid party."

He laughed and spun me to face him. "Please, do not lie to me. I recognized that defiance and determination on your face from across the room."

"Oh, did you? I'm surprised you can see anything besides her."

"You're one to talk," he snapped back.

"What does that mean?"

"Nothing." He scowled and released me.

I stalked away from him. This room was too damn small with him in it. Fragrant candles burned on the desk, and a large globe bristling with pins sat nearby.

Turning toward him, I lifted the hem of my dress and snapped, "Are you still sleeping with her?"

"Why would you ask me that?" he snarled, his head whipping toward me.

My chest heaved. My already unstable emotions had gone haywire the second that door closed. I hadn't talked to him in days, yet it felt longer. I'd been trapped in my damn routine again, and I was losing it.

"You are, aren't you?" I huffed. "What? You get worked up with me, then run to her to finish the job?"

His lips thinned, his brow darkening in anger. He took a step toward me. "Is that what you think?"

We danced around each other. Vincent stalked me like a predator, but I was done giving him what he wanted. Every step he took, I countered, staying out of his reach. I was just so . . . frustrated with him. The stolen glances and midnight kisses had heightened my need and made me . . . hope. He made me believe that maybe there could be something, that maybe I wasn't alone. Then I had to watch him put his hand on her waist and laugh with her as they danced. The way she couldn't keep her hands off of him made my blood boil.

"You know, you talk a big game when it comes to her, but gods, do you play your part right. You can't keep your hands off each other. And don't even try to lie to me. I know it isn't all just for show. I heard the two of you together the night before last."

"Camilla." He reached for me, but I darted away, heading for the door. I was beyond mad, but the heartbreak threatened to bring me to my knees. Here I was, second best again. It was the same in everything. No matter what I did or how powerful I was, I was still not enough. Not for her, for my family or the world, and not for him. Tears pricked my eyes, and I blindly ran the last few steps to the door. I couldn't let him see me cry. I refused to give him my pain.

His hand slammed against the door, shutting it and cutting off my exit. I leaned my forehead against the door, willing my tears not to fall. He braced his hands on either side of my head, and I could feel his powerful form towering over me.

"As if you have any right to say that to me when you have Kaden following you around like a leashed pet. Everyone saw it down there, how you can't keep your hands and mouths off each other."

So Kaden's ruse had worked. It didn't matter. All of this back and forth was just a prelude to the inevitable. Nismera's claws were in Vincent far too deep, and I'd never had a chance.

"Me?" I scoffed and turned around to face him. I leaned back against the door, his scent and the heat of his body surrounding me. I threw my next words at him with every bit of the hurt and pain I felt. "Please, I saw the way you looked at her, how you smiled at her when you can't even look at me. It's bullshit. I took care of you when your *king* left you to rot in that bed. She didn't even care if you lived or died. Did you know that? I sure as fuck did. I made sure your wounds didn't fester and kept you alive, yet your unwavering loyalty still bends to her every whim. Why do you let her do whatever she wants?" The last part left my lips on a cry.

Vincent dropped his gaze. "What choice do I have?" he asked, and even though he didn't move away from me, I felt him drawing back.

This time, I wouldn't let him retreat back into that persona he wore so well. I wouldn't let him hide behind his fear of Nismera and her retribution, going back to pretending he cared for nothing and no one.

"Me," I whispered. "You have me."

Something broke and cracked within him. I felt it, watched as his body went rigid, the veins along his forearms bulging as if he were trying to will himself to say something but was blocked.

"I can't," he gasped the words.

"You can, though." I grabbed his arms and gazed up at him. "And if not, I refuse to let this be my life. I will not have half of you. Stolen kisses behind closed doors are not enough. I will not stay here under her rule. I will leave when I get the chance, despite the risk of her killing me if I am caught, but I refuse to be a ghost here, unfulfilled and lonely." His eyes dilated at my words, his chest heaving. My fingers dug into his arms. "Fight, Vincent. Fight for something you want for once. Otherwise, let her kill you. Because this? This is not living. Not for you and not for me."

Something flickered in his eyes. Hope, promise, or maybe determination, but it was a change, nonetheless. I had half a second to guess before his lips crushed mine. It wasn't sweet or slow as before. No, this was feral, wild, and possessive. I gasped as his hands cupped the back of my head, and he tilted my head. His fingers wove into my hair, and he tugged, demanding entrance. My lips parted, and he deepened the kiss, his tongue running across mine in a hot, blazing trail. My arms wrapped around him, my nails digging into his back.

A desperate moan escaped him as he pushed his body against me. I gasped as his mouth left mine, trailing hungry kisses along my jaw and neck. No, this wasn't like before.

I pushed against his chest, panting. "Don't kiss me after you've been with her!"

"I haven't," he whispered against my throat before lifting his head. His hands framed my face, forcing me to look at him. "For months now. She has left me alone, focusing on whatever power she's obsessed with now."

"But she has been visiting you, using you again."

His eyes darted to my lips. "Tedar died because of Dianna. She destroyed his entire legion. It was the final call to war for Nismera. Nismera is worried that the rebels see Dianna as their new hope, so she . . . The East is no more, but she has had me commanding the soldiers as they retrieve parts for a weapon."

My chest heaved, and my pulse quickened, but I knew what I'd heard. "But I heard," I said, wanting to believe so much, but I would not ignore what I knew. "I went to check on you the other night, and I heard you in your room. The sounds . . ."

Vincent stood a fraction taller, pressing every hard edge of himself into me. He stepped between my legs and ground his hardness where I ached for him, those cerulean blue eyes burning as he stared down at me.

"Myself." His thumb caressed my lips in one sweep, and he thrust his hips against me. "After *you* got me worked up, as you put it."

My chest felt lighter at his words, but my core went heavy and burned, thinking of him pleasuring himself. We stared at each other, the truth nipping at us. We were in way over our heads, and there was no easy solution for the predicament each of us was in.

Vincent stared down at me, his body heavy against mine, one breath, then two, as if contemplating what he was doing. His hand left my face and dipped to my shoulder, brushing the stray hairs from my collarbone before placing his hand not just atop my breast but over my heart.

"Vincent." My voice was as breathless as I felt.

"Don't." His eyes darted to mine, and I knew this was a mistake. "Don't leave me. I've hurt and pushed everyone away, everyone that meant anything. You are all I have now."

My lashes lowered, shuttering my expression, hiding my confusion. That's what this was. My words had hit some part he'd buried damn deep, and it had raged forward. I sighed and swallowed back my tears and sorrow. Maybe I was never meant for a happily ever after, but I could stand by this broken man. I would stand by him because it was already too late for me.

My hand caressed the side of his face. "I won't leave you." I placed a kiss on his lips and then pulled back a fraction. "We go together or not at all. Deal?"

He nodded, our breaths mingling before his lips crushed mine.

LXXVIII

Vincent

I could kiss Camilla for the rest of eternity and never tire of it. It was the only time my bruised and wounded soul knew peace. The only time I felt anything besides that gnawing, aching emptiness. I craved her, this, and especially the soft sounds she made as my hand roamed over her body, squeezing at her breasts. She had truly terrified me when she said she would leave. Something in me had snapped, awakening the ugly beast in me. Protective and feral, it feared losing this haughty witch more than the demon goddess that had created it.

"Vincent," she moaned against my mouth. I kissed her once more before forcing myself away from her lips. I lowered my head and traced the neckline of her dress, her skin soft against my tongue. She tasted of the sea, a raging, powerful force that had the potential to drown me, and gods above, I wanted to drown.

Her fingers slid into my hair at my nape and fisted as I pulled the top of her dress down with my teeth, exposing her nipple. My mouth clamped over it before she had time to register what I was doing. Camilla's head lolled against the door, and her body rocked forward on a gasp, her hips writhing against mine. I lapped at the tight bud, pulling at it with my teeth. She hissed, grinding into me a fraction harder with every deep suck. It drove me wild, and I slid my hand into her dress, plucking at her other nipple.

Camilla's hand tightened in my hair. "Vincent!"

I slid my hands down her sides and reluctantly released her nipple, leaving it swollen and slick from my mouth. I grasped her dress and gathered it in my fists, pulling it up her body.

"I'd fall to my godsdamn knees right now to have just a taste of you," I said, trailing a blistering path up the column of her throat. "To see how far I could stick my tongue in you before you screamed, but she'd taste it."

"Good," was Camilla's breathless response before she nipped at my lips.

I groaned as I lifted her dress to her hips and pressed my leg between her thighs, spreading them wider. "I want to fuck you so badly, Camilla. You are all I think about, all I dream about, all I want."

Camilla moaned as I pressed into her harder, her lips slanting over mine as she cupped my face. She ground against my leg, but it wasn't enough, not for me, and definitely not for her. My hand splayed against the door near her head, my other slipping beneath her thigh. She lifted her knee and hooked it at my hip, opening eagerly to me. I shifted my thigh away from her core to allow my hand access, dancing my fingers across her panties and lightly brushing at her clit.

Her eyes widened a fraction, lust pooling in their depths as her lips parted on another gasp.

"I want to have you, every single part, but not here, not like this. So can I have a small taste instead?"

I slid my fingers across her once more, marveling at the wetness that I could feel through the thin fabric.

Her hands dropped to the lapels of my jacket, and she fisted the fabric. "Y-yes," she stammered.

I smiled before kissing her once more. One yank, and I ripped the thin, smooth fabric of her panties before tossing them aside. My hand cupped her pussy, her slick heat coating my fingers as I moved them over her sex, back and forth. She arched into my touch, her hands pulling at my jacket as she pressed herself into my hand. My lips slanted over hers, my tongue swirling in the way I wished I could taste between her legs.

Camilla deepened the kiss, her body trembling as my fingers circled her clit. I slipped my middle finger into her, and she moaned, letting me taste her pleasure. Wet, tight heat greeted me, and I damn near combusted. She rode my hand, clamping around my finger, crying small, desperate sounds into our kiss. My dick grew harder, my pants constricting painfully. I longed to pull my finger from her and replace it with my cock, but I didn't care about my pleasure. I only cared about her.

All I cared about was Camilla.

She rocked against me, desperate and hungry. Her lips left mine, her eyes wild and filled with need. She panted, her hands pulling on my jacket, using me as leverage to chase her pleasure. Gods, she was the most beautiful woman in any realm.

"Another," she whispered, and I didn't have to ask what she meant. I pulled out, her pussy quivering, and then slipped two fingers inside of her.

She moaned and clenched around me so tightly it was almost uncomfortable. I groaned, imagining feeling that around my cock. Her head fell back, and she ground her clit against my palm.

"Gods, Camilla. I want to feel you dripping down my cock as I take you."

"Fuck me," she begged. "Please, Vincent. I need . . ."

Camilla begging was my new favorite. I knew I wanted to hear her do it over and over again. Her pussy clenched and trembled around my fingers. Her mouth was mere inches from mine, our breath mingling. It was the perfect fucking torture to have her, yet not.

I twisted my hand and curled my fingers inside her, sliding firmly along her inner wall. Her head tipped back, and she grabbed my wrist, grinding my palm against her clit. "Come for me," I whispered and leaned forward to suck her nipple into my mouth. She went rigid and then came apart, hot liquid pouring from her quivering pussy. I covered her mouth with my free hand, and she screamed into my palm. Her entire body trembled, and I leaned against her, pressing her against the wall to keep her upright. Her eyelids fluttered, and she rocked helplessly against my hand as I wrung every last bit of her orgasm from her.

Camilla panted as I gently pulled my fingers from her. She kept a hold of my wrist and raised my hand to her lips. I watched in pure amazement as she sucked both fingers into her mouth, licking them clean, and I swore I could feel her tongue doing the same to my cock. My shaft throbbed painfully, and I groaned as she played her tongue over my fingers. I met her gaze and saw the magic swirling in her eyes, and I knew what she was doing. She sucked harder, and her cheeks hollowed, my body jerking.

"Camilla," I whispered, and I could hear the pleading in my voice.

She took my fingers deeper into her mouth, sucking and licking. My head fell back, and I widened my stance. My hips thrust against hers as if I could feel her head between my legs and her lips around my cock. She lovingly continued, gagging wetly on my fingers. My spine tingled, and my balls tightened.

"Fuuuck, Camilla." Her eyes watered, and her cheeks were flushed a beautiful pink. "Please . . . please."

I didn't even know what I was begging for, only that I couldn't stop. Another swirling caress of her tongue over my fingertips, and my hand slammed against the wall next to her as I came. And came.

She released my fingers with a pop and licked across her swollen lips. She smiled up at me, and I devoured it, claiming her mouth and the taste of her happiness. I curved into her, her hands holding me close as she returned the kiss as if she never wanted to let me go. I pulled back, my forehead on hers as we tried to catch our breath. We stared at each other, something sharp and forbidden between us, something that would damn us both.

"Camilla, you are . . . I don't have words."

She smiled, and godsdamn, how did I not notice that it was the most beautiful thing I had ever seen?

A low whistle cut through the room, and my heart stopped. I pulled her away from the door, and it cracked open to reveal Cameron on the other side.

"You know, if you two were so desperate to slip away for a quickie, you should probably have found a place that is a little more private. I mean, these doors aren't exactly soundproof."

LXXIX

Vincent

"Don't forget your panties," Cameron said to Camilla.

She grabbed the ruined scrap of material off the floor and gave me a small smile before turning and leaving the room, holding her head high as she brushed past Cameron.

"If I had a coin for every time I walked in on you ruining some woman's panties, I could buy this fucking palace."

"What do you want?" I asked, gritting my teeth.

"I can't believe you'd make Camilla another notch on your bedpost when your goddess from Iassulyn is right downstairs. But then again, I don't know you at all."

"Cameron," I said, his name a plea. "She can't know."

"Oh, she can't?" Cameron pushed away from the door. The way he spoke and moved was so him, but I knew he had been changed on a fundamental level. The shadows in the room followed him, the light trying to hide.

That connection between us was forever severed, and not just because of my betrayal. The beast that inhabited his skin now owned him. I saw the flicker of red in his irises even now.

"You should probably shower before heading back to your evil goddess. Can't walk around smelling like hot witch sex, now, can you? Nismera will execute her in front of everyone, but you know that already."

Worry flared in my gut. "You can't say *anything*."

Cameron whistled. "Don't tell me that the betrayer himself gives a shit about anyone but himself? Please, the Vincent I knew, or thought I did, died long ago. I now know you're just as heartless as the bitch who made you."

"I'm serious," I sneered. "Nismera will cut her hands off and lock her in a dungeon to spite me."

"Okay," Cameron shrugged, "but I want something."

I stepped forward, anger replacing worry. He would dare to use Camilla against me? "Are you blackmailing me?"

Cameron squared his shoulders without a flicker of fear. He seemed larger now, more filled out. I wondered if he had gained muscle in training or if it was another perk of dying and being reborn. "I'm taking a page out of your playbook. Doesn't feel good, does it?"

"You can hate me all you want, Cameron, but you were right there with me when everything happened."

"As if I had a choice. You knew as soon as he went after Xavier that I would choose him. Don't act surprised or innocent."

I did neither.

"That's what you want? Xavier? Even if he is mindless?"

Cameron's fist shot out, connecting with my jaw. The punch was hard enough to rock my head to the side.

"Watch what you say," he said, a hint of a beastly snarl threaded through his words.

I rubbed at my jaw and snorted. "It's the truth, and we both know it. What you want, you can no longer have. There is no way to turn them back."

Red flared in his eyes, flooding his irises. "And whose fault is that?" he snapped, a hint of his fangs showing.

"Mine," I said, and he reared back in shock, obviously not expecting me to say it. "It's mine. Look, I don't know where Xavier is."

"But you know something?"

I was quiet for a second, Camilla's words playing over in my head. *Fight for something.* How often had I heard them? But for her, for her safety, I would fight until it killed me.

"Pauule. It's a war camp, but Nismera has a plan to draw Dianna out. Get there first. Maybe she can help you." I shrugged. "A team is being sent out. They leave tomorrow morning."

Cameron said nothing more before turning away, and a part of me ached for the brother I had lost.

"You won't make it far looking as you do," I said before he could leave. "I'd steal a general's persona for it. It's a tight-lipped mission. Nismera doesn't want anyone to know. She is nervous, and if you're caught, you're dead."

Cameron folded his arms and nodded once. "You know what's funny?"

"What?"

"You hated Dianna so much, but she was willing to die for those she loved. She may have teeth and claws and be every bit of the monster, you believe, but she at least has a heart. You . . ." Cameron shook his head. "I'm just surprised I didn't see how heartless you were before."

Heartless. That was one word to describe how I felt.

"I'll get you the mission. Don't say anything about Camilla."

Cameron had started for the door again but stopped and looked over his shoulder. I saw the Ig'Morruthen that now lived under his skin. He was all predator now, the beast keeping him safe. I had done that.

He gave me a smile filled with malice. "Unlike you, I wouldn't damn someone else."

"But you would risk everything for Xavier?" I asked.

Cameron turned to face me again. "Maybe if you loved someone more than yourself, you would understand, but I seriously doubt you are capable."

I only nodded, chewing the inside of my lip. "Nismera moved his station several times. She knows you're looking for him, and I think she plans to use him like a leash to keep you under control. I don't know where he is."

His eyes flared bright red. “Why didn’t you tell me this before?”

I shrugged one shoulder. “I’ve caused you enough pain. I wasn’t going to give you false hope, too.”

Cameron paused a moment to study me suspiciously before turning to leave. I didn’t stop him this time.

LXX

Dianna

Samkiel rubbed his eyes as Orym went on about some ceremony Veruka had sent him a letter about. Apparently, rulers far and wide had flown to swear their loyalty after what happened in the East. I still couldn't wrap my head around it. The whole East was gone. When you looked toward the eastern sky, nothing but dust and scattered rock remained.

We had returned to pack everyone up and move them to the new castle, but Orym had pulled us aside the moment we'd arrived. I knew that grim look well, and every little bit of happiness had fled upon seeing it. We had been in this study for hours as Orym and Samkiel discussed what to do next.

I was back to being frustrated. It had been months. We barely had Logan and didn't know where the others were. Orym said Nismera kept their locations and who they were with under lock and key.

"I hate this." I sighed loudly, sinking further into the chair. "We are no closer to ridding the world of her, and gods, the second we stop and take a minute to ourselves, the world burns."

Orym and Samkiel turned toward me, Samkiel's eyes softening. "Dianna."

"I know," I said, sitting up. "I'm being selfish. Half the realm is dust, and my worry is our honeymoon lasted zero point five seconds."

Orym cleared his throat and stood a bit straighter. "I am sorry to put this on you two just after the ceremony, but—"

Samkiel raised his hand. "Orym, you are fine. We need to know, and we need to plan our next course of action."

"I have an idea!" I said, raising my hand. "We kill her."

They looked at me like I'd grown two heads, and I shrugged.

"It's a terrible plan. I don't even know if she's fireproof like you." I sighed. "But we have to do something. She is still in her seat of power. What's to stop her from doing what she did in the East to any others that don't kiss her ass?"

Orym shuffled on his feet as Samkiel leaned across the desk.

"I agree it would be the best course of action if we could achieve it, but Nismera is not just any goddess. She is gifted in battle, fast and ruthless."

"And I'm not?"

His eyes held a deep warmth. "Akrai, baby, she is a conqueror in the purest form. Alone, she is not easily defeated, but with her army and guards defending her, she is nearly untouchable."

"He is not wrong," Orym added, rubbing his chin. "They nicknamed her *The Shadow* in her death camps. She is far quicker than most goddesses, and they say when she fights, you only see a flash of her silver hair before your body meets death."

Irritation filled me, and I wiggled in my seat. "Everyone and their stupid nicknames."

A small snort left Samkiel's nose, and he leaned back. His hands tapped lightly against the assorted scrolls strewn across the desk. The moon hung behind him, the crescent shape listening in as we plotted.

"I'm not afraid of her," I said, and I meant it.

"I am well aware." Samkiel smiled, and I knew he was remembering me running into that damned room for him. "But we have to think rationally when it comes to her. We can't let emotions direct our actions."

"You fought her. I saw you two in that blooddream way back when. You held your own, and you've helped train me."

"Yes," he agreed, "but I barely survived, and I had all my power then. It wasn't burning in the sky. Plus, you also saw her beat me and nearly take my head off. You've kissed the scar that proves it."

"But you have me now."

"That I do." A look of pure contentment crossed his face at my words.

Orym ignored us, but his eyes darted to Samkiel's throat, looking for the scar.

"Now think of the years I spent locked away, the years she has had time to train and perfect her swordsmanship," he said. "She will not be easy to dethrone. No matter how strong we are. We have to be smarter."

An idea formed in my head as I chewed the inside of my lip. "You mean destroy her from the inside out?"

Samkiel's smile sent a chill down my spine. "Exactly."

LXXI

Dianna

"And this is your room," I said, opening the door. I stepped aside so Reggie could pass.

"It's quite lovely."

"You like it?" I asked.

I walked to the desk in the corner, eager to show him the massive globe and large colorful map of the realms and their stars that we'd found.

Reggie lifted his gaze to the glass-domed ceiling. It was sometimes hard to tell with Reggie, but I could feel the happy surprise coming off of him. While he explored, I opened the windows, letting a sweet, warm breeze slip in.

"We are so high you can see the mountain tops and, at night, nearly the whole galaxy," I said. He watched me flit about the room, seeming to enjoy my excitement. I stroked my hand down the large brass telescope. It pointed toward the open window above. "And if you really miss your home, you can look through here."

Reggie nodded, grinning indulgently. "This is truly lovely. Thank you, Dianna."

I folded my hands in front of me. "You're welcome. I made sure there was a small table and chairs here. Maybe we can get you some of those board games you enjoy."

Reggie said nothing as he glanced toward the small table.

"Maybe Miska can bring you those teas you love so much."

He only nodded.

"Okay." I tossed my hands up. "Say it. What's wrong with you?"

Reggie's eyes met mine. "I do not know what you mean."

My hands fell to my hips. "You spout off about some weird message which you haven't done in a while. I have not seen you use those eyes in a while either, and you have been consuming a lot of tea, so I asked Miska. I know they are laced with both a sedative and painkillers. What's wrong?"

Reggie nodded. "I see. There is nothing particular, I suppose. Just minor aches and pains here and there."

"Since the tunnel?"

He nodded.

I stepped toward him, concern twisting in my gut. "Is there anything I can do?"

Reggie shook his head. "I am afraid not, but I shall be fine, Dianna. Nismera is a powerful goddess, but the aftereffects of what she did to me shall wear off. It merely takes time."

It didn't completely ease my worry, but I smiled and nodded, not wanting to pester or push further. I patted his shoulder and left him to settle into his new room. I was happy that he seemed to like it.

My footsteps were light as I skipped downstairs toward Samkiel's study. It had taken him a while, but I was glad he'd finally picked a room out of nearly the hundred here. I had finally suggested he take the one on the third floor. It was near our room and huge, with plenty of room for all the scrolls and books I knew he would eventually hoard. I had no doubt he would fill the shelves with his treasures in no time.

I couldn't help my grin when I thought about the desk we'd moved into his office. We had found it on one of the lower levels, and it was big enough for him to spread out and make a complete mess of it. We had tested the sturdiness of it three times, just to make sure it was exactly what we needed.

My giggle preceded me as I pushed open the large double doors. Sunlight spilled through the windows on the left, dust motes sparkling in the beams. Samkiel and Orym seemed to be in the middle of a debate, but they both turned toward me. I caught the apprehension on Samkiel's face and how Orym's mouth was set in a thin line, and I knew there was trouble. A tall, lean female elf stepped around Samkiel. She had been standing so close to him that I hadn't even noticed her, but I saw her now, and she was way too close. My lip must have curled, and I knew my eyes had gone red because Orym stepped in front of her and held out his hand.

"Dianna," Orym said, "this is Veruka."

I blinked, startled enough to pause. "Veruka? As in works-for-Nismera Veruka? And you just let her into my house?"

Before any of us had time to process my questions, I had her pinned against the very sturdy desk. It creaked under the pressure as my grip around her throat tightened. I leaned forward and inhaled deeply. My fangs lengthened, but my diction was still perfect. "You report to that bitch, and I'll eat your fucking heart out."

Samkiel's arms went around me, holding me in a vise grip as he hoisted me off her, my feet dangling in the air.

"Dianna!" he snapped. "Calm down."

"Calm down?" I shrilled. "Are you out of your fucking mind? You let her in my house when she reports to that bitch?"

"She comes in peace to provide information." Samkiel placed me on my feet but kept his arms around me, holding me against him. My gaze remained locked on her as Orym helped her to her feet and supported her as she caught her breath.

"Yeah?" I straightened my shirt and glared at them both from within the cage of Samkiel's arms. "You know what information I smell? I smell Isaiah on you. That is what I smell. Do you know what he did to Samkiel?"

"Listen," Veruka said, a breeze slipping in through the window and blowing her scent my way again. "I'm not—"

My nostrils flared, and I gasped. "Sami!" I cried in a whisper, my heart thudding and a brief wash of relief making my body melt against his. I had hoped, but I'd never dared to believe.

"Dianna?" Samkiel asked, sensing the shift in my mood.

I turned in his arms and grabbed his hand, gazing up at him as I spoke mind to mind.

"She smells like Cameron and Imogen. I smell it. I do. It's faint but there. They are alive, Sami, but they are there."

His head whipped toward Veruka, his chest expanding as he took a deep breath. I felt it from him, too. It was an overwhelming sense of pure, blinding hope. We knew where two more were. Gods above, I wanted them home already.

"You are close to my family?" Samkiel asked her.

Veruka's eyes widened a fraction before she nodded. "Yes, they are there. Imogen is under Isaiah, in his legion."

"Okay," I said. "He will be the first I kill."

Her eyes flashed to mine, then back to Samkiel. "And Cameron is a commander of his own."

"What?" Samkiel asked. "He'd never work for her, serve her."

My hand fisted in his shirt, and I tugged. *"He might if he had no choice. I did it, remember?"*

I felt Samkiel's cool touch across my mind and emotions, easing the burn of the memories of who I had been and what I had done. It soothed the beast that lived beneath my skin, and I leaned into his caress.

Veruka went on. "He searches for the other member of The Hand."

"Ah," Samkiel nodded, "I see."

Orym glanced between us, more relaxed now that the tension had mostly subsided. "Veruka came with a note. She knows the next place we need to strike."

I turned in Samkiel's embrace again, and he pulled my back to his chest, holding me close. I knew we both needed the comfort and held tight to his forearm where it crossed my breasts. "Okay, and this time, you decided to show and tell?"

Veruka nodded. "Yes, because they will label me a traitor after this."

Samkiel stood in front of the mirror and tipped his head, cleaning up the hair across his chin and along his hairline. He edged it shorter, not bothering to remake the marks I had shaved into his hair. At least now, when he removed his helmet, they wouldn't automatically assume he was a part of The Eye. All they would see was a handsome soldier.

"Flirt." He grinned at me as I sat on the bathroom sink.

I leaned back, admiring the flex of muscle across his broad chest and how the white towel wrapped low around his hips contrasted with his tanned skin. "Are you always in my head?"

He tapped the razor blade against the sink and ran it beneath the water. The rush of blue from the faucet was still new to me. The color reminded me of the ocean, but it was crisp and almost sweet. Samkiel said it was fed through the mountain or something, the minerals giving it the unique color and taste.

"No." He smiled. "It's easier to slip in when you think of me, and I, you. Plus, I only peek when your eyes do that thing."

I tipped my head. "What thing?"

He just smiled before grabbing a small towel and wiping it under his chin and throat. He tossed it on the counter and stepped around me, keeping his distance after his shower. Veruka planned to wash my scent from his skin after our morning activities. She had said it would make sneaking into the war camp easier.

I jumped off the counter but waited for him to disappear into the closet before heading into the bedroom. I flopped onto the bed, my arms and legs spread out as I gazed at the canopy above. I heard the dresser drawers open and close as Samkiel rummaged for clothes. It was good he'd made us a bit of a wardrobe, even if I had bitched about him conserving his power.

"I'll still be close by."

I heard his soft chuckle. "Dianna, I will be fine, and you know you cannot leave that venue."

I groaned, flipping onto my front. "I already hate this plan."

I heard Samkiel's footsteps and pushed up on my elbows just as he walked into the room. He was wearing the dark, fitted, long-sleeve shirt and pants he usually wore beneath his armor. I had a moment to appreciate how it molded to all my favorite parts before he flicked his ring, and his silver armor formed over his body. He removed the helmet and held it beneath his arm.

I propped my chin on my hand and dragged my gaze over him. "What time do we have to leave again?" I purred and bit my lower lip.

Samkiel chuckled and patted the bed before walking toward the door. "Come on, before I have to take another shower. You are much too tempting, akrai."

I pouted but followed him out of our bedroom. As we walked down the hall toward his study, I glanced up at the tapestry hanging on the wall and the empty rectangular tables.

"I need to decorate this place, honestly."

He chuckled. "We are preparing to infiltrate one of Nismera's war camps, and you are worried about decorations?"

"Yes," I said as he opened the door to the study. He waited for me to pass before walking in. Orym and Veruka were deep in conversation. I honestly had not seen Orym happier. His smile was wide and true, showing off his canines. Their tails thrashed almost in unison, and I wondered how long they had been separated. They stood as we entered, both wearing the gold armor of Nismera's legion. I took a deep breath and released it, reminding myself they were not a threat.

Veruka's eyes ran up and down Samkiel, not in a lustful way, but assessing.

"The silver is a dead giveaway. We will not be able to slip past security."

"I am aware," he said. He ran his thumb over his ring, and a flush of color crept over his armor. The silver turned gold, and a bit of tan cloth with Nismera's war symbols draped from his hip. Two long, legless, winged beasts etched themselves into his breastplate, crisscrossing each other, forming a large X over his chest. The helmet under his arm was the last to change color, and I hated seeing her mark form in the metal.

"That is truly amazing, my king," Veruka said, admiration clear in her voice.

"*Relax.*" My brow lifted as Samkiel's voice flooded through my mind.

Orym caught the change in my attitude, though. He caught my eye and gave me a deliberate nod before nudging his sister. Veruka dipped in a small bow that had me a bit confused.

"Veruka hereby swears her loyalty to House Martinez."

"House Martinez?" I looked toward Samkiel.

There was no humor in his gaze. "Yes, we can discuss it later."

Veruka rose, smiling at Samkiel and me. "With the King and Queen of Rashearim back, maybe there is hope after all."

I didn't know how to respond. The last few weeks had been a whirlwind, and I wasn't sure I would ever get used to being called a queen. It wasn't that I minded, but Samkiel and I hadn't even had a chance to discuss any of this yet.

Veruka looked at Samkiel again. "That works. You look like most of the soldiers, and I have the rancid, so I will also smell like them for a short time."

She reached into a small pocket in the smooth pants she wore beneath her armor and pulled out a small braided bracelet. As soon as Samkiel touched it and placed it on his wrist, it was like I'd lost the scent of him. Oddly, I hadn't realized how accustomed I was to his scent. As soon as he slipped the bracelet on, I ached with the loss of it. I didn't like it, nor did my Ig'Morruthen, for that matter. My fangs slipped past my gums, and it wasn't until they all turned toward me that I realized a growl had slipped from me. I clamped a hand over my mouth.

"Sorry," I said, dropping my hand. "I just . . . It felt like he was gone for a second."

Samkiel's eyes softened, and he reached for me but stopped short.

Veruka stepped closer to me, holding out another bracelet. "This one's for you, and I apologize for the smell."

I knew what she meant the moment I slipped it on. Orym sneezed and pressed the back of his hand to his nose. Samkiel's eyes started to water, but he stoically tried to keep from reacting.

"Great," I said before placing my hands on my hips. "How did you get this, anyway?"

Veruka shrugged. "A witch."

"Camilla?" I asked. It had slipped out. I hadn't dared to hope she was still alive, but she'd disappeared with Vincent and Kaden when they went through that damn portal, and I knew of no one else who would have this kind of power. Samkiel stared at Veruka, as interested in her answer as I was.

Veruka frowned, looking between us. "I mean, I know of her, but no, I have another on the inside." She looked at me, confusion filling her eyes. "You know her?"

"She's still alive?" I asked, my voice catching.

Veruka's eyes widened a fraction, and she nodded. "Yes, and under Nismera's watchful eye. She isn't even allowed to piss by herself, I hear. Nismera has her making spells and items for her when she is not sneaking glances at Nismera's High Guard."

"High Guard?"

But it was Samkiel who answered in a voice as cold as death. "Vincent?"

"Yes. Your old second," Veruka said.

"As in recently?" I asked.

Veruka looked confused, but she nodded. "Yes."

Samkiel and I looked at each other.

"I swear I killed him," I said.

"You?" Veruka took a step back, and Orym stood a tad straighter.

"That was the legion member who attacked us at the prison?" Orym asked.

I nodded and started to pace. How had he survived being stabbed in the heart, especially with that weapon? I knew I hadn't seen his light burn across the sky, and here was the confirmation.

"I am not surprised," Samkiel said. "If he is still alive, he and Camilla must share a bond."

I scoffed. "A bond? Since when?"

Samkiel shrugged. "He visited her cell repeatedly on Rashearim. Camilla had alluded to a relationship between the two of them."

Veruka shrugged, a small smile curving her lips. "There is something between them. Everyone knows it, and they are both dumb to think Nismera doesn't as well."

That made my skin prickle, and I looked at Samkiel.

"If she is alive, I want her back."

Samkiel's eyes narrowed a fraction, and his jaw clenched.

"She is more than just an ally. She hid me from you for months. Imagine what Nismera can make her do. We need her, and you know it. She also brought my sister back to me when she didn't have to. I will not let her suffer."

The flicker of jealousy left his gaze, and he smiled ruefully. "Spoken like a true queen fighting to protect her people."

Veruka cleared her throat. "Well, there won't be any titles if we don't get there soon. Luckily, I know a shortcut to Pauule."

LXXII
Samkiel

Clouds swirled behind us as we cut through the billowing misty masses. We descended, and my thighs tightened against the metal saddle, the air growing warmer the lower we went.

"I hate this," Dianna said through our connection. *"Why do I have to be a giant flying worm?"*

The wind ate my chuckle. *"Technically, you're not a worm. Ryphors are ancient beasts and much more intelligent than a worm."*

"It's a fucking worm, Sami, and I hate you."

I merely patted her soothingly as she grumbled. I supposed the creature's overall shape did look like a giant worm. The thick metallic gray plate that covered its head in a semicircular crown ran the length of its body, tapering toward the tail. The smooth underbelly had round vents that somehow lifted it into the air. Its mouth was nothing short of a nightmare. The serrated teeth and split jaws were bad enough, but it was the smaller tentacle tongue with the mouth at the end that was truly unnerving. Ryphors were unpredictable, violent, and aggressive, yet somehow, Nismera had managed to tame at least one and breed it.

"Mm-hmm. I feel they are more closely related to those hoklok that lurk in the reefs, not worms. You know, they are slimy, vicious, stupid, and attack anything that moves."

"I still hate you."

I threw my head back and laughed. Veruka's eyes widened as her ryphor curved through the sky next to us. I hadn't told her of the power I had crafted into our rings because, no matter what Orym said, I did not trust her fully. Dianna was right. Veruka smelled of my brother, and I wasn't convinced it was just for the sake of the mission.

We broke through the low-hanging clouds, and rows and rows of hexagonal tents came into focus below us. My eyes caught on one tent in the middle of the camp that sat a little higher than the rest. Soldiers crawled over the camp, voices reaching us even up here.

Veruka whistled, and we turned and sailed toward the southern end of the camp. We sailed over the ryphors locked on their posts, and they raised their heads as we passed. I prayed Veruka's witch was strong enough to mask our scents. I knew we were in the clear when none of them screamed or chased after us.

Veruka pulled back on her reins, hovering near an elongated tent, and Dianna followed suit. Dust curled around our feet as Veruka and I hopped off. She nodded toward the tent behind me before heading to the one just on the other side. Dianna followed me in, her long serpentine body coiling to fit. She changed back to her lithe form as soon as the flap fell, a shudder of relief going through her.

"I counted at least a hundred as we passed over," she said, peeking out. "Not counting the ones inside the stable."

Dianna stepped back, and Veruka walked in, one of those small wisps darting around her head. Her tail whipped behind her, and she stopped short, not wanting to crowd Dianna. "Orym is atop the nearest hill. No one has come or gone besides us in the last hour, so Illian is here."

I nodded. Illian was the commander here, his legion the one that frequented the area. The information Veruka provided said that he was a carviann, a species with four arms, skin the color of the ocean, with spikes protruding from his elbows.

It was astounding to me that those who hated the gods so desperately seemed eager to join Nismera's legions and work for her. Even the most vicious and rebellious bent to her will, and I didn't understand why. Why work for a goddess who destroyed your way of life?

"All right," I said. Dianna came to my side, careful not to touch me. I hated it. "We need to find his tent first, then gather the documents."

"Okay, well, we passed over that large one. My bet is that's his," Dianna said.

Veruka and I both shook our heads.

"Wouldn't be," Veruka said. "It would be waving a flag to anyone attempting to raid this place. If anything, it's a trap in case someone comes snooping."

"Correct," I added. "I saw a smaller one toward the back. We can check there first."

Veruka shook her head again and tapped her chin. "Too close to the forest's edge. He will still be in the middle of the camp but hidden. Nismera is too on edge right now. She wouldn't leave things lying around. We need to look for the one where soldiers are hanging around outside but trying not to act like they are guarding it."

"All right," I said, nodding.

I turned toward Dianna, who just watched us both.

"I'll be back as soon as we collect it, and then we leave. Dianna, you wait here and stay hidden."

"Quietly," Veruka added.

Dianna's lips thinned. "Well, it seems like you all have the perfect plan. I'll just wait here." She bared her teeth at Veruka. "Quietly."

I reached for her but stopped short, my hand collapsing into itself. She said nothing. She just wiped her hands on her dark pants and stepped back. Dark mist boiled from her skin and expanded, coalescing into the large, formidable form of the ryphor again. Veruka nodded toward the tent exit, and I tossed a thin smile to Dianna from beneath my helmet before we left.

We strode side by side, blending in with the soldiers we passed. Veruka received a barely-there nod from those who passed, but I remained quiet until we passed another tent.

"Watch how you speak to her," I said, keeping my voice low and my eyes forward.

I felt the tension leaking from Veruka as she cleared her throat. "I meant no disrespect, but she is not battle-trained."

My hand went to her arm, and I pulled her to the side, turning her to face me. "She will be your queen."

I could see the resignation in her eyes, and I let her go. "Does she know that?"

"What is that supposed to mean?" I asked in a hushed voice as a few soldiers passed.

"I barely know her, mostly only what Orym has said. Her will and alliance are to you and your family, but the realms? She does not act for them. He told me what she had done. What the others see as a rebellion seeking freedom from Nismera's tyranny was merely to keep you safe."

I said nothing.

"Are you sure she even wants to be queen, or does she merely wish to be with you? Did you ask her, or are both of you blinded by love and not focused on duty?"

A shriek filled the air, and we glanced up. A few ryphors flew past, turning toward the right and settling away from the stable tents in a plume of billowing dust. I recognized the commander riding atop the largest beast. Veruka and I shared a glance and nodded, refocusing on our mission.

"I suppose we don't have to guess what tent," she said as we walked toward the noise.

Soldiers passed us, headed the opposite way, returning to where they should have been. It seemed he had been gone long enough for them to decide to take a break. Now, break time was over. Veruka and I ducked around a neighboring tent near where he had landed. We pretended to be deep in conversation while we looked around. The ryphors were tethered to their posts, but Illian and his personal guards were nowhere in sight.

"I am going to do a quick perimeter sweep," Veruka said, taking another glance. "Then we can move in. Stay here."

I nodded, and she hurried past. I moved toward a few crates, doing my best to seem busy.

"Dianna." My mind stretched eagerly toward her. I felt the tug of the connection, but there was no answer. *"Dianna,"* I said again, more firmly this time.

"What? Tired of your new girlfriend already?" Her frustration felt like a brush of ice across my mind.

"Funny."

"Just saying I could have stayed at the top of the hill with Orym instead of in a sweaty tent that smells like worm shit."

My hand clenched, tightening my grip on the ring that I wore beneath my gauntlet. *"I wish it was you instead. I've only been around Orym's twin for mere moments, and she's already annoyed me."*

Her anger felt like needles prickling across my scalp. *"What did she do?"*

I focused, showing Dianna the actual conversation. She listened to what Veruka had said to me, and I felt the knot in my gut tighten. It was true that I had never asked Dianna if she even wanted to be queen. I had been far too excited to be with her, dragging her into my world and responsibilities without ever—

"Sami." Her voice was a soothing balm that brought my thoughts to a screeching halt. *"You dragged me into nothing I did not want. I chose you, Sami, and I will, over and over again. Plus, I knew you were king when I tried to kill you the first time."*

I laughed and covered it with a cough as a passing soldier glanced at me. He didn't say anything and just continued on his way.

"It changes nothing, and Veruka can mind her own godsdamn business. You stuck me with nothing I do not want. This whole saving the world and ruling kingdoms is a package deal with you, and I'd have it no other way."

"But I never asked, Dianna, and now we're married. It was selfish."

"Not in the least. I'm a smart girl, and I knew what this came with. I'd have you with or without a crown. As long as I have you."

That warmth spread, not just in my head or through my body, but it flooded my fucking heart. This woman . . . she was my everything. Veruka appeared next to me, and I turned to meet her gaze.

Veruka nodded. "I found his tent. He just stepped out with a general, so our window is limited," she said. "We need to go now."

LXXIII

Samkiel

Veruka and I waited until two soldiers passed before we ducked into the tent. A wave of uneasiness swept over me, and I stood still, looking in every corner. I didn't see anything, yet I felt as if we were not alone.

"What?" Veruka asked as she walked toward the small table near the back.

I shook my head and followed her. "Nothing," I said, focusing on the bundle of scrolls and books scattered across the desk. Veruka nodded, heading back to the front of the tent as she kept a watchful eye.

I ran my hand over a few papers with numbers scribbled on them. These looked like payments for shipments, each line with a name next to it. I grabbed them, folded them, and placed them in my pocket. These could be names of benefactors, people who work for her, or people she had extorted into an alliance. I rifled through another stack, pausing when red ink caught my eye. Shifting a few documents aside, I spread the scroll out fully and leaned forward, bracing my hand on the corner of the map.

"Veruka."

Her head whipped toward me.

"This isn't just a map of this world. It's a map of every single one she's planning to hit."

I looked up at her, and her eyes widened. At first, I thought she was reacting to what I'd said, but her gaze was focused on a spot just past the desk. I whipped my head to the side, but it was too late. A woman stepped out of the opened portal and stabbed a serrated dagger through my hand, where it rested on the table. Something shifted in me as a silver pool of blood built on the map. I gritted my teeth in pain, bright cerulean blue eyes locking on me in a death stare.

"Neverra," I gasped, shock chasing away the pain.

There was a flicker. It was brief but there when I said her name. The tent sides rippled as portals opened one after the other, disgorging soldiers. Illian appeared in the middle of them all, his thick, armored arms clasped behind his back.

He grinned at me and said, "Well now, you were not expected."

He raised one hand. Veruka yelped as two soldiers appeared next to her and rammed a blade into her gut. They pulled it out, and she fell forward, right into their arms.

"She, however, was," Illian said, flicking his wrist. "Put her in the caravan with her traitorous brother. We leave soon."

My eyes widened. They had gotten Orym. Sweat formed on my back. Had they gotten to Dianna, too? No, this place would be covered in flames if they had. My mind reached for her right as Neverra twisted the blade in my hand, and I hissed.

The soldiers dragged a limp Veruka from the tent as Illian pulled a glowing green pendant from the collar of his armor. I recognized it as a glamor created by a very powerful witch.

"Now," he walked toward me, his head tipped to the side. "You were not what we were waiting for. Nismera said Kaden's whore would show, but you, my friend, are bigger than even my most ruthless soldier, and you are male. Are you with his whore now?"

I bared my teeth. "Say that again, and I'll rip your face from your skull."

He chuckled, and his broad smile made me feral. "So you are." He rubbed his chin. "Nismera will be pleased to know that she has another working for her, but I do wonder who you are?"

He rounded the table, and Neverra twisted the blade cruelly. My eyes cut to her, and it was a mistake as Illian's hand whipped out, reaching under my helmet and grabbing my throat. My brain burned thanks to those damned hands and their paralytic components. He was a perfect commander, able to touch anyone and render them useless. My shoulders eased as he tugged at my helmet, the cool air teasing over my chin. What he didn't know was that I had backup.

"*Dianna.*" It was a whisper from my subconscious to hers, hoping she would hear me before our entire cover was blown. "*It's time for Plan B.*"

She didn't say anything, but I felt the whisper of her smile, and even unable to move, goosebumps broke out over my skin. A roar, thicker and louder than any I'd heard from her before, ripped through the sky, every guard and soldier turning toward it.

Illian dropped his hand and spun, ripping the tent flap open. He glanced back at Neverra and uttered a word under his breath. I didn't quite hear it, but her head whipped toward him, and she nodded. While she was distracted, I reached out and slammed my hand against her chest, sending her flying across the tent. I ripped the knife from my hand, hissing through my clenched teeth.

I looked down at Neverra. She was crumpled on the ground, but she was breathing. I didn't know what he had said, but I suspected it was some type of kill code. My palm opened, and I summoned a small portal beneath her. I only had enough power to send her to the edge of the forest, but she would be safe there from Dianna's Plan B. Her body bent as it fell, and I watched until she lay unconscious upon the grass until I closed it. I'd get her as soon as I was done here.

I heard boots rush past and strode out of the tent. Chaos reigned in the once-organized camp. Soldiers bolted from their tents, others stopping mid-stride to stare in shock.

The ground shook and quaked as Dianna's massive form lunged toward the sky, blocking out the sun. Powerful black wings unfurled from her back, the remains of the tent falling from her spikes.

"Ig'Morruthen!"

The shout rang out, and then the world erupted in flames.

LXXIV

Samkiel

I jumped over a high wall of flame, rolling to my feet on the other side. Dianna roared with every pass above me, thick dark smoke blocking out the sun and making it hard to breathe. Massive wings flapped through the air, screams turning to dust wherever she passed. On the plus side, I was not sure what had changed, but her fire no longer burned me. However, the heat alone made me sweat. I cleared a path through the guards, who ran in retreat. Others tried to gather a defense, but they had no weapons that would be effective against her. All the Ig'Morruthens left in this world were on Nismera's side.

I surged through the smoke, throwing two blades. They connected, sinking deep into the skulls of a couple of guards. Their bodies dropped, creating a cloud of dust as they hit the ground in a heap.

"*You're going the wrong way,*" Dianna growled in my head.

"*Oh, I apologize. I must not be able to see through thick clouds of smoke.*" I stopped, squinting to see if I could even make out the guard tower from here.

"*Over here.*"

My head whipped to the right, and I saw the orange and gold flames pour from the sky. I turned and ran toward them, her tail swishing through the clouds, making them roil. I needed to get Veruka and

Orym and get out of here. All it would take was for word to get back to Nismera, and she would rip a portal to get here. I wasn't ready for her, not yet.

Illian had run the moment he saw her, heading for the ryphors, but Dianna had killed his beast before he could get to it.

I ran faster, dodging guards and burning tents, working my way toward the tower. Somehow, over the noise of the chaos, I heard the scuff of a boot against the ground. I grunted as I was tackled from the side, my back breaking the wooden bench we fell against. I groaned and opened my eyes, rolling out from under the sword aimed at my head. Neverra. She must have woken up and ran the entire way here to end me. Yeah, it was definitely a kill code.

I hopped to my feet, summoning a blade as Neverra came at me, aiming for my throat. I blocked, and steel crashed against steel, the vibration echoing down my arm. Her eyes were pure cerulean flame as she pressed harder. I pushed off her, and she twirled her blade above her head. I blocked the attacks she threw, letting her push me back. The last thing I wanted was to hurt her, and killing her was out of the question. I felt Dianna whisper through my mind, but I was too focused on Neverra to pay attention.

"Neverra," I said as she slammed her blade against mine once more. "I know you're in there."

I pushed back, and she sailed through the air, landing in a squat. Her face held no emotion. There was no sweat on her skin. She was a perfect weapon.

"I already have, Logan," I said. "It's time for you to come home, too."

She stood slowly and raised the sword between us but stopped at my words. Gods, my heart faltered. If she could be reached, they all could. Hope burst in my chest. They could all be saved.

She shifted the sword, gripping the hilt and the end of the blade before slamming it across her knee. With a snap, the one blade became two. She tossed one piece at me. I leaned back, hitting it away, but it was already too late. Neverra was my quickest, my strongest, and my cleverest. She wasted no time in taking advantage of my distraction. She was behind me in a blink, the other half of the sword coming toward my throat. There was a clap as Dianna's hand grabbed Neverra's wrist, stopping the blade's descent.

"Hey, Nev," Dianna said. "Long time no see."

Neverra didn't hesitate to drop the blade and twist free, delivering a spinning kick that pushed Dianna into me, sending us crashing into the side of a nearby tent.

My arm wrapped across Dianna's middle as she landed on top of me, my body breaking her fall.

Her hand covered mine where it rested on her abdomen. "Fuck. She's stronger."

"No," I said, rolling to my feet and lifting Dianna with me. "Neverra has always been humble and sweet, but she, by far, is my strongest celestial."

"Oh. Great."

Neverra reached down and grabbed the broken blade, ready to complete her mission.

I reached out and gripped Dianna's shoulder. She glanced at me but was obviously reluctant to take her eyes off Neverra. "I need you to go take care of Illian."

"No," she said, "I'm not leaving you here."

"He has Orym and Veruka. If he takes them back to Nismera, they are dead."

Her face scrunched as she debated it, and I knew a part of her didn't care. It wasn't because she was cold or callous, as everyone assumed, but because she loved me, and she was so tired of losing the ones she loved.

"I will be fine. I trained Neverra, and I can subdue her."

Something flickered in Neverra's gaze, but it was gone a moment later. She started to pace, her movements as graceful and elegant as always. I knew we didn't have much time before she came at me again. She was just figuring out how to get past Dianna.

"Dianna," I prompted.

"You're so bossy," she said and clenched her fists. I knew she'd not leave me, the world be damned, but I needed her to. We'd lose Orym and Veruka if she didn't.

"Please," I said, sending a wave of my desperation to her but also my love. "Save the others. I can take care of Neverra."

"I don't even like them."

"Dianna."

Dianna growled softly and walked a distance away before changing her form and launching herself into the air, her wings pounding the ground with a rush of wind threatening to flatten everything around us. I knew it was her way of having the last word.

I took a deep breath and held my hands up. "No weapons, Nev," I said. "I will not hurt you. Logan would kick my ass." Again, there was that flicker in the depths of her eyes. "You remember him, don't you?"

She lunged, aiming for my chest with that broken piece of her sword. I dodged, raising my arm to take the brunt of her strike. It clanged against my armor, and my forearm tingled from the force of the hit. I snatched the hilt from her grip, leaning back when her fist came at my face, the punch just missing my jaw.

She came at me with punches and kicks, relentless in her mission. Most I either blocked or took, but I refused to fight her. She was not my enemy, only my family.

"All the women in my life want to kick my ass," I joked. She brought her knee up hard enough to make me grunt from the impact. I pushed back, and we circled each other. I heard another roar of flames behind me. Dianna must have found them.

"You know, I was thinking the other day of how reluctant you were to join The Hand."

Neverra sent another jab toward my face, and when I moved out of her way, she lifted her elbow and caught me across the chin. The impact sent my helmet flying. She followed it with a kick to my chest, my head ringing when I landed on my back.

"Now look at you," I groaned and sat up. "One of my strongest."

Neverra raised her foot to stomp me. I jerked back, sliding over the ground on my ass. She kicked out at me again, but I caught her foot this time and pushed, sending her flying through a pile of crates. I jumped to my feet and walked toward her. She pushed herself up, debris scattered all around her.

"You know, a fate told me once that love has power. I want to test that theory."

I knew I shouldn't, and it would cost me, but I had to save my family, regardless of the power I used. They came first. Neverra charged, and I opened a portal to our new home right in her path. Logan sat in a cell, blue bars gleaming behind him. His empty cerulean eyes stared at us, and it broke my heart to see him look at his amata like that. I had never seen anything but love in his gaze when he looked at her.

Neverra skidded to a stop, her hands dropping to her sides. She blinked just once as she looked at him. Her lip quivered, and I knew it had worked.

Her eyes darted to mine. "Sa-Samkiel. How? What's going on?"

"You are in there." I couldn't help the tears that burned my eyes, but my joy was short-lived. She dropped to her knees, her scream bloodcurdling as she grabbed her head. I ran, falling to my knees and skidding to a stop beside her. I held her clawing hands, keeping her from pulling at her scalp.

"Neverra. It's okay, I'm here. You're—"

She twisted out of my grip, and her fist shot out, catching me in the nose and sending me reeling back. My eyes watered, but I could feel it already healing. Her boots stomped against the turned-up ground as she stood up, looming over me. I looked up at her, and my heart sank. Whatever had been there was gone, but it had happened. I'd seen it, and I heard her voice. That was all I needed to give me hope. If they could be reached, nothing would stop me from saving my family.

Neverra may be my fastest, but she wasn't faster than me. I rose to my feet and appeared behind her. My fingers found the pressure point between her neck and shoulder, and she slumped into my arms. I lifted her and stepped through the portal, calling for Roccurem.

LXXV
Dianna

I was a killing machine, one made of fire and sharp edges. A weapon was what they all said, and a weapon was what I felt like. Chunks of the ryphors fell from the sky, the pieces of their massive bodies littering the war camp below. Claws, teeth, and flame bit into every single one that thought they could escape me. Their blood stained my jaws, taking any that took flight to the ground. Only a handful remained, and one of them carried that damn commander.

Illian and one of his guards rammed into me, ryphor teeth biting into my skin. My hip exploded with pain, and I burned his ally to a crisp, my tail hitting the commander's beast hard enough to crack bone. They tumbled to the ground, and I followed, landing next to him. I shifted back to my mortal form.

He grunted, pushing to his hands and knees. Blood dripped down his face from a wound on his head, turning his teeth red as he laughed at me.

"I don't see what's so funny," I said. "You are bleeding more than I."

His grin only widened as he rose to his feet, cradling his injured arm. The ryphor between us took one last breath, then went quiet and seemed to deflate.

"So you are her? You've been making quite a fuss, you know?"

"Yeah, yeah, I heard Nismera is mad, so mad she decimated planets. Talk about a temper tantrum."

"You're a fool, girl, if you think it was merely that," he spat. "She has a weapon now that will leave nothing behind. I guess you can thank your dead ex-lover for that."

My hand was around his throat before he stopped speaking. I lifted him and tried to speak, but my body decided that wasn't necessary, and a cool, tingly feeling washed through every muscle and nerve. My legs wobbled, and he laughed, clamping an enormous hand around my wrist. I sank to the ground, my limbs giving out.

"I was hoping you were as easy to piss off as they said." He tightened his grip, that cool feeling spreading. His eyes blazed with victory as he leaned forward, pushing more of that paralyzing agent into me. "I will wear a medal for your capture."

I heard a swish, and something sliced through the air. Illian's gaze remained fixed on me, but his eyes went wide, and blood rushed through my body once more as his hand went limp. His mouth opened and closed, but no sound came out. A bright line bubbled and grew across his throat as he blinked once more before his head rolled to the side, bouncing off his shoulder.

Samkiel kicked Illian's body aside and held his hand out for me. "I leave you alone for five minutes." He lifted me and supported me as I regained the use of my limbs.

"It was more than five, and look around. I pretty much sacked the whole place while you were saving Neverra," I joked before growing serious. "Is she okay?"

"Yes," he said with a heavy sigh. "Orym and Veruka?"

My hand, nice and mobile once more, whipped out, popping him in his armored chest plate. He looked at me, confused. "Don't do that again."

"What? Destroy those who threaten you with my blade?"

"No. You don't ask me to choose."

His eyes softened. "Dianna."

"Don't *Dianna* or *baby* or *akrai* me," I said, meaning every word as I pushed him again. He didn't stumble or even move, really, and that just made me even more mad. "You will not like the outcome if you ask me to choose between you and someone else again. And I don't care if you huff or roar or stay pissed at me. I am not the hero. That's your job."

The corner of his lips twisted. I felt the warmth of his admiration flutter across my mind, and there was even a hint of arousal at my protectiveness. "So, what's your job, then?"

"Keeping you alive and making sure you don't make stupid mistakes." I folded my arms and cocked my hip to the side, watching how his eyes stroked the curve. "You're terrible at it."

His laugh was short. "All right then. Where are they? Orym and Veruka?"

I nodded, pointing my thumb behind me. "Safe. I stopped the caravan that tried to escape with them. The commander was what was left."

His hands slid over my arms, checking me for injuries, and I let him. I knew fighting him would only hold up the process. He noticed the small cuts and tears on my clothes, but I knew he wouldn't find anything major. Even my hip wasn't hurting as much. The ryphor teeth must have only grazed me.

"I'm fine."

"Mm-hmm," he added before rubbing his hands over my head, his fingers tangling in my hair.

I slapped him away. "Seriously, I'm fine. What about you?"

"I'm good," he said, glancing around the burnt camp. "More wounded emotionally, but I'll tell you later."

"Okay," I said. "We need to go get Veruka and Orym. They are both banged up pretty bad."

"All right."

I turned, leading the way as we walked past the burning remains of ryphors and tents. We came up to the charred caravans surrounded by the corpses of the burnt guards. Veruka held her side and groaned, Orym still passed out in her lap.

"I cauterized her wounds the best I could before the commander escaped."

Samkiel went to his knees next to her, silver light glowing on his hand as he placed it over her gut. She groaned, and he looked up at me.

"Excellent work," he said, smiling at me as he healed her.

I shrugged. "I suppose. Commander Poison-Hands nearly caught me."

"That was my mistake," he said as Veruka groaned again. "I should have warned you."

I shrugged. "No big deal. You saved me."

Veruka sat a little straighter, and Samkiel shifted Orym to an upright position. He moved his hand over his head, the silver light glowing brightly. The sky split with a loud crack, and we all looked up as three ryphors appeared, one of them carrying a general. They hovered above us, staring for a moment before fleeing.

"Fuck."

"Dianna." Samkiel surged to his feet as I watched them race away.

"They saw you!" I snapped. "Saw that silver power. They will tell her."

My body didn't even ache as I reached for my beast form, the change coming faster than ever before. I shot back into the sky, leaving Samkiel standing beside the destroyed carriage with Veruka and Orym.

"Dianna." His voice was filled with fear. *"Do not go after those ryphors!"*

"If they reach her, we are fucked," I said. *"I'll be fine."*

A screech pierced the air as I forced the flame from my throat, scorching the closest ryphor. Its burning body spiraled toward the ground like a flaming ribbon.

"See?" I smiled in my head, and I wondered if he felt it.

"I did," he answered.

I streamlined my body and pushed harder, beating my wings against the air, gaining on the remaining two. I had flown far enough away that I couldn't see him, but I still felt him. It was like a tether linking us, and even though I couldn't see or hear him, I felt it pull tight, thrumming with the essence of him. That part of me that was hollow and lonely all those years was finally filled. It was just another perk of the ring he'd made me. Maybe this marriage thing was all it was cracked up to be.

The ryphors split, one going left and the other right. Fuck. I couldn't let them get away. They knew he was here, and now, they knew what I'd been protecting all this time. If they made it back to her, everything would be over. I flew hard, cutting across the wind as I darted left. If I could just catch one quickly, I could circle back.

Smoke bellowed up, blocking my view within snout reach, so I relied on sound instead of my eyes. I extended my wings, gliding on the wind, and listened. A soft whistle of the wind to my right had me pivoting, and I saw the legless beast whip into the clouds. My wings beat once, twice, and I gained speed, forcing myself against the wind, its shape coming into view. The general glanced back, his eyes widening when I opened my jaws. Flame bubbled up, the heat caressing my throat, but his surprised look quickly turned into a satisfied smile, and he dove.

I snapped my jaws shut, preparing to follow, when a reflective shine caught my eye. The smoke separated, and two more ryphors appeared on either side. A net stretched between them, attached to their saddles. It wasn't made of rope but pure silver light meant to slice me to bits. They stretched it tight, and I realized this was a trap. All of this was a trap made for me.

Fuck.

We can only be mortally wounded in our true forms. Tobias's words echoed in my head. Nismera knew.

I was flying too fast, and I couldn't stop. This time, my arrogance may truly be the death of me. I flung my head and mantled my wings, trying to slow my forward momentum, but it was too late.

"*Sami.*" I hadn't realized I had reached out to him along our bond until his terror flooded me. He felt my fear, my apprehension, and I heard him scream my name.

I took a deep breath, preparing for the pain of hitting that net, but it didn't come. Instead, a massive gray and black form slammed into my chest from below, forcing me up. It screeched in pain, a hollow, deadly sound. I echoed his cry, the edges of our Ig'Morruthen wings shedding embers from where they'd touched that net.

His eyes met mine, and my breath caught. It wasn't just any Ig'Morruthen. It was Cameron. We were both flightless now and spiraling toward the ground, our wings damaged. The air ripped at us, and despite my anger and hate, I curled my damaged wings around him, cocooning us both. We crashed to the ground in a heap of dust and gravel.

LXXVI

Cameron

A soft hum filled my ears, and blistering, raging pain shot up my spine and into my arms. My eyes opened, and I blinked them, trying to get the room to come into focus. I lay on my stomach, the cot beneath me covered with thick comforters and furs. I stared at the cerulean bars with their spinning runes and knew where I was.

"And what would you have me do?" Dianna snapped, her voice hoarse as if she had been screaming for hours. We had fallen a long way, so maybe she had.

I had almost been too late. The portal I had used to get there opened and spat me out into chaos. The entire war camp was ablaze and smoking, but I hadn't hesitated when I saw her take flight, heading straight into their trap. I had never transformed before, not once, but some innate power rose in me, and I just followed my instincts. My body stretched, power filled me, and then I was airborne, rocketing toward her. I had no idea what those nets were. I had never seen them before today, but now I knew why Nismera had been working late, why she and Vincent had not smelled like each other for months. Dianna was her main priority now.

"It was so stupid that they thought you'd fight that hard for Reggie." I groaned, the sound as hoarse and harsh as Dianna's voice had been.

Reggie stood on the other side of the room, his hands folded in front of him. I forced my eyes to focus on the fate, keeping as still as possible because even breathing hurt right now. "No offense."

Reggie said nothing, and my gaze flicked to Dianna. Her arms were more healed than mine, with only a little discoloration that I knew would be gone in days. Only one person could heal her from godly weapons that well, and I knew it was the man standing next to her.

My head spun, and I couldn't help the sound that left my lips. My eyes burned, and I wondered if I had lost my mind. Or maybe I had died, and this was Iassulyn, being forced to face all of them. I had felt something when I arrived, but I thought it was Dianna I was sensing. I pushed myself up, trying to stand and go to him. My scream bounced around the cell as my back tore open, and I collapsed onto the cot with a sob. Samkiel rushed past the bars and kneeled before me, gripping my hand.

"It's okay. I'm here," he said.

His voice was like music to my fucking ears. I hadn't just lost my leader and my king when I thought he'd died, but also my best fucking friend.

"Are you real?" My voice cracked. "Or is this another sad dream?"

His eyes softened, but it was true. Every time I closed my eyes, I dreamed I had saved him. I dreamed I had fought, saved Xavier, and we had stayed. Gods, I hated myself. It hurt to cry, the sobs racking my body and reopening my wounds. I couldn't stop the tears. Every bit of fear and guilt and regret and grief came pouring out.

"I'm real." His hand was gentle on my shoulder, and a soothing coolness settled over my aching, cracked skin. I knew he had tried to heal me, too, just from the parts of me that weren't split open. I suspected after healing Dianna, whatever power he had was depleted. It had to be since it still colored the sky. He leaned against me in the weirdest hug I had ever been a part of, his head on mine as if he was afraid to hurt me.

"But you died. We all felt it," I choked out between gasps for air.

"Dianna brought me back."

I lifted my head and turned toward Dianna, nearly throwing Samkiel off me. Tears still flowed from my eyes as I stared at her in shock. Dianna smirked and shrugged.

"Brought back? From the dead?" I practically screamed. "How is that even possible?"

"It's a long story," Dianna said. "I'll write a book one day. Now, what do you know about Nismera and her whereabouts?"

Samkiel ignored her as he patted the back of my head. "I missed you too, Cameron."

Another cry left me. "Oh, gods, it's really bad then if you are saying that."

Samkiel's touch suddenly disappeared, and the cool balm of his healing dissipated. The pain was still bad, but nowhere near the agony it had been. Panic squeezed me like a vise. Had this been another dream? Was this all just punishment for what I had done? I looked up and saw Dianna holding his wrist.

"Samkiel, you have to stop," Dianna commanded, tugging him away from me. "You've already used too much power trying to heal us both. You can barely stand, and this is further draining you."

"I can't leave him in pain," Samkiel protested.

"We won't, but you're no good to any of us if you sleep for a week from exhaustion," she snapped back. "Miska can make him some healing teas. It will be a slower process, but it will help."

Another sob tore from me, and they both spun toward me. "Gods, I've missed hearing you two bicker."

Dianna shook her head as Samkiel snorted, a single hand running across his brow.

"Do you remember where you were? Where Nismera is?" Dianna asked again.

I opened my mouth, eager to tell them, but my throat tightened. My brows furrowed as I tried to force it, but nothing came. I wanted to tell them where I'd been and what I had seen, but only flashes of gold and cream pierced the fog of my memory. "I . . . I don't remember."

"How can that be?" Dianna asked, glancing between us.

Samkiel shrugged. "Witches, perhaps. Camilla was strong enough to cloak Kaden and you from me."

Dianna's gaze raked over me. "Is she? Is she cloaking her?"

"I highly doubt it." I groaned as I turned toward them. "Camilla is too busy being obsessed with Vincent and vice versa. I know she's working with her, but I don't think she is doing that. Nismera has more witches than Camilla. It is possible one of them is doing so."

Samkiel sighed. "That proves my other theory."

"Which is?"

I watched how they worked together and smiled, resting my head on the soft furs. He had been looking for this for so damn long. Samkiel finally had his queen, and she was worthy of him in every way. She would have torn the realms apart for him and hadn't even let death come between them. I sunk deeper into my cot. Despite the pain of the burns, my body finally relaxed after months of constantly being on guard. Samkiel was alive, and I was finally safe.

"There are no maps to her kingdom or palace because she does not want to be found. I had assumed it was because of The Eye, and I think that is true. Maybe she isn't cloaked, but perhaps she has a spell that makes those who leave her premises lose the memory of it," Samkiel said.

Dianna cast a flirtatious grin toward him. "Gods, you're so hot and so smart."

"I agree," I said against my smooshed pillow. "You look great for a half-dead guy. Or a recently dead guy. How did that work? Your light burns in the sky. I felt it. We all did."

Samkiel went to open his mouth when Dianna's warning growl stopped him. He cut her a look, and she glared back, her brows shooting up in disagreement. For a second, I wondered if they were speaking mind to mind, but I didn't see the mark on them. Another warning growl rumbled in her throat. A skitter of fear tripped down my spine, but Samkiel seemed intrigued by the sound. His eyes glowed a bit brighter before she huffed and folded her arms in defeat. He gave her a small smile before turning back to me.

"Regardless of Dianna's shameless flirting, she is right," Samkiel said. "This does put us in a predicament. We are no closer to finding Nismera, and even beings who have been to her stronghold can't tell us where it is."

"I'm sorry. I wish I could be more helpful," I said.

Dianna cocked her head. "Who said you won't be?"

Worry crept up my spine, a chill curving around my neck. "Okay, why does it feel like you want to rip my head off when you look at me like that?"

"She doesn't." Samkiel gave her a pointed look.

"So what happens now?" I asked, not convinced he was right.

Dianna shrugged, tapping her nails against her biceps. "We keep you locked up."

"Temporarily," Samkiel enunciated the word.

It truly was comical watching them. Dianna was one destructive force, and Samkiel was the one who kept her and everything together. They really were two sides of the same coin.

"Okay," I said, my eyes darting to Dianna. "Why? I would never . . . I wouldn't. Not again . . ."

The room grew silent, the air thickening between us. It felt like an anvil pressing on my chest. How could I apologize when I'd done it for Xavier?

She held my gaze. "You are still in peak Thrash, which means whatever Kaden wants from you, you'll do."

"No, I won't," I all but snapped, hissing as I tried to push up off the cot.

"Cameron. You've been turned for months. Has he helped you feed? Change forms? Train? I highly doubt it. Do you have your hunger under control? Hmm?"

I glanced away, staring at the fate. He watched all this unfold with something akin to wonder in his eerie eyes.

"Exactly," she pressed. "You'd probably blow him if he asked at this point."

My head whipped toward her. There was disgust on her face, and

Samkiel looked at her with worried eyes. I knew he was wondering if Kaden had demanded the same from her when she'd first been changed.

Dianna held up her hands. "I'm just saying, okay? I am not saying it happened. In the beginning, you are very bonded with the being that made you. It takes a bit to work it out of your system. Think about it. Hasn't he asked you to do things, and you agreed? I assume you even went back after whatever missions he sent you on, even though we both know you normally wouldn't."

Samkiel watched me carefully, and I didn't turn away this time because she was right. I had done just that. An odd sense of home pulled me back to her damned palace even though I hated it, hated him. I assumed it was because I thought Samkiel was dead and I had no place to go, but if what Dianna said was true, then I was fucked.

"Okay." I sighed. "Keep me locked up. I don't want to answer his call or act on anything he wishes. More than anything, I don't want to hurt you again," I said and eased back down on the cot, my head feeling too heavy to hold up any longer. I hoped they could hear the sincerity in my voice.

"I promise to make it as comfortable as I can until we figure this out," Samkiel said, crouching beside me once more. I had forgotten how massive he truly was. He placed a hand on my shoulder, and I inhaled deeply, taking in his familiar scent. That was what home felt like.

LXXVII

Cameron

Sleep would not come, my body refusing to allow me the solace of unconsciousness. The castle had quieted down, and my internal clock told me it had to be well past midnight. The fresh air that circulated into my cell smelled sweet, bringing thousands of new scents I would normally be eager to explore. But right now, they just added to the throbbing in my head. I could only focus on the burn in my throat and the rumble in my stomach.

I tossed, sweat beading on my skin as an aching need ripped at my gut. Dianna was right. I wasn't out of Thrash, not at all. Those damn underground fights and the blood had been my way of sublimating it. I turned onto my side, trying to get comfortable, and gasped. A pair of red eyes glowed at me from the darkness outside my cell. My body jerked in instinctive fear, my back screaming with the movement.

Dianna emerged from the shadows, holding a tall glass. The aroma hit me, and I jumped to my feet, my fangs descending. The pain in my back and arms was non-existent compared to the hunger. My stomach growled loud enough for her to hear, and claws replaced my nails. She stepped back, not out of fear but gauging me and my reaction. She swirled the liquid in the cup, the smell driving me mad. Without thinking, I reached out and gripped the cerulean bars. I hissed in pain and yanked them back.

"I was right," she said, stepping forward. "You have been starving. Kaden didn't teach you how to feed, did he?"

"I know how to feed," I said.

"Have you killed?" she asked, her voice low.

I fisted my healing hands and leaned against the wall, dropping my lips over my fangs.

"Yes," I said, keeping my gaze down.

I heard her step closer and the sound of the glass scooting across the stone floor. I looked up to see her kneeling before the bars, pushing it past the barrier. My hand trembled as I grabbed it and pressed it to my lips, gulping at the dark liquid. It hit my tongue first, my jaw clenching from the tang of it before it spilled down my throat.

Dianna just sat and watched me as I fed. My eyes roamed her lean, lithe form, and my stomach growled again. She stared at me, crossing her legs and leaning back on her hands. I fought the desire but couldn't seem to help the way my body reacted. I had never felt a single hint of lust toward Dianna, not once, but I was starving and for more than just food.

"You want to eat me?" she asked, her smile bordering on a smirk.

I finished the blood and lowered the glass. "No," I practically snapped. "Yes . . . No . . . Not like that."

Her smile faded, and worry filled her eyes. "It's okay. It's Thrash, and it's natural. You've been starved, Cameron. He didn't take care of you at all. He turned you into a weapon and left you to pick up the pieces. Your entire being is just reacting to every primal need it has. Don't make it into something it's not."

I nodded, wiping my mouth with the back of my hand and sliding down the wall, sitting on the floor. "Maybe send Samkiel in here to feed me."

"It won't help. You'd still want to feed and fuck him, too."

A snort left my lips. "Who doesn't?"

Dianna's eyes lit up before she tipped her head back and laughed, a full, hearty sound that invited me to join her.

She sighed and sat up, resting her hands against her thighs. "I'll help you as much as I can. Teach you how to feed without killing once we get the last wave of Thrash out of the way. You'll be right as rain or whatever they used to say on Onuna."

I forced a smile and brought my knees up, resting my forearms on them.

"Have you had sex since he turned you?" she asked.

"No."

"Why?"

"Because it's what drove Xavier away in the first place." I felt my chest tighten, and moisture pricked my eyes. "It's what got him caught in the first place. Me and Elianna."

Dianna nodded. "I wondered how Kaden got him."

I swiped the back of my hand across my cheeks. It was the first time I'd talked about it in months. "We had a fight after the party you and Samkiel had. I'd waited too long to tell him how I felt, and Elianna sealed the deal for him. He was going to marry his boyfriend. He told me and left. Then I got a call from him, only it was Kaden. He lured me out, and the rest is . . ." My voice trailed off.

It was quiet for a long moment, and I worried she would blame me now. I glanced up at her and caught the haunted look in her eyes.

She saw me watching her and shook her head, shuttering her expression. "I'm sorry."

"You?" I scoffed and sat up straighter. "I'm sorry for—"

She raised her hand, cutting off my words, and every part of me surrendered. I didn't know if it was because her Ig'Morruthen demanded respect or that she was the embodiment of a queen and stood at Samkiel's side, but I listened. "Don't apologize, Cameron. I've done far worse than you ever have for my sister. I get it. If anyone does, I do."

"Sometimes I think it may be better if I gave in like you did when you lost Gabby," I admitted. The thought had crossed my mind several times in that damn palace of horrors. "Burn the world. Maybe it would all hurt less."

"It wouldn't," she said.

My gaze flicked to hers. "You made it seem like it did."

Dianna ran a hand over her face and sighed deeply before meeting my eyes again. I was worried that my words felt like a slap to her. I hadn't meant for it to seem like I was throwing her past in her face.

"That's different. I was . . . very sad and very lonely, and it was the only thing that helped me feel something, or so I thought. The feeding? Yes, it makes you stronger, but you don't have to be a killer like me. And the sex? It was meaningless. You're right about that. All I did was hurt Samkiel, which you know was my intention. I wanted to drive him away, proving to myself that it was never real, that it never meant anything. I wanted him to hate me like I hated myself, maybe even punish me. All I was doing, though, was lying to myself and trying to bury my feelings. I loved him before Gabby died, and I blamed him and myself for her death. I truly believed my love for him was what killed her. Of course, it wasn't. It was the psychopath that turned you, ruled by another psychopath who wants to rule the realms. So no, it doesn't help."

I studied her, feeling a deep kinship snap into place between us. Dianna understood. "I hate myself."

"Why?"

Words bubbled in my throat, wanting to spill out. They burned and begged for freedom and freedom I would give them. Dianna had to admit so much to heal, and it was time I started.

"Because I got his sister killed."

As soon as those words left my lips, I felt a weight lift off my shoulders. It was as if keeping it to myself for so long had trapped me in a pit of self-hatred. It had been stupid and foolish, putting us all at risk.

Her brows drew together. "What?"

"It was way before The Hand formed, way before I was friends with anyone." I swallowed the growing lump in my throat. "That's my dirty secret, and Kaden used it against me. I got Xavi's sister killed because I stayed out too late. Instead of going on the mission with Athos, I wanted to sleep off my hangover. They sent Kryella and her team instead, and . . . Maybe I was always meant to be Ig'Morruthen. It's the only thing that feels right now, and I guess that's how you feel at times, too."

Dianna held my gaze and said, "I won't lie. I do feel more myself when I turn. Knowing I have the power to protect the ones I loved was a dream come true, and I reveled in it. But, Cameron, you didn't kill his sister. You were young and drunk and wanted to sleep in. So what? You had no idea what would happen, nor could you predict it. Stop blaming yourself, and if you love him, fight for him. Regardless of what happened between you two, I know he would fight for you."

Her words touched on the broken, damaged pieces of me. The ones I covered with humor, laughter, and words to make others happy while I felt like I was dying inside. She was right on some level. I knew that, but I could never forgive myself. Xavier lost the most important person to him, and it was my fault. Maybe he was better off without me. That was why I never told him how I truly felt. How could I? Our whole friendship was built on my guilt. I loved a man who I had damned. I was the definition of fucked up.

I shook my head, wrapping my hands across my knees. "I feel so guilty."

"It wasn't intentional," she said.

"My friendship with him was," I said, wrapping my arms around my legs. Even the pull of the still-healing burns didn't match the pain in my chest. "He was so sad, Dianna. I just wanted to make it better, and I did, but . . . I can never tell him. He'll hate me."

She raised a single brow at me. "Let's save him first, then you decide what he needs to know. But trust me when I say that lying will only hurt you both more."

The corners of my lips lifted in a sad smile. It was so strange to see how much she had changed. She had been a being of pure rage and wrath, and now here she was, comforting me and giving me relationship advice. Samkiel had really helped her, but he had always seen her. He had been right all along. We never knew the real her before she lost her sister. Dianna was always a protector. Now, she had the firepower to back it up.

"Does the speech giving come from you two finally being together?" I asked.

"Maybe." Dianna smiled, one that made her eyes light up and not with the red of her beast, although I suspected her Ig'Morruthen felt the same. But what I saw in her gaze was pure, unadulterated love. "Samkiel's good. He always has been, just like Gabby. They see the good in everyone and everything, and if I say I love them, I have to try to be worthy of them. So, I try every day to live up to the person they see when they look at me. At least a mild attempt. Though the truth is, I am lucky to have known what it means to be loved by them, and I will do anything to protect him."

A smile tugged at my lips. "You've said you love him twice now. Have you guys . . .?"

The atmosphere in the room changed, and the smile that suffused her face was one I had never seen from her before. It was a pure, radiant joy.

"Oh, even better." She lifted her hand and wiggled a single finger. A ring shone there, shining even in the darkened cell. I recognized the stone and knew it was only formed from molten rock. I wondered if he had told her.

"No fucking way." I gasped and jumped to my feet. Ignoring the pain screaming through my every nerve, I stepped closer. "Does that mean what I think it does?"

She nodded and looked at the ring like it meant more than the world to her. "Yes, I lost our amata mark when I brought him back to life."

"What?" I exclaimed.

Dianna waved her hand. "It's a long story. I'll tell you later, but he decided this was the next best thing."

I shook my head, trying to process everything she just told me. "I knew you guys were fucking mates. No one else could handle him, honestly. The man has an ego."

She threw her head back and laughed, and I joined her. Warmth spread across my chest, knowing he had finally found the one thing he had been searching for all his life. A wave of sadness followed because I remembered placing a bet on it with Xavier before everything went to shit. I wished he was here because I just fucking missed him.

She smiled. "You're not wrong about that."

"Where?" I asked, fumbling over the words. I wanted every single detail. We all had wanted Samkiel to be happy, truly happy, and now he finally was. They both were. "Where?"

"We actually had the ceremony here." She glanced around. "I'll show you the rest of the castle when you're free."

"Wait until the others hear. They are going to . . ." I stopped when her smile dropped.

Silence fell, the unspoken truth hanging between us all. I glanced behind her at Logan, who stood in his cell, and then Neverra across from him. Both had their backs straight, their eyes glowing a bright cerulean blue. Neither of them moved, standing like perfect statues.

"Do you think they will come back?"

"Samkiel does." Dianna didn't hesitate, holding my stare. "And I will try my damnedest to make sure they do."

"Thank you." And I meant it so damn much. "For everything."

Dianna nodded, sighing as she stood. She wiped her hands along her sleek black pants. "Yeah, well, that's what family is for, and you said I was a part of yours a long time ago. I won't let you take it back." She smiled once more at me before heading up the stairs.

"She has an armada, Dianna," I called out. "That much I do remember. A fleet large enough to take over every realm, and you're her first priority."

Dianna stopped, and darkness built in the room. "She will find, like so many others, that taking me, army or not, is no easy task." She looked at me over her shoulder, her eyes burning and blazing red. "I fear no gods and no kings."

My smile was brief. "I think she knows that, too."

LXXVIII

Dianna

The door closed with a click behind me, and I heard Cameron settle for the night. It was deep into the night, and the castle was dimly lit, but I didn't need night vision to know a grumpy god was there.

"Eavesdropping, huh?"

Samkiel leaned against the wall, his arms folded. He seemed relaxed, but by the way he held his body, I knew he was pissed. "You're not allowed to feed him alone."

I snorted, not needing my ring to know what he was feeling. His eyes were hard and glittering, and I could read every emotion that flickered in their depths. Yup, definitely grumpy. I grinned before standing on my toes and grabbing the front of his shirt, pulling him down to place a kiss on his lips.

"Are you sure you're not part Ig'Morruthen?" I asked against his lips. "The jealousy and territoriality are identical."

He made a noise in the back of his throat before returning my kiss. I pulled back before we could get carried away and nipped at his lower lip.

"He can't help how he feels," I said. "Don't make this more difficult on him, okay? He was turned, used, and left."

"Like you?" he asked.

I chewed the inside of my lip, thinking of how to word the next part gently. "Not really. Kaden helped me more."

That didn't help. Samkiel bristled, the perfect line of his jaw flexing. "Before or after he asked you to . . . How did you word it? Blow him?" Samkiel said, and I felt the storm in his voice.

I rolled my eyes. "Okay, that was a poorly timed joke. Kaden may be scum and evil incarnate but we . . . He and I . . . We weren't together until after I survived Thrash, and it was always consensual, even if he turned out to be a cheating asshole afterward. It wasn't always like that."

It was the truth, and Samkiel told me that was what he wanted from me, so I'd give it even if it pissed him off. There had been good times between Kaden and me, but they were brief, and the bad far outweighed them.

Samkiel looked away, his jaw clenched. "I like this fantasy I have in my head where you are mine and mine alone, and you have been for centuries."

I couldn't help the small laugh that left my mouth, thinking of a few other fantasies I had shown him. "I like that fantasy too, but if that were true, I wouldn't know how to do that one thing you like so much."

He shrugged with every bit of arrogance and confidence I had come to love so much. He nuzzled my neck, his breath hot against my ear as he whispered, "You'd be surprised. I'm a great teacher."

I snickered and swatted his shoulder, pushing away from him. "Okay, teacher. Now, tell me why you were really eavesdropping. Miss me?"

"Actually, yes," he said, straightening. "But also because Orym sent a message."

Orym and Veruka had taken a few days to heal before they packed and left. It was bittersweet. I knew Orym wouldn't stay once he got his twin back, but Miska took it the hardest. She was so used to having no friends that she latched onto the ones she had made. Orym promised to send her wisps and visit when he could, but I knew those would be few and far between. They were spies and hunted ones at that.

I crossed my arms. "He found something?"

Samkiel nodded. "Yes, he and Veruka both did. I am assuming it's another member of The Hand. I say we both go, but now I'm concerned about Cameron."

I bit my lower lip as I thought about it. "We won't be gone that long. I can bring him another meal before we leave. Even starved, blood like that can last for a full day, two at most."

Samkiel looked at the door, his brow furrowed with worry. "Will he be okay?"

I didn't know which part he truly meant. Physically, yes, he would, but emotionally? That type of healing could take years, and even then, he wouldn't be as he was before. Pain that cut that deeply left scar tissue.

"Yes," I said, knowing he read what crossed my mind even if he did not say it. So I changed the subject. "I think we have a few more weeks before he can practice feeding on others without killing, and yes, before you say anything, I planned for you to come with me for those super fun adventures."

Samkiel grinned, and it took my breath away. "Thank you."

"So what's the plan?"

Samkiel sighed, rubbing at the stubble on his chin. "We meet at a local safe house. I plan to take Miska in case we get into a true fight, and someone is injured. I thought we should take Roccurem as well."

"Why Reggie?" I asked.

"I may love Cameron, but I heard him feed. If, for some reason, he breaks out, I do not wish to leave anyone behind he could feed on. I know he'd burn himself to pieces trying to get to Neverra and Logan."

I nodded in agreement. Thrash was a tricky thing and one I didn't fully understand. I barely remembered my change. The memories were fuzzy until I had it under control.

"Okay, when do we leave?"

"Now."

I sighed and started up the stairs. "I think we are already way overdue for a vacation."

Samkiel was a step behind me, just as he always was. He was my soul given form. It was the only way I could put into words how I felt about him. It was as if a part of me lived in him.

He cleared his throat. "I heard what you said."

"I assumed, given the way you were all puffed up in my defense." I smirked.

"Not just that," he said.

I paused and looked back at him, one foot on the next step. "Everything?"

Samkiel nodded twice.

"Nosy."

"Did you mean it?" Emotions were swirling deep in his eyes. They glowed, but not Otherworldly, not as if he were angry, but with a raw, keening vulnerability, and I knew what he was referring to before he even said his next words. "The part where you said you loved me. Before . . ."

I smiled as I turned to face him fully and stepped down one step so we were eye to eye. I lifted my hand and lightly placed it against his cheek, his stubble rubbing against my palm. In the chaos of everything that had happened to us these last few months and both of us finally admitting what our hearts already knew, I realized I'd never told him. "Samkiel, I have loved you since we left Reggie's vortex, and sometimes, when I think about it, I think I loved you before that too."

Samkiel leaned forward, his lips pressing lightly against mine. It was not a kiss of want or need but of pure love. Even if my body was a hollow, aching thing, if no soul filled its darkness, and the only thing sustaining it was the beating of my heart, he owned every part of it, every part of me.

"You own me as well." He smiled against my lips, pulling back.

I swatted his arm, a small playful pat, and he grinned at me. "I keep forgetting you can read my mind. That's cheating."

He grinned and slipped his hand into mine, leading me upstairs.

"I'm still not used to this," I said, wiggling my fingers around his.

He grinned at me and winked. "It's okay. I'm a great teacher."

I laughed, the sound echoing off the walls and filling our new home.

LXXIX

Camilla

Two days later

My nerves were shot. Even though I knew I had to do it, I still didn't want to. Hilma, Tessa, and Tara watched closely as I held the last piece of the medallion up. They held their breath as I spoke the last incantation. Magic, powerful and fierce, bound our hands, the sparking emerald vines reaching for the pieces. I had a newfound strength and purpose, and I would succeed.

The last piece snapped into place, and a silent explosion detonated in the room. We were all slammed to the ground by whatever force wished for that medallion to stay in a million pieces. I used the table for balance and pulled myself to my feet. Hilma's eyes were huge as she looked at me over the tabletop, her hair sticking up in every direction as Tessa and Tara whopped from the other side of the room.

"You did it," Hilma whispered.

"I did."

I sat on my bed, holding the medallion. The circular cross covered my palm, the ends of each branch flaring to points. At the center, a face was carved into the dark metal, its eyes and mouth wide open and blank. Magic, thick and heavy, pulsed behind it, iridescent swirls against the darkness, reminding me of oil on water. I traced the loops and swirls etched into each leg of the cross. The patterns did not look familiar, but I could tell it wasn't just a random design. I flipped it over, trying to identify the metal, but ended up wondering if it was stone. Either way, it wasn't something I had ever seen. I slid my fingers over the precisely engraved letters, words of a language I did not know.

I looked out the window at the setting sun, tracing the shape of the medallion absently. Hilma had wanted to tell Nismera immediately, but I told her to wait, to give me a day to make sure it wasn't defective and wouldn't crumble. Some of the pieces we had combined had done just that, so it was a valid reasoning.

It was a lie, though. I had another plan, and it helped that Nismera was nowhere to be found. Apparently, she had left. No one knew where she had gone or when she would return, but I assumed she was up to more threats and intimidation. The realms were finally settling into their place and accepting her as their ruler. The witches hadn't heard anything else about the rebels since she burned the East.

The sudden knock on my door startled me from my thoughts, and I hopped to my feet. I tucked the medallion under my pillow and hurried to the door. Vincent grinned at me when I opened it and stepped past me. The door had barely shut before he pulled me into his arms, his mouth covering mine. Warmth like thick syrup flowed through me, pooling low in my belly, but I pulled back, tasting the tension in him. His arms tightened a fraction more as if he feared I would try to break contact with him. I slid my hands over the back of his neck, stroking soothingly, and rested my forehead against his.

"What's wrong?" I asked, nuzzling my cheek against his, careful not to break contact or pull away from him.

He shook his head. "Long day."

"Oh," I said, knowing better than to ask for more details.

He kissed me before stepping back, a sudden bitter cold sweeping between us.

"I did it," I said.

Vincent's eyes went flat. "You finished it?"

I nodded and walked to the bed. I pulled the medallion from the ridiculous hiding spot and hurried back to him. He hadn't moved, but his eyes focused on the medallion. His eyes danced across it before he held his hand out. "Can I?"

I nodded and placed it on his palm. He shivered and said, "Powerful."

"Yes," I agreed. "I have no idea what magic broke it, but putting it back together was nearly impossible."

"But you did it," he said, placing it in his pocket. "Nismera will be happy."

"Yeah." I shook my head. "Only, I don't plan to give it to her. I told Hilma to give me a day to make sure it wouldn't combust and that my magic was strong enough to hold it together. But this is it, Vincent. We take it, and we leave. We can leave now."

"I'm not going anywhere, Camilla," he said, his smile fading. "But you are."

"What?" My heart thudded in my chest, echoing the sound of his boots as he stomped to the door and flung it open. A soldier entered, holding a long, blunt-ended golden trident. Electricity shot from the prongs, wrapping me in a net of sizzling sparks. My body shook, and my magic fizzled as my knees hit the floor.

My eyes widened and filled with tears. "You treacherous snake."

Vincent folded his arms over his broad chest. "I never lied about who I was. You were just too simple to believe it."

"I'll kill you!" I gritted my teeth, sweat beading on every bit of my exposed skin as I tried to summon my magic to fight, but nothing came.

"No," he said as the world drew dark. "No, you won't."

My head lolled to the side as they dragged me by my arms to the floors below the palace. Voices pierced the darkness clouding my mind, and

I blinked, trying to dispel the fog. Commanders and generals lined the perimeter of the room, but she was what I focused on. I knew who the biggest threat was.

Nismera stood in the center of the room next to a stone block, her soldiers surrounding her and a large one-eyed man at her side. His smirk turned my blood to ice as I was dragged toward them, and I saw a hunger that bordered on lust in his gaze. He wore dark gray leather, his collar held tight by a line of buttons, but his arms were completely bare. He held the handle of a large ax in one enormous three-fingered hand. Its edges were worn and caked in dried blood, but the power coming off it sent a frisson of fear down my spine.

The soldiers stopped and yanked me up by my arms as Vincent passed. He didn't even spare me a glance as he walked toward her.

"I heard my medallion is done."

My face heated, and pain twisted inside of me. How much had Vincent told her? Vincent's eyes blazed as he stopped before her and went to one knee, lifting the medallion on one palm in offering. I turned my head away, unable to bear the sight of him handing it over so easily.

"Wonderful," Nismera purred, snatching the medallion from his hand and holding it up to the light, watching the dark magic swirling inside. Nismera looked at Vincent on the floor, her eyes blazing.

"Did you really believe I would not know what happens in my kingdom? I have spies everywhere," she hissed at me.

Nismera snapped the fingers of her free hand, and Vincent rose to stand beside the one-eyed man. My heart slammed against my ribs, and I fought to summon my magic as I heard soft footfalls approaching. Hilma walked in and strode to Nismera's side, completely at ease. Nismera placed the sealed medallion in her hand, and Hilma bowed with a cold smile. She smacked a kiss on her war queen's hand before stepping back, not even looking at me as she left the room.

Nismera took a step closer to me. "And you just became useless. I think it's time to show you what happens when people touch my belongings."

I saw Vincent's throat bob, and my eyes cut to his. He'd told her . . . everything. "Bring her forward. It's time to dispose of my witch."

I didn't whimper, didn't cry, as the guards dragged me toward the block. They yanked my arms in front of me, keeping the net coiled around my body, making me jerk as they sent another wave of electricity through it. I made no move to escape, accepting my fate. Truth be told, I should have died with my coven.

Every legion member stood behind their generals, watching my public punishment. Nismera wanted to make a mockery of this, to have others bear witness to what happens when they are no longer necessary or convenient to her. Most of all, she wanted to hurt me in front of Vincent because of his transgressions. Only he was on her side.

The soldiers lay me across the stone block, pressing my chest to its cold surface.

"Idiots," she hissed. "I want her hands, not her head!"

The soldiers dragged me back and forced me to kneel, placing my wrists on the stone slab. My hands! Oh gods, she wanted to take my magic. My eyes locked with hers, pure panic ripping through me.

"Yes," she said with a smirk, savoring my fear. "I will take your hands, rid you of that precious magic, and watch day in and day out as you suffer. Just like this."

She stepped forward and grabbed Vincent's chin, grinding her mouth over his. I tried to turn away so I didn't have to watch, but the soldiers forced me to remain still. Nismera's tongue darted into his mouth, and he opened to her.

Magic, thick and violent, swirled around my fingertips, and the soldiers gasped. Nismera pulled back with a look of pure pride, happy to have gotten a reaction from me. She finally understood just how strong I was. I kept my gaze focused on Vincent, his image blurring through my tears. He looked worried, but I didn't care. Nismera chuckled and waved the one-eyed man forward. Everyone went silent. The only sound was the scratch of steel being dragged across the dark stone floor. I stared at it, trying to slow my breathing as my executioner hobbled forward. Nismera turned to the room and raised her arms triumphantly, a deep emerald glow beaming from within the medallion.

"As you can see, the final stage in our grand scheme has come to fruition. Here lies the last key before The Rise. And once it is done, these realms, the few that still remain, will have no choice but to kneel to their rightful king. The new world is in our grasp, and so shall end the old."

The cheers and howls of glee died as she turned back to me. Every eye was on me, and suddenly, I was the center of attention.

Nismera clasped her hands around the medallion. "But before that, I need a test of true loyalty because these coming months will be challenging, and the outcome will determine the future."

The executioner stopped, placing the massive serrated ax beneath his scaly chin.

"You, my beloved," she said to Vincent. "This girl is the last tether to your old life. I fear you may slip, and since she has fulfilled her purpose, we do not need any more distractions." Nismera's eyes bored into Vincent's. "You can make up for your transgressions, and then I can forgive you."

My body went rigid as she pulled my head up by my hair. My neck ached with the strain as I glared at Vincent, my hands held tight against the stone.

"I can forgive it all and not have you skewered on a pike outside the city with all those who failed me. Just disarm the witch. I want her hands as a trophy for all to see what happens when they touch what's mine."

Vincent's brow furrowed. "But what of the medallion?" he asked. "What if her magic is volatile, and it cracks before the ritual?"

A hush washed over the room as Nismera smiled. Everyone knew she was at her most dangerous when she smiled. "Don't worry about that, pet. One celestial event, and it will be of no worry any longer. She finished just in time. Seven more moons, and the merge happens. We have plenty of time."

A cool calm smoothed Vincent's face, and I swallowed. That was why she had pushed so hard. She needed another celestial event, just as with Samkiel's death.

I stared at Vincent. Acceptance was a bitter taste in my mouth, but I was okay. This was a fate I thought I deserved after helping Kaden for so long. I deserved to be punished for what I'd done to Dianna, to the world. Nismera released my hair, stepping toward Vincent for a better view of my humiliation.

"Now take her hands," Nismera whispered, placing her hand on his shoulder. "I command you."

A sick and twisted realization hit my gut, but I swallowed it. Vincent turned back toward me, and Nismera took his silence as compliance, waving the executioner over. He stopped a mere inch away from Vincent and handed him the ax. Vincent took it, and a small breath left my lips. I bowed my head, the thick brown waves of my hair spilling around me, blocking my view of the world. My body slumped with resignation, my arms stretched tight, and my palms lifted as if in supplication. I curled my fingers once more, feeling the heat of the emerald glow one last time before I lost my hands and my magic forever.

Vincent and I were pawns. Both of us sought punishment for our betrayal of those who had loved us, for what we helped orchestrate, and in the process, we allowed ourselves to be used to commit even worse crimes.

The room went deadly silent as Vincent's armored boots drew near, and my pounding heart skipped a beat. I heard him grunt, and then steel sliced through the air with a nearly musical whistle. I closed my eyes tight, and I swore I heard him whisper, "I'm sorry."

The sound of metal rending flesh and steel hitting stone rang through the silent room. Pain shattered my mind, and I screamed.

Kaden

Screams echoed from the blood-soaked battlefield below. The coin flipped between my fingers as the last of the Di'llouns fought for their small village. The armored shells along their backs offered no defense after Nismera supplied her soldiers with weapons that carried a touch of her godly light. It was just a tiny amount, not enough to burn the user to ash, but strong enough that any who came up against them would match the dirt they fought on. I watched from atop a rock jutting out from a small cliff.

"What is that?" a deep voice next to me asked.

My fist closed over the coin, and I turned toward Bash. He stood eye level with me, the quills on top of his head quivering as he eyed my hand.

"Nothing."

He quirked a brow, holding the collar of his armor. "Seems like something. You fondle that damn thing every day."

"What a shame," I said, watching another small beam of light rip apart a few rebels. "Nismera lost one of her favorite generals in a waste of a place like Di'lloune."

Bash's barking laugh could be heard even over the sounds of battle. He shrugged. "Just a question."

"Drop it," I said with a sneer.

He held his hands up, the small quills along their backs flaring too. "Okay, okay."

Sighing, I turned back, watching the dust lift above the battlefield, the memory refusing to be denied.

"You kept it?" Her voice caught me off guard, and I looked up. How well she had adapted that she could sneak up on even me now.

I fisted the coin and slid the dark stone plate under a stack of scrolls before pushing to my feet. Dianna stood there with a smile on that devastatingly perfect face, holding a bag in her hand.

"You're back a day early," I said.

Her face scrunched. "No, I'm not. You told me a week, and it's been a week. Unless you want me to go back?"

I hadn't realized I'd moved until I was in front of her, blocking the door. Her smile grew.

I hated that, hated how I reacted to her. She was not supposed to be here, smiling and looking at me like that, touching me as she did. She did not belong to me, and as Nismera had said only moments earlier, she was supposed to be dead. My blood should have made her a beast like the others, but I would be lying if I said I wasn't upset that she had survived intact. She had awakened, and I had become utterly attached in the months she had been here. It was becoming a problem. Was I so starved for the smallest affection that even a smile made me want to crumble?

She was not mine.

The words echoed in my head, but I'd keep her, regardless. I just needed to figure out how to eradicate the false king before he found her.

"Do you want to do something?" she asked, shaking me from my thoughts.

"What?"

"Just us." Her hand landed on the dark fabric of my tunic. "No Tobias or Alistair around to make snide comments they think I don't hear."

"Why?"

She laughed, the sound brushing over my skin like a caress. "You've never had a friend, have you?"

"What would we do?"

Her shoulders lifted. "I've never been out of Eoria my whole life. Now we're on this island for however long. Show me around. Maybe I'll find you a new, less bloody coin."

Dianna's hand brushed mine, and I tightened my fist around it. "No, I like this one."

Her hands stayed on mine, and she looked at me as if I were something worth looking at, but she did not know me, not truly. She did not know the evil deeds I had done in the name of vengeance because our father had wished Isaiah and me dead. Yet a touch or smile from her and that hollow aching pit inside me hurt a bit less.

"Okay," I said, eager to see what pleasure she would show me next.

The sound of a portal closing behind me shook me from my thoughts. Bash looked behind me, but I didn't need to see his expression to know who had arrived. I knew the feel of my brother as well as I knew my reflection.

"We're ready," he said.

I glanced toward Isaiah as he shook the blood from his armored hands. "It's done?" I asked.

Annoyance sparked in his gaze. We both had things that set us off. Mine, of course, was abandonment. Isaiah hated to be tricked or lied to. He had handled the situation in his usual fashion. His methods were what had earned him his reputation, and he did nothing to dispel the fear it instilled.

Isaiah leaned close to the edge of the cliff and looked down at the battle raging below. "Do you think you can handle the rest of them?" he asked Bash.

Bash's grin turned feral, and his helmet flowed over his head in a slither of metal. He gave us a single nod that was just a bit too low, looking like a shallow bow, before jumping into the fray. The harrowing screams erupted tenfold, and more dirt shot skyward. Bash flattened a path through the Di'llouns every way he turned. It was another reminder of why he was one of Nismera's favorites.

"Are you ready?" Isaiah asked again.

I nodded and took one last look at the coin in my hand, running my thumb over the worn sides and the line across the center. I placed it in my pocket before turning with my brother. He ripped another portal open, and I followed, leaving the crashing city of Di'lloune in smoke and embers.

XCI

Nismera

The crowd parted, creating a clearing as I landed the massive ryphor. Dust blew as its mighty body whipped and curled before coming to a stop. Several guards still hovered above me, keeping the perimeter secured.

"The legion," I heard someone whisper and saw a mother slap her hand across her whispering child's face.

Others landed and dismounted as I jumped to the ground. The whispers died, people clinging to their loved ones. Shops didn't dare close their doors or windows, afraid to draw my attention to them. Gods above, I loved the smell of fear. It was almost as intoxicating as my other favorite indulgence.

I removed my helmet, my hair spilling down my back as I placed it on the saddle.

"He's still here," my lead commander said, and a smile bloomed across my face.

"Excellent."

We moved as one, a whole legion behind me, shuffling down the road. Those who did not move out of the way of my army were shoved to the side, elbowed, and kicked. People murmured and stared, watching to see where we were going, making sure we weren't coming toward them.

I loved the control I had over the realms. I had built the fear from the ground up and secured my own crown. This was paradise to me. To me, this was peace. I would never again be beneath another as I had been so many eons before. I finally had the crown and throne I deserved, and I'd be damned if I allowed anyone or anything to take it from me. The Eye would fall. They couldn't hide forever, and today I was taking the next step in flushing them out. I was here to cut off their supply of weapons.

The alleyway was rank and filthy, and I curled my lip as I walked down it. I heard the click of locks before I even rounded the corner. Murmured moans turned to whispered shouts and then the sound of scurrying feet. These people lived like vermin, and I thought about just exterminating them all.

I flicked my wrist, and the golden-tipped spear appeared in my hand. My guards and commander stepped back. I aimed it at the door and pushed my power through it, leaving a gaping hole where the door had been. I stepped into the brothel and the screaming began.

XCI

Dianna

The wind died in a swirling mass of littered trash as the portal closed behind us. Miska adjusted the straps of her bag around her shoulders, holding the small compass Orym had given her. My eyes darted toward Samkiel as he pulled the hood a bit tighter around his head. All of us had dressed to blend in amongst the citizens of the small industrial town.

Samkiel nodded toward me and gave me a ghost of a smile, once again reading the worry that fluttered across my mind.

"*Would you even tell me the truth if you were not okay?*" I asked through our bond.

"I'm fine. I swear."

But I knew it was a half lie. Now, I could not only hear Samkiel's thoughts if I tried, but I could feel him, too. I felt the weight on his shoulders, the apprehension of us being here, and above all, the wave of exhaustion that swept through him as the portal closed. He had been using far too much power, pushing himself past his limits for weeks. With his power spread across the sky, he wasn't as strong and burned out quickly.

He fell into a deep sleep every night, exhaustion pulling him under. He didn't even stir when I got up to use the bathroom, and I'd caught him nodding off during the day. My eyes dropped to his side, but he waved me off and clasped my hand in a firm grasp.

We walked out of the alley, blending in with the crowd as they shopped or looked for somewhere to eat. We rounded a corner and stopped, Samkiel nodding at a building up ahead, three guards chatting outside the door. Miska lingered behind us, pretending to find interest in a shop window. We started forward again, Reggie walking a few paces ahead of us as we passed the small cottage-style home.

Reggie pretended not to be able to hold his liquor. "You'll pay your due!" he yelled, drawing attention. The crowd parted around him, not stopping, but giving him a wide berth. Samkiel and I stepped to the side and stopped. Two of the guards glanced at him, one elbowing the third. While all eyes were on the drunken man walking toward them, we moved in behind them.

Samkiel towered over the man as he wrapped his hand around his throat. He pulled the guard back against him and applied pressure, the man going limp in his arms. His friend spun and opened his mouth to yell, but my fist shot out. I heard bones crunch, and the whites of his eyes flew upward as he fell backward. Samkiel looked at me, still holding the limp guard in his arms, and I shrugged. His eyes widened a fraction as the third guard charged at me from behind, but I spun and raised my foot, the kick catching him in the chest. His body sailed through the front door.

"I said quietly!" Samkiel hissed at me.

"This is quiet to me," I hissed back.

Someone roared behind us. Several guards within the small room saw us and turned to run. Samkiel tossed his unconscious guard inside, knocking a few of them off their feet. I followed him inside, closing the half-broken door behind me.

Reggie moved the last guard into the small closet, and I tried and failed to shut the door twice. A stupid boot was in the way. I leaned down, moving it inside before finally shutting it with a click.

I stood, wiping my hands on my pants. Miska headed down a small hall, and we followed after her. Samkiel stood by a desk covered in sheets of parchment and scrolls. A heavy, odd-shaped paperweight held a thick, worn page down on one side, and Samkiel's hand held the other edge. He ran his index finger over it, his head jerking up as we entered.

"Orym was right," Samkiel said. "This was a small meeting, but this is just a diagram of the water supply system here and in the neighboring town. There are also a few scrolls listing places they grow crops and some information about a shipping company. It's a lot."

"That's good, right?"

"Yes." He nodded. "It would be if I had more manpower to spread. I'd never make it to all of these in time. She seems intent on cutting off supply chains. These places nearby are ones that hang in between long treks. The Eye may depend on them to feed their soldiers."

"If," I interjected, "if she still keeps at it. If we have them, she may change plans."

His eyes searched mine. "That does not make me feel any better."

"No, but this map." I came around the desk to stand beside him, gazing down at it. "This gives you an advantage and gives us a peek at how her brain works. It also tells us what posts she is interested in."

He smiled and swept his hand across my hair. I felt that warm feeling spread across my skin as he looked at me with pride, or maybe it was just pure, unbridled affection. Regardless, I didn't care.

"See." I smiled up at him. "I'm more than just a pretty face."

Samkiel chuckled, but it was short-lived as the small device in his pocket vibrated. He pulled it out, the round, dark circle beeping. He placed it on the table, and two lightly shimmering images appeared.

"Samkiel," Orym greeted. "Did you find it?"

Samkiel reached back and grabbed the nearby chair, pulling it close as he sat.

"Yes," Samkiel said. "I found a map and a few pieces of information regarding Havrok Bay and shipments. I can look at the rest tomorrow once we are home."

"Perfect, but you're going to love this," Veruka piped in, taking up more of the shadowy image. "We're at a bar off the coast of Ravinne.

Two commanders just landed on the outskirts with a crate. We think they are carrying weapons and taking a quick break before returning to her."

Samkiel sat up a bit straighter, casting me a look. I nodded, and he turned back to them.

"Okay, perfect. You two stay there to make sure they don't leave. Dianna and I will be there shortly."

Orym and Veruka agreed to stay put before disappearing back into that device. Samkiel gathered the pages he'd found before turning to me.

"I have an idea," I said.

"No," he responded before moving around the desk.

"You didn't let me finish."

"I already know what you are going to say, and it's a no."

I tossed my hands up and followed him from the room. He made it to Miska and Reggie before I caught up with him.

"Listen, it will take me less time to get the weapons. You won't be seen, and I can bring them back here. Besides, if they are so concerned about the water, maybe we need to make sure they haven't already tried to poison it or interrupt the supply."

Samkiel and Reggie looked at me, the muscles in Samkiel's jaw working.

"Listen, if the bond works off a strong emotional connection, we will be fine. I'm just a thought away." The line in Samkiel's jaw flexed again, and I raised my hand. "I can handle a crate of weapons, and besides, Veruka and Orym will be there."

Samkiel's eyes bore into mine. "I don't like the idea of us splitting up. It never works in our favor."

Reggie tipped his head toward Samkiel in agreement.

"Hey, stay out of this," I snapped at Reggie, but the fate feigned innocence.

Samkiel shook his head once more. "I don't approve, akrai. I know you're strong, but Nismera has been on a rampage. We have already witnessed her setting traps for you at the war camp. This is just another. We will figure something else out."

"These are weapons we are talking about. We already saw what she did in the East. What if what she is shipping back is something far larger and worse?" I said. "What if we don't have another chance?"

"Who is to say we will not?" Samkiel asked, growing a tad agitated.

"Think of it as an aalxat's nest."

His brow flicked up.

I waved my hand. "Okay, or some other stingy insect from your world. Regardless, she has a nest, and we have kicked it. Now, all her guards are spilling out to find out where that kick came from. We need to act while they are out and before they go back, regroup, and make an even stronger nest."

The room went silent, and I feared my analogy had gone over all their heads.

Samkiel sighed, his fingers gripping the bridge of his nose. He dropped his hand and glared at me. I bit my lower lip, knowing I'd won.

"If," he paused as if the words were difficult to get out, "if you do this, you leave before the sun sets tonight. I doubt they will stay at the station for long. You go in, take them, and leave. If it even looks like a trap, come back immediately. Do you understand?"

"Yes." I smiled, hope beaming in my chest. If these crates had even the smallest form of weapons or parts, it would give us some insight into what she was truly making. The East was floating rocks now, and the nets that had managed to capture me had freaked both Samkiel and me out. If she had the power to make something that large and powerful, enough to cut an Ig'Morruthen into ribbons, I was growing more concerned about what else she had.

He held up a single finger. "No unnecessary fighting and no unnecessary risks."

I raised my hand, extending my pinky. "I promise. Besides, I'm meeting Orym and Veruka there. I'm not going alone."

His nostrils flared. "I mean it, Dianna."

"*Stop clenching your jaw before you break a tooth,*" I whispered in his head.

"*It will just grow back.*"

"I'll be fine. The first sign of danger, and I'm running straight to you. Promise." I wiggled my pinky finger at him, speaking that part out loud.

His eyes softened, and he raised his hand, his pinky finger wrapping around mine briefly. Still, I felt his apprehension and worry slide into my mind. *"I just hate being away from you."*

My heart fluttered, and I watched as he squared his shoulders, finally giving up the fight.

"No aerial flight." He pointed again, and my smile grew a tad bit more. "I do not trust her not to use those nets at every location. Only fly when I am with you."

"Okay." I smiled, knowing how protective he was. It had only increased tenfold since he had gotten me back, and I wasn't complaining in the slightest. It was nice to be loved, after all.

"And you will keep in contact with me the entire time." He nodded toward my hand, and my gaze dropped to my ring.

I twisted the precious piece around my finger. "Will it work that far away?"

"It should, as long as you don't remove it. It is bound to both of us."

XCIII

Dianna

Samkiel watched me until the portal closed, and all I could do was shake my head. Overprotective godly bastard. I loved him.

I crossed the street to the small bakery where I was supposed to meet Orym and Veruka, my boots tapping against the cobblestones. It had the perfect view of the docks. The door opened as I approached, and I waited for the man to exit before I stepped in. The small woman behind the counter nodded to me, but one glance told me Orym and Veruka were not there. I looked out the window toward the docks but didn't see any ryphors either.

"Excuse me," I asked the owner. "I'm looking for two of my friends. Have you seen them? About this tall, pointed ears, elves?"

"Oh, yes." She beamed and put the finishing touches on a display behind the counter. "They were in here earlier. They chatted together for a moment before leaving. I saw them head that way," she said, pointing toward the docks.

"Okay, thanks," I said, forcing a smile. My gut was telling me something was not right.

I took one last look at the woman as she waddled, one hand on her growing stomach, toward another glass case of sweets. She didn't smell dead. Some parts of me would never stop looking over my shoulder for

Tobias. I also didn't detect the stench of a lie coming from her. Okay, perhaps it wasn't a trap.

The door behind me closed with a creak as I pulled my hood higher on my head. The cobblestone was rough and uneven as I pressed forward. A reflection of small eyes caught my attention, and I looked up. There, on a broken sign, a bird made of midnight sat watching me. Its beak was as dark as its feathers, and its body was as long as my forearm. I inhaled deeply, but no scent flowed to my nose. My eyes narrowed. It was not a shifter. The lack of scent proved that. I hissed, baring my fangs at the creature, and it took flight, disappearing into the night. I shook my head and continued toward the docks.

The moon hung far closer here than in other worlds, covering most of the horizon and ringed by rocks. It was quiet on the docks, with no sign of anyone, and I could only smell a hint of the ryphors. I stopped short when I saw a dagger embedded in a pier post. I ripped away the paper it was holding in place and read.

Meeting changed to Torkun. Hurry, they decided this place wasn't good enough for a rest. Left a transporter for you under the pier.

Orym

I crumpled up the note and incinerated it with a small flash of my flames. Grabbing the edge of the pier, I slipped over the side and gripped the worn wood with one hand. I saw one of the gauntlet transporters tucked under a beam and grabbed it with my free hand. With a soft grunt, I swung my legs and propelled myself back up.

I walked back up the hill. The mud clinging to my boots caused me to slip when I hit the slick cobblestones. I flipped the latch on the gauntlet open, and runes burst into the air, surrounding a small circular map. A red dot flashed, pinpointing my destination. Orym, you beautiful elf, you already set the coordinates.

My finger paused over the button to send me. I knew I needed to tell Samkiel I was changing locations, but he would only show up, protesting he needed to go with me. Realistically, I needed to do this alone. I had to show him that we couldn't do every mission together, and I'd be okay without him at my side. We could not save the world while connected at the hip. These realms were far too vast. I took one last look at my wedding ring and pressed the button.

The gauntlet hissed in my hand, and I shook it, the top sparking and sizzling. I looked closer and saw a small dent and a crack. It must have gotten damaged when Orym and Veruka stole it. Luckily, I had made it to Torkun before it gave out, but I hadn't realized how far this planet was. It was definitely a pit stop between worlds.

A ryphor's cry rent the air, and my head shot up. The beast hovered beside a tavern. I didn't see the box of weapons, but I figured Orym and Veruka had to be nearby. Chucking the gauntlet into the trash, I pulled the hood of my cloak up and strode toward the small building.

"Everything okay?"

I jumped, damn near squealing as I whirled, expecting to see Samkiel behind me.

"Gods, I still have to get used to that," I responded.

His laugh floated through my head. *"Are you all right?"*

"Yes," I said, stopping just outside the tavern. I didn't know if he would be able to hear the music, but I didn't want to take any chances. *"What music?"*

"Uh, there's a band," I said. *"In town. Weird, right?"*

"Yes, actually."

I hummed in my head as if I were listening to the music, hoping it would drown out my other thoughts. *"Everything is fine. I need to concentrate, though. I found the ryphors. Now, I just need their weapons. I'll check in as soon as I have them."*

Samkiel was silent, and I swore I could hear him thinking. *"Five minutes."*

"What?" I mentally snapped, stepping closer to the door.

"Check in with me in five minutes, or I'm on my way."

"Oh, my gods."

"Tick-tock."

My eyes rolled as I smiled and pushed him out before storming into the tavern. I'd have to hurry because I knew Samkiel meant what he said. Music, smooth and smokey, filled the room. People sat around small tables, some drinking, some just talking and laughing. Everyone seemed to be having a good time.

I stood on my tiptoes, glancing around a few taller beings, trying to spot my elf companions. I didn't see them, and my lips twisted to the side. Fuck. Where were they? I absently side-stepped a stumbling drunk, half pushing him out of my way. My gaze restlessly roamed the tavern. My instincts were screaming at me, but there were no soldiers here that I could see, and I couldn't locate the danger. Everything here seemed exactly what you would expect from a place like this.

"Can I help you, miss?" a voice asked over the chatter and music.

I turned to see a green, spiky-headed bartender wiping at the bar.

"Yes," I said, sliding into an empty seat. "I'm looking for my friends. Have you seen them?" I raised my hand as I spoke. "Tall girl and guy, kinda look alike? Pointed ears and tails?"

He looked down the bar as someone yelled for him. He held his finger up before grinning at me. "One second."

I sighed and leaned against the bar as I waited.

"Anything?"

"You know, I didn't know gods were so protective," I murmured, glancing around the busy tavern.

"It's been five minutes."

I turned on my stool and looked around the room. A bathroom sign flashed in the corner, portraying images of beings washing their hands.

"They are in the bathroom. I have not been kidnapped or maimed, and all your favorite bits are in place."

He chuckled. *"All right."*

"Talk to you in five more minutes, you worrywart."

A deep rumble vibrated through me before the warmth of our connection faded, and I was alone in my head again.

I turned back toward the bar, looking at the array of clear and multicolored bottles on the back wall. The bartender returned and dropped a platter down in front of me. Blood dripped from the edges, the scent nearly overwhelming. Veruka and Orym's heads lay atop it, their eyes drawn back and mouths agape as if they'd died screaming.

"Is this what you were looking for?" the bartender asked with an amiable smile.

My stool clattered as I jumped up from my seat. A chill raced across my spine. The oracle's sick, wet laugh mocked me. *I wouldn't follow her, headless boy, or you'll have a twin to match.* And match they did. My eyes darted to the smiling bartender as I shook my head slowly. "That is not what I'm looking for."

A deep voice a few steps down asked, "You sure you're not looking for the two-for-one special?" He sipped at the blood in his glass, and a sound of contempt left his lips. "A liar and a traitor?"

He resembled Samkiel and Kaden so much you'd have to be ignorant not to know he was their brother. I felt so dumb for not seeing the resemblance between Kaden and Samkiel sooner. Their demeanor, arrogance, over-the-top cockiness, and the enormous egos that made them believe that nothing living or dead could touch them.

"So, what's your superpower? Are you like Alistair? Mind control an entire city to do your bidding?"

He held up a pure emerald stone. "Witches, actually."

He crushed the stone in his fist, and the room flashed. All the beings that had been chatting, dancing, drinking, and laughing now lay dead. Pieces of them splattered across the walls and bar as if they had exploded from the inside out. The blood he drank looked like it had come from the bartender, who was half slumped in the seat next to him.

"It's a glamour," he said, lifting his glass and taking another drink. He pointed with the same hand toward the platter. "Except them, of course. They've been dead for hours."

My heart thudded, and I took a step back, sliding a bit on the blood-slicked floor.

He stared at me, his tongue sliding over his teeth. He watched me as a predator would prey before it went in for the kill. "So you're her? We haven't been properly introduced. I am Isaiah. I didn't get a good look at you when you stormed in and caused all kinds of chaos before running away with the corpse of my little brother."

My fists clenched at my sides, nails biting into my palms.

Isaiah was suddenly on his feet and invading my space. My head tipped back as he stared down at me. His gaze moved over me from head to toe, not in lust but in clear disappointment.

"This is what you'd risk everything for? Where is the rest of her?" he asked, his eyes dropping to my chest. "She barely has any tits."

My skin prickled, and my breathing quickened at the familiar sound of those boots against the floor, the measured steps I had conditioned myself to listen for. One step, then another, and every cell in my body went on high alert.

"She makes up for it in other places."

Kaden.

My body trembled, the Ig'Morruthen in me thrashing and biting. It wanted to crawl to the surface and rip him to pieces for every single thing he had done, everything he had taken from me, but the rational part of my brain, the part Samkiel had trained, told me to wait and calculate my odds first. They lured me here to this desolate planet for a reason, and the fact that both of them were here meant they had no intention of leaving without me.

I turned toward him, the very bane of my existence. I forced myself to relax, refusing to let him see that every cell in my body was on high alert. They hadn't come alone. A handful of his generals fanned out behind him. I forced a smile. Holding my hands out to my sides, I spun, noting every window and door. "I've got to say it was smart to drag me so far away, Kaden. Were you worried I'd torch a place you like?" I stopped and smirked at him. "I'm flattered, really."

I angled my body and clasped my hands behind my back, slipping my ring off and placing it into my pocket. Samkiel couldn't know what was going on here. He wasn't healed, and if he showed up, not only would he be in danger, but they would know he was alive. They would go straight to Nismera with that information, and she couldn't know. Not yet.

Kaden leaned against the door frame, a small smirk on his face revealing just a hint of his dimple. How could such an evil creature like him have a dimple? It just wasn't right. "I'll admit, I truly underestimated you through the years, but after everything, I won't make that mistake again. No one will."

"Good."

Isaiah sighed, and I felt him shift behind me. "So, how does this go? You come quietly, or we take you screaming?"

I squared my shoulders and stepped forward, my words laced with venom. "Oh, baby, you couldn't make me scream on your best day."

Flame engulfed my hand, and I reared back, slamming the fireball into his face. Isaiah yelped and lunged away as Kaden charged.

One thing about battle was that you learned a few things if you did it long enough. If you faced the same opponent enough times, you started to remember their tells. Kaden taught me how to survive. Samkiel taught me how to live, and now I would do everything in my power to make sure Samkiel did both. I grabbed Kaden by his arm and bent. Twisting my body, I tossed him over the bar.

Isaiah ran at me, and I squared my feet. His fist shot out, and I leaned back, dodging the punch and landing one of my own against his chin. He was quick, both of them were. The guards joined the chaos, but they were easily disposed of. Arms, throats, anything I could touch, I ripped, painting the room red.

"Hold her if you get her!" Kaden screamed. But he was such a fool if he thought anything would keep me here. I growled, sinking my fangs deep into a guard who had charged at me. I tore out his neck and then used his body as a wrecking ball, tossing it toward them. Kaden and Isaiah came at me with a melee of kicks and punches. I blocked almost as many as I took, but all of my strikes bounced off of that damned armor.

Fuck.

I wasn't going to win this by beating on them. I would have to carve them out of that fucking armor, and I didn't have the time. My mind cycled through my possibilities, and I scanned the room, looking for a weapon. I dodged a kick from Isaiah. Perfect. I faked a slip. He lunged, intent on grabbing me when I was unbalanced. I allowed myself to fall, and planting my foot in his gut, I let his momentum aid me in tossing him through the tavern wall. The lights flickered as he hit a support beam with a hollow thud. I scrambled to my feet and spun to face Kaden. He curled his fingers at me, beckoning me closer.

"Come on, pretty girl. It's been a while since I had an actual romp."

"You're disgusting," I sneered.

"You'd know."

"Your obsession with me is getting a little out of hand, don't you think?" I taunted as Kaden tossed a fist at me. I caught it and slammed the bottle I'd picked up off the floor across his face. He stumbled back but recovered quickly.

He smiled and ran his hand under his bleeding nose. "Not an obsession. Love."

"I'm in a room with dead bodies, but that comment alone makes me want to barf."

"Stop fucking around!" Isaiah yelled from the broken rubble. "Stab her so we can go home."

Stab me? I stepped away from Kaden. He smiled and unsheathed a glowing dagger.

I snickered, my fear draining away. "Typical Kaden. I've been stuck by bigger."

"Doubtful." He grinned.

Isaiah crawled out of the hole his body had made in the wall. I pivoted to keep them in sight, waiting for their next move.

"This blade will fix everything, Dianna. No more blind hatred or broken heart."

I looked closer at the dagger, and my breath hitched. It wasn't just some glowing artifact to scratch his ego. No, that blade was drenched in magic. Magic made to . . .

"Are you fucking kidding me?"

Kaden shook his head. "I can make it all go away. You won't remember anything. I can make you love me again."

My lip curled back, and I hissed, my fangs forming. "What we had was not love. You can't love and treat each other the way we did. You know nothing of that word."

"That is a lie. I know I miss you."

My eye caught on Isaiah as he took one step to the right, just as Kaden moved to the left. I adjusted, keeping them both in my line of vision. Kaden was trying to distract me and get close enough to touch.

Kaden shifted his grip on the hilt of the blade. "I know that I still care, and no matter what I've tried, I cannot remove you from my fucking veins. You're it, Dianna. You always have been."

"You killed my sister." I spat the words at him like acid, keeping my fists raised between us. "You killed my amata, and now you want to erase the memories of the only man I ever loved?"

"We had something," Kaden snapped. "You and I. No one is here but us now. You cannot deny it."

"Deny it?" I scoffed. "You are the epitome of a walking contradiction. Of course you'd beg me to come back after I finally destroyed every ounce of feelings I ever had for you. We had something? Maybe eons ago. I tried. You pushed me away. Actually, you quite literally gave up on me."

"I had to," Kaden practically screamed at me. Isaiah watched him, his eyes blinking rapidly at Kaden's confession. "You know everything now. The whole truth. Why I acted the way I did, why I had to . . ."

"Say it!" I snapped. "Tell me why you had to kill her, rip her from me, or how about you explain why it was okay for you to use her to make me obey you. Huh? Say that part."

Kaden's jaw worked, but he didn't explode in anger like I expected. "I can erase it. The pain you felt, the pain you have. We can go back to how it was before everything."

"You mean when you forgot every birthday I ever had? Or when you couldn't even remember what food I absolutely hate? What about my favorite color, huh? The places I love to visit? My most precious memories. What makes me laugh, Kaden? What makes me smile? What makes me cry? You don't know because you weren't there. You never were. There is no *us*. No happy moments or love, because I was nothing more than your puppet. A weapon you pointed and used. There was nothing. There is nothing. *You. Are. Nothing. To. Me.*"

The room shifted, and so did my form, my hands dropping to my sides. I was tired of this game, tired of him. By the old gods and new, I was no longer the scared girl who held back but a queen born of darkness, flame, and anger.

"And now I am going to rip you both to pieces for what you've done, and when you wake up on the other side, hopefully writhing in agony, you'll finally understand that I have not an ounce of love for you."

A ghost of a smile twisted Kaden's lips. "No matter. You will be mine. I taught you how to fight to survive. You are not trained in war."

"You did." I nodded, bracing my feet. "But I've learned a lot since I left you." I hoped my eyes burned with as much hate as I felt. "Only one of us is leaving this place. And it will be me."

"You always were a dreamer." Kaden tossed the blade before placing it back in its sheath.

I knew Kaden sensed what I was about to do and saw him look at Isaiah. I grinned and tossed a ball of flame at him. He dodged, stepping to the side, and the next one sailed for Isaiah. He ducked, and the wall behind him exploded.

Claws slid from my fingers, and I roared a challenge as my beast surged to the surface. Kaden and Isaiah changed between one breath and the next. The building erupted as we took to the skies, all teeth and wings and unbridled hatred. The sky was lit with flames and ash, the ground trembling beneath the weight of our fury.

XCIV

Samkiel

It's fine. Everything is fine. I repeated the words to myself, running my fingers over the thick band of my ring. Perhaps it was the loss of her soul that had spurred this overprotectiveness. Or perhaps I had always been this way with her. I hated being apart from her for any length of time. Something terrible always seemed to happen. I sighed and gripped my ring, closing my eyes as I ran my thumb and forefinger over it. It had been longer than five minutes since I reached out this time. I just needed to hear her voice across my mind, and then I'd be fine . . . at least for another five minutes.

I pulled on our connection but was stopped by a thick wall. My eyes snapped open, my blood running cold. There was nothing there. No spark or tingle across my subconscious. No warmth. She'd taken her ring off. My heart pounded, terror gripping me. I knew there was only one reason she would do so. It meant she was in danger, and she thought she was keeping me safe.

Damn stubborn woman.

"Roccurem!" I bellowed, and he immediately formed in the room. I was already on my feet and pulling on my coat.

"Yes, my—"

His words died on shattered glass and broken wood. The windows erupted into the room, and we both looked down as the small devices came to rest on the floor. They beeped once before exploding into a cloud of piercing white noise and deep gray smoke.

My ears rang as I sat up, my chest heaving. I coughed, trying to clear my lungs, and rubbed my eyes. My vision cleared, and the world came rushing back. Sound returned as my ears healed, and the first thing I heard clearly were the screams. I pushed a large wooden support beam off me and started shifting the stone, trying to dig myself out.

"Secure the fate," I heard someone say. "She needs it whole."

I stilled and lifted my head. The fate? They were here for Roccurem.

Smoke filled the room in a thick haze, but I could make out the shine of gold and black armor. Nismera's soldiers. Fuck. They had found us, which meant this was all a setup. I pushed from the rubble and lunged to my feet, several of those golden helmets turning toward me. One soldier held chains that shimmered with silver power. They were wrapping them so tightly around Roccurem that I was glad the fate didn't need to breathe to live.

"Who—"

I kicked him across the room, watching as he hit the wall and lay still. My back erupted in pain, and I hissed before spinning. The soldier held his sword to his side, already preparing for another attack. I darted forward, and we met in the middle. He raised the blade, and I grabbed his wrist, twisting until I felt his bones snap. His sword fell, and I snatched it out of the air before it could hit the ground. His eyes dilated a fraction as he witnessed my speed. One swipe, and I sliced his head clean off.

The air moved behind me, and I shifted my weight to kick out, catching the charging soldier in the stomach. His body slammed against the wall, and I chucked the sword at him so hard it pierced his chest plate. The force of the blade held him impaled against the wall.

I squinted. It was still too hazy to see clearly, and from the sounds Roccurem was making, those chains were also designed to hurt him. Fuck. Footsteps echoed, and I dropped to the floor as two soldiers swung their blades toward my head. Summoning an ablaze dagger, I swept my leg out in a low kick, taking both men to the ground and stabbing them through the neck.

Roccurem was coughing and moaning when I reached him, his skin fluttering as his form begged to be released from the shell he wore. I hauled him over my shoulder and ran out the door without bothering to look back. He coughed as I jumped the stairs, landing in a crouch.

Shouts came from above, various cries for backup, which meant I only had a few minutes to get out of there and find Dianna.

"Miska," I muttered. "Where was she?"

Roccurem coughed again. "Study."

"Okay," I said. "This is going to hurt, but once you get the chains off, find Dianna. She's in danger."

Without waiting for his response, I tossed him through the broken door and into the empty shop building across the street, away from the smoke. Perhaps I was helping him, or perhaps I was still mad about how much he had kept from me, the secrets he had shared with my wife. Above the chaos, I heard him land and take a deep breath, sighing in relief, not pain.

I started toward the study door behind the staircase but stopped when guards pounded down the stairs.

"While my first instinct is to beat you all until you explain how you found us and this place." I gathered power in my palm. "I have more important things to worry about."

I lifted my hand, and a blast of wind slammed into them. As strong as any violent storm, it twisted the soldiers in a circle. A tornado of gold armor and debris spun, held in place by my power. I threw it toward the doors, tossing them down the road and away from the house. My side screamed, and my legs nearly collapsed from the effort that alone took. I needed to get this done and quickly.

On the plus side, the small tornado had sucked the smoke out with it, making breathing much easier. I ran to the study and threw open the door. Miska lay on the floor by the desk. The markers Roccurem had given her were still in her hand, and the journal she'd been coloring in was opened before her.

I lifted her to me, cradling her small form against my chest. I headed for the door, pulling her closer to check on her. Relief flooded me to feel her heart still beat, and while her breaths were short and shallow, she was alive. I wondered if the smoke had knocked her out, but I didn't question it further as I stepped out of the broken building. Roccurem solidified from dark mist, whole and unharmed.

Roccurem held his arms out, and I gently transferred Miska to him.

"The gas may have been too strong for her, but she's alive and breathing," I said.

Roccurem nodded. "They know where we are, which means they know where she is."

"I know," I said, blinking to clear my vision further. "I need to get to her. Did you find her?"

A look crossed Roccurem's face before he shook his head. "The smoke's effects are still too strong. I'll need time."

"We don't have time," I growled. "I'll send you back to the castle. Wait for us there."

Roccurem glanced at my side, knowing the wound might slow me down. "As you wish."

The air blinked in and out as the portal tried and failed to open. The pain in my abdomen doubled me over, but I gritted my teeth and tried again. This time, the portal formed with a whoosh, and I sucked in a deep breath, fighting against the pain. I felt Roccurem's eyes on me, and I nodded. He turned to the open portal but paused and looked over his shoulder. I felt it, too. Fuck.

I steeled my back, straightening my posture. A group of gray-winged soldiers stood in the middle of the road. At their head stood Ennis. He was the older brother to Milani, the Queen of Trugarum, and one of the most prolific and ruthless generals I'd ever encountered.

"You . . . It's been you all along. You're the one she has been protecting, not the fate." Ennis placed one powerful hand on his midsection and threw his head back as he laughed, his powerful wings flaring behind him. The guards around him did not move.

The way his armor curved around his shoulders always reminded me of talons, and a feather-like pattern was etched into his boots, chest plate, and helmet.

"Roccurem." My thumb rotated the ring on my middle finger, and silver armor, starting at my toes, raced up my body, stopping at my neck. "Take Miska and go home. I'll be there shortly with Dianna," I said.

It was the first time I'd ever seen apprehension from the fate. He stared at the small army in front of us and nodded. "As you wish, but please be careful."

A half-smirk graced my lips as my helmet formed. "This will not take long."

Roccurem stepped through the portal, and I closed it behind him.

Ennis curled his lip, gripping his helmet a fraction tighter. "Still so arrogant."

I cocked my head and summoned an ablaze longsword, pointing it toward him.

"You mistake arrogance for the truth. You are no match for me, not even with all your men behind you."

Ennis grinned a fraction wider before placing his helmet on his head and securing it under his chin. He grabbed the feather-tipped broadsword from its sheath across his back. "The great and powerful World Ender escapes death itself. I should be surprised, yet . . . I'm not. Want to tell me how you did it?"

I shrugged. "I'd rather just split your head from your shoulders."

He raised his blade toward the sky, and the army charged.

XCV

Dianna

Below us were scorched plains and the remnants of buildings crumbling in pieces, destroyed by creatures who had been far larger and far too powerful. Kaden had once told me of creatures far older than us that could block out the sun. The old days had been brutal.

I whipped and dove away from Kaden's snapping jaws and Isaiah's razor-sharp claws. Blood leaked from my side, one eye half shut, but I refused to surrender or stop fighting. I wanted blood for what Kaden had done, and I planned to take it. My wing hurt from where I hadn't been quick enough, and Isaiah's claw had ripped at the membrane. I saw the outline of his tail as he moved between clouds of smoke and ash. I drew in another thunderous breath and unleashed a tunnel of flame. Isaiah's screech was music to my ears.

Thunder roared behind me, the sound of Kaden's wings. In all of our thousand years, I had never seen his true form. He'd never shown me, just like he'd never shared anything with me. The girl in the desert would have cowered at the sight of this massive beast. The jet black and crimson scales flowed like ink over his heavy, muscled body, and he wore the array of spikes that jutted from his head like a crown. But me? This Dianna? The girl who fought and bled and carved her way to some semblance of peace saw it and saw fucking red.

Kaden followed me across the sooty, crimson sky. A raw screech emitted from my throat as I tossed flame at his chasing form. I had hurt Isaiah, and I had already learned in this fight that Isaiah was one of Kaden's weaknesses. He loved his brother, and I would do everything in my power to maim him.

I swooped to the right and down just as he lunged forward. My smaller, sleeker form was faster than his heavy, massive one, but that didn't mean he still wasn't agile and skilled. I heard him spin above me to follow. I coasted before banking left, my wings widespread. Another half turn, and I tipped my head to the side, using my good eye to watch the sky for the Ig'Morruthen, who was just as wounded as me. I didn't need to see through the smoke to smell the blood.

My nostrils flared, and I slammed my wings against the air, charging through the clouds, prepared to rip and claw. My body jerked sideways. Two against one was an unfair fight, and I was paying for it.

Fuck.

My side screamed and bled where Kaden's jaws clamped around me. I angled my neck, reaching for him, jaws snapping and peeling scales from his skin. He roared but gripped me tighter. His teeth sank deeper into my body, and I felt his fangs scrape against bone. I whipped my tail, slamming it against him, desperate to get him to let me go. He dove, the ground coming into focus just before he tossed me toward the crumbling buildings. Wood split as I tumbled through two or more houses. My body came to a stop, my form shaking as I returned to myself. I pushed up on shaky arms, spitting blood as I cupped my side. My hand came away covered in blood.

"Fuck."

It wasn't deep enough to kill, but it would definitely slow me down. My heart hammered in my chest, and with every rapid beat, more of my blood poured out of me. Every single part of me ached, and my lungs hurt with each gasped breath, but I would not surrender to him, to them, to any fucking one. I'd drag them to Iassulyn with me.

My head whipped up when I heard a loud thud that caused the ground to shake. It was quickly followed by another. They were on the ground. I had a split second to wonder what I was going to do before the side of the house was ripped away.

"I forgot how good you tasted," Kaden said as he walked in. He swiped my blood from his chin and licked his fingers clean.

I grimaced in revulsion as I held my side, scooting back on the broken floor. "I hate you."

Kaden's smile only widened. "That was smart, Dianna. Hurt us in our true forms, and you'd be able to kill us. Who told you that? I didn't. Was it your dead boyfriend?"

Isaiah snapped his fanged teeth as they returned to normal. The spikes over his head disappeared as he reclaimed his mortal form.

"Actually," I spat blood to the floor, "it was Tobias before I cut him in half. Wanna join him so you can take him to task for sharing secrets? Come here."

Isaiah whistled, clearly amused. I watched their shadows throw disjointed shapes on the walls as they stepped inside the ruined building. "So she did kill a King of Yejedin?"

Kaden's brow flicked up. "She did," he said, pride filling his voice. "But you weren't trained in aerial fights, Dianna."

They both stepped over broken wooden planks, pieces of cracked stone crunching beneath their boots. Half of Kaden's face and his shoulder were covered in blood, and I saw the bite marks where my teeth had sunk deep into his armored chest. Isaiah grinned, following a few steps behind Kaden and nearly as battered.

Satisfaction filled me, and I forced myself to my feet. I may be in immense pain, but I'd given just as good as I'd got. My entire being was suffused with agony, but I wouldn't show it. I'd never give him the satisfaction.

I flexed my hand, letting them see the wound along with the cuts on my head and arms. "I don't know. I think I did pretty well."

Isaiah's grin widened, showing off his bloody teeth. "Not nearly."

I grabbed my twisted, broken wrist and reset it. "Wipe the grin from your face. I've been fucked harder than you hit. You've done nothing."

"She is a nasty little thing," Isaiah said, glancing at Kaden. "Is that why you are in love with her?"

"That, among other reasons," Kaden answered.

Isaiah smirked, and I watched as his crimson eyes went a shade darker. The blood on his arms and brow moved of its own accord, racing back to the cuts it had escaped from, sealing the skin. My stomach sank as Kaden's wound healed as well.

He controlled the blood. Not only could he heal himself, but he could heal others.

I didn't ask how because it didn't matter. I now knew I wasn't leaving here alive. They wouldn't change forms again. I had already lost my edge. Arrogance would be my downfall.

"Pretty cool, huh?" Isaiah quipped, raising a brow in complete and utter confidence.

I lifted one shoulder in a negligent shrug. "I guess if you can't heal on your own."

I lunged for a piece of broken wood and hurled it at him. Kaden glanced at his brother, and I charged. Isaiah lifted his arm, and the wood broke when it hit the spikes on his thick dragonbane armor.

"That was stupid." Isaiah laughed, shaking the splinters off.

"It's called a distraction, you idiot," I said. Pain shot through my knee when it connected with the armor over his midsection, but it was what I needed. Kaden was sloppy when it came to his brother, and he reached for me at the same time I lowered my head. The momentum of his missed grab spun him, exposing his back and the dagger. I twisted, and the wounds over my torso protested vehemently. Ignoring the pain, I grabbed the dagger, ripping it from its sheath. I darted back as Kaden whipped around. He blinked in surprise, watching as I spun the gleaming crystal blade on my palm.

"I don't want to fight you, Dianna," Kaden said, his tone careful.

"Too bad," I sneered. "I do."

My fist shot out. Kaden blocked one hit and then the next, but I didn't stop. Every kick, twist, or punch he sidestepped or dodged, but he was still pushed back. Isaiah went to grab me, and I let him pull me close before rearing back and head-butting him in the face. He let go of me with a curse, his nose streaming blood. I spun and jumped, kicking him in the chest. The blow was hard enough to send him sailing across the room.

"You're faster and deadlier. I love it," Kaden said from behind me.

I flipped the dagger in my hand. "You shouldn't."

"It won't work if she uses it on you, Brother," Isaiah snapped, pushing himself to his feet.

"I know that," Kaden gritted his teeth, watching me carefully.

"Oh." I smiled around the blood that filled my mouth and stained my lips. "Damn magic and their tricky rules. But don't worry, I wasn't going to use it. I am going to break it."

Kaden yelled a denial and lunged toward me as I tossed the blade to the ground. I lifted my leg, ready to smash it under my boot, but suddenly, my body was no longer under my control. My leg stopped moving as if hundreds of hands stilled it. My body bent on its own accord, arms spread wide at my sides, back bending, and my gaze snapped forward.

Isaiah glared at me, his eyes a dark, eerie red that seemed to swirl. My blood felt as if it were hooked to tiny strings, and Isaiah was the puppeteer. Kaden raced forward and grabbed the dagger. My leg snapped down, and my knees hit the ground. Every cell and molecule screamed as if being torn in two as I fought. My arms were yanked to my sides, the muscles obeying only Isaiah.

Isaiah stood beside Kaden, broken glass and wood crunching beneath his armored boots. I tried to jerk my arms, move and fight, but I was immobile as they stood over me.

I grimaced, holding back every scream I so desperately wanted to make. I wouldn't give them the satisfaction.

"Not so much," Kaden demanded.

Isaiah's eyes flicked toward him, and the pressure eased a fraction. The pain in my head lessened, and it was no longer a struggle to breathe. I growled low in my throat. "Is this your guys' thing? Tying someone down to beat them. Once is a mistake, twice is a pattern."

Kaden kneeled before me. I wanted to back away, but my body would not let me.

"I didn't want to fight, not really." He reached out, brushing the blood-soaked hair from my face, and despite my inability to control my body, it shuddered at his touch. "I want you to come back in one piece. I always did."

"Pretty sure I remember your Irvikuva ripped me to pieces to bring me back to you."

"They can be a tad rough, especially given how hard you fight, talons and all, but those you didn't kill died when they returned to me. I never wanted you dead, no matter what you think. I wanted you with me forever."

"Sorry to disappoint you, but that was never going to happen, and I'm not going anywhere with you now. I'd rather die." I tried and failed to bite the hand so damn close to me.

He smiled at my attempt and held up the dagger. The hilt glowed with magic, the blade itself taunting me.

Kaden spun the blade by the hilt. "You know, your father helped me sculpt it, although he had no choice in the matter. I needed a loophole. After all she made me take from you, I knew you'd hate me."

I was silent, my heart pounding painfully.

Isaiah patted his brother's shoulder. "Kaden was always smarter than me. He was always ten steps ahead of me. Even Mera knows that. One little stick of that dagger, and when you wake up, all your feelings and love for Samkiel will be gone. Replaced and given to my brother."

Heat flashed beneath my skin, the Ig'Morruthen thrashing and fighting to come to the surface. The need to protect her mate was nearly overwhelming.

"No."

Kaden nodded. "I have never stopped loving you, Dianna. I just need to get rid of all that anger. You will be mine again, and this time for eternity."

Terror gripped me at what they planned to do.

"No. I'd rather die than have you ever touch me again."

"I'd never let you die, Dianna, and I promise to keep you safe."

The muscles in my arms, my legs, and my whole body ached as I tried to regain control. Sweat broke out on my brow. I wouldn't let him take me.

Kaden raised his hand, the blade carving a path to my heart, threatening to rip out the love I harbored there. He was threatening to take from me the one person who defied nature itself to help me, love me, protect me. Something snapped in me. Fire raged in my blood, and for a moment, I felt it in my eyes. A scalding hot fire flowed from my heart and, with each beat, reached more of my body. A flicker of bright orange flame danced across my hands, and the man from my dreams, the one who sat atop his throne made of bone, stood. His orange eyes glowed brighter, and a wide smile revealed his sharp white teeth.

"*Finally.*" His voice scraped over my brain like molten steel.

My arms jolted forward, my hands clasping Kaden's wrist. Isaiah reeled back a step, his mouth dropping open as I broke his hold on me. The whites of Kaden's eyes shone as I easily held the blade inches from me. A trail of flame flared along my fingers, and Kaden hissed as if it even burned him.

"Never." It was my voice, but deeper, raw, and pissed.

Isaiah covered Kaden's hands. I tried to stand, but only my upper body seemed to be free. It would be enough. They grunted, pushing to drive the dagger into me.

I held on, using everything I had left. The flames on my hands rose and then sputtered. I gritted my teeth, sweat running down my face, stinging the myriad of cuts. The fire flared, hot and intense, but then fell, smoke curling around my knuckles. A wave of nausea slid over me so quickly that I almost doubled over.

The blade moved an inch closer.

XCVI
Samkiel

I strode toward Ennis, slinging blood from my sword before calling it back. I grabbed him by the front of his now tarnished armor and lifted him off the blood-soaked ground, his torn wing hanging limp and useless.

"Where is she?" I snapped.

"Rot in Iassulyn," he hissed.

My eyes burned silver, the light surging forward so hot and intense it cut through his arm and severed it just below the shoulder. He screamed, spit forming on his lips at the pain.

"Where. Is. She."

He swallowed, the pulse in the column of his neck beating visibly. "Someone intercepted her arrival. Change of plans, you know the drill."

"Changed to where?" Ennis shook his head, staring at me defiantly even through the pain. His scream ripped through the air as I burned his other arm off. "Tell me!"

His mouth twitched as if he wished to laugh. "It is so humorous to see you concerned with another. She will know it now. All will. The great World Ender has a weakness."

I dropped him to the ground and placed my foot on his chest, looking at the destruction surrounding us. His fleet was destroyed, the battlefield littered with the dead and dying. "There will be no one alive to tell the tale, I'm afraid. Even you."

"My sister will look for me. I am already late checking in. She's probably on her way now. You remember her, don't you?" His smile was bloody and just as nasty as mine.

My shoulders lifted in a shrug. "I've fucked a lot of sisters. Can't say she was anything special."

Ennis jerked beneath my armored boot. "You will die for that."

"And you'll die if you don't tell me where she is." I leaned down and gripped his injured wing, grinding the broken bones together. He screamed, all the color draining from his face. "Tell me where she is. Where is the new location?"

He gritted his teeth with a cold, bitter smile. "I hope they rip her to pieces and send the parts back to you."

"They?" My boot dug into his chest a fraction harder, and I crushed the bones between my fingers.

He writhed but managed to gasp out, "Oh, yes. Your brothers."

A cold sweat broke out along my spine, but the familiar killing calm washed over me.

"Oh." Ennis chuckled wetly. "So that does scare the mighty king. Kaden plans to take her back and keep her as his."

My hand gripped his throat so hard that I felt something crunch and break within his neck. "Tell me where she is, or I'll take your eyes next. There are no more Jade Healers to restore them, and we know how your *sister* feels about those who are no longer of use to her."

He gasped and croaked, trying to speak, but I held on a moment longer before letting up. He choked, gasping for air. "They changed the meeting to Torkun. All I heard was that he had a blade made by her father. One stab and the victim becomes whatever you wish, and I'm thinking Kaden wishes for his old bitch back, which means no more memories of you."

I didn't know if time could actually stop. I'd never met a single being capable of it, but I imagined this was what it would feel like. Rain stood midair, and each beat of my heart seemed to take minutes. He was going to erase me? Us? All so he could convince her that she was his? Hate slammed into me with volcanic and overwhelming wrath, but the fear was even greater than that. I was terrified that I would lose her, that I had wasted my time with Ennis and not rushed to find her. If I was too late . . .

"My king," Reggie's voice filtered through the turbulent haze of my emotions.

The world came rushing back. Thunder roared in the sky, and I saw Roccurem's head whip up out of the corner of my eye. I didn't ask why he'd come back. I didn't care, not when my entire world was about to be stripped from me.

Ennis groaned beneath me. "You won't make it. That blade we used was supposed to kill you. If you are here and alive while your power burns in the sky, you'll never make it in time."

I hesitated, and it was all Ennis needed. He used his good wing as leverage, propelling himself up. His head collided with mine, and I stumbled back as he hopped to his feet. He spread his wings wide and awkwardly took to the sky. His flight was labored as he disappeared between the roiling clouds.

"My king." My head bowed. Reggie placed a hand on my shoulder, and I heard him gasp and pull back. He looked down at his burned palm.

"Torkun is realms away. I don't have all my power. I'll never make it in time." The pain returned, familiar and nauseating, the same viselike grip that held me on the remains of my homeworld. My chest felt as if it was collapsing in on itself. My Dianna is strong and brave, but she's alone and outnumbered. One Ig'Morruthen was already an unfair fight to most of the highly trained, but two? And two of the deadliest. She needed me. "She's too far away from me," I said, my voice breaking.

"If I may, Your Majesty," Roccurem said as the sky opened and rain pelted us. I turned to him, blinking against the water soaking my face. "I once told you that love has power, and the purest, truest of it can defy great odds. It is something I have witnessed before, and I will witness it again. If it gives power, take it. Harness it. This," he pointed up, "is your power in the sky, no one else's. To save her, simply call it home."

"Home?" I had asked as she leaned near the bathroom sink, hope flickering to life in my chest.

She smiled then, a small half-thing that blossomed further as she shrugged, no longer trying to hide her feelings. "That's what it feels like with you."

The rain sizzled and popped as it hit my armor, my brow. My body burned alongside my rage, sparks of electricity dancing across my shoulders, my legs, and my arms. My head throbbed as the sky above us rumbled and then cracked wide open. Dirt turned to mud, and I heard Reggie step back.

I remembered when I was younger, remembered the exact moment puberty hit. I remembered the sky shaking as my mother ran into my room. My scream had torn my throat as my mind opened, and the secrets of the cosmos had ripped into me. She held me, tears staining my face as the first stage of ascension began.

We had stayed like that until I heard my father's footsteps enter my room. I had peered past her shoulder, watching my father stare at the sky as I tried to process the new power filling me. He hadn't said anything that night, but later, he spoke of how I was just like him, how a great power, far beyond our understanding, ran through our blood. He explained that I would need to harness it, control it, or I could destroy worlds. It wasn't until later that we would realize how foretelling his words were.

It rained on Rashearim for weeks after. I remembered how others avoided me, the power rippling around and off my skin for weeks. I was such a danger then. My father increased my training and studies. When my mother passed, and my world was once more in turmoil, instead of losing control, I focused all of that dark rage and forged the Oblivion ring and sword. As soon as it rested on my finger, all of those harrowing feelings left, and now I knew why. Now I understood the look on my father's face and my mother's tears as she held me that night. I did not make Oblivion. I *was* Oblivion.

Power rippled across my knuckles in electric, purple streaks. Ennis had laughed, like so many others, about how easy it was to take her away from me. He had mocked me, telling me what Kaden planned to do, and something inside me snapped, ripped, and coiled. It had taken me this long to know the truth, to accept it, and I was going to use that knowledge to my advantage. Every last godsdamn part of it meant keeping the ones I loved safe.

It felt like fire erupted across my skin, flowed through my veins, and ignited in my soul. The world shook, and another peal of thunder rocked the air. The swirling mass of power in the sky halted and turned as if it had just been waiting. I threw a single arm up, and my power rushed forward, the silver racing so fast night turned into day. It crashed into my fingertips before spreading, surging into me in waves.

My body claimed the power, my cells soaking in the energy. I dropped my arm as my helmet slid over my face, the ground burning under my boots.

Reggie smiled at me, and it was the first real one I had seen from him in a long time. "Bring your queen home."

I gave him a curt nod and shot into the sky, leaving the sound of thunder in my wake.

XCVII

Dianna

I couldn't tell if thunder cracked in the distance or if the bones in my hands snapped from the pressure. I groaned, holding the hilt of the dagger with both hands while Kaden and Isaiah tried to push it closer to my chest. We were three unmovable forces, unrelenting and refusing to surrender. Wood cracked beneath my knees, and I gritted my teeth.

My arms shook, and a trickle of moisture ran down my cheek. I thought it was sweat until the iron smell spilled into the air. My nose had started to bleed, and my entire body ached. Isaiah's eyes bore into mine, and I realized he was using that damn power on me again. I wasn't going to let them just take me. My will was not to be underestimated, and I wasn't going down without a fight.

I sneered, blood pooling in my mouth and slipping past my lips. A pop sounded behind my eyes and then another in my ears as my blood vessels began to burst. It wouldn't matter how strong or powerful I was if it reached my brain. I would be unconscious in seconds.

My beast roared, her body writhing within the confines of my skin. She poured more strength, more power into me, trying to bolster my waning reserves. Wood continued to crack under me, and I sank deeper into the floor as they pushed. The muscles in my arms screamed, and the blade slipped a fraction closer. My chest heaved. One more push, and I was done. Gone.

They were going to win.

I was going to be taken and never see Samkiel again.

"You give me the best memories."

I had said it that night, and he had. Under stars, on a lake at night with sparklers and moonkrest who were rare and eternal. And now I wouldn't remember that or the first time he made me laugh. I wouldn't remember the festival and the face he made the first time he tried cotton candy, my heart fluttering as I laughed—really laughed—for the first time in ages. I wouldn't remember the photo booth he could barely fit in, that stupid garden at Drake's, or that damned flower I'd tossed away the first time we fought. That was when I thought he despised me, but I'd stared at it for days as it wilted. I wouldn't remember the castle he made me when I wanted nothing but to be left alone. I wouldn't remember the ocean and how I dipped my toes in the edge as he watched, waiting and making sure I did not break. I wouldn't remember how he healed me or our ice skating and laughing. I wouldn't remember our small but perfect wedding. I wouldn't remember what we had, the fights, the laughs, the playfulness. None of it. All of it would be gone and tainted by Kaden. I failed Samkiel like I failed Gabby. I should have told her I loved her more. I should have told him more. Now, I'd never get the chance.

A cry left my lips, a wordless plea playing over in my mind. The blade slipped closer. Even with all my strength, my body was giving out. Blood ran down the blade from my leaking fingertips as I tried to grip it tighter, but Isaiah was causing every blood cell in my body to seize. He pushed even harder, and I couldn't tell if I was crying or if it was blood flowing from my eyes. A hollow, aching sob tore from my throat.

No. I couldn't forget. I wouldn't.

Even as my hands slipped on the hilt, I promised to claw, rip, and tear my way back to Samkiel. I swore it.

My muscles finally seized. A battle lost. My arms dropped. My eyes closed.

"I'll remember that I love you." I knew he couldn't hear me, but I made the vow just in case.

Silence fell, and the world paused. Everything stopped, and I fought to find a way to lock a part of him away in my mind, to choose just one memory for safekeeping. I could save him, revisit it. It was a lifeline for me to hold on to until I made it back to him because I would make it back to him.

My world. My heart. My lost soul.

A sonic boom broke the silence, so loud and violent that I wondered if the sky was still intact. My eyes snapped open on a gasp. I fell forward and felt control of my body return to me. I tossed my hair out of my face, rubbing my eyes to clear them of the blood and tears so I could see. My mouth dropped open as I sat up, looking around in awe.

It was as if I had been transported to another world. The building I'd been in was gone. Every building had been reduced to ash, a world littered with gray snow. There were no trees, mountains, or living beings. Everything around me was suddenly gone. A residual vivid silver light skittered across the sky where a hole had been punched open. A portal. I took a shaky breath when I noticed that Isaiah and Kaden were gone, nothing left of them but ashes floating on the wind.

And I knew.

"Samkiel." My voice emerged as a whisper. I knew what this meant. Everyone would know he was alive. *She* would know he was alive.

I wrapped my arms around myself because I finally understood the stories and the legends. Samkiel never needed the Oblivion blade to be feared. It was clear now why so many bowed, why they chanted, why they followed. Looking around the desolate wasteland that he had created, I finally understood the true nature of his destructive power and why they called him World Ender.

XCVIII

Samkiel

The air above the Isle of Detremn tore, shuddering beneath the weight of the portal. The entire planet was wrapped in plant life but otherwise deserted. It didn't even have any animals, but more importantly, it was several realms away from Dianna.

Trees broke and fell, the ground bunching beneath Kaden and Isaiah as I threw them to it. Power I had not used since my father's reign wafted from my skin in silver tendrils, reaching and stretching, eager to defend and avenge her. It disrupted the atmosphere, clouds curling and darkening before rain poured. Lightning struck all around them, the wind holding them in place. My feet hit the ground, sending a shudder through the planet.

Kaden and Isaiah struggled to their feet, their faces masks of pure shock and hate. One by one, their Dragonbane helmets slid over their heads in an effort to protect them, but it was too late.

"You are supposed to be dead," Kaden snarled from behind his horned helmet.

I flexed my wrist, the power flickering over my skin to coalesce in my hand. The shadow of a blade formed in my palm as dark and hateful as they'd made me. The sword solidified, purple and black tendrils of magic reaching, searching for their next victim. I pointed it at Kaden. "I am not, but you soon will be."

"Oblivion," Isaiah whispered. "How did you get that from Mera?"

My lips curled in disgust. "I did not *get* it. I *am* it. Oblivion is not something anyone can take from me."

He took an involuntary step back, but his fear and good sense were short-lived. The serrated blades protruding from the armor above their wrists were as sharp and twisted as the two of them. Isaiah's eye twitched before he looked at Kaden. I knew how powerful they were. Separate, they were deadly, but together, they could tear the world to ribbons with only claws and teeth. I had to be smarter. My father had preached intelligence during a fight.

"Even the strongest of your enemies has a weakness. We may be fierce warriors, but we are flesh and blood. Above all, we are emotional beings, no matter how hard or tough we think we are. Emotions, my son, run faster through the system than blood."

He spun his spear above his head as we sparred, the tip coming to rest against my heart.

"Find a weakness, and use it if you must. No fight is fair, not even between gods."

"I understand your obsession with her, *Brother*," I spat the last word as if it was poison. Even if I denied it, his obsession and love for Dianna were as strong and potent as mine. "After having her, I understand why you can't leave her alone."

Kaden's eyes burned with fiery rage, and he clenched his fists hard enough to draw blood, his talons digging deep into his palms.

"Shall I show you why she would never return to you? Why father would never choose you?" I smirked, gauging his reaction before twisting my blade of words a bit harder. "Do you wish to see why I am king, and you two are a forgotten page in history, torn and tossed aside?"

Rage bubbled off them. Isaiah took a single step forward, but Kaden raised his hand, halting him.

"So the prodigal son returns," Kaden hissed, the orange and red flames beneath his armor sparking. "Do you truly think a few jabs will make us react so blindly? I know the power that lies beneath your skin. It is just like father's."

"I think you're a fool. Truly. You believe you can beat me here and return to Dianna." I raised my hand and willed the gauntlet away to reveal the ring I had made, the one that matched hers. "Dianna will never choose you, even with all your conniving and fail-proof plans. She chose me and has every day from the moment she laid eyes on me. She left you then and never once looked back. Not. Once."

"What is that?" Kaden hissed.

"You stole our amata mark, so I did the next best thing. She is my wife, my only, and she will never again be yours. *Never.*"

Kaden snapped, attacking with the same blind rage and fury he had proclaimed himself above. And Kaden fell first.

I twisted to the side, the gauntlet reforming over my hand. Using my momentum to complete the spin, I swung out with the sword. Kaden's knees hit the ground with a dull thud, his eyes wide with shock. I watched with satisfaction as his head lolled to the side before slipping from his shoulders.

I stood with my feet planted and my body relaxed but ready, holding Oblivion casually with the tip pointed toward the ground. I flicked my eyes to Isaiah. He jerked to a stop mid-step as his brother's body wilted and dissolved into dark ash, the particles floating between us in a haze. He glared at me, his crimson eyes filled with pained rage. I held his gaze with calm satisfaction, knowing Kaden would never again come after Dianna. I spun Oblivion in my hand and adjusted my grip on the hilt. Isaiah eyed the sword as if he wanted to flee instead of fight.

I smirked and called the sword back, holding my hands up in mock surrender. I saw his cold, red eyes narrow. "Come on, I won't even use it on you."

"What is this?" he spat. "Trickery?"

"I want you to see why it took chains and ancient runes to beat me."

He didn't move.

"Don't be shy now. You're embarrassing yourself, *Blood Scorn.*" I said his fabled name in a mocking tone.

Isaiah snarled. He ran toward me, his blade raised and angled to slice me in half.

I sidestepped.

He swung.

I grabbed the back of his armor and pulled him down. At the same time, I brought my knee up, breaking his spine before gripping his head and twisting.

The portal closed above me as I drifted toward the ground, Isaiah gripped in my hand, unconscious but breathing . . . for now. Thunder rumbled in the sky, the rain coming down in silvery sheets. The air was gray, and ash had turned to mud on the ground. It was complete desolation, destruction in its purest form. This was what I fought against unleashing.

My armored boots had barely touched the ground before a body collided with mine, strong, slender arms wrapping tightly around me. Warm cinnamon tinted the brutally burnt air, her scent a part of every breath. I dropped Isaiah in a heap at her feet and held her to me. With just her touch, the cold rage of battle was replaced by peace and comfort. I pulled her tighter against me, but she struggled, trying to push me away. I barely felt it. Her strength was depleted.

I cupped her face with my hands, searching her eyes. "Are you okay, akrai?"

She slapped at my armored chest. "You left me here, you ass!"

"For merely a second," I said, happy to even hear her voice.

She forced a small smile etched in pain, the world an ashen gray mist around her.

"Are you okay?" I asked again, running my hand along the side of her neck. She hissed, her body starting to tremble. Between the rain, blood, and mud smeared over her, I couldn't tell where she was actually hurt. "Where are you hurt?"

"Everywhere." She smiled, then grimaced. "I really thought I had the upper hand, but I feel like I've been ripped to pieces and put back together again."

"Dianna, my akrai. You did more than phenomenal. Two Ig'Morruthens? Gods have had their light bleed across the sky from one. Not to mention, my brothers were trained for war by my father. You were not."

She nodded and grimaced in pain at the movement. "I want more training. No more holding back with me. My enemies will not."

"We will talk about that later," I said, tipping her jaw up so I could see the marks on her throat. It looked like one of them had grabbed her. I could see the handprint already forming. "But my main concern is why your ring is off?"

Her expression grew guarded as if she knew whatever she was about to say wouldn't make me happy.

"I had a plan. A stupid plan." She nodded and tapped her pocket. "I still have it."

My thumb swiped across her cheek. "I couldn't find you."

She nodded, her body shuddering with pain. "I didn't want you to show up. They would know you were alive. Nismera would know you were alive."

Thunder cracked across the sky, the rain picking up speed. "I do not care about them or Nismera, only you. Never do that again."

She smiled, the wound on her lower lip threatening to crack. "Pinky promise."

I made a noise low in my throat before placing both of my hands on either side of her head gently, letting my power flow into her. I smiled as she closed her eyes, relaxing into the warmth. She started to glow, and gods above, she was beautiful. The small cuts along her scalp knitted themselves back together, and her busted lip closed. I slid my thumb over its plump fullness, and she parted her lips, opening to me. I heard a few snaps as her bones popped back into place, and I fought the urge to kill Isaiah. Dianna sighed, and her hands wrapped around my wrists. She opened her eyes, and I slowly pulled my power back, easing out of her.

"I forgot how much that tingles," she whispered, a pale line of red running down her face, the rain washing the fight off her bit by bit. I was relieved that her wounds were healed, but all the dried blood on her made me want to go back and kill him again.

"Feel better?"

She nodded and took a breath that wasn't labored. "Are other worlds like this?"

"No." I shook my head, casting a glance around the ruined and devastated planet. "Only this one. Only where you were."

"Oh." She sighed, pushing the hair that escaped her ponytail away from her face. "Also, I knew you could fly fast, but . . ."

I glanced up at where I had entered the atmosphere and shrugged. "Depends on the realm, technically. Some places are faster than others, gravity and all, or lack thereof."

Her eyes dropped back to mine. "You destroyed a world for me?"

Dianna said it in utter disbelief. She did not fully understand the lengths I would go for her. Destroying a world was not even a fraction of it. She thought me a hero, but a hero would defy others for the greater good. She was mine, and for her, I'd do the unthinkable. My strong, fierce, beautiful girl who thought she could take the world on all by herself. Only she had me now, and gods above and below help anyone who thought they could hurt or take her from me.

My brows furrowed at her surprise. "I'd destroy several worlds if it meant keeping you safe. You have no idea the limits I'd go for you."

"Shameless flirt." She smiled through the rain, and it was the most beautiful thing I'd ever seen. I chuckled, but I did not deny her claim.

She nodded to Isaiah's slumped form. "I'm assuming Kaden is dead?"

"Long overdue, but you assume correctly."

Dianna sighed, closing her eyes in relief, and I wished I could have given it to her sooner. When she opened them again, she seemed lighter, as if a weight had been lifted off her shoulders.

"And Isaiah? You're going to interrogate?"

I nodded. "After we take care of you."

"Such a gentleman." A soft sigh left her lips, and she glanced down. She bent and picked up the dagger she must have dropped when she threw herself at me. The crystal blade shimmered, an aquamarine gem in the center. "We need to talk about this too, and trust me when I say you will not be happy."

I lifted my hand, and a gently swirling vortex appeared beside us. The vast, gorgeous landscape below our castle appeared. The imposing mountains rose in the background, and I could just make out the towering walls of the outer bailey peeking through the trees.

Sweeping her off her feet, I picked Dianna up, supporting her back with one arm, the other looping behind her knees. She smiled up at me and rested her head against my chest as I kicked Isaiah's body through the portal. "Trust me, I am already not happy."

XCIX
Camilla

Thunder cracked and clashed above the palace, and I wondered how loud it must be to reach down here. I shivered on the floor, my cell dark and cold. I tucked my arms in close against my body, my wrists bandaged but still throbbing and burning. Water dripped from the ceiling as someone far off and down below hummed a tune. A door clanged, and three sets of armored boots grew closer.

They stopped outside my cell, and I rolled over, lifting to my knees while trying not to jar my arms. Vincent stood between two guards, towering over them in his half-cloak and lightweight armor.

"Nismera's trained pet come to piss on me for amusement now?" I spat, and the guards shuffled, trying to hide their smiles. They loved seeing me powerless, it seemed.

Vincent's cold, blank expression did not waver. "I told you. I will always choose her. You were a fool to think otherwise."

"Why are you here?"

"To make sure you haven't died of sepsis yet. The king has work for you yet," one of the guards said, and Vincent nodded.

"I mean, despite having no hands, the rest of her looks fine," the other guard said. "Say, Vincent, can we have a turn with your ex-whore now?"

They laughed viciously, looking at each other and then at him hopefully. Wet gurgles replaced their laughter as twin silver blades erupted from Vincent's folded arms, piercing their throats. Blood sprayed the cell floor in vibrant red as they fell, grabbing at their necks. Vincent stepped over their bodies, leaving them to drown in their blood behind him.

Vincent kneeled in front of me and pushed his cloak to the side. He pulled out a folded bundle and unwrapped it, revealing my hands. I held out my wrists, and when he carefully cut away the bandages, I felt my magic crawl forward. I jolted back as my hands mended to my wrists, feeling that comforting cool balm wash over me, my power settling into my veins again.

I glanced up at Vincent. He still kneeled in front of me, staring at my hands. "You got your rings back?" I asked, nodding at his decorated hands.

It jarred him out of whatever thoughts had claimed him. "Oh," he flexed his fingers, "yes, I hid these from her when I first arrived. I told her I wanted nothing that reminded me of Samkiel. It worked."

I saw the pain in his expression over his fallen friend. He'd helped drive a blade through Samkiel and, in the process, damned the world. I knew he had nightmares, and I wondered how many of them revolved around his family. He shook his head and leaned forward. Bracing a hand under my elbow, he helped me up, his eyes still locked on my hands.

"I'm fine," I said, holding them up and even wiggling my fingers for effect. "I swear."

Vincent's mask slipped, pain etching his features as he gently grabbed my hands and placed a kiss to each palm. "I'm still so sorry, Cami."

Cami. Why did I love that nickname now?

I smiled and placed a hand against his cheek. "It had to look convincing. Nismera is brutal. We have to match that to trick her. Besides, it was a simple regeneration spell. A child could do it."

He nodded. "I hated that plan."

"It had to be convincing," I said again. He had been so against this plan that I knew nothing I said right now would make him feel better.

"I didn't mean what I said." Tears filled his eyes, and not knowing what else to do to help him, I pressed my lips to his.

I pulled back just enough to whisper, "I know."

Vincent kissed me again, sweet and slow, before moving back a step. He dropped one of my hands and dug into his armor, pulling out a key. "I got this, as you said. She will return once she hears the prisoners have escaped, and we need to be gone."

I nodded. "Let's go."

Guards rushed past our hiding place in the alcove. Once they were gone, Vincent moved first. He refused to let go of my hand, holding tight as if he were afraid I would disappear. We darted toward the war room, ducking inside as another wave of guards passed.

"What are you doing in here?" a voice snapped. We spun, surprised to see Elianna standing near the table. Her eyes were red-rimmed, and she clutched papers to her chest.

"What are you doing?" I asked.

She took one look at Vincent, and her face flushed. So we weren't the only ones attempting a coup.

"Kaden hasn't come back. I don't think he is going to. The sky no longer burns with Samkiel's power. He has returned."

Vincent and I looked at each other in disbelief. "What?"

Elianna nodded, but I saw the grief in her eyes. "He's dead. Kaden's dead. I don't know how or why, but I know it. I feel it."

"Samkiel's alive?" Vincent whispered.

Elianna nodded again and pointed to the window. We nearly ran around the table. The night exhaled in our faces as we pushed the large balcony doors open. I was dumbfounded, but I saw it and felt it. His return. The sky no longer held the shimmers of silver. There was nothing but pure open sky, the stars flickering and flashing in celebration of the return of hope and the one true king. I turned toward Vincent and pressed my hands to his chest. He swallowed hard, and the shine of tears in his eyes glittered in the moonlight.

"He's alive," I said. "I can feel it. My magic tells me he summoned that power back in seconds. Dianna must have found a way to resurrect him. Maybe that's why she was burning through the world."

Vincent said nothing, seeming unwilling to look away from the sky. I stepped closer to him, brushing my body against his, and he finally looked at me.

"Glad we have that covered," Elianna said. "I'm leaving, and if you guys are smart, you will too. Things are about to get very, very ugly."

My head snapped toward her. "And how do you know that?"

Vincent moved with celestial speed, and Elianna yelped when he appeared behind her. He gripped her shoulders and asked, "And why are you stealing documents?"

"I'm leaving. Are you insane? Nismera fears him. Who doesn't? We all know he's pissed, and these papers will ensure I can hide until this damned war passes over. I don't have anyone else but myself."

Vincent's eyes darted to me, and I knew what he was thinking.

"Come with us?" I asked.

Elianna shook her head. "You? Why?" she asked.

"One, you have far more information than we do, and two, we need those pages. I can see the writing from here."

"Okay, what's in it for me? It's not like you two can ensure my safety. We all heard what went down in those chambers."

"Camilla wants to return to Dianna," Vincent interjected.

"Are you insane?" Elianna all but gasped. "She will gut us alive for what we did to Samkiel, even if he still breathes. We're better off staying here with Nismera."

"No." I glanced at Vincent. "I know Dianna. War is brewing, and she cares about her family above all. I don't just bring her information but also a way to protect them. She will help us. No heads will roll. I promise."

Elianna held the documents a fraction closer. "How can you be so sure?"

"Because even at her lowest, her deadliest, she didn't kill me," I said. "And besides, we have this."

Vincent opened his cloak, revealing the medallion inside. Elianna's eyes widened. "How?"

"It's not important. Are you with us or not?"

Elianna stared at us, her fingers tightening on the papers. "Vincent won't make it past the front door after everything he's done. I know that above all."

"Then, if he dies, so do I, but we're leaving," I said, giving Vincent a small reassuring smile. "Together or not at all."

A small smile tugged at his lips. They were the same words I had said before and the same ones he said to me when he spoke of our plan.

Elianna's bottom lip wobbled, and I saw the longing in her eyes for something more than council meetings, death, and destruction. She shrugged as much as she could under Vincent's hands. "Fine, whatever. We're all going to die anyway, right?"

She said it so calmly, almost like a joke, but my magic stirred as if reacting to it like an omen.

Nismera

The walls sizzled where magic had burned them, and a thousand and one pieces of metal lay scattered about. The last table clattered to the floor as my guards ransacked Killium's makeshift shop. I twirled my spear, crunching the ashes of mercenaries beneath my boot. I stopped and spun, pointing the tip toward Killium. "A little birdie told me you made a strange weapon for a strange man. So tell me. Where is the fate?"

Killium laughed, his teeth bleeding pale white blood. "You think fate needs a weapon?"

My boot collided with his chest. I kicked until I heard a bone break, and he screamed.

I flipped my hair back, smoothing the sides. "Answer the question, or I will decorate the walls with you." I grabbed his jaw, forcing him to look at the dust smear nearby. "Like I did with sweet old Jaski."

"You have already taken everything from me. I hope you rot."

The world shook, and I stumbled off my feet. My guards rushed forward, grabbing my arms and helping me stand back up. I pushed them off, sneering. "I'm fine."

There was another deep rumble, and parts of the ceiling began to crumble.

I straightened myself once more, wiping my hands over the front of my armor. A wet, deep laugh came from the corner of the room.

"Something funny?" I snarled at him.

Killium sat up, his hand holding his cracked ribs. "You think I made a weapon for a fate? You're as dumb as you look. I made a weapon to bridge a gap, to fix what you broke."

My hand whipped out, grabbing him by the throat. "What does that mean?" I hissed.

Thunder echoed across the sky, and a soldier burst through the door a heartbeat later.

"My liege."

"Not now, Grog." I spun, still holding Killium, my spear drawn. "Can you not see I am in the middle of maiming?"

His eyes were so wide they took up most of his face. He stammered and pointed up. "The sky, my liege. It's moving."

"What?" I asked, my brows furrowing. Killium started laughing again, even though it obviously hurt. I shook him and growled, "What do you know?"

"You're out of time." He smiled at me. "The true king has returned."

He was still smiling when I rammed the spear through his midsection. His body disintegrated into a heap of dust, and I turned toward the stairs. My generals let me pass and then followed me up the steps to the front door.

The town gathered outside, everyone gasping and pointing toward the sky. I looked up and watched in disbelief as the silver disappeared and the clouds bellowed. The sky split, and rain poured down. Thunder roared, so loud and violent that everyone on the streets cringed and scrambled toward their homes. My eyes stayed drawn to the sky.

"Our next order, my liege?" one soldier asked.

I gripped the spear deathly tight, steel creaking in my hand.

"Prepare for Tatil'ee."

Isaiah

They had talked about him. Nismera had the old records that recorded Samkiel's rise and fall from Rashearim. I remembered being enamored with the way they painted his accomplishments. I'd even wished to be like him. He was this powerful, brave figure everyone looked up to. He was faster than any and extremely deadly with a blade, any blade. I just never thought I'd see it in real life. Mera had said he was trapped behind the realms, and he'd be long dead for them to open, yet there he stood. He'd ripped the very sky open for her, and now, all it did was pour.

Blind rage poured into his eyes, and tendrils of destructive, raw power struck at the air around him. My chest ached. Kaden had fallen so easily as if killing him were nothing. Samkiel was so fast my eyes hadn't even registered his movements, and as my body begged to retreat, I realized what we were dealing with. We had dared to touch her, and now there was no mercy in the creature I faced.

I swallowed my fear and charged him, striking out with my sword. Samkiel dodged the blow easily, effortlessly. Too quick. I felt his hand at the back of my armor, then a sickening crunch from somewhere deep in my body. Too damn quick. I had only seen one other person move that quickly, only one, and I'd helped murder him because no one else could. Unir. Our father. There was searing pain and then nothing but darkness.

My wrists and head throbbed. I shifted, trying to alleviate some of the strain on my shoulders. My eyes flew open when I realized my body was pulled tight and aching everywhere. I was on my knees with my arms stretched out to my sides, thick metal cuffs wrapped painfully tight around my wrists. Shallow cuts covered my body, blood stained me, pooling around me on the floor. The color was almost black where it had dried. They had been bleeding me out for a while now, it seemed. I wondered how long I had been unconscious.

The room faded in and out. When my vision cleared, my breath stuttered in my chest. Samkiel stood framed in the doorway, and for a moment, I saw our father. The same stance, the same lean, the same posture, and above all, the same power. Curse the old gods and the dead. He had it all back. He'd ripped his power from the very sky for *her*.

Samkiel had always been the weak one in our story, a means to an end. He was merciful and kind, a guardian and protector, but always below us. Now, he leaned against the doorjamb with a predator's intent, waiting patiently for the right moment to strike. He was no untried youth. This man had been tempered, tried, and driven to the edge. He was a god in the true sense of the word: terrible, beautiful, and overflowing with power. We were all wrong. She was so wrong.

He carelessly tossed a silver dagger into the air, catching it easily by the hilt. I saw the blood staining the edge of the blade and knew instinctively it was mine. I tried to move but struggled to make my body work, feeling so weak and tired.

"When I was younger, Unir constantly scolded me for not being where I should be. Instead of training or participating in the council meetings, I would be off looking for fun, adventure, and, as I got older, partners. His punishment was always to lock me in the athenaeum. I'd study for hours, sometimes days, depending on what trouble I had caused. He wanted me to be a great king, a smart one. I remember reading about a powerful race that could bend water at will, and then there were those who learned to bend blood."

Samkiel paused, appraising me with molten silver eyes. They burned with barely contained rage, reminding me of Nismera.

"The trick with magic or power is to find the source and stop it just like a dam in a river. Stop the flow. Blood is your power, but it is also your weakness. I made a few cuts. I hope you don't mind. They won't seal since the blade I used is ablaze. It is what hurts you that can kill you, but Unir didn't teach me that. She did."

Ablaze. He had used the ablaze weapons on me and not that swirling death blade. Until he'd killed Kaden, I had never seen it, never been close to it. I'd only seen the aftermath of his destruction and learned why they called him the World Ender. Nismera had the ring. I had seen it, and I knew it didn't rest on his hands. It shouldn't have been possible for him to summon it, but if what he said was true, he didn't need it for Oblivion. He *was* Oblivion. My heart broke as I remembered how quickly Kaden fell, becoming nothing but dark ash.

"Kaden . . ." I didn't realize the word left my lips until he made a noise in his throat.

"Is dead."

I lowered my head with a small sob. I wished I could weep, but nothing would come. He had practically desiccated me. Kaden was gone, and I had no doubt I would soon join him. My chest felt like it was about to cave in. I'd never see Imogen again and left unattended with the others . . . I wanted to scream.

"You cry for him?"

I raised my head and swallowed the hatred, sadness, and fear that lodged in my throat. When I met his gaze, my body involuntarily tried to shift further away from him. The look he gave me was filled with wrath and a need for vengeance. He hated Kaden for what he had done to his amata. His anger was a living, breathing thing, and I could feel it mantling in the room. I pulled at my chains, even though I knew I wasn't going anywhere. I saw now why they waited, why they distracted him for so long, why The Order needed those marks and chains to hold him. It made sense why they did not want their mating mark to form. One of him was enough, but the two of them together would be undefeatable.

I steadied myself, trying to calm my racing heart. I wouldn't give him the satisfaction of seeing my fear.

"I see Father in you, *Brother*." I said it like the curse it was.

He pushed off the wall and strolled into the room, still wearing his infamous battle-worn silver armor. He moved in it as if it were light as a feather.

"I'm not your brother. I am your judge and executioner."

He stopped in front of me, and the Ig'Morruthen in me recoiled, desperate to move away from him. I forced myself to remain still. If I were to die, I wouldn't falter or whimper like a child.

"Then execute me because I will tell you nothing."

He sighed and shook his head, an expression I wasn't familiar with flashing in his silver eyes.

"Not tonight. Tonight, I wish to go upstairs and lay with the woman I love. The woman you, Kaden, and Nismera keep trying to take from me. I also need to find a way to get my family back because you all tried to take them, too. So I'll let you wallow here for a while. Let the silence and the walls drive you mad. Then, when it's time, I will return and ask you questions. You will refuse to answer, and I will resort to something very unkind. The cycle will repeat until I have what I wish for. But tonight, I am tired, and I wish to spend the rest of my evening with this realm's future queen."

My lip curled, and I turned my head away.

"I want you to know while you wallow and hate and curse my very name and existence that this, all of this, is your fault, Kaden's fault, and Nismera's. It never had to be this way. I was never the monster she told you I was. You should have come to me. I would have given you all a home, a family."

Something twisted and broke inside of me. Family. It was the one thing Kaden and I had craved most of all, and we had learned a long time ago we were not made to have. Weapons of war. That was all we were. My jaw clenched, longing to violently rip him to shreds for even suggesting such a thing.

"But you chose a different path. Had you all come to me and told me what and who you were, had you helped me, this would not have happened. You would not be here, and Kaden would not be dead because despite what vile, vicious lies Nismera has planted into your brain, I am not the bad guy here. I never was. I love and protect those who seek it, and I love and protect my family with everything I have."

His hand whipped out, grabbing my jaw and forcing me to look at him. A growl, deep and guttural, seeped from my lips. I squinted against the light burning from his eyes. The glow was too bright in this dark room, the heat of it threatening to burn me alive.

"With. Everything. I. Have. Isaiah."

He released my chin with a shove and turned, stalking toward the door, his steps silent despite the armor. My chin burned where his rings had touched my skin, his power leaving its mark.

"I'll tell you nothing. No matter what you do to me, what you threaten, or what you break."

Samkiel paused in the doorway, and bright cerulean bars formed across the front of my cell, sealing me in. He stared at me for a moment and gave me a shadow of a smile, then without saying anything, he left. I think out of all that had happened, that interaction scared me the most.

I lowered my head and sighed, my arms screaming in pain. I'd find a way to get out of here, find a way to get back to—

An icy wind swept through my cell, colder than the harsh climate of Fvorin. I shivered, my skin prickling, and lifted my head. My wrists burned as I jerked back on my chains because there in the doorway stood Veruka.

"How?" I asked. Her hollow, empty eyes stared at me. "You're dead. I killed you."

She took a step forward, then another, passing through the bars as if she didn't exist on this plane any longer, and she didn't. Her head tilted at an ungodly angle, and the red, jagged line across her throat where I'd ripped it off was still spilling blood. She stopped in front of me and leaned forward.

She had no smell, no scent. She was hollow.

"What are you?"

A ghostly smile curved her lips as she reached toward me. I tried to jerk back, but Samkiel had chained me to the ceiling and floor. I had nowhere to go.

Her hand hovered over my chest, and I felt a tug as a small ball of flame emerged. She grabbed and crushed it in her fist, a cold, empty smile on her face.

I heard a crash above me and whipped my head back, looking at the ceiling. When I looked back, I was alone in my cell. I blinked a few times, my mind reeling. Of course, I was alone. Why would I assume I wasn't alone in my cell? Samkiel had left me here. I had been alone the whole time.

CII

Dianna

The stone beside my head cracked from the pressure of his hand as he pounded into me. My back hit the wall with his every thrust, both of us panting and groaning as we took, took, took. There were no soft words or whispered pleading, just a primal need to feel, to know that we were both alive and together. His mouth dominated mine, stealing my breath, and I gladly gave it. His free hand clenched my jaw, his palm spanning my throat. My heart thudded, matching the same rhythm as his, my one and only.

I needed to not just know that this was real. I needed to feel that this was real, that I was not locked inside my head, and that Kaden had not won.

My nails raked across his back, and he groaned against my lips, tongue swiping across mine. "Tell me you love me," I moaned, arching against him, crushing my breasts against the hard planes of his chest. My nails raked across his shoulders, his arms, anything I could attach myself to.

He angled my head up with his thumb and scraped his teeth along my neck, thrusting into me a fraction harder.

"I love you."

Another heated kiss.

"I love you."

Another.

"I love you."

I clenched around him, and he pushed me harder against the wall, fucking me into it. I could feel his need to anchor himself in me, assuring himself I was here with him, alive and safe. Pleasure rippled across my skin with every thrust, his chest dragging across my nipples. I was burning alive with desire, whimpering against him. It was bliss, pure blinding bliss, and everything I needed. Wanted. I hadn't realized how much he had been holding back. The part of my mind that was still capable of thought was worried about the foundation of our bedroom and this wing of our home.

My eyes closed, and I held on to Samkiel, wrapping my legs tighter around him, pulling him in until he was fighting my hold to thrust into me. I kept seeing that damned blade, their faces drawing closer, along with the destruction of my future. I had never been so close to losing before, never been scared of it, but today I was terrified. It had scared us both badly. Now, there was this insatiable need to claim, mark, and take what we both needed.

"Akrai, I . . ." He panted, and I felt the muscles in his thighs strain. I knew he was close.

"Me too. Me too."

Pleasure built coiling low in my belly as he grunted and groaned, whispering filthy words in my ear. My back arched, white-hot pleasure sparking through every part of me as I came beneath him. He cupped my ass, driving deep and grinding against me until I saw stars, and he followed me over. He pressed his body against me, crushing me against the wall as we fell apart and came back together again. Silence fell, rain pelting the window as a flash of light illuminated our room.

Emotions bubbled to the surface after my release, and this time, when my body shook, it wasn't from pleasure. Without having to ask, Samkiel's arms tightened around me, and I buried my face against his neck and cried. With others, I could pretend that nothing touched me, protected by spikes, fangs, and claws, but there was no hiding from him.

"It's cold," I complained. Samkiel lay against my back, half of his massive body covering mine, his weight pressing me into the bed. I needed that, needed him that close. He always seemed to know what I needed. My hand wrapped around his, and I tugged it close, tucking it under my chin.

"I must have gotten the seasons wrong. Usually, it is bearable at nightfall this time of the year," he said, his breath tickling my upper back.

"Hmm." I felt his chest rise and fall. "I'm sorry for jumping you the second you walked in the door," I said, and I was. I'd left the shower the second I heard our bedroom door open, not wanting to be alone, and jumped into his arms before the door even latched fully, my lips crashing against his.

"Never apologize." He made a noise of contentment as we lay still, the covers bunched around us. "I'll welcome it even when I'm old and feeble."

My thumb passed slowly across the back of his fingers. "Will you grow old and feeble now that your powers are back?"

He took a deep breath, the muscles across his chest and abdomen flexing against my back. "Eventually. All gods do. My true immortality was tied to the realms, remember?"

"Vividly." I glanced out the window. None of his power danced in the sky now, only the building storm as rain continued to fall. "Did you break the sky when you got your powers back?"

"Hmm?" he asked, the sound drowsy. I wiggled beneath him, and he adjusted, shifting to lie on his back. Scooting close, I placed my head on his chest. "I'm not sure, nor do I particularly care."

"How did you do it?" I whispered the question, needing to know. I couldn't sleep without knowing, no matter how relaxed I was. "How did you kill Kaden?"

"I taunted him," he said, his eyes fluttering open. "With you." A crack of lightning illuminated the room. The flash echoed in his eyes.

"Me?"

"Regardless of how vile or cruel, he loved you above all else. His methods may have been twisted and wrong, but we felt the same for you. So, I said things I knew would burn me to my core if said to me. He reacted, and I took his head with Oblivion."

I drew random patterns over his chest, soothing the tension I could feel tightening his muscles. Samkiel brushed a kiss to the top of my head and took a deep breath. I was quiet for a moment, picturing Kaden's death. A draft whispered over us, and I reached for the covers, pulling them tighter around us. I nestled closer and whispered, "No one has ever protected me like you do. I'm always the one taking care of everything and everyone else. You're supposed to protect the world, not me."

"You are my world." He pulled me flush against him and tipped my head back to kiss my forehead, his hand running idly up and down my back. "I'll always protect you, akrai. No matter the consequences," he whispered against my forehead. "Even if I break the sky."

I snorted at the last part, his breath tickling the hairs on top of my head. But I knew without a shadow of a doubt that he meant it. He was my sword, my shield, my heart, and my home.

"I'm sorry I don't tell you I love you more often." His hand paused the idle stroke down my back, and he pulled back to look at me. His brows furrowed as if he had not expected me to say that, but I went on. "I do love you. It is the only thing I know with absolute certainty in this crazy new world. Everything we've done, everything we've been through, I love it all. I was scared tonight."

Samkiel raised up on his elbow as if preparing to battle even my own fears. "Dianna."

"No, I was scared I wouldn't be able to tell you. You are the love of my life, Samkiel. You are it for me, and I don't always have the pretty words to tell you, but I can show you every single day."

Another flash of lightning lit up the room, and I swore his eyes shimmered with unshed tears. He smiled softly. "Every day, huh?"

I nodded.

"Well, that will be a very long time, considering we have eternity."

My head reared back even as my heart swelled. "Eternity? I don't know if I agreed to that."

His lips formed a half smile, and he pointed to my ring. "You kind of did. Now, not even death will separate us. That's what was in our vows. You said it."

"I did?" I joked. "I was distracted. Can we change them? Is it too late?" I cringed. "I don't know. Maybe we should rethink everything I just sa—"

He grabbed me and rolled, forcing me against the bed. I squealed and then laughed as his hands found that sensitive spot just beneath my ribs. His lips slanted over mine, and warmth seeped through my skin and into my bones. My words had built upon our bond, forging something stronger between us, brighter than fire and harder than steel.

Samkiel pulled back and gazed down at me, brushing a few strands of my hair from my face. "The love of your life, huh? I've never heard that before."

"Is that why you're grinning like a fool?"

His smile brightened. "Perhaps. I may need to hear that more."

I fake scoffed as we settled back into bed. "How often?"

"Hmm, maybe every single day?"

"Absolutely not."

He shrugged. "Okay, once or twice. Here and there."

I fake-flopped back on the bed in mock disgust. "You're pushing it. You are so needy."

He placed a kiss on my forehead and then my cheek. His hand cupped the curve of my jaw, his thumb flicking my bottom lip. "I have no idea how I've survived this long without you."

"Me either."

He chuckled and brushed his lips along mine. "Go to sleep."

I smiled and placed a chaste kiss on his lips before turning over and pushing back into him. His massive body curled around mine protectively, and his arms tucked me in close as I settled. "I don't show it a lot, right? Because if people start thinking I'm nice . . ."

His laugh rumbled through the room, the sound chasing away the darkness.

CII Roccurem

It fascinated me that the two neighboring planets were so close to this one, their massive forms ghostly shadows hiding behind the veil of night. You would think that after seeing a thousand-plus worlds, I would be accustomed to all the wonders the universe had to offer, but it pleased me to know I could still be surprised. A bird made of night coasted through the window and landed on the table behind me. Nails tapped on the polished wood before silence fell.

"I witnessed it once, the future and how peace could be attained. Dianna is a flame that will spark a revolution," I said, lifting the teacup to my lips.

"And?" asked the bird of night, the room growing a fraction colder.

"And now all I see is destruction and ruin. The laughter has faded, screams taking its place. I see fire to the West, a wasteland of the East, and . . . what changed?"

I moved away from the large window and sat at the circular table in the center of the room.

"Death of one."

"So it is true, then?"

"For now."

I poured a cup of tea and slipped it toward my kinsman before topping off my own. Darkness crawled from every corner of this room, entrapping the bird before manifesting its massive self in the seat before me. The worn and tattered suit he wore was riddled with bullet holes, and his hair stuck to his head in a red smear. His taut pale skin pulled tight as if it were an ill-fitting mask. One of the Formless Ones, the most ancient, and he preferred to wear the forms of those who had passed his gates.

"I've come for a reason, kinsman." Death carefully picked up the fragile cup and took a sip.

My fingers tapped lightly against the arm of the chair. "If you have come for the boy, I fear it would be a fight. She is quite protective of him, and he of her."

Death's pale, dead eyes fixed on me as he lowered his teacup. I knew he hated to be cheated, and that was exactly what Dianna had done.

"No one escapes me." His voice was reminiscent of the hollow void we all came from. "I will have them both in the end. Make no mistake."

"I am aware. I have seen that, too." It had been a strange experience to watch them both perish. I was certain that if I had been in a body that permitted emotion, I would have felt that sadness. "What I am unaware of is why. Why bring him back? Risk it? Barter her soul in exchange for his life?"

"You have seen the end. You have seen several, kinsman." Death scoffed as if even thinking about admitting what he was about to annoyed him. "The opposite was far more damaging."

"Destruction."

Death only leaned back as he agreed. "Annihilation. You had but a fraction of it on Onuna."

"You fear her?"

"We all should. Dianna is no longer the promised princess of Rashearim or the destined queen. The other sibling has polluted her blood. What she carries within her now could turn worlds to ash if she willed it. You all should fear her as they once feared Ro'Vikiin."

I chuckled. "You know as well as I that he hated that name. He always preferred Gathrriel."

"It does not matter what he prefers. His blood lives in this realm once more."

I sat up straighter. "And it has come to pass again. That's the shift. Every being in this realm and the next felt that spark once more."

"Right, you are. The witches feel it, your moirai, the beings with no legs, and ones with too many. Every. Single. One."

"Is this why my vision has changed? Because of her?"

"No." Death folded its cold hands upon his lap. "Because of them. The brother has slaughtered his blood. It seems to be a repeat of the family tradition, but have no fear. I plan to correct it."

I raised my teacup. "And so Death intervenes, as does fate."

"Intervene suggests I stopped the inevitable. I did not. I merely saw a loophole, but I would not worry about the rules of this existence much longer, kinsman. If Nismera wins, if they return, there will be nothing left of any of us."

My hand tightened on the cup. Had he seen the same tragic ending I had? A murky pit giving birth to beings long forgotten. I stilled, needing the answer to my next question. "What of her soul?"

Death tilted his head toward me. "That's what worries you? Not the return, but her soul?"

I said nothing.

"Soul?" Death tsked. "The fractured thing it is. It's a jagged, crushed thing, the remnants buried within him."

My back straightened, and Death caught it. My mind whirled. I had not seen that outcome either.

"Her soul is in Samkiel?"

"What is left of it. Two beings in one. It seems Samkiel was strong enough to bear it," Death said and sipped his tea.

Mortals felt fear and anxiety. Beings such as us did not, but I could not deny the feelings that rushed through me. It may sound like a good thing that Death had found a way for them to survive, and I knew there would be a cost. I just never expected it to be so ghastly.

I took another drink of my cold tea, trying to calm the unfamiliar emotions clouding my mind. "But how did you do this?"

Death raised a brow and shook his head, a small, rueful smirk quirking his lips. "I have no power over Samkiel. I never did. Dianna brought him back. She didn't know it at the time, but she used the power of that mark. Without even realizing what she was doing, she did the reverse of what Vvive did. She forfeited the mark for the power to split her soul, and then she tied it to his life. Dianna resurrected Samkiel. As much as I hated being bested, it was both terrifying and intriguing to witness something that has only happened once before. The love she has for him is a power."

"How?" I gasped out, never having expected this.

"Love has power. We have both witnessed empires rise and fall for it. And the love that Dianna has for him is a *power*. Just like Vvive's."

"But Dianna laughs, breathes, and loves. She is not just flesh and—"

"And she is void. As was Ro'Vikiin, a soulless, empty monster," Death interrupted and then paused. "My apologies. I mean, Gathrriel was void before Vvive. He died on that battlefield, and when Vvive split her soul to save him, the mark formed. Samkiel dies, and Dianna, refusing to accept that reality, absorbs the power of her mark and merges the pieces of her soul that his passing hadn't shredded. She left herself empty. She is Gathrriel once more."

"Her anger, feedings . . ."

"All of it." Death tilted his bloody, bruised head. "I would make sure they stay close to one another if I were you. If there is too much separating, the body realizes it's void. It tries to revert to its most basic, primal urges."

"That's why she is okay with Samkiel." I swallowed. "She knows."

"More or less," Death said. "Some primal instinct knows that her soul lies within him, her true morality."

My chest grew tight as if I had a heart to feel it. I had not seen this in any reality. This was one of the few times an action or thought surpassed the timeline souls were destined to stay on. Perhaps I could not see it since it was decided after Nismera had ripped into me. If fear could touch even the Formless Ones, it placed its hand upon me now.

Death studied me, sipping at his tea. "You seem frightened, Roccurem. Perhaps you have walked amongst the living for far too long. Their emotions are sticky things, attaching themselves to everyone around them as they weep, laugh, and moan."

"What happens to her if she dies?" I asked the next question that weighed heavily on my mind.

Death placed his teacup down between us, the cold in the room growing. "If she dies now, her body fades to nothing, but you already know that, don't you?" Death said, his anticipation obvious. I couldn't help but wonder what he had planned for her.

"That may be a problem, given Samkiel would destroy you if you tried to take that girl."

The laugh that left Death's lips made even my form crawl. "I do not fear the God King. I have collected several. Even the greatest powers have limits, and he will pass as the rulers before him have. No one escapes me. So, no, *the boy* does not worry me. Besides, time is my counterpart. It fades the pain I inflict until those who are used to me welcome me as a friend. I am infinite, and he will mourn and move on. They all do."

I shook my head and folded my hands across my midsection. "You, like so many others, underestimate his love for her. You just got through telling me that her love for him is a power, but do not think it is not reciprocated wholeheartedly. The mark may be gone, but they were made for each other. You will drive him mad."

"Unir carried the same love for his beloved. Did he strike the skies to embers looking for me? No, because he knew—"

I placed my cup down, the sound cutting him off as I folded my hands in my lap. "Samkiel is not his father."

"Perhaps not, but I have seen him love thousands. He will love a thousand more."

"We both know that was not love."

"Love. Bed." Death waved his cold, pale hand. "What is the difference to the ones who bear flesh and blood? You have witnessed it, too. Only you believe those grand gestures and words. How many have you seen slain in the name of this *love*? We both know my kingdom is filled with those once in love."

"And how many have been born from it?" I questioned. "What of the sacrifices they make in the name of it? Those also show up at your door. I have witnessed that, too. Those who never recover from that lost love mourn until they are reunited. Or the ghosts who beg at your gates, screaming for one last glimpse at the ones they left behind. Do you deny it?"

Death's darkness mantled behind him, hating the mere challenge. Ice formed on the glass windows and spread across the floor. "Are you truly willing to bet countless worlds and lives on that? We both know how quickly a heart, even as pure as his, can change. How many heroes have fallen since the beginning of time, and how many realms have suffered for it? Do you truly wish to ruin the last bit of hope any of us have in this realm or the next by testing that?"

The cold receded a fraction, and Death folded his pale, bruised hands, completely unbothered by the consequences he threatened to unleash by permanently taking her away from Samkiel. Death watched me with a crooked smile.

"You're enjoying this?" Worry swamped me. "Because she threatened you? You are happy with her having no eternal peace."

"You blame me as if I took her soul. As if I am holding it hostage." Death placed a hand on the table, the stone beneath cracking from the burning cold.

"We both know your power, *kinsman*."

Death tapped his skeletal fingers on the table, the lifeless eyes of the man who crossed his gates staring back at me, but Death did not scare me. He, along with others, came into existence when the universe was born, and even with our ancient quarrels, we were bound in ways mortals and deities could never understand.

Finally, Death leaned back, interlacing his fingers. "You think that threat she made in those tunnels was an idle one? You witnessed what she did on Onuna over a sister who was not even blood. Now, imagine what she would do for her mate, the one created for her. She would have no tether, no moral compass, no love. So do not look at me that way. If I truly wanted the end of the world, I would have fought her there for the God King. Nismera will leave the realms desolate if she gets her way and succeeds with the Great Return. So I did what I must. Dianna, as you all call her, was meant to rule. Do you think she was meant to be Ig'Morruthen? He, a living corpse? No, Nismera interfered. She spread lies and deception through the House of Unir, and it worked. She gathered and honed her power for eons, and now *we* must interfere. I do not wish to witness another War of Wars."

The air grew thicker. "It will not matter once Samkiel finds out about her fate. That is what he will focus on, the war be damned. She is all he sees. He loves her, truly loves her."

"How bothersome." Death tapped his fingers once more. "You are no better. You care for the child. You always have. We've seen it. You have a father's love for her. It's immoral. You are above emotions."

"Ah, merciless Death, who cares for nothing and no one." The corner of my lip raised. "In my long existence, it is nice to find something worth protecting."

Death did not falter or move, but something shifted across those hollow, dead eyes.

I crossed one leg over the other. "You know I will not keep this from her. She has been betrayed enough in her long life."

The darkness in the room seemed to quiver in irritation before settling near his frame.

"Just as you are aware that I collect a little part of everyone who passes through my gates, yes?" He picked up his cup and drained the last of his tea before setting it back down. "Dianna was kind enough to send me Alistair."

Realization slapped the air from the room.

"You would not dare."

"I would dare." Death rose, adjusting the bullet-riddled jacket he wore. "So, kinsman, you will not remember this, but know I do want the new world, and I will help you attain it. That I can promise you."

Darkness swelled and then faded. I shivered, cold seeping across the room. I sat up straighter, blinking as I glanced toward the window. Had I left it open? The candles flickered atop the nearby mantle, and music filled the air. I shook my head, rubbing at my temples. Ever since Nismera's light burned, my visions had been scattered and incoherent. I was becoming increasingly afraid she had damaged me on a level so deep I may not recover.

A knock sounded at the door before it slowly cracked open.

"Reggie?" Miska called, her voice a whisper as she stepped into the room. She must have been working late in the greenery Samkiel had made for her. It wasn't anything like what Jade City had, but she was making it her own. Her nightshirt was littered with small bits of herbs. Miska loved all the clothes Dianna had asked Samkiel to make for her. She had never been allowed her own personal attire before.

"Yes, Miska?"

"Who were you talking to?"

I glanced around the room, wondering if I had missed something. "No one. I haven't spoken to anyone but you tonight. I must have mumbled a vision. My apologies."

She shrugged one shoulder. "It's fine, it happens. Do you want to try the new tonic I made? I think I got the ingredients right this time."

"Why are you up so late working? It's well past midnight."

"I couldn't sleep. It's freezing in here, and it keeps storming, so I figured, why not work?"

A smile formed on my lips as I rose. "Well then, let us try your new tonic, shall we?"

I never said anything about her failed attempts. Miska worked hard, trying to remember what she had learned and what her mother had taught her. She was already such a powerful healer, yet she had only just begun.

"Perfect." She waved her hands in the air in pure excitement. "I'm trying to target the pain receptors associated with burns for Cameron. His back is pretty bad, but Dianna said he'd heal once he got his feeding better under control because godly burns are worse, especially in his Ig'Morruthen form, and . . ." Her voice stopped as her eyes caught on something behind me. "Why is your tea frozen? Did you leave a window open?"

I frowned, perplexed. "Perhaps. I'm not sure."

CIV

Kaden

My soul screamed as bone and tissue became muscles, followed by skin to cover it all. My fingers curled into soft soil as I pushed myself up. Sharp, blistering pain radiated from my spine, skipping along newly regrown nerves. I screamed as my body put itself back together, every cell burning with agony. I rested on my hands and knees, panting, taking in as much air as possible.

He had killed me.

Samkiel had killed me.

Everything came back as consciousness took form. He'd stood there, exhaling anger, hate, and rage with every breath as he held that blackened death blade. His eyes burned as Father's had, and the hair along my arms had prickled. I had timed it right, timed my movements, but he was too quick, too fast. I hadn't even seen him move, and I hadn't felt the blade. There had only been a brief pinch and then absolute nothingness, no pain, no fear, just absolute and complete nothingness. I did not even exist anymore.

My heart pounded in my chest. Death. I had experienced true death.

"Oblivion," a deep, hollow voice said, and my head whipped toward it.

Only the empty battlefield greeted me.

"What?" My voice didn't even sound like my own, as if my body was still struggling to heal.

"It should never have happened. What Oblivion does is forbidden and quite bothersome, but at the same time, it does make my job a fraction easier. Fewer souls entering my kingdom, you see?"

My mind reeled. I couldn't catch my breath, and my vision swam as I tried to bring the old, half-burned woman into focus. Her wrinkled hands were propped on her hips, the apron she wore covered in soot and smoke.

"You brought me back? Who . . . Who are you?"

"I have many names," she said, her eyes raking over me as if assessing my injuries or lack thereof. "This will do."

I started to ask what she meant, but her form burst into a bird the color of night and shot into the sky, a caw raking across the sky before disappearing past the tree line.

What the fuck?

I rolled my neck to the side and pushed to my feet, trying to remember everything about that night, and then I remembered Isaiah.

I spun, looking in every direction for scattered armor, a limb, or even dust. There was nothing but me and my own remains here.

I was no fool. Samkiel had ripped the sky apart to get to his . . . wife. His ear-splitting roar had shaken the planet and me to the core. I'd felt it then, how similar he was to our father. I had been a fool. Everything we'd heard of him was true. Samkiel was that powerful, that strong. He was the World Ender. I hadn't wanted to believe how lucky we had been to survive our previous encounters with him. I could sense the same thunderous power that had flowed through Unir's veins, but it was combined with Samkiel's power, and it was devastating. Did he know just how powerful he was?

I shook my head, forcing clarity into my thoughts. I needed to get Isaiah back. If he had not fallen here, that meant Samkiel took him and would try to get every bit of information out of him. Regardless of the fear and apprehension that ate at me, I could not fail the one person who had never failed me.

CV

Xavier

One foot in front of the other, the repetition was mindnumbing. Days turned into nights, and nights into days. This was my life now. I stayed in the darkest parts of my mind, watching out of eyes that were no longer my own, existing within a body that was no longer my own.

I had claimed so many lives since I had been taken, and I knew I would never forget the screams and the blood. There had been times I wished for death, prayed for it, anything to end the torment. Yet, no matter how bad it got, a flicker of hope sat idly by. It was a spark of life, an ember I protected with all my will. It was the memory of shimmering hair, the color of the sun, the scent of mistwood, the rich fragrance heralding the turn of fall, and a laugh that could heal heartaches and broken bones. He was home, and he was so far away from me now that it felt as if a part of my soul was missing. I would have sworn he was a dream, only I did not dream here. Yes, death would be better.

"The sky, general!" a soldier on my left shouted.

The general in question held up his hand and whispered those damn words that made my body go rigid. I stopped in my tracks as he stepped forward. We stood on the large stone bridge that connected one part of the crumbling castle to another. The sea nipped at the shore, and a few ships floated in the bay.

A soldier pointed up, and a few others removed their helmets. I watched their mouths fall open in shock, and then they all started speaking at once. My body remained relaxed, but still, no matter how much I willed it, I could not look up. It was the only thought I had until everything went to shit.

The air seemed to compress just before a loud boom made the stone bridge shudder. Explosions came from all around me, and in my peripherals, I saw flames and wooden chunks shoot toward the sky. Yells followed as pieces of the ships flew toward us, guards either ducking or placing their helmets back on as the general shouted.

Whatever was attacking us had enough power to make the general who had kept me by his side like a leashed pet tuck tail and run in the other direction.

There was a crack of thunder, and the world turned dark. Rain pelted me even if I could not feel it.

The stone bridge rocked, and the guards I could see turned to look. I knew whatever had landed behind me was bad because they turned and ran. Hot, blinding silver light raced past me, and my heart leaped. I knew that light, knew what it meant, knew how it felt. It was not Nismera, but it was a god.

Samkiel.

If I could breathe, I'd lose my breath. I knew whose power filled the sky. I knew Nismera had killed him. Grief was still my constant companion. I had spent hours in taverns beside Nismera's guards as they sang of his demise, yet I knew this power. It called to a part of me that those damned words could not touch.

More of that light washed over me, and I basked in it even as the stone bridge rocked. Silver armor skirted past me, not even bothering to stop as they sprinted after the retreating guards. I watched with cold malice as one reached that damn general. He fought and then bled when an ablaze weapon gutted him. He fell to his knees and glared up at the god standing over him, clutching the ropes of his intestines. There was a blur and the familiar hiss of an ablaze sword cutting the air. His head rolled over the ground. Freedom! My mind reeled. But freedom was not guaranteed.

As soon as the battle started, it ended. The stone bridge stopped vibrating ominously, but smoke obscured the world. It whipped and curled, blanketing me. Fear sank its claws in deep. Had Dianna come? Had she set the world ablaze once more as she had on Yejedin?

I heard steel boots draw close, and I started to pace within the dark confines of my mind. A lithe, feminine form suddenly crashed to a stop in front of me, her body covered head to toe in silver armor. No, this wasn't Dianna. Dianna did not wear our crest or armor, but then again, she was a weapon and did not need it. Other figures appeared at the woman's side, all wearing the same silver steel. Two men towered over the women directly in front of me, but I saw the crowd growing behind them.

The woman twisted her wrist, and her helmet melted away.

No, not Dianna at all.

"Xavier," she purred. "My yeyras. I've missed you."

Kryella.

Her hands clamped down on the sides of my head. My vision burned green, and I screamed inside my head, her power burning me to my core. I screamed as my soul burst into flames, and for the first time in the last few months, my mouth moved under my own control. My knees buckled, but she continued to pour more of her magic into me. Iassulyn would be a fucking paradise compared to this torture, the acidic burn making me want to claw my skin off.

Kryella finally stopped, and my hands slapped down on the bridge as I panted, sweat beading on my skin. I panted, realizing it was me who made that motion, me who finally had control over my body.

My head snapped up, my eyes brimming with tears. "I-I," I stammered. "I can move. You fixed it. Me," I damn near sobbed.

Kryella kneeled, her armor bending to points at her knees. She reached forward, and I flinched, expecting pain again, but when she cupped my cheek, there was nothing but the comfort of her touch. "Of course."

Kryella dropped her hand and rose to her feet with easy grace before turning to the woman next to her. She slid her helmet back, and blonde hair spilled past the breast of her suit.

Athos. The goddess Athos. It was impossible.

My mind swam, and my blood pounded. They were dead. They had been thought to be dead since the Gods War, but . . . the proof was standing before me. My mind reeled. We never saw a body or their light burn through the sky. Samkiel never spoke of it, but we assumed.

"How are you alive?" I choked out.

Athos did not hesitate. "We are The Eye." The lethal soldiers behind her stood tall, holding the thick silver shields I remembered from before the fall of Rashearim. Gods, so many gods. "We are the last rebellion against Nismera the Conqueror. What we need to know now is how many more of you are alive?"

CVI

Dianna

My eyes shot open, my breath catching in my throat. I could tell by how clear my vision was in the dark that my eyes glowed crimson. The dream receded, just a fleeting memory I couldn't remember or catch. I finally focused on the Ig'Morruthen, and a chill ran up my spine when I heard what the beast was screaming.

Danger!

Danger!

Danger!

I went predator still, assessing the room. Firelight flickered against the walls, and the curtains on the large bay window danced lightly with the cool breeze. Rain, a slow drizzle, emptied from the dark gray clouds. Lightning streaked across the sky, followed by a low rumble of thunder.

Heat blanketed my back, and a slow, even breath tickled my shoulder. Samkiel's head rested against mine as he slept, his arms holding me in a vise-like grip, protecting me even in his sleep. I tried to calm my raging heart, wondering what startled me from my sleep. But I didn't see anyone in our room, not even a single book, candle, or tablecloth out of place, so why had I awakened as if someone was watching us from the end of the bed? Why was my beast going crazy with distress?

I sighed and relaxed back against Samkiel, deciding it was just the remnants of the forgotten dream. I wrapped his arm tighter around me, but I felt it again as soon as I closed my eyes.

My instincts screamed at me to wake, urging me to leave. An insistent thread pulled tight, wanting me to follow it.

I forced my eyes closed a fraction tighter, denying the pull, telling myself it was nothing, just the echo of the nightmare. Kaden was dead. He wasn't here, and Isaiah was locked deep beneath the castle.

Still, a tug pulled at me, beckoning me, and I wondered if something was wrong in the castle. I carefully lifted Samkiel's arm and slid beneath it as quietly as I could. He sucked in a breath before groaning and turning over onto his back, his arm now draped across his bare chest, the other above his head. Gods, he was beautiful. I forced myself to turn away and slipped off the bed, reaching for the robe on the nearby armchair. I slipped it on, taking one last look to make sure he was still asleep.

Samkiel's chest rose and fell evenly, the sheets tangled around his thighs now. He was deep asleep in all his naked glory, but besides my normal appreciation of the godly body he was blessed with, my eyes caught on his midsection. Where that deep, bruised scar had slashed across his abdomen, there was now nothing but smooth, healed skin. I had felt it earlier when he had stripped first himself and then me before taking me against the wall. I had run my hand over it to make sure it was real.

A part of me still hoped that it had all been just another nightmare. Looking at the absence of the wound, I could almost believe he hadn't been ripped from me, but the gaping ache where my soul had once been proved the truth. The only thing that eased the throb of the loss was being close to him.

I peered out the open window, still unsure how he had taken all his power back. I had asked Reggie for clarification once we returned, and Samkiel dragged Isaiah downstairs. Reggie said the sheer force of will and drive to protect me had been the catalyst. He said he willed them back into his body faster than he had time to process, and he still wasn't sure what he had done was possible. Gabby loved me, but I had never been loved like Samkiel loved me. No one had cared for or protected me as he did. I still was unsure I was even worth it after everything I had put him through. But my cold, dead, aching heart swelled, thinking of such love and how, no matter what, it was mine.

I left his massive sleeping form and headed out the door, going quietly so as not to disturb him. As soon as I stepped into the hall, that damn tug happened again. My body jerked to a stop, and I glanced down. Whatever was pulling at me wanted me to go down. My blood ran cold.

Had something happened to Logan, Neverra, or Cameron? Had Isaiah escaped? Was he on a rampage downstairs, and we hadn't heard it? I didn't stop to think as I ran down the hall, taking the steps three at a time. Logan was down there, as were Neverra and Cameron. Even with Cameron's increased strength, I knew Isaiah would rip him apart with his bare hands.

I ran down the hall, doorways blurring. I turned a corner and sped past the open door to Samkiel's study before skidding to a halt. The hem of my robe tangled around my thighs as I backed up, my eyes narrowing. My heart thudded in my chest, alarm bells screaming in my head.

Danger!

Danger!

Danger!

The large masculine shadow detached from the darkness, moving stealthily within the room. I growled low in my throat, my hands lighting with bright orange flames. My foot made contact with the door in a vicious kick, and it flew wide open, parts of it splintering as it thudded against the far wall with a crack. I knew those shoulders, knew what kind of powerful beast lay beneath them. I threw enough fire into him to send him sailing out of my home. One fireball, then another, sailed through the air and right through him, burning the wall behind him.

What the fuck? The fire died in my hands as he turned around, a peculiar look on his face as he looked between me and the hole with its still-burning edges in the wall.

"Your vicious, feral nature makes up for your small frame."

I swallowed the lump in my throat, and my mouth suddenly went dry. Ice skittered through my veins because I wasn't looking into Kaden's eyes. I was looking into a god's.

"Unir."

"You know me?"

I couldn't even nod my head, let alone respond. He was the shadow I had seen or sensed in every corner since we arrived here, the one I saw in the market. There, but not. It was never Kaden watching me, hunting me.

"How?" It was a whisper of pure and utter disbelief.

He looked every bit like the God King I had seen in Samkiel's memories, right down to the thick silk robes that draped battle-worn silver and gold armor. Armored boots came to a point at the knee, with intricate patterns carved along every bit of silver. He smiled, just the corner of his lips lifting, a gesture so familiar to the man asleep upstairs that my heart faltered.

"The how is not important." Even his voice demanded power, and the Ig'Morruthen beneath my skin snarled in response. "The why should be more concerning to you."

"Okay, then." I mustered every ounce of false bravado. "Why?"

Unir smiled, stepping through the table before halting in front of me. He towered over me, far taller than any of his sons, and my head reared back. He stared at the ring on my finger before meeting my eyes again.

"The dead have much to discuss with you, daughter-in-law."

His hands engulfed my skull as darkness filled my mind, and I screamed.

"The dead have much to discuss with you, daughter-in-law."

His hands engulfed my skull as darkness filled my mind, and I screamed.

KEEP READING FOR A SNEAK PEEK AT THE NEXT STAGE OF DIANNA AND SAMKIEL'S STORY . . .

Prologue

The town had started to settle for the night as I left my home. I waved at a few shopkeepers as they closed up and sidestepped two drunkards, stumbling and laughing their way to wherever they were headed. The night was beautiful, the sky alive with stars, and I enjoyed the walk to work. I did better working nights, preferring fewer crowds. Plus, the lake came alive once the sun set, with or without the moon.

"You're early," my boss said, adjusting his straw hat. His white shirt strained around his lower midsection, the bulge of his belly enhanced by the worn dark pants he'd tucked into his knee-high boots.

The dock was abandoned, the lake empty, and the usual crowds were absent. All the boats were still tied to the pier, and from the looks of it, none of them had gone out.

"Slow night for lovers?" I asked.

He shrugged. "It's not that. The moonkrests are nowhere to be seen."

I frowned, and he nodded toward the lake, telling me to look for myself. The boards creaked as I crossed them. I stopped at the edge of the pier beside the barrels of sparklers and leaned against the railing. The trees were silent, and no bugs floated around the hanging branches that teased the surface. There were no signs of the moonkrests, even with the full moon casting bright beams of light deep into the inky depths. That was very odd. They were always active when the moon was out.

I turned to ask him what he thought was happening, but I was alone on the dock. Nothing seemed amiss, the stars twinkling above and the breeze forming soft ripples at the lake's edge. Weird. Where had he gone? He wouldn't just leave, and he wasn't quiet or fast.

Screams and sounds of fighting pierced the peaceful night, and I spun toward town. I started back down the dock but froze when I heard the thick beat of wings above me. Something landed behind me, hitting the wood hard enough to jar me. When I turned around, I realized why every living thing around the lake had gone into hiding.

The massive creature folded its four wings against its back, the transparent membranes flashing iridescent in the moonlight. Dark brown, plated armor wrapped his shoulders and molded to his body, stopping just above his backward-bent legs. His lower bony mandible split into pincers and flickered, creating an ominous chittering noise. The sound activated my primal brain, sending shivers of alarm through me. I didn't know what this creature was, but every instinct I had screamed that I was in danger.

I took a step back just as another thud sounded behind me, and the dock shuddered beneath my feet. I turned to run and slammed into the hard exoskeleton of a second creature. My ass hit the boards hard, and the creature reached for me with his four arms. Adrenaline surged through me, and I rolled toward the railing, scrambling to get back on my feet. I grabbed a paddle from a stack and swung. The creature blinked and chittered angrily as the wood splintered against his shoulder, but then he was atop me.

My chest hit the ground, dust scattering as my breath exploded from my lungs. My wrists stung from where they'd bound my arms behind my back, and despite my struggles, there was no give in the bindings. I groaned as long nails dug into my twisted and tied limbs. He hoisted me up, and I gasped in horror at the carnage around me. I blinked, certain I had died, and arrived in Iassulyn.

Flames crackled off the remains of the tavern and surrounding buildings, the dark smoke acrid and clogging. Creatures ransacked the shops, breaking windows and chirruping in their strange language. Screams rent the air as men, women, and children were dragged from their houses. Some had managed to escape and were running into the woods, creatures following both on the ground and in the air. Those who were able to arm themselves and do what they could to fight were quickly overtaken and consumed. I swallowed hard and closed my eyes as the sound of bones crunching filled the air.

It wasn't just a nightmare. My mind could never imagine this horror. The Otherworld had opened up its horrible, rancid jaws, and a plague of demons had descended upon our town. My heart thudded in my chest as the scent of death clogged my nose. The monster dragging me further into town chittered with what sounded like excitement. My feet scrambled against the ground, and my muscles strained in the creature's powerful grip. But no matter how hard I fought, I knew I couldn't escape. The beast shook me violently until I stopped struggling, its talons digging into my shoulders. My chest heaved, my nostrils burned, and my eyes stung, terror consuming any hope I had.

I heard heavy, thick footsteps approach, and dread trickled down my spine, turning my guts liquid. My eyes shuttered, and I started praying to any gods still left in this world, praying to Samkiel himself. I kept my eyes closed, not wanting to see what was coming. The sounds were bad enough. The creature shook me again and screeched in my face, his hot breath hitting me hard enough to blow my hair back. My eyes snapped open, and I wished I had followed my instincts and kept them closed.

The beast loomed in front of me, his face inches from mine. His pincers clicked a few more times before withdrawing. He closed his bony mandibles and stood straight and at attention. It took a few moments for me to find the courage to look away, and when I did, there was a new nightmare to make my legs go weak.

He was taller than any being had the right to be. From the deep black pits of his eyes, poreless pale skin, and sharply pointed crown atop his head, it was clear this was not a man standing before me. He wore a dark coat that split into two large flaps in the back, the odd fabric flaring around his feet. He stood inside a double circle, and I recognized the runes within the perimeter. It was a teleportation mark. It glowed weakly and flickered. The power he had infused it with to transport himself and summon the ghastly horrors he'd brought with him was fading.

Fear was an overwhelming force that turned me almost numb. I found myself focusing on his chest because I couldn't look at his face and stay upright. I squinted, watching as the material of his intricately embroidered clothing bunched and moved. Both his skin and clothes were ill-fitting, and I wondered if this wasn't his true form. Power pulsed from him, and I forced myself to lift my eyes to meet his cold, otherworldly ones. My throat went dry as I finally put the pieces together. I knew who this was.

"I can smell the fear on you. Stronger than the piss that runs in your streets. Stronger than the blood decorating the ground. You know who I am?" he asked, his voice as deep and dark as the realm he'd ascended from. He crouched in front of me, his body moving in a nauseatingly alien way. Even in that position, he towered above me.

"Y-yes," I managed to get out. "I heard rumors about the new age, a rebellion amongst the princes, and a newly crowned ruler. You're the King of the Otherworld. Umemri."

"Correct," he said with a smile, and my stomach churned again. The twin lines that bracketed his mouth bisected his sharp features, ending where his ears should have been in this form. His mouth was way too wide, and I feared what I would see if he truly opened it. His hair looked stark black in the firelight, but when he turned to his general, I saw it wasn't hair but jagged spikes vibrating with his every breath. He was a genuine horror brought to life. No one I knew had ever laid eyes on any of the princes of the Otherworld, much less its dark lord.

Unable to hold his gaze, my eyes flickered restlessly. Flames crackled throughout the ruined town, and a few feet away, two people lay face-first on the ground, bleeding out from their throats. Whatever answers he'd demanded, they had not given. Hope flared in me. Maybe if I answered his questions correctly, he would spare me.

"W-what do you want?" I asked, forcing myself to look at him again. "Whatever it is, I can give it."

"Can you now?" Umemri tilted his head, his black eyes boring into me as if he could pluck the answers from my mind. "I am looking for someone important to me. Her last bit of communication was from this town. Since then, there has been nothing but . . . silence."

The way he spoke the last part of that sentence made me wonder if something as horrid as he might have a heart.

I shook my head, blinking. "I haven't . . . We haven't seen anyone from the Otherworld here."

He flicked his hand open, the long, curved claws tipping his three long fingers clicking against each other. I flinched, even though he had made no move toward me. "Oh, but I think you have. Her scent lingers in this town, and I can smell her blood on these wretched streets."

Recollection hit me like a brick wall, and my heart started beating so hard it sounded like a drum to war. Umemri heard it, his cold, dark eyes dropping to my chest.

"Where is my murrak?"

Panic clenched my gut, and sweat formed on my brow. Oh gods. I couldn't lie. I couldn't hide the fact that she was . . .

"Dead."

I blurted it out, fast and harsh. Some dark and devastating emotion flared to life on his face. The chaos around the town drew closer as if the others sensed his emotions and were preparing to rip me to shreds. Umemri laughed, his dark, thick voice vibrating my bones. His generals joined in his mirth, the sound growing more grating and animalistic. He reached out and grabbed me by the throat, his laughter abruptly morphing into a snarl as he lifted me off my feet. His face split and opened, the transition making bile rise in my throat. I saw the pincers waiting within, and I was certain he was going to eat me.

"Impossible," Umemri said, holding me as if I weighed nothing. "No one I have an allegiance with would touch her. Even if they tried, none could stop her if she was in her true form and on a rampage. I doubt a town full of Itians could even scratch her."

I struggled against his hold, my heart thudding in panic. He eased up just enough that I could choke out, "Samkiel." I said his name as if it were a prayer, and it alone could grant me my life, and it did.

Umemri's eyes flared, and the creatures halted as if I'd spoken a curse. Everything went oddly silent. The only things I could hear were the crackle of the fire and the whisper of the wind. He suddenly released me, and I fell to the ground. I panted, blood dripping down my neck from the puncture wounds his talons had left. It felt like hours passed before Umemri finally blinked, and I saw realization rip through him. It was as if just the sound of his ancient enemy's name was enough to prove to him that his murrak was dead. His shoulders bunched and fabric ripped as thick, spiny, dark appendages broke free, curling around him in agitation.

"You're lying," he snapped, his lip curling and his tentacles snapping toward me in agitation.

I wasn't, but I could tell he wished, above all else, I was. "No," I said, my entire body shaking with uncontrollable tremors. "I'm not. He was here with a woman. They left after the murrak attacked and he killed it."

The sharp point of an appendage pierced my shoulder. I screamed, and Umemri smiled cruelly, seeming to savor the sound.

"A woman?" Umemri enunciated with a painful twist.

"Yes!" I cried. "I never got her name, but she was an Ig'Morruthen. I don't know why she was with him."

The talon twisting in my flesh stopped before it ripped through my shoulder. Umemri's head snapped toward his cursed army, and he barked an obvious command in a language I did not know. One of his creatures took flight before he brought his attention back to me. The look in his eyes only increased my fear.

"It seems I do not need you any longer, then."

He raised one thick tentacle, the sharp point aimed at my head. Just as he brought it toward me, I yelled, "I can take you to her! Where we buried your murrak!"

He dropped me so fast that I fell forward. One of his guards caught me and lifted me to my feet, arms still bound.

Umemri tilted his head, his eyes flashing with grief and rage. "Very well, lead the way."

I took a shuddering breath and started walking, knowing exactly where her large, twisted body was. A few of the other townspeople and I had buried her. I always knew doing good deeds would eventually fuck me up. His guards fell into step beside and behind us as I led them forward, past the tree line, until we reached the freshly churned dirt mound near the base of a thick, gnarled tree.

A soldier pushed me to my knees, my shoulder aching and seeping blood as he held me there. Umemri stepped forward as his guards formed a circle around the grave. He lifted a hand and squeezed it into a tight fist, the ground shifting and rolling in response. What powers did he possess? I thought only gods had telekinesis. I had heard rumors that some witches had powers to rival the gods, but I didn't know of any, and he wasn't a witch.

The ground split, thousands of bugs and worms oozing from the grave on his command. With a nauseating pulse of their bodies, a head emerged from the dirt. I'd braced for the monstrous, crystallized one with pinchers and large, oval eyes. Only that was not what they delivered. Umemri kneeled and brushed his talons through hair the color of moonlight. The insects retreated, and the guards in the clearing bowed their heads in a sign of respect and shared grief.

A sound of despair left the King of the Underworld, but he cut it off as if he'd had no control over the making of it. He stood and turned toward me, his tentacles raised threateningly behind him. My eyes were drawn to the head he cradled against his chest as if it were the most precious thing in the world to him. She stared at me with wide, lifeless eyes glazed a milky white. Her features were feminine and delicate, with the same lines around her mouth that he had. I saw nothing of the monster we'd buried.

I realized now why the town burned, why he'd slaughtered everyone. He was the same as any being who had abruptly lost someone they loved. The murrak hadn't been just something to him. She was *someone*. From the level of his despair and anger, I suspected she was a lover, or worse, his mate.

"This woman he was with. Tell me more about her," Umemri demanded.

I didn't think there was a way out of this for me, but I knew this was my only hope, so I didn't hesitate. I told him about the boat ride and how they acted with each other. A tremor went through him, and his tentacles lashed the air when I told him how they'd fought for each other, describing how they killed the female he held so close. When I was finished, I swallowed the growing lump in my throat and waited.

A bird of night landed in the trees just above Umemri, its glittering eyes boring into me. Watching. Waiting. It stretched its wings and cawed loudly, but neither Umemri nor his guards seemed to notice it at all. I blinked up at it. The damn thing seemed curious about our conversation. The peculiar thing, though, was that birds had fled this area hundreds of years ago.

Leaves crunched, drawing my attention back to the King of the Otherworld. His guards watched me, their eyes reflecting the light from the crescent moon peeking through the trees.

"Am I free?" I stumbled across my words. "I told you everything I know, and I won't speak of anything that happened here today. Whatever you wish."

A ghost of a smile pulled at his mouth. "You cannot give me what I wish for now," Umemri said. "But I shall grant your request. I'll set you free."

The warmth of relief spread through my body. I knew some would call me a coward at how I gave up everything to save myself. Some would say that I was without honor, but I wanted to live. Pain exploded across my neck, and then I felt nothing.

I watched from the forest floor as my body thudded inches away from me, my head missing. I blinked as the last of my life held fast. The ground shook and hissed, splitting as steam rose. Orange runes appeared, casting a bright glow around each being. The beasts sank one by one, the ground swallowing them whole as the king and his army returned to the Otherworld. My mouth gaped open, trying to form words I could no longer utter. I blinked once more as the bird made of midnight spread its wings far too wide. My vision faded as it landed, taking the shape of a man made of darkness.

ACKNOWLEDGMENTS

First and foremost, how do we feel guys? How are we doing? Does it get better or worse? Who knows? Definitely not me . . .

In all seriousness I want to say thank you to all the readers. The fact that you even wanted to pick up this book means the world to me! Thank you endlessly. Also, thank you to every single person I have met and become friends with on this journey, and I hope you enjoyed this installment of Samkiel and Dianna's epic journey.

Next, I want to say thank you to the Rose & Star Publishing team for believing in me! There is not a single day that I am not grateful for all you have done for me. Thank you for letting a mixed kid who never thought she would see herself in stories flourish. You all own my very heart. Thanks for letting me blow your phones up with a thousand messages and regular Facetimes. Samkiel may have lost his home, but I found mine with you!

Thank you to Kensington and Hachette for believing in me and taking a chance on these books and this series. I cannot praise you all enough. This has been quite a ride, and I am so lucky to have a home for my crazy, loveable, chaotic characters.

Mikayla, my bestie and PA, I truly could not do this without you, and I hope you know that. Minus the seventeen phone calls per day and just gossiping about this series, you have truly helped me so much and now you have it in writing how much I love and adore you!

Aisling, my amazing editor, thank you so much for seeing my world and loving every single part. Thank you for believing in me as well and not being afraid of Dianna and her chaotic ways. I also apologize in advance for the rest of this series.

I also want to say thank you to my Found Family who has listened to me vent and cry and accepts me all the same. I'd burn the world for you guys, too! Thank you for loving me!

I want to say thank you to the beta readers (you know who you are). Thank you for being the best beta readers a girl could ever ask for. Your feedback means the world, and I treasure you guys.

Thank you to my mom and sister, whom I love dearly. The family bond in this entire series is a reflection of them for me—the undying love and the ability to do anything for the ones you love. We have been through hell and back, and I hope you both know how much I love you.

Lastly, once again, I just want to thank my readers. You all mean the world to me, and I appreciate every comment, post, DM and meme made. Without you guys there would be no Samkiel or Dianna. You are everything, and you all deserve the world, and I hope you find someone (if you don't have someone already) who would end the world for you, too. Thank you, Thank you, and Thank you!